LOGIC AND COMPUTER DESIGN FUNDAMENTALS

FIFTH EDITION
GLOBAL EDITION

M. Morris Mano
California State University, Los Angeles

Charles R. Kime
University of Wisconsin, Madison

Tom Martin
Virginia Tech

PEARSON

Boston Columbus Indianapolis New York San Francisco Hoboken
Amsterdam Cape Town Dubai London Madrid Milan Munich Paris Montreal Toronto
Delhi Mexico City São Paulo Sydney Hong Kong Seoul Singapore Taipei Tokyo

Vice President and Editorial Director, ECS: *Marcia J. Horton*
Executive Editor: *Tracy Johnson*
Acquisitions Editor: *Julie Bai*
Assistant Acquisitions Editor, Global Editions: *Aditee Agarwal*
Executive Marketing Manager: *Tim Galligan*
Marketing Assistant: *Jon Bryant*
Senior Managing Editor: *Scott Disanno*
Production Project Manager: *Greg Dulles*
Project Editor, Global Editions: *Donald Villamero*
Program Manager: *Joanne Manning*
Global HE Director of Vendor Sourcing and
    Procurement: *Diane Hynes*

Director of Operations: *Nick Sklitsis*
Operations Specialist: *Maura Zaldivar-Garcia*
Senior Production Manufacturing Controller, Global Editions:
    Trudy Kimber
Media Production Manager, Global Editions: *Vikram Kumar*
Cover Art: © *Shaparniy/Shutterstock*
Manager, Rights and Permissions: *Rachel Youdelman*
Associate Project Manager, Rights and Permissions:
    Timothy Nicholls
Composition: *Jouve India*

Pearson Education Limited
Edinburgh Gate
Harlow
Essex CM20 2JE
England

and Associated Companies throughout the world

Visit us on the World Wide Web at:
www.pearsonglobaleditions.com

British Library Cataloguing-in-Publication Data
A catalogue record for this book is available from the British Library.

ISBN 10: 1-292-09607-1
ISBN 13: 978-1-292-09607-0

Typeset by Jouve, in 10/12 Times Ten LT Std

Contents

□ Chapter 3 **129**

□ Chapter 4 **213**

□ Chapter 10　**547**

☐ Chapter 11 **601**

☐ Chapter 12 **635**

PREFACE

The objective of this text is to serve as a cornerstone for the learning of logic design, digital system design, and computer design by a broad audience of readers. This fifth edition marks the continued evolution of the text contents. Beginning as an adaptation of a previous book by the first author in 1997, it continues to offer a unique combination of logic design and computer design principles with a strong hardware emphasis. Over the years, the text has followed industry trends by adding new material such as hardware description languages, removing or de-emphasizing material of declining importance, and revising material to track changes in computer technology and computer-aided design.

NEW TO THIS EDITION

The fifth edition reflects changes in technology and design practice that require computer system designers to work at higher levels of abstraction and manage larger ranges of complexity than they have in the past. The level of abstraction at which logic, digital systems, and computers are designed has moved well beyond the level at which these topics are typically taught. The goal in updating the text is to more effectively bridge the gap between existing pedagogy and practice in the design of computer systems, particularly at the logic level. At the same time, the new edition maintains an organization that should permit instructors to tailor the degree of technology coverage to suit both electrical and computer engineering and computer science audiences. The primary changes to this edition include:

- Chapter 1 has been updated to include a discussion of the layers of abstractions in computing systems and their role in digital design, as well as an overview of the digital design process. Chapter 1 also has new material on alphanumeric codes for internationalization.

- The textbook introduces hardware description languages (HDLs) earlier, starting in Chapter 2. HDL descriptions of circuits are presented alongside logic schematics and state diagrams throughout the chapters on combinational and sequential logic design to indicate the growing importance of HDLs in contemporary digital system design practice. The material on propagation delay, which is a first-order design constraint in digital systems, has been moved into Chapter 2.

- Chapter 3 combines the functional block material from the old Chapter 3 and the arithmetic blocks from the old Chapter 4 to present a set of commonly occurring combinational logic functional blocks. HDL models of the functional blocks are presented throughout the chapter. Chapter 3 introduces the concept of hierarchical design.

- Sequential circuits appear in Chapter 4, which includes both the description of design processes from the old Chapter 5, and the material on sequential circuit timing, synchronization of inputs, and metastability from the old Chapter 6. The description of JK and T flip-flops has been removed from the textbook and moved to the online Companion Website.

- Chapter 5 describes topics related to the implementation of digital hardware, including design of complementary metal-oxide (CMOS) gates and programmable logic. In addition to much of the material from the old Chapter 6, Chapter 5 now includes a brief discussion of the effect of testing and verification on the cost of a design. Since many courses employing this text have lab exercises based upon field programmable gate arrays (FPGAs), the description of FPGAs has been expanded, using a simple, generic FPGA architecture to explain the basic programmable elements that appear in many commercially available FPGA families.

- The remaining chapters, which cover computer design, have been updated to reflect changes in the state-of-the art since the previous edition appeared. Notable changes include moving the material on high-impedance buffers from the old Chapter 2 to the bus transfer section of Chapter 6 and adding a discussion of how procedure call and return instructions can be used to implement function calls in high level languages in Chapter 9.

Offering integrated coverage of both digital and computer design, this edition of *Logic and Computer Design Fundamentals* features a strong emphasis on fundamentals underlying contemporary design. Understanding of the material is supported by clear explanations and a progressive development of examples ranging from simple combinational applications to a CISC architecture built upon a RISC core. A thorough coverage of traditional topics is combined with attention to computer-aided design, problem formulation, solution verification, and the building of problem-solving skills. Flexibility is provided for selective coverage of logic design, digital system design, and computer design topics, and for coverage of hardware description languages (none, VHDL, or Verilog®).

With these revisions, Chapters 1 through 4 of the book treat logic design, Chapters 5 through 7 deal with digital systems design, and Chapters 8 through 12 focus on computer design. This arrangement provides solid digital system design fundamentals while accomplishing a gradual, bottom-up development of fundamentals for use in top-down computer design in later chapters. Summaries of the topics covered in each chapter follow.

Logic Design

Chapter 1, Digital Systems and Information, introduces digital computers, computer systems abstraction layers, embedded systems, and information representation including number systems, arithmetic, and codes.

Chapter 2, Combinational Logic Circuits, deals with gate circuits and their types and basic ideas for their design and cost optimization. Concepts include Boolean algebra, algebraic and Karnaugh-map optimization, propagation delay, and gate-level hardware description language models using structural and dataflow models in both VHDL and Verilog.

Chapter 3, Combinational Logic Design, begins with an overview of a contemporary logic design process. The details of steps of the design process including problem formulation, logic optimization, technology mapping to NAND and NOR gates, and verification are covered for combinational logic design examples. In addition, the chapter covers the functions and building blocks of combinational design including enabling and input-fixing, decoding, encoding, code conversion, selecting, distributing, addition, subtraction, incrementing, decrementing, filling, extension and shifting, and their implementations. The chapter includes VHDL and Verilog models for many of the logic blocks.

Chapter 4, Sequential Circuits, covers sequential circuit analysis and design. Latches and edge-triggered flip-flops are covered with emphasis on the D type. Emphasis is placed on state machine diagram and state table formulation. A complete design process for sequential circuits including specification, formulation, state assignment, flip-flop input and output equation determination, optimization, technology mapping, and verification is developed. A graphical state machine diagram model that represents sequential circuits too complex to model with a conventional state diagram is presented and illustrated by two real world examples. The chapter includes VHDL and Verilog descriptions of a flip-flop and a sequential circuit, introducing procedural behavioral VHDL and Verilog language constructs as well as test benches for verification. The chapter concludes by presenting delay and timing for sequential circuits, as well as synchronization of asynchronous inputs and metastability.

Digital Systems Design

Chapter 5, Digital Hardware Implementation, presents topics focusing on various aspects of underlying technology including the MOS transistor and CMOS circuits, and programmable logic technologies. Programmable logic covers read-only memories, programmable logic arrays, programmable array logic, and field programmable gate arrays (FPGAs). The chapter includes examples using a simple FPGA architecture to illustrate many of the programmable elements that appear in more complex, commercially available FPGA hardware.

Chapter 6, Registers and Register Transfers, covers registers and their applications. Shift register and counter design are based on the combination of flip-flops with functions and implementations introduced in Chapters 3 and 4. Only the ripple counter is introduced as a totally new concept. Register transfers are considered for both parallel and serial designs and time–space trade-offs are discussed. A section focuses on register cell design for multifunction registers that perform multiple operations. A process for the integrated design of datapaths and control units using register transfer statements and state machine diagrams is introduced and illustrated by two real world examples. Verilog and VHDL descriptions of selected register types are introduced.

Chapter 7, Memory Basics, introduces static random access memory (SRAM) and dynamic random access memory (DRAM), and basic memory systems. It also describes briefly various distinct types of DRAMs.

Computer design

Chapter 8, Computer Design Basics, covers register files, function units, datapaths, and two simple computers: a single-cycle computer and a multiple-cycle computer. The focus is on datapath and control unit design formulation concepts applied to implementing specified instructions and instruction sets in single-cycle and multiple-cycle designs.

Chapter 9, Instruction Set Architecture, introduces many facets of instruction set architecture. It deals with address count, addressing modes, architectures, and the types of instructions and presents floating-point number representation and operations. Program control architecture is presented including procedure calls and interrupts.

Chapter 10, RISC and CISC Processors, covers high-performance processor concepts including a pipelined RISC processor and a CISC processor. The CISC processor, by using microcoded hardware added to a modification of the RISC processor, permits execution of the CISC instruction set using the RISC pipeline, an approach used in contemporary CISC processors. Also, sections describe high-performance CPU concepts and architecture innovations including two examples of multiple CPU microprocessors.

Chapter 11, Input–Output and Communication, deals with data transfer between the CPU and memory, input–output interfaces and peripheral devices. Discussions of a keyboard, a Liquid Crystal Display (LCD) screen, and a hard drive as peripherals are included, and a keyboard interface is illustrated. Other topics range from serial communication, including the Universal Serial Bus (USB), to interrupt system implementation.

Chapter 12, Memory Systems, focuses on memory hierarchies. The concept of locality of reference is introduced and illustrated by consideration of the cache/main memory and main memory/hard drive relationships. An overview of cache design parameters is provided. The treatment of memory management focuses on paging and a translation lookaside buffer supporting virtual memory.

In addition to the text itself, a Companion Website and an Instructor's Manual are provided. Companion Website (www.pearsonglobaleditions.com/Mano) content includes the following: 1) reading supplements including material deleted from prior editions, 2) VHDL and Verilog source files for all examples, 3) links to computer-aided design tools for FPGA design and HDL simulation, 4) solutions for about one-third of all text chapter problems, 5) errata, 6) PowerPoint® slides for Chapters 1 through 8, 7) projection originals for complex figures and tables from the text, and 8) site news sections for students and instructors pointing out new material, updates, and corrections. Instructors are encouraged to periodically check the instructor's site news so that they are aware of site changes. **Instructor's Manual** content includes suggestions for use of the book and all problem solutions. Online access to this manual is available from Pearson to instructors at academic institutions who adopt the book for classroom use. The suggestions for use provide important detailed information for navigating the text to fit with various course syllabi.

Because of its broad coverage of both logic and computer design, this book serves several different objectives in sophomore through junior level courses. Chapters 1 through 9 with selected sections omitted, provide an overview of hardware for computer science, computer engineering, electrical engineering, or engineering students in general in a single semester course. Chapters 1 through 4 possibly with selected parts of 5 through 7 give a basic introduction to logic design, which can be completed in a single quarter for electrical and computer engineering students. Covering Chapters 1 through 7 in a semester provides a stronger, more contemporary logic design treatment. The entire book, covered in two quarters, provides the basics of logic and computer design for computer engineering and science students. Coverage of the entire book with appropriate supplementary material or a laboratory component can fill a two-semester sequence in logic design and computer architecture. Due to its moderately paced treatment of a wide range of topics, the book is ideal for self-study by engineers and computer scientists. Finally, all of these various objectives can also benefit from use of reading supplements provided on the Companion Website.

The authors would like to acknowledge the instructors whose input contributed to the previous edition of the text and whose influence is still apparent in the current edition, particularly Professor Bharat Bhuva, Vanderbilt University; Professor Donald Hung, San Jose State University; and Professors Katherine Compton, Mikko Lipasti, Kewal Saluja, and Leon Shohet, and Faculty Associate Michael Morrow, ECE, University of Wisconsin, Madison. We appreciate corrections to the previous editions provided by both instructors and students, most notably, those from Professor Douglas De Boer of Dordt College. In getting ready to prepare to think about getting started to commence planning to begin working on the fifth edition, I received valuable feedback on the fourth edition from Patrick Schaumont and Cameron Patterson at Virginia Tech, and Mark Smith at the Royal Institute of Technology (KTH) in Stockholm, Sweden. I also benefited from many discussions with Kristie Cooper and Jason Thweatt at Virginia Tech about using the fourth edition in the updated version of our department's Introduction to Computer Engineering course. I would also like to express my appreciation to the folks at Pearson for their hard work on this new edition. In particular, I would like to thank Andrew Gilfillan for choosing me to be the new third author and for his help in planning the new edition; Julie Bai for her deft handling of the transition after Andrew moved to another job, and for her guidance, support, and invaluable feedback on the manuscript; Pavithra Jayapaul for her help in text production and her patience in dealing with my delays (especially in writing this preface!); and Scott Disanno and Shylaja Gattupalli for their guidance and care in producing the text. Special thanks go to Morris Mano and Charles Kime for their efforts in writing the previous editions of this book. It is an honor and a privilege to have been chosen as their successor. Finally, I would like to thank Karen, Guthrie, and Eli for their patience and support while I was writing, especially for keeping our mutt Charley away from this laptop so that he didn't eat the keys like he did with its short-lived predecessor.

TOM MARTIN
Blacksburg, Virginia

GLOBAL EDITION

The publishers would like to thank the following for their contribution to the Global Edition:

Contributors

Chiranjib Koley, Associate Professor, *National Institute of Technology,* Durgapur
Lyla B. Das, Associate Professor, *National Institute of Technology,* Calicut

Reviewers

Debaprasad Das, Professor, *Assam University*
Moumita Mitra Manna, Lecturer of Computer Science and Applications at *Bangabasi College, University of Calcutta*
Piyali Sengupta, Freelance

CHAPTER

1

DIGITAL SYSTEMS AND INFORMATION

This book deals with logic circuits and digital computers. Early computers were used for computations with discrete numeric elements called *digits* (the Latin word for fingers)—hence the term *digital computer*. The use of "digital" spread from the computer to logic circuits and other systems that use discrete elements of information, giving us the terms *digital circuits* and *digital systems*. The term *logic* is applied to circuits that operate on a set of just two elements with values True (1) and False (0). Since computers are based on logic circuits, they operate on patterns of elements from these two-valued sets, which are used to represent, among other things, the decimal digits. Today, the term "digital circuits" is viewed as synonymous with the term "logic circuits."

The *general-purpose digital computer* is a digital system that can follow a stored sequence of instructions, called a *program*, that operates on data. The user can specify and change the program or the data according to specific needs. As a result of this flexibility, general-purpose digital computers can perform a variety of information-processing tasks, ranging over a very wide spectrum of applications. This makes the digital computer a highly general and very flexible digital system. Also, due to its generality, complexity, and widespread use, the computer provides an ideal vehicle for learning the concepts, methods, and tools of digital system design. To this end, we use the exploded pictorial diagram of a computer of the class commonly referred to as a PC (personal computer) given on the opposite page. We employ this generic computer to highlight the significance of the material covered and its relationship to the overall system. A bit later in this chapter, we will discuss the various major components of the generic computer and see how they relate to a block diagram commonly used to represent a computer. We then describe the concept of layers of abstraction in digital system design, which enables us to manage the complexity of designing and programming computers constructed using billions of transistors. Otherwise, the remainder of the chapter focuses on the digital systems in our daily lives and introduces approaches for representing information in digital circuits and systems.

1-1 INFORMATION REPRESENTATION

Digital systems store, move, and process information. The information represents a broad range of phenomena from the physical and man-made world. The physical world is characterized by parameters such as weight, temperature, pressure, velocity, flow, and sound intensity and frequency. Most physical parameters are *continuous*, typically capable of taking on all possible values over a defined range. In contrast, in the man-made world, parameters can be discrete in nature, such as business records using words, quantities, and currencies, taking on values from an alphabet, the integers, or units of currency, respectively. In general, information systems must be able to represent both continuous and discrete information. Suppose that temperature, which is continuous, is measured by a sensor and converted to an electrical voltage, which is likewise continuous. We refer to such a continuous voltage as an *analog signal*, which is one possible way to represent temperature. But, it is also possible to represent temperature by an electrical voltage that takes on *discrete* values that occupy only a finite number of values over a range, for example, corresponding to integer degrees centigrade between −40 and +119. We refer to such a voltage as a *digital signal*. Alternatively, we can represent the discrete values by multiple voltage signals, each taking on a discrete value. At the extreme, each signal can be viewed as having only two discrete values, with multiple signals representing a large number of discrete values. For example, each of the 160 values just mentioned for temperature can be represented by a particular combination of eight two-valued signals. The signals in most present-day electronic digital systems use just two discrete values and are therefore said to be *binary*. The two discrete values used are often called 0 and 1, the digits for the binary number system.

We typically represent the two discrete values by ranges of voltage values called HIGH and LOW. Output and input voltage ranges are illustrated in Figure 1-1(a). The HIGH output voltage value ranges between 0.9 and 1.1 volts, and the LOW output voltage value between −0.1 and 0.1 volts. The high input range allows 0.6 to 1.1 volts to be recognized as a HIGH, and the low input range allows

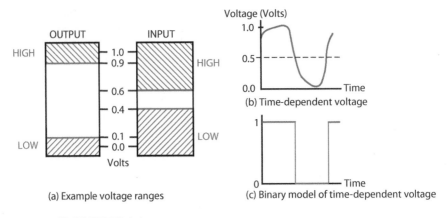

(a) Example voltage ranges   (c) Binary model of time-dependent voltage

☐ **FIGURE 1-1**
Examples of Voltage Ranges and Waveforms for Binary Signals

−0.1 to 0.4 volts to be recognized as a LOW. The fact that the input ranges are wider than the output ranges allows the circuits to function correctly in spite of variations in their behavior and undesirable "noise" voltages that may be added to or subtracted from the outputs.

We give the output and input voltage ranges a number of different names. Among these are HIGH (H) and LOW (L), TRUE (T) and FALSE (F), and 1 and 0. It is natural to associate the higher voltage ranges with HIGH or H, and the lower voltage ranges with LOW or L. For TRUE and 1 and FALSE and 0, however, there is a choice. TRUE and 1 can be associated with either the higher or lower voltage range and FALSE and 0 with the other range. Unless otherwise indicated, we assume that TRUE and 1 are associated with the higher of the voltage ranges, H, and the FALSE and 0 are associated with the lower of the voltage ranges, L. This particular convention is called *positive logic*.

It is interesting to note that the values of voltages for a digital circuit in Figure 1-1(a) are still continuous, ranging from −0.1 to +1.1 volts. Thus, the voltage is actually analog! The actual voltages values for the output of a very high-speed digital circuit are plotted versus time in Figure 1-1(b). Such a plot is referred to as a *waveform*. The interpretation of the voltage as binary is based on a model using voltage ranges to represent discrete values 0 and 1 on the inputs and the outputs. The application of such a model, which redefines all voltage above 0.5 V as 1 and below 0.5 V as 0 in Figure 1-1(b), gives the waveform in Figure 1-1(c). The output has now been interpreted as binary, having only discrete values 1 and 0, with the actual voltage values removed. We note that digital circuits, made up of electronic devices called transistors, are designed to cause the outputs to occupy the two distinct output voltage ranges for 1 (H) and 0 (L) in Figure 1-1, whenever the outputs are not changing. In contrast, analog circuits are designed to have their outputs take on continuous values over their range, whether changing or not.

Since 0 and 1 are associated with the binary number system, they are the preferred names for the signal ranges. A binary digit is called a *bit*. Information is represented in digital computers by groups of bits. By using various coding techniques, groups of bits can be made to represent not only binary numbers, but also other groups of discrete symbols. Groups of bits, properly arranged, can even specify to the computer the program instructions to be executed and the data to be processed.

Why is binary used? In contrast to the situation in Figure 1-1, consider a system with 10 values representing the decimal digits. In such a system, the voltages available—say, 0 to 1.0 volts—could be divided into 10 ranges, each of length 0.1 volt. A circuit would provide an output voltage within each of these 10 ranges. An input of a circuit would need to determine in which of the 10 ranges an applied voltage lies. If we wish to allow for noise on the voltages, then output voltage might be permitted to range over less than 0.05 volt for a given digit representation, and boundaries between inputs could vary by less than 0.05 volt. This would require complex and costly electronic circuits, and the output still could be disturbed by small "noise" voltages or small variations in the circuits occurring during their manufacture or use. As a consequence, the use of such multivalued circuits is very limited. Instead, binary circuits are used in which correct circuit operation can be achieved with significant variations in values of the two output voltages and the two input ranges. The resulting transistor circuit with an output that is either HIGH or LOW is simple, easy to design, and extremely reliable. In addition, this use of binary values makes the results calculated repeatable in the sense that the same set of input values to a calculation always gives exactly the same set of outputs. This is not necessarily the case for multivalued or analog circuits, in which noise voltages and small variations due to manufacture or circuit aging can cause results to differ at different times.

The Digital Computer

A block diagram of a digital computer is shown in Figure 1-2. The memory stores programs as well as input, output, and intermediate data. The datapath performs arithmetic and other data-processing operations as specified by the program. The control unit supervises the flow of information between the various units. A datapath, when combined with the control unit, forms a component referred to as a *central processing unit*, or CPU.

The program and data prepared by the user are transferred into memory by means of an input device such as a keyboard. An output device, such as an LCD (liquid crystal display), displays the results of the computations and presents them to the user. A digital computer can accommodate many different input and output devices, such as DVD drives, USB flash drives, scanners, and printers. These devices use digital logic circuits, but often include analog electronic circuits, optical sensors, LCDs, and electromechanical components.

The control unit in the CPU retrieves the instructions, one by one, from the program stored in the memory. For each instruction, the control unit manipulates the datapath to execute the operation specified by the instruction. Both program and data are stored in memory. A digital computer can perform arithmetic computations, manipulate strings of alphabetic characters, and be programmed to make decisions based on internal and external conditions.

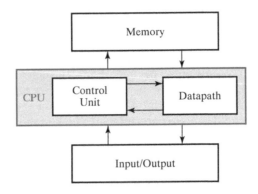

☐ **FIGURE 1-2**
Block Diagram of a Digital Computer

Beyond the Computer

In terms of world impact, computers, such as the PC, are not the end of the story. Smaller, often less powerful, single-chip computers called *microcomputers* or *microcontrollers*, or special-purpose computers called *digital signal processors* (DSPs) actually are more prevalent in our lives. These computers are parts of everyday products and their presence is often not apparent. As a consequence of being integral parts of other products and often enclosed within them, they are called *embedded systems*. A generic block diagram of an embedded system is shown in Figure 1-3. Central to the system is the microcomputer (or its equivalent). It has many of the characteristics of the PC, but differs in the sense that its software programs are often permanently stored to provide only the functions required for the product. This software, which is critical to the operation of the product, is an integral part of the embedded system and referred to as *embedded software*. Also, the human interface of the microcomputer can be very limited or nonexistent. The larger information-storage components such as a hard drive and compact disk or DVD drive frequently are not present. The microcomputer contains some memory; if additional memory is needed, it can be added externally.

With the exception of the external memory, the hardware connected to the embedded microcomputer in Figure 1-3 interfaces with the product and/or the outside world. The input devices transform inputs from the product or outside world into electrical signals, and the output devices transform electrical signals into outputs to the product or outside world. The input and output devices are of two types, those which use analog signals and those which use digital signals. Examples of digital input devices include a limit switch which is closed or open depending on whether a force is applied to it and a keypad having ten decimal integer buttons. Examples of

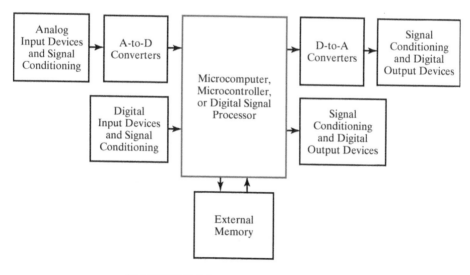

☐ **FIGURE 1-3**
Block Diagram of an Embedded System

analog input devices include a thermistor which changes its electrical resistance in response to the temperature and a crystal which produces a charge (and a corresponding voltage) in response to the pressure applied. Typically, electrical or electronic circuitry is required to "condition" the signal so that it can be read by the embedded system. Examples of digital output devices include relays (switches that are opened or closed by applied voltages), a stepper motor that responds to applied voltage pulses, or an LED digital display. Examples of analog output devices include a loudspeaker and a panel meter with a dial. The dial position is controlled by the interaction of the magnetic fields of a permanent magnet and an electromagnet driven by the voltage applied to the meter.

Next, we illustrate embedded systems by considering a temperature measurement performed by using a wireless weather station. In addition, this example also illustrates analog and digital signals, including conversion between the signal types.

 EXAMPLE 1-1 Temperature Measurement and Display

A wireless weather station measures a number of weather parameters at an outdoor site and transmits them for display to an indoor base station. Its operation can be illustrated by considering the temperature measurement illustrated in Figure 1-4 with reference to the block diagram in Figure 1-3. Two embedded microprocessors are used, one in the outdoor site and the other in the indoor base station.

The temperature at the outdoor site ranges continuously from −40°F to +115°F. Temperature values over one 24-hour period are plotted as a function of time in Figure 1-4(a). This temperature is measured by a sensor consisting of a thermistor (a resistance that varies with temperature) with a fixed current applied by an electronic circuit. This sensor provides an analog voltage that is proportional to the temperature. Using signal conditioning, this voltage is changed to a continuous voltage ranging between 0 and 15 volts, as shown in Figure 1-4(b).

The analog voltage is sampled at a rate of once per hour (a very slow sampling rate used just for illustration), as shown by the dots in Figure 1-4(b). Each value sampled is applied to an analog-to-digital (A/D) converter, as in Figure 1-3, which replaces the value with a digital number written in binary and having decimal values between 0 and 15, as shown in Figure 1-4(c). A binary number can be interpreted in decimal by multiplying the bits from left to right times the respective weights, 8, 4, 2, and 1, and adding the resulting values. For example, 0101 can be interpreted as $0 \times 8 + 1 \times 4 + 0 \times 2 + 1 \times 1 = 5$. In the process of conversion, the value of the temperature is quantized from an infinite number of values to just 16 values. Examining the correspondence between the temperature in Figure 1-4(a) and the voltage in Figure 1-4(b), we find that the typical digital value of temperature represents an actual temperature range up to 5 degrees above or below the digital value. For example, the analog temperature range between −25 and −15 degrees is represented by the digital temperature value of −20 degrees. This discrepancy between the actual temperature and the digital temperature is called the *quantization error*. In order to obtain greater precision, we would need to increase the number of bits beyond four in the output of the A/D converter. The hardware components for sensing, signal conditioning, and A/D conversion are shown in the upper left corner of Figure 1-3.

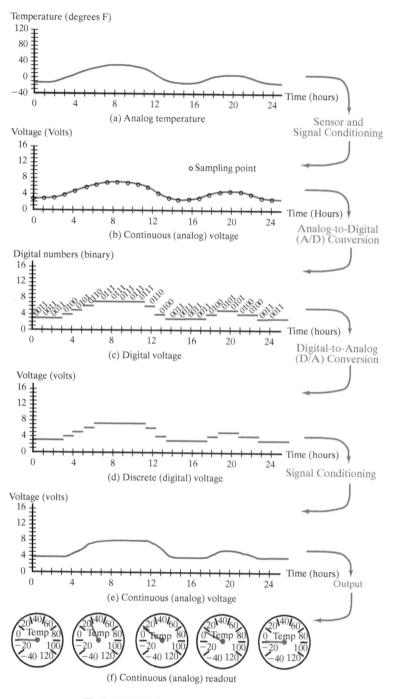

□ **FIGURE 1-4**
Temperature Measurement and Display

Next, the digital value passes through the microcomputer to a wireless transmitter as a digital output device in the lower right corner of Figure 1-3. The digital value is transmitted to a wireless receiver, which is a digital input device in the base station. The digital value enters the microcomputer at the base station, where calculations may be performed to adjust its value based on thermistor properties. The resulting value is to be displayed with an analog meter shown in Figure 1-4(f) as the output device. In order to support this display, the digital value is converted to an analog value by a digital-to-analog converter, giving the quantized, discrete voltage levels shown in Figure 1-4(d). Signal conditioning, such as processing of the output by a low-pass analog filter, is applied to give the continuous signal in Figure 1-4(e). This signal is applied to the analog voltage display, which has been labeled with the corresponding temperature values shown for five selected points over the 24-hour period in Figure 1-4(f). ■

You might ask: "How many embedded systems are there in my current living environment?" Do you have a cell phone? An iPod™? An Xbox™? A digital camera? A microwave oven? An automobile? All of these are embedded systems. In fact, a late-model automobile can contain more than 50 microcontrollers, each controlling a distinct embedded system, such as the engine control unit (ECU), automatic braking system (ABS), and stability control unit (SCU). Further, a significant proportion of these embedded systems communicate with each other through a CAN (controller area network). A more recently developed automotive network, called FlexRay, provides high-speed, reliable communication for safety-critical tasks such as braking-by-wire and steering-by-wire, eliminating primary dependence on mechanical and hydraulic linkages and enhancing the potential for additional safety features such as collision avoidance. Table 1-1 lists examples of embedded systems classified by application area.

Considering the widespread use of personal computers and embedded systems, digital systems have a major impact on our lives, an impact that is not often fully appreciated. Digital systems play central roles in our medical diagnosis and treatment, in our educational institutions and workplaces, in moving from place to place, in our homes, in interacting with others, and in just having fun! The complexity of many of these systems requires considerable care at many levels of design abstraction to make the systems work. Thanks to the invention of the transistor and the integrated circuit and to the ingenuity and perseverance of millions of engineers and programmers, they indeed work and usually work well. In the remainder of this text, we take you on a journey that reveals how digital systems work and provide a detailed look at how to design digital systems and computers.

More on the Generic Computer

At this point, we will briefly discuss the generic computer and relate its various parts to the block diagram in Figure 1-2. At the lower left of the diagram at the beginning of this chapter is the heart of the computer, an integrated circuit called the *processor*. Modern processors such as this one are quite complex and consist of tens to hundreds of millions of transistors. The processor contains four functional modules: the CPU, the FPU, the MMU, and the internal cache.

□ **TABLE 1-1**
Embedded System Examples

Application Area	Product
Banking, commerce and manufacturing	Copiers, FAX machines, UPC scanners, vending machines, automatic teller machines, automated warehouses, industrial robots, 3D printers
Communication	Wireless access points, network routers, satellites
Games and toys	Video games, handheld games, talking stuffed toys
Home appliances	Digital alarm clocks, conventional and microwave ovens, dishwashers
Media	CD players, DVD players, flat panel TVs, digital cameras, digital video cameras
Medical equipment	Pacemakers, incubators, magnetic resonance imaging
Personal	Digital watches, MP3 players, smart phones, wearable fitness trackers
Transportation and navigation	Electronic engine controls, traffic light controllers, aircraft flight controls, global positioning systems

We have already discussed the CPU. The FPU (*floating-point unit*) is somewhat like the CPU, except that its datapath and control unit are specifically designed to perform floating-point operations. In essence, these operations process information represented in the form of scientific notation (e.g., 1.234×10^7), permitting the generic computer to handle very large and very small numbers. The CPU and the FPU, in relation to Figure 1-2, each contain a datapath and a control unit.

The MMU is the *memory management unit*. The MMU plus the internal cache and the separate blocks near the bottom of the computer labeled "External Cache" and "RAM" (*random-access memory*) are all part of the memory in Figure 1-2. The two caches are special kinds of memory that allow the CPU and FPU to get at the data to be processed much faster than with RAM alone. RAM is what is most commonly referred to as memory. As its main function, the MMU causes the memory that appears to be available to the CPU to be much, much larger than the actual size of the RAM. This is accomplished by data transfers between the RAM and the hard drive shown at the top of the drawing of the generic computer. So the hard drive, which we discuss later as an input/output device, conceptually appears as a part of both the memory and input/output.

The connection paths shown between the processor, memory, and external cache are the pathways between integrated circuits. These are typically implemented as fine copper conductors on a printed circuit board. The connection paths below the bus interface are referred to as the processor bus. The connections above the bus interface are the input/output (I/O) bus. The processor bus and the I/O bus attached to the bus interface carry data having different numbers of bits and have different ways of controlling the movement of data. They may also operate at different speeds. The bus interface hardware handles these differences so that data can be communicated between the two buses.

All of the remaining structures in the generic computer are considered part of I/O in Figure 1-2. In terms of sheer physical volume, these structures dominate. In order to enter information into the computer, a keyboard is provided. In order to view output in the form of text or graphics, a graphics adapter card and LCD (*liquid crystal display*) screen are provided. The hard drive, discussed previously, is an electromechanical magnetic storage device. It stores large quantities of information in the form of magnetic flux on spinning disks coated with magnetic materials. In order to control the hard drive and transfer information to and from it, a drive controller is used. The keyboard, graphics adapter card, and drive controller card are all attached to the I/O bus. This allows these devices to communicate through the bus interface with the CPU and other circuitry connected to the processor buses.

1-2 ABSTRACTION LAYERS IN COMPUTER SYSTEMS DESIGN

As described by Moggridge, design is the process of understanding all the relevant constraints for a problem and arriving at a solution that balances those constraints. In computer systems, typical constraints include functionality, speed, cost, power, area, and reliability. At the time that this text is being written in 2014, leading edge integrated circuits have billions of transistors—designing such a circuit one transistor at a time is impractical. To manage that complexity, computer systems design is typically performed in a "top down" approach, where the system is specified at a high level and then the design is decomposed into successively smaller blocks until a block is simple enough that it can be implemented. These blocks are then connected together to make the full system. The generic computer described in the previous section is a good example of blocks connected together to make a full system. This book begins with smaller blocks and then moves toward putting them together into larger, more complex blocks.

A fundamental aspect of the computer systems design process is the concept of "layers of abstraction." Computer systems such as the generic computer can be viewed at several layers of abstraction from circuits to algorithms, with each higher layer of abstraction hiding the details and complexity of the layer below. Abstraction removes unnecessary implementation details about a component in the system so that a designer can focus on the aspects of the component that matter for the problem being solved. For example, when we write a computer program to add two variables and store the result in a third variable, we focus on the programming language constructs used to declare the variables and describe the addition operation. But when the program executes, what really happens is that electrical charge is moved around by transistors and stored in capacitive layers to represent the bits of data and

Algorithms
Programming Languages
Operating Systems
Instruction Set Architecture
Microarchitecture
Register Transfers
Logic Gates
Transistor Circuits

□ **FIGURE 1-5**
Typical Layers of Abstraction in Modern Computer Systems

control signals necessary to perform the addition and store the result. It would be difficult to write programs if we had to directly describe the flow of electricity for individual bits. Instead, the details of controlling them are managed by several layers of abstractions that transform the program into a series of more detailed representations that eventually control the flow of electrical charges that implement the computation.

Figure 1-5 shows the typical layers of abstraction in contemporary computing systems. At the top of the abstraction layers, algorithms describe a series of steps that lead to a solution. These algorithms are then implemented as a program in a high-level programming language such as C++, Python, or Java. When the program is running, it shares computing resources with other programs under the control of an operating system. Both the operating system and the program are composed of sequences of instructions that are particular to the processor running them; the set of instructions and the registers (internal data memory) available to the programmer are known as the instruction set architecture. The processor hardware is a particular implementation of the instruction set architecture, referred to as the microarchitecture; manufacturers very often make several different microarchitectures that execute the same instruction set. A microarchitecture can be described as underlying sequences of transfers of data between registers. These register transfers can be decomposed into logic operations on sets of bits performed by logic gates, which are electronic circuits implemented with transistors or other physical devices that control the flow of electrons.

An important feature of abstraction is that lower layers of abstraction can usually be modified without changing the layers above them. For example, a program written in C++ can be compiled on any computer system with a C++ compiler and then executed. As another example, an executable program for the Intel™ x86 instruction set architecture can run on any microarchitecture (implementation) of that architecture, whether that implementation is from Intel™ or AMD. Consequently, abstraction allows us to continue to use solutions at higher layers of abstraction even when the underlying implementations have changed.

This book is mainly concerned with the layers of abstraction from logic gates up to operating systems, focusing on the design of the hardware up to the interface between the hardware and the software. By understanding the interactions of the layers of abstraction, we can choose the proper layer of abstraction on which to concentrate for a given design, ignoring unnecessary details and optimizing the aspects of the system that are likely to have the most impact on achieving the proper balance of constraints for a successful design. Oftentimes, the higher layers of abstraction have the potential for much more improvement in the design than can be found at the lower layers. For example, it might be possible to re-design a hardware circuit for multiplying two numbers so that it runs 20–50% faster than the original, but it might be possible to have much bigger impact on the speed of the overall circuit if the algorithm is modified to not use multiplication at all. As technology has progressed and computer systems have become more complex, the design effort has shifted to higher layers of abstraction and, at the lower layers, much of the design process has been automated. Effectively using the automated processes requires an understanding of the fundamentals of design at those layers of abstraction.

An Overview of the Digital Design Process

The design of a digital computer system starts from the specification of the problem and culminates in representation of the system that can be implemented. The design process typically involves repeatedly transforming a representation of the system at one layer of abstraction to a representation at the next lower level of abstraction, for example, transforming register transfers into logic gates, which are in turn transformed into transistor circuits.

While the particular details of the design process depend upon the layer of abstraction, the procedure generally involves specifying the behavior of the system, generating an optimized solution, and then verifying that the solution meets the specification both in terms of functionality and in terms of design constraints such as speed and cost. As a concrete example of the procedure, the following steps are the design procedure for combinational digital circuits that Chapters 2 and 3 will introduce:

1. **Specification:** Write a specification for the behavior of the circuit, if one is not already available.

2. **Formulation:** Derive the truth table or initial Boolean equations that define the required logical relationships between inputs and outputs.

3. **Optimization:** Apply two-level and multiple-level optimization to minimize the number of logic gates required. Draw a logic diagram or provide a netlist for the resulting circuit using logic gates.

4. **Technology Mapping:** Transform the logic diagram or netlist to a new diagram or netlist using the available implementation technology.

5. **Verification:** Verify the correctness of the final design.

For digital circuits, the specification can take a variety of forms, such as text or a description in a hardware description language (HDL), and should include the respective symbols or names for the inputs and outputs. Formulation converts the specification into forms that can be optimized. These forms are typically truth tables or Boolean expressions. It is important that verbal specifications be interpreted correctly when formulating truth tables or expressions. Often the specifications are incomplete, and any wrong interpretation may result in an incorrect truth table or expression.

Optimization can be performed by any of a number available methods, such as algebraic manipulation, the Karnaugh map method, which will be introduced in Chapter 2, or computer-based optimization programs. In a particular application, specific criteria serve as a guide for choosing the optimization method. A practical design must consider constraints such as the cost of the gates used, maximum allowable propagation time of a signal through the circuit, and limitations on the fan-out of each gate. This is complicated by the fact that gate costs, gate delays, and fan-out limits are not known until the technology mapping stage. As a consequence, it is difficult to make a general statement about what constitutes an acceptable end result for optimization. It may be necessary to repeat optimization and technology mapping multiple times, repeatedly refining the circuit so that it has the specified behavior while meeting the specified constraints.

This brief overview of the digital design process provides a road map for the remainder of the book. The generic computer consists mainly of an interconnection of digital modules. To understand the operation of each module, we need a basic knowledge of digital systems and their general behavior. Chapters 1 through 5 of this book deal with logic design of digital circuits in general. Chapters 4 and 6 discuss the primary components of a digital system, their operation, and their design. The operational characteristics of RAM are explained in Chapter 7. Datapath and control for simple computers are introduced in Chapter 8. Chapters 9 through 12 present the basics of computer design. Typical instructions employed in computer instruction-set architectures are presented in Chapter 9. The architecture and design of CPUs are examined in Chapter 10. Input and output devices and the various ways that a CPU can communicate with them are discussed in Chapter 11. Finally, memory hierarchy concepts related to the caches and MMU are introduced in Chapter 12.

To guide the reader through this material and to keep in mind the "forest" as we carefully examine many of the "trees," accompanying discussion appears in a blue box at the beginning of each chapter. Each discussion introduces the topics in the chapter and ties them to the associated components in the generic computer diagram at the start of this chapter. At the completion of our journey, we will have covered most of the various modules of the computer and will have gained an understanding of the fundamentals that underlie both its function and design.

1-3 NUMBER SYSTEMS

Earlier, we mentioned that a digital computer manipulates discrete elements of information and that all information in the computer is represented in binary form. Operands used for calculations may be expressed in the binary number system or in the decimal system by means of a binary code. The letters of the alphabet are also converted into a binary code. The remainder of this chapter introduces the binary number system, binary arithmetic, and selected binary codes as a basis for further study in the succeeding chapters. In relation to the generic computer, this material is very important and spans all of the components, excepting some in I/O that involve mechanical operations and analog (as contrasted with digital) electronics.

The decimal number system is employed in everyday arithmetic to represent numbers by strings of digits. Depending on its position in the string, each digit has an associated value of an integer raised to the power of 10. For example, the decimal number 724.5 is interpreted to represent 7 hundreds plus 2 tens plus 4 units plus 5 tenths. The hundreds, tens, units, and tenths are powers of 10 implied by the position of the digits. The value of the number is computed as follows:

$$724.5 = 7 \times 10^2 + 2 \times 10^1 + 4 \times 10^0 + 5 \times 10^{-1}$$

The convention is to write only the digits and infer the corresponding powers of 10 from their positions. In general, a decimal number with n digits to the left of the decimal point and m digits to the right of the decimal point is represented by a string of coefficients:

$$A_{n-1}A_{n-2}\ldots A_1 A_0 . A_{-1} A_{-2} \ldots A_{-m+1} A_{-m}$$

Each coefficient A_i is one of 10 digits (0, 1, 2, 3, 4, 5, 6, 7, 8, 9). The subscript value i gives the position of the coefficient and, hence, the weight 10^i by which the coefficient must be multiplied.

The decimal number system is said to be of *base* or *radix* 10, because the coefficients are multiplied by powers of 10 and the system uses 10 distinct digits. In general, a number in base r contains r digits, $0, 1, 2, \ldots, r^{-1}$, and is expressed as a power series in r with the general form

$$A_{n-1} r^{n-1} + A_{n-2} r^{n-2} + \ldots + A_1 r^1 + A_0 r^0$$

$$+ A_{-1} r^{-1} + A_{-2} r^{-2} + \ldots + A_{-m+1} r^{-m+1} + A_{-m} r^{-m}$$

When the number is expressed in positional notation, only the coefficients and the radix point are written down:

$$A_{n-1}A_{n-2} \ldots A_1 A_0 . A_{-1} A_{-2} \ldots A_{-m+1} A_{-m}$$

In general, the "." is called the *radix point*. A_{n-1} is referred to as the *most significant digit* (*msd*) and A_{-m} as the *least significant digit* (*lsd*) of the number. Note that if $m = 0$, the lsd is $A_{-0} = A_0$. To distinguish between numbers of different bases, it is customary to enclose the coefficients in parentheses and place a subscript after the right parenthesis to indicate the base of the number. However, when the context makes the base obvious, it is not necessary to use parentheses. The following illustrates a base 5 number with $n = 3$ and $m = 1$ and its conversion to decimal:

$$(312.4)_5 = 3 \times 5^2 + 1 \times 5^1 + 2 \times 5^0 + 4 \times 5^{-1}$$
$$= 75 + 5 + 2 + 0.8 = (82.8)_{10}$$

Note that for all the numbers without the base designated, the arithmetic is performed with decimal numbers. Note also that the base 5 system uses only five digits, and, therefore, the values of the coefficients in a number can be only 0, 1, 2, 3, and 4 when expressed in that system.

An alternative method for conversion to base 10 that reduces the number of operations is based on a factored form of the power series:

$$(\ldots((A_{n-1}r + A_{n-2})r + (A_{n-3})r + \ldots + A_1)r + A_0$$
$$+ (A_{-1} + (A_{-2} + (A_{-3} + \ldots + (A_{-m+2} + (A_{-m+1} + A_{-m}r^{-1})r^{-1})r^{-1} \ldots)r^{-1})r^{-1})r^{-1}$$

For the example above,

$$(312.4)_5 = ((3 \times 5 + 1) \times 5) + 2 + 4 \times 5^{-1}$$
$$= 16 \times 5 + 2 + 0.8 = (82.8)_{10}$$

In addition to decimal, three number systems are used in computer work: binary, octal, and hexadecimal. These are base 2, base 8, and base 16 number systems, respectively.

Binary Numbers

The binary number system is a base 2 system with two digits: 0 and 1. A binary number such as 11010.11 is expressed with a string of 1s and 0s and, possibly, a binary point. The decimal equivalent of a binary number can be found by expanding the number into a power series with a base of 2. For example,

$$(11010)_2 = 1 \times 2^4 + 1 \times 2^3 + 0 \times 2^2 + 1 \times 2^1 + 0 \times 2^0 = (26)_{10}$$

As noted earlier, the digits in a binary number are called bits. When a bit is equal to 0, it does not contribute to the sum during the conversion. Therefore, the conversion to decimal can be obtained by adding the numbers with powers of two corresponding to the bits that are equal to 1. For example,

$$(110101.11)_2 = 32 + 16 + 4 + 1 + 0.5 + 0.25 = (53.75)_{10}$$

The first 24 numbers obtained from 2 to the power of n are listed in Table 1-2. In digital systems, we refer to 2^{10} as K (kilo), 2^{20} as M (mega), 2^{30} as G (giga), and 2^{40} as T (tera). Thus,

$$4K = 2^2 \times 2^{10} = 2^{12} = 4096 \quad \text{and} \quad 16M = 2^4 \times 2^{20} = 2^{24} = 16{,}777{,}216$$

This convention does not necessarily apply in all cases, with more conventional usage of K, M, G, and T as 10^3, 10^6, 10^9 and 10^{12}, respectively, sometimes applied as well. So caution is necessary in interpreting and using this notation.

The conversion of a decimal number to binary can be easily achieved by a method that successively subtracts powers of two from the decimal number. To

□ **TABLE 1-2**
Powers of Two

n	2^n	n	2^n	n	2^n
0	1	8	256	16	65,536
1	2	9	512	17	131,072
2	4	10	1,024	18	262,144
3	8	11	2,048	19	524,288
4	16	12	4,096	20	1,048,576
5	32	13	8,192	21	2,097,152
6	64	14	16,384	22	4,194,304
7	128	15	32,768	23	8,388,608

convert the decimal number N to binary, first find the greatest number that is a power of two (see Table 1-2) and that, subtracted from N, produces a positive difference. Let the difference be designated N_1. Now find the greatest number that is a power of two and that, subtracted from N_1, produces a positive difference N_2. Continue this procedure until the difference is zero. In this way, the decimal number is converted to its powers-of-two components. The equivalent binary number is obtained from the coefficients of a power series that forms the sum of the components. 1s appear in the binary number in the positions for which terms appear in the power series, and 0s appear in all other positions. This method is demonstrated by the conversion of decimal 625 to binary as follows:

$$625 - 512 = 113 = N_1 \qquad 512 = 2^9$$
$$113 - 64 = 49 = N_2 \qquad 64 = 2^6$$
$$49 - 32 = 17 = N_3 \qquad 32 = 2^5$$
$$17 - 16 = 1 = N_4 \qquad 16 = 2^4$$
$$1 - 1 = 0 = N_5 \qquad 1 = 2^0$$
$$(625)_{10} = 2^9 + 2^6 + 2^5 + 2^4 + 2^0 = (1001110001)_2$$

Octal and Hexadecimal Numbers

As previously mentioned, all computers and digital systems use the binary representation. The octal (base 8) and hexadecimal (base 16) systems are useful for representing binary quantities indirectly because their bases are powers of two. Since $2^3 = 8$ and $2^4 = 16$, each octal digit corresponds to three binary digits and each hexadecimal digit corresponds to four binary digits.

The more compact representation of binary numbers in either octal or hexadecimal is much more convenient for people than using bit strings in binary that are three or four times as long. Thus, most computer manuals use either octal or hexadecimal numbers to specify binary quantities. A group of 15 bits, for example, can be represented in the octal system with only five digits. A group of 16 bits can be represented in hexadecimal with four digits. The choice between an octal and a hexadecimal representation of binary numbers is arbitrary, although hexadecimal tends to win out, since bits often appear in strings of size divisible by four.

The octal number system is the base 8 system with digits 0, 1, 2, 3, 4, 5, 6, and 7. An example of an octal number is 127.4. To determine its equivalent decimal value, we expand the number in a power series with a base of 8:

$$(127.4)_8 = 1 \times 8^2 + 2 \times 8^1 + 7 \times 8^0 + 4 \times 8^{-1} = (87.5)_{10}$$

Note that the digits 8 and 9 cannot appear in an octal number.

It is customary to use the first r digits from the decimal system, starting with 0, to represent the coefficients in a base r system when r is less than 10. The letters of the alphabet are used to supplement the digits when r is 10 or more. The hexadecimal number system is a base 16 system with the first 10 digits borrowed from the

☐ **TABLE 1-3**
  Numbers with Different Bases

Decimal (base 10)	Binary (base 2)	Octal (base 8)	Hexadecimal (base 16)
00	0000	00	0
01	0001	01	1
02	0010	02	2
03	0011	03	3
04	0100	04	4
05	0101	05	5
06	0110	06	6
07	0111	07	7
08	1000	10	8
09	1001	11	9
10	1010	12	A
11	1011	13	B
12	1100	14	C
13	1101	15	D
14	1110	16	E
15	1111	17	F

decimal system and the letters A, B, C, D, E, and F used for the values 10, 11, 12, 13, 14, and 15, respectively. An example of a hexadecimal number is

$$(B65F)_{16} = 11 \times 16^3 + 6 \times 16^2 + 5 \times 16^1 + 15 \times 16^0 = (46687)_{10}$$

The first 16 numbers in the decimal, binary, octal, and hexadecimal number systems are listed in Table 1-3. Note that the sequence of binary numbers follows a prescribed pattern. The least significant bit alternates between 0 and 1, the second significant bit between two 0s and two 1s, the third significant bit between four 0s and four 1s, and the most significant bit between eight 0s and eight 1s.

The conversion from binary to octal is easily accomplished by partitioning the binary number into groups of three bits each, starting from the binary point and proceeding to the left and to the right. The corresponding octal digit is then assigned to each group. The following example illustrates the procedure:

$$(010\ 110\ 001\ 101\ 011.\ 111\ 100\ 000\ 110)_2 = (26153.7406)_8$$

The corresponding octal digit for each group of three bits is obtained from the first eight entries in Table 1-3. To make the total count of bits a multiple of three, 0s can be added on the left of the string of bits to the left of the binary point. More importantly, 0s must be added on the right of the string of bits to the right of the binary point to make the number of bits a multiple of three and obtain the correct octal result.

Conversion from binary to hexadecimal is similar, except that the binary number is divided into groups of four digits, starting at the binary point. The previous binary number is converted to hexadecimal as follows:

$$(0010\ 1100\ 0110\ 1011.\ 1111\ 0000\ 0110)_2 = (2C6B.F06)_{16}$$

The corresponding hexadecimal digit for each group of four bits is obtained by reference to Table 1-3.

Conversion from octal or hexadecimal to binary is done by reversing the procedure just performed. Each octal digit is converted to a 3-bit binary equivalent, and extra 0s are deleted. Similarly, each hexadecimal digit is converted to its 4-bit binary equivalent. This is illustrated in the following examples:

$$(673.12)_8 = \quad 110 \quad 111 \quad 011. \quad 001 \quad 010 \quad = \quad (110111011.00101)_2$$
$$(3A6.C)_{16} = 0011 \; 1010 \; 0110. \; 1100 \quad = (1110100110.11)_2$$

Number Ranges

In digital computers, the range of numbers that can be represented is based on the number of bits available in the hardware structures that store and process information. The number of bits in these structures is most frequently a power of two, such as 8, 16, 32, and 64. Since the numbers of bits is fixed by the structures, the addition of leading or trailing zeros to represent numbers is necessary, and the range of numbers that can be represented is also fixed.

For example, for a computer processing 16-bit unsigned integers, the number 537 is represented as 0000001000011001. The range of integers that can be handled by this representation is from 0 to $2^{16} - 1$, that is, from 0 to 65,535. If the same computer is processing 16-bit unsigned fractions with the binary point to the left of the most significant digit, then the number 0.375 is represented by 0.0110000000000000. The range of fractions that can be represented is from 0 to $(2^{16} - 1)/2^{16}$, or from 0.0 to 0.9999847412.

In later chapters, we will deal with fixed-bit representations and ranges for binary signed numbers and floating-point numbers. In both of these cases, some bits are used to represent information other than simple integer or fraction values.

1-4 ARITHMETIC OPERATIONS

Arithmetic operations with numbers in base r follow the same rules as for decimal numbers. However, when a base other than the familiar base 10 is used, one must be careful to use only r allowable digits and perform all computations with base r digits. Examples of the addition of two binary numbers are as follows (note the names of the operands for addition):

Carries:	00000	101100
Augend:	01100	10110
Addend:	+10001	+10111
Sum:	11101	101101

The sum of two binary numbers is calculated following the same rules as for decimal numbers, except that the sum digit in any position can be only 1 or 0. Also, a carry in binary occurs if the sum in any bit position is greater than 1. (A carry in decimal occurs if the sum in any digit position is greater than 9.) Any carry obtained in a given position is added to the bits in the column one significant position higher. In the first example, since all of the carries are 0, the sum bits are simply the sum of the augend and addend bits. In the second example, the sum of the bits in the second column from the right is 2, giving a sum bit of 0 and a carry bit of 1 ($2 = 2 + 0$). The carry bit is added with the 1s in the third position, giving a sum of 3, which produces a sum bit of 1 and a carry of 1 ($3 = 2 + 1$).

The following are examples of the subtraction of two binary numbers; as with addition, note the names of the operands:

Borrows:	00000	00110		00110
Minuend:	10110	10110	10011	11110
Subtrahend:	−10010	−10011	−11110	−10011
Difference:	00100	00011		−01011

The rules for subtraction are the same as in decimal, except that a borrow into a given column adds 2 to the minuend bit. (A borrow in the decimal system adds 10 to the minuend digit.) In the first example shown, no borrows occur, so the difference bits are simply the minuend bits minus the subtrahend bits. In the second example, in the right position, the subtrahend bit is 1 with the minuend bit 0, so it is necessary to borrow from the second position as shown. This gives a difference bit in the first position of 1 ($2 + 0 - 1 = 1$). In the second position, the borrow is subtracted, so a borrow is again necessary. Recall that, in the event that the subtrahend is larger than the minuend, we subtract the minuend from the subtrahend and give the result a minus sign. This is the case in the third example, in which this interchange of the two operands is shown.

The final operation to be illustrated is binary multiplication, which is quite simple. The multiplier digits are always 1 or 0. Therefore, the partial products are equal either to the multiplicand or to 0. Multiplication is illustrated by the following example:

Multiplicand:	1011
Multiplier:	× 101
	$\overline{1011}$
	0000
	1011
Product:	$\overline{110111}$

Arithmetic operations with octal, hexadecimal, or any other base r system will normally require the formulation of tables from which one obtains sums and products of two digits in that base. An easier alternative for adding two numbers in base r is to convert each pair of digits in a column to decimal, add the digits in decimal, and then convert the result to the corresponding sum and carry in the base r system. Since addition is done in decimal, we can rely on our memories for obtaining the entries from the familiar decimal addition table. The sequence of steps for adding the two hexadecimal numbers 59F and E46 is shown in Example 1-2.

EXAMPLE 1-2 Hexadecimal Addition

Perform the addition $(59F)_{16} + (E46)_{16}$:

Hexadecimal	Equivalent Decimal Calculation		
	$1 \leftarrow$	$1 \leftarrow$	
5 9 F	5 Carry	9 15	Carry
E 4 6	14	4 6	
$\overline{13E5}$	$1\ \overline{19} = 16 + 3$	$\overline{14} = E$ $\overline{21} = 16 + 5$	

The equivalent decimal calculation columns on the right show the mental reasoning that must be carried out to produce each digit of the hexadecimal sum. Instead of adding F + 6 in hexadecimal, we add the equivalent decimals, 15 + 6 = 21. We then convert back to hexadecimal by noting that 21 = 16 + 5. This gives a sum digit of 5 and a carry of 1 to the next higher-order column of digits. The other two columns are added in a similar fashion. ■

In general, the multiplication of two base r numbers can be accomplished by doing all the arithmetic operations in decimal and converting intermediate results one at a time. This is illustrated in the multiplication of two octal numbers shown in Example 1-3.

EXAMPLE 1-3 Octal Multiplication

Perform the multiplication $(762)_8 \times (45)_8$:

Octal	Octal		Decimal	Octal
762	5×2	=	$10 = 8 + 2$	= 12
45	$5 \times 6 + 1$	=	$31 = 24 + 7$	= 37
4672	$5 \times 7 + 3$	=	$38 = 32 + 6$	= 46
3710	4×2	=	$8 = 8 + 0$	= 10
43772	$4 \times 6 + 1$	=	$25 = 24 + 1$	= 31
	$4 \times 7 + 3$	=	$31 = 24 + 7$	= 37

Shown on the right are the mental calculations for each pair of octal digits. The octal digits 0 through 7 have the same value as their corresponding decimal digits. The multiplication of two octal digits plus a carry, derived from the calculation on the previous line, is done in decimal, and the result is then converted back to octal. The left digit of the two-digit octal result gives the carry that must be added to the digit product on the next line. The blue digits from the octal results of the decimal calculations are copied to the octal partial products on the left. For example, $(5 \times 2)_8 = (12)_8$. The left digit, 1, is the carry to be added to the product $(5 \times 6)_8$, and the blue least significant digit, 2, is the corresponding digit of the octal partial product. When there is no digit product to which the carry can be added, the carry is written directly into the octal partial product, as in the case of the 4 in 46. ■

Conversion from Decimal to Other Bases

We convert a number in base r to decimal by expanding it in a power series and adding all the terms, as shown previously. We now present a general procedure for the
operation of converting a decimal number to a number in base r that is the reverse of
the alternative expansion to base 10 on page 32. If the number includes a radix point,
we need to separate the number into an integer part and a fraction part, since the
two parts must be converted differently. The conversion of a decimal integer to a
number in base r is done by dividing the number and all successive quotients by r
and accumulating the remainders. This procedure is best explained by example.

EXAMPLE 1-4   Conversion of Decimal Integers to Octal

Convert decimal 153 to octal:

The conversion is to base 8. First, 153 is divided by 8 to give a quotient of 19 and a
remainder of 1, as shown in blue. Then 19 is divided by 8 to give a quotient of 2 and a
remainder of 3. Finally, 2 is divided by 8 to give a quotient of 0 and a remainder of 2.
The coefficients of the desired octal number are obtained from the remainders:

$$153/8 = 19 + 1/8 \qquad \text{Remainder} = 1 \qquad \text{Least significant digit}$$
$$19/8 = 2 \ + 3/8 \qquad\qquad\quad = 3$$
$$2/8 = 0 \ + 2/8 \qquad\qquad\quad = 2 \qquad \text{Most significant digit}$$
$$(153)_{10} = (231)_8$$

    Note in Example 1-4 that the remainders are read from last to first, as indicated
by the arrow, to obtain the converted number. The quotients are divided by r until
the result is 0. We also can use this procedure to convert decimal integers to binary,
as shown in Example 1-5. In this case, the base of the converted number is 2, and
therefore, all the divisions must be done by 2.

EXAMPLE 1-5   Conversion of Decimal Integers to Binary

Convert decimal 41 to binary:

$$41/2 = 20 + 1/2 \qquad \text{Remainder} = 1 \qquad \text{Least significant digit}$$
$$20/2 = 10 \qquad\qquad\qquad\qquad = 0$$
$$10/2 = 5 \qquad\qquad\qquad\qquad = 0$$
$$5/2 = 2 + 1/2 \qquad\qquad\qquad = 1$$
$$2/2 = 1 \qquad\qquad\qquad\qquad = 0$$
$$1/2 = 0 + 1/2 \qquad\qquad\qquad = 1 \qquad \text{Most significant digit}$$
$$(41)_{10} = (101001)_2$$

Of course, the decimal number could be converted by the sum of powers of two:

$$(41)_{10} = 32 + 8 + 1 = (101001)_2$$

The conversion of a decimal fraction to base r is accomplished by a method similar to that used for integers, except that multiplication by r is used instead of division, and integers are accumulated instead of remainders. Again, the method is best explained by example.

Example 1-6 Conversion of Decimal Fractions to Binary

Convert decimal 0.6875 to binary:

First, 0.6875 is multiplied by 2 to give an integer and a fraction. The new fraction is multiplied by 2 to give a new integer and a new fraction. This process is continued until the fractional part equals 0 or until there are enough digits to give sufficient accuracy. The coefficients of the binary number are obtained from the integers as follows:

$$0.6875 \times 2 = 1.3750 \qquad \text{Integer} = 1 \qquad \text{Most significant digit}$$
$$0.3750 \times 2 = 0.7500 \qquad\qquad\quad = 0$$
$$0.7500 \times 2 = 1.5000 \qquad\qquad\quad = 1$$
$$0.5000 \times 2 = 1.0000 \qquad\qquad\quad = 1 \quad\downarrow \quad \text{Least significant digit}$$
$$(0.6875)_{10} = (0.1011)_2$$

Note in the foregoing example that the integers are read from first to last, as indicated by the arrow, to obtain the converted number. In the example, a finite number of digits appear in the converted number. The process of multiplying fractions by r does not necessarily end with zero, so we must decide how many digits of the fraction to use from the conversion. Also, remember that the multiplications are by number r. Therefore, to convert a decimal fraction to octal, we must multiply the fractions by 8, as shown in Example 1-7.

EXAMPLE 1-7 Conversion of Decimal Fractions to Octal

Convert decimal 0.513 to a three-digit octal fraction:

$$0.513 \times 8 = 4.104 \qquad \text{Integer} = 4 \qquad \text{Most significant digit}$$
$$0.104 \times 8 = 0.832 \qquad\qquad\quad = 0$$
$$0.832 \times 8 = 6.656 \qquad\qquad\quad = 6$$
$$0.565 \times 8 = 5.248 \qquad\qquad\quad = 5 \quad\downarrow \quad \text{Least significant digit}$$

The answer, to three significant figures, is obtained from the integer digits. Note that the last integer digit, 5, is used for rounding in base 8 of the second-to-the-last digit, 6, to obtain

$$(0.513)_{10} = (0.407)_8$$

The conversion of decimal numbers with both integer and fractional parts is done by converting each part separately and then combining the two answers. Using the results of Example 1-4 and Example 1-7, we obtain

$$(153.513)_{10} = (231.407)_8$$

1-5 DECIMAL CODES

The binary number system is the most natural one for a computer, but people are accustomed to the decimal system. One way to resolve this difference is to convert decimal numbers to binary, perform all arithmetic calculations in binary, and then convert the binary results back to decimal. This method requires that we store the decimal numbers in the computer in such a way that they can be converted to binary. Since the computer can accept only binary values, we must represent the decimal digits by a code that contains 1s and 0s. It is also possible to perform the arithmetic operations directly with decimal numbers when they are stored in the computer in coded form.

An n-bit *binary code* is a group of n bits that assume up to 2^n distinct combinations of 1s and 0s, with each combination representing one element of the set being coded. A set of four elements can be coded with a 2-bit binary code, with each element assigned one of the following bit combinations: 00, 01, 10, 11. A set of 8 elements requires a 3-bit code, and a set of 16 elements requires a 4-bit code. The bit combinations of an n-bit code can be determined from the count in binary from 0 to $2^n - 1$. Each element must be assigned a unique binary bit combination, and no two elements can have the same value; otherwise, the code assignment is ambiguous.

A binary code will have some unassigned bit combinations if the number of elements in the set is not a power of 2. The ten decimal digits form such a set. A binary code that distinguishes among ten elements must contain at least four bits, but six out of the 16 possible combinations will remain unassigned. Numerous different binary codes can be obtained by arranging four bits into 10 distinct combinations. The code most commonly used for the decimal digits is the straightforward binary assignment listed in Table 1-4. This is called *binary-coded decimal* and is commonly referred to as BCD. Other decimal codes are possible but not commonly used.

Table 1-4 gives a 4-bit code for each decimal digit. A number with n decimal digits will require $4n$ bits in BCD. Thus, decimal 396 is represented in BCD with 12 bits as

$$0011 \quad 1001 \quad 0110$$

with each group of four bits representing one decimal digit. A decimal number in BCD is the same as its equivalent binary number only when the number is between

□ **TABLE 1-4**
Binary-Coded Decimal (BCD)

Decimal Symbol	BCD Digit
0	0000
1	0001
2	0010
3	0011
4	0100
5	0101
6	0110
7	0111
8	1000
9	1001

0 and 9, inclusive. A BCD number greater than 10 has a representation different from its equivalent binary number, even though both contain 1s and 0s. Moreover, the binary combinations 1010 through 1111 are not used and have no meaning in the BCD code.

Consider decimal 185 and its corresponding value in BCD and binary:

$$(185)_{10} = (0001 \quad 1000 \quad 0101)_{BCD} = (10111001)_2$$

The BCD value has 12 bits, but the equivalent binary number needs only 8 bits. It is obvious that a BCD number needs more bits than its equivalent binary value. However, BCD representation of decimal numbers is still important, because computer input and output data used by most people needs to be in the decimal system. BCD numbers are decimal numbers and not binary numbers, even though they are represented using bits. The only difference between a decimal and a BCD number is that decimals are written with the symbols 0, 1, 2, ..., 9, and BCD numbers use the binary codes 0000, 0001, 0010, ..., 1001.

1-6 ALPHANUMERIC CODES

Many applications of digital computers require the handling of data consisting not only of numbers, but also of letters. For instance, an insurance company with thousands of policyholders uses a computer to process its files. To represent the names and other pertinent information, it is necessary to formulate a binary code for the letters of the alphabet. In addition, the same binary code must represent numerals and special characters such as $. Any alphanumeric character set for English is a set of elements that includes the ten decimal digits, the 26 letters of the alphabet, and several (more than three) special characters. If only capital letters are included, we need a binary code of at least six bits, and if both uppercase letters and lowercase letters are included, we need a binary code of at least seven bits. Binary codes play an important role in digital computers. The codes must be in binary because computers can handle only 1s and 0s. Note that binary encoding merely changes the symbols, not the meaning of the elements of information being encoded.

ASCII Character Code

The standard binary code for the alphanumeric characters is called ASCII (American Standard Code for Information Interchange). It uses seven bits to code 128 characters, as shown in Table 1-5. The seven bits of the code are designated by B_1 through B_7, with B_7 being the most significant bit. Note that the most significant three bits of the code determine the column of the table and the least significant four bits the row of the table. The letter A, for example, is represented in ASCII as 1000001 (column 100, row 0001). The ASCII code contains 94 characters that can be printed and 34 nonprinting characters used for various control functions. The printing characters consist of the 26 uppercase letters, the 26 lowercase letters, the 10 numerals, and 32 special printable characters such as %, @, and $.

The 34 control characters are designated in the ASCII table with abbreviated names. They are listed again below the table with their full functional names. The control characters are used for routing data and arranging the printed text into a

□ **TABLE 1-5**
American Standard Code for Information Interchange (ASCII)

$B_4B_3B_2B_1$	$B_7B_6B_5$							
	000	001	010	011	100	101	110	111
0000	NULL	DLE	SP	0	@	P	`	p
0001	SOH	DC1	!	1	A	Q	a	q
0010	STX	DC2	"	2	B	R	b	r
0011	ETX	DC3	#	3	C	S	c	s
0100	EOT	DC4	$	4	D	T	d	t
0101	ENQ	NAK	%	5	E	U	e	u
0110	ACK	SYN	&	6	F	V	f	v
0111	BEL	ETB	'	7	G	W	g	w
1000	BS	CAN	(	8	H	X	h	x
1001	HT	EM	)	9	I	Y	i	y
1010	LF	SUB	*	:	J	Z	j	z
1011	VT	ESC	+	;	K	[	k	{
1100	FF	FS	,	<	L	\	l		
1101	CR	GS	-	=	M	]	m	}
1110	SO	RS	.	>	N	^	n	~
1111	SI	US	/	?	O	_	o	DEL

Control Characters

NULL	NULL	DLE	Data link escape
SOH	Start of heading	DC1	Device control 1
STX	Start of text	DC2	Device control 2
ETX	End of text	DC3	Device control 3
EOT	End of transmission	DC4	Device control 4
ENQ	Enquiry	NAK	Negative acknowledge
ACK	Acknowledge	SYN	Synchronous idle
BEL	Bell	ETB	End of transmission block
BS	Backspace	CAN	Cancel
HT	Horizontal tab	EM	End of medium
LF	Line feed	SUB	Substitute
VT	Vertical tab	ESC	Escape
FF	Form feed	FS	File separator
CR	Carriage return	GS	Group separator
SO	Shift out	RS	Record separator
SI	Shift in	US	Unit separator
SP	Space	DEL	Delete

prescribed format. There are three types of control characters: format effectors, information separators, and communication control characters. Format effectors are characters that control the layout of printing. They include the familiar typewriter controls such as backspace (BS), horizontal tabulation (HT), and carriage return (CR). Information separators are used to separate the data into divisions—for example, paragraphs and pages. They include characters such as record separator

(RS) and file separator (FS). The communication control characters are used during the transmission of text from one location to the other. Examples of communication control characters are STX (start of text) and ETX (end of text), which are used to frame a text message transmitted via communication wires.

ASCII is a 7-bit code, but most computers manipulate an 8-bit quantity as a single unit called a *byte*. Therefore, ASCII characters most often are stored one per byte, with the most significant bit set to 0. The extra bit is sometimes used for specific purposes, depending on the application. For example, some printers recognize an additional 128 8-bit characters, with the most significant bit set to 1. These characters enable the printer to produce additional symbols, such as those from the Greek alphabet or characters with accent marks as used in languages other than English.

Adapting computing systems to different world regions and languages is known as *internationalization* or *localization*. One of the major aspects of localization is providing characters for the alphabets and scripts for various languages. ASCII was developed for the English alphabet but, even extending it to 8-bits, it is unable to support other alphabets and scripts that are commonly used around the world. Over the years, many different character sets were created to represent the scripts used in various languages, as well as special technical and mathematical symbols used by various professions. These character sets were incompatible with each other, for example, by using the same number for different characters or by using different numbers for the same character.

Unicode was developed as an industry standard for providing a common representation of symbols and ideographs for the most of the world's languages. By providing a standard representation that covers characters from many different languages, Unicode removes the need to convert between different character sets and eliminates the conflicts that arise from using the same numbers for different character sets. Unicode provides a unique number called a *code point* for each character, as well as a unique name. A common notation for referring to a code point is the characters "U+" followed by the four to six hexadecimal digits of the code point. For example, U+0030 is the character "0", named Digit Zero. The first 128 code points of Unicode, from U+0000 to U+007F, correspond to the ASCII characters. Unicode currently supports over a million code points from a hundred scripts worldwide.

There are several standard encodings of the code points that range from 8 to 32 bits (1 to 4 bytes). For example, UTF-8 (UCS Transformation Format, where UCS stands for Universal Character Set) is a variable-length encoding that uses from 1 to 4 bytes for each code point, UTF-16 is a variable-length encoding that uses either 2 or 4 bytes for each code point, while UTF-32 is a fixed-length that uses 4 bytes for every code point. Table 1-6 shows the formats used by UTF-8. The x's in the right column are the bits from the code point being encoded, with the least significant bit of the code point placed in the right-most bit of the UTF-8 encoding. As shown in the table, the first 128 code points are encoded with a single byte, which provides compatibility between ASCII and UTF-8. Thus a file or character string that contains only ASCII characters will be the same in both ASCII and UTF-8.

In UTF-8, the number of bytes in a multi-byte sequence is indicated by the number of leading ones in the first byte. Valid encodings must use the least number

□ **TABLE 1-6**
   UTF-8 Encoding for Unicode Code Points

Code point range (hexadecimal)	UTF-8 encoding (binary, where bit positions with x are the bits of the code point value)
U+0000 0000 to U+0000 007F	0xxxxxxx
U+0000 0080 to U+0000 07FF	110xxxxx 10xxxxxx
U+0000 0800 to U+0000 FFFF	1110xxxx 10xxxxxx 10xxxxxx
U+0001 0000 to U+0010 FFFF	11110xxx 10xxxxxx 10xxxxxx 10xxxxxx

of bytes necessary for a given code point. For example, any of the first 128 code points, which correspond to ASCII, must be encoded using only one byte rather using one of the longer sequences and padding the code point with 0s on the left. To illustrate the UTF-8 encoding, consider a couple of examples. The code point U+0054, Latin capital letter T, "T", is in the range of U+0000 0000 to U+0000 007F, so it would be encoded with one byte with a value of $(01010100)_2$. The code point U+00B1, plus-minus sign, "±", is in the range of U+0000 0080 to U+0000 07FFF, so it would be encoded with two bytes with a value of $(11000010\ 10110001)_2$.

Parity Bit

To detect errors in data communication and processing, an additional bit is sometimes added to a binary code word to define its parity. A *parity bit* is the extra bit included to make the total number of 1s in the resulting code word either even or odd. Consider the following two characters and their even and odd parity:

	With Even Parity	**With Odd Parity**
1000001	01000001	11000001
1010100	11010100	01010100

In each case, we use the extra bit in the most significant position of the code to produce an even number of 1s in the code for *even parity* or an odd number of 1s in the code for *odd parity*. In general, one parity or the other is adopted, with even parity being more common. Parity may be used with binary numbers as well as with codes, including ASCII for characters, and the parity bit may be placed in any fixed position in the code.

 EXAMPLE 1-8   **Error Detection and Correction for ASCII Transmission**

The parity bit is helpful in detecting errors during the transmission of information from one location to another. Assuming that even parity is used, the simplest case is handled as follows—An even (or odd) parity bit is generated at the sending end for all 7-bit ASCII characters—the 8-bit characters that include parity bits are transmitted to their destination. The parity of each character is then checked at the receiving end; if the parity of the received character is not even (odd), it means that at least one bit has changed its value during the transmission. This method detects one, three, or any odd number of errors in each character transmitted. An even number of errors is undetected. Other error-detection codes, some of which are based on additional parity bits, may be needed to take care of an even number of errors. What is done after an error is detected depends on the particular application. One possibility is to request retransmission of the message on the assumption that the error was random and will not occur again. Thus, if the receiver detects a parity error, it sends back a NAK (negative acknowledge) control character consisting of the even-parity eight bits, 10010101, from Table 1-5 on page 43. If no error is detected, the receiver sends back an ACK (acknowledge) control character, 00000110. The sending end will respond to a NAK by transmitting the message again, until the correct parity is received. If, after a number of attempts, the transmission is still in error, an indication of a malfunction in the transmission path is given. ■

1-7 GRAY CODES

As we count up or down using binary codes, the number of bits that change from one binary value to the next varies. This is illustrated by the binary code for the octal digits on the left in Table 1-7. As we count from 000 up to 111 and "roll over" to 000, the number of bits that change between the binary values ranges from 1 to 3.

For many applications, multiple bit changes as the circuit counts is not a problem. There are applications, however, in which a change of more than one bit when counting up or down can cause serious problems. One such problem is illustrated by an optical shaft-angle encoder shown in Figure 1-6(a). The encoder is a disk attached to a rotating shaft for measurement of the rotational position of the shaft. The disk contains areas that are clear for binary 1 and opaque for binary 0. An illumination source is placed on one side of the disk, and optical sensors, one for each of the bits to be encoded, are placed on the other side of the disk. When a clear region lies

☐ **TABLE 1-7**
   Gray Code

Binary Code	Bit Changes	Gray Code	Bit Changes
000		000	
001	1	001	1
010	2	011	1
011	1	010	1
100	3	110	1
101	1	111	1
110	2	101	1
111	1	100	1
000	3	000	1

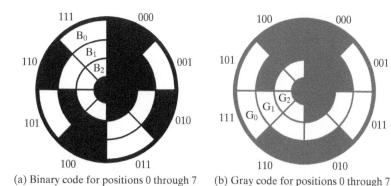

(a) Binary code for positions 0 through 7   (b) Gray code for positions 0 through 7

□ **FIGURE 1-6**
Optical Shaft-Angle Encoder

between the source and a sensor, the sensor responds to the light with a binary 1 output. When an opaque region lies between the source and the sensor, the sensor responds to the dark with a binary 0.

The rotating shaft, however, can be in any angular position. For example, suppose that the shaft and disk are positioned so that the sensors lie right at the boundary between 011 and 100. In this case, sensors in positions B_2, B_1, and B_0 have the light partially blocked. In such a situation, it is unclear whether the three sensors will see light or dark. As a consequence, each sensor may produce either a 1 or a 0. Thus, the resulting encoded binary number for a value between 3 and 4 may be 000, 001, 010, 011, 100, 101, 110, or 111. Either 011 or 100 will be satisfactory in this case, but the other six values are clearly erroneous!

To see the solution to this problem, notice that in those cases in which only a single bit changes when going from one value to the next or previous value, this problem cannot occur. For example, if the sensors lie on the boundary between 2 and 3, the resulting code is either 010 or 011, either of which is satisfactory. If we change the encoding of the values 0 through 7 such that only one bit value changes as we count up or down (including rollover from 7 to 0), then the encoding will be satisfactory for all positions. A code having the property that only one bit at a time changes between codes during counting is a *Gray code* named for Frank Gray, who patented its use for shaft encoders in 1953. There are multiple Gray codes for any set of n consecutive integers, with n even.

A specific Gray code for the octal digits, called a *binary reflected Gray code*, appears on the right in Table 1-7. Note that the counting order for binary codes is now 000, 001, 011, 010, 110, 111, 101, 100, and 000. If we want binary codes for processing, then we can build a digital circuit or use software that converts these codes to binary before they are used in further processing of the information.

Figure 1-6(b) shows the optical shaft-angle encoder using the Gray code from Table 1-7. Note that any two segments on the disk adjacent to each other have only one region that is clear for one and opaque for the other.

The optical shaft encoder illustrates one use of the Gray code concept. There are many other similar uses in which a physical variable, such as position or voltage, has a continuous range of values that is converted to a digital representation. A quite different use of Gray codes appears in low-power CMOS (Complementary Metal Oxide Semiconductor) logic circuits that count up or down. In CMOS, power is consumed only when a bit changes. For the example codes given in Table 1-7 with continuous counting (either up or down), there are 14 bit changes for binary counting for every eight bit changes for Gray code counting. Thus, the power consumed at the counter outputs for the Gray code counter is only 57 percent of that consumed at the binary counter outputs.

A Gray code for a counting sequence of n binary code words (n must be even) can be constructed by replacing each of the first $n/2$ numbers in the sequence with a code word consisting of 0 followed by the even parity for each bit of the binary code word and the bit to its left. For example, for the binary code word 0100, the Gray code word is 0, parity(0, 1), parity(1, 0), parity(0, 0) = 0110. Next, take the sequence of numbers formed and copy it in reverse order with the leftmost 0 replaced by a 1. This new sequence provides the Gray code words for the second $n/2$ of the original n code words. For example, for BCD codes, the first five Gray code words are 0000, 0001, 0011, 0010, and 0110. Reversing the order of these codes and replacing the leftmost 0 with a 1, we obtain 1110, 1010, 1011, 1001, and 1000 for the last five Gray codes. For the special cases in which the original binary codes are 0 through $2^n - 1$, each Gray code word may be formed directly from the corresponding binary code word by copying its leftmost bit and then replacing each of the remaining bits with the even parity of the bit of the number and the bit to its left.

1-8 CHAPTER SUMMARY

In this chapter, we introduced digital systems and digital computers and showed why such systems use signals having only two values. We briefly introduced the structure of the stored-program digital computer and showed how computers can be applied to a broad range of specialized applications by using embedded systems. We then related the computer structure to a representative example of a personal computer (PC). We also described the concept of layers of abstraction for managing the complexity of designing a computer system built from millions of transistors, as well as outlining the basic design procedure for digital circuits.

Number-system concepts, including base (radix) and radix point, were presented. Because of their correspondence to two-valued signals, binary numbers were discussed in detail. Octal (base 8) and hexadecimal (base 16) were also emphasized, since they are useful as shorthand notation for binary. Arithmetic operations in bases other than base 10 and the conversion of numbers from one base to another were covered. Because of the predominance of decimal in normal use, Binary-Coded Decimal (BCD) was treated. The representation of information in the form of characters instead of numbers by means of the ASCII code for the English alphabet was presented. Unicode, a standard for providing characters for languages worldwide, was described. The parity bit was presented as a technique for error detection, and the Gray code, which is critical to selected applications, was defined.

In subsequent chapters, we treat the representation of signed numbers and floating-point numbers. Although these topics fit well with the topics in this chapter, they are difficult to motivate without associating them with the hardware used to implement the operations performed on them. Thus, we delay their presentation until we examine the associated hardware.

REFERENCES

1. GRAY, F. *Pulse Code Communication*. U. S. Patent 2 632 058, March 17, 1953.
2. MOGGRIDGE, B. *Designing Interactions*. Boston: MIT Press, 2006.
3. PATTERSON, D. A., and J. L. HENNESSY, *Computer Organization and Design: The Hardware/Software Interface*, 3rd ed. San Francisco: Morgan Kaufmann, 2004.
4. The Unicode Consortium. "Unicode 6.3.0." 13 November 2013. http://www.unicode.org/versions/Unicode6.3.0/
5. WHITE, R. *How Computers Work: Millennium Edition*, 5th ed. Indianapolis: Que, 1999.

PROBLEMS

The plus (+) indicates a more advanced problem, and the asterisk (*) indicates that a solution is available on the Companion Website for the text.

1-1. This problem concerns wind measurements made by the wireless weather station illustrated in Example 1-1. The wind-speed measurement uses a rotating anemometer connected by a shaft to an enclosed disk that is one-half clear and one-half black. There is a light above and a photodiode below the disk in the enclosure. The photodiode produces a 3 V signal when exposed to light and a 0 V signal when not exposed to light. **(a)** Sketch the *relative* appearance of voltage waveforms produced by this sensor (1) when the wind is calm, (2) when the wind is 10 mph, and (3) when the wind is 100 mph. **(b)** Explain verbally what information the microcomputer must have available and the tasks it must perform to convert the voltage waveforms produced into a binary number representing wind speed in miles per hour.

1-2. Using the scheme in Example 1-1, find the discrete, quantized value of voltage and the binary code for each of the following Fahrenheit temperatures: -34, $+31$, $+77$, and $+108$.

1-3. *List the binary, octal, and hexadecimal numbers from 16 to 31.

1-4. Calculate the exact number of bits in a memory that contains **(a)** 8K bits, **(b)** 4M bits, and **(c)** 2G bytes?

1-5. Calculate the exact number of bits in 2 Tb, with the help of following steps: use the formula of $2^{20} = 1,000,000_{10} + d$, where d is the difference between 2^{20} and $1,000,000_{10}$, to calculate exact number for 2^{20}; then expand the power equation for 1 Tb into a sum-of-products form; insert the value of d; and then find the sum for 1 Tb; thereafter, calculate the exact number of bits for 2 Tb.

1-6. What is the decimal equivalent of the largest binary integer that can be obtained with **(a)** 11 bits and **(b)** 25 bits?

1-7. Convert the binary numbers into decimal numbers: 1011001, 1100111.001, and 10110010.10101.

1-8. Convert the following decimal numbers to binary: 255, 452, 124.5, and 587.625.

1-9. *Convert the following numbers from the given base to the other three bases listed in the table:

Decimal	Binary	Octal	Hexadecimal
369.3125	?	?	?
?	10111101.101	?	?
?	?	326.5	?
?	?	?	F3C7.A

1-10. *Convert the following decimal numbers to the indicated bases, using the methods of Examples 1-4 on page 39 and 1-7 on page 40:

(a) 7562.45 to octal   (b) 1938.257 to hexadecimal   (c) 175.175 to binary.

1-11. *Perform the following conversion by using base 2 instead of base 10 as the intermediate base for the conversion:

(a) $(673.6)_8$ to hexadecimal   (b) $(E7C.B)_{16}$ to octal   (c) $(310.2)_4$ to octal

1-12. Perform multiplications of the following binary numbers:

(a) 100×1110 (b) 1100×1011 (c) 10100×11010

1-13. +Division is composed of multiplications and subtractions. Perform the binary division $1010110 \div 101$ to obtain a quotient and remainder.

1-14. Assume a new number system has a base of 4. There are at most four integer digits. The weights of the digits are 4^3, 4^2, 4^1, and 4^0. Special names are given to the weights as follows: $4 = 1\,C, 4^2 = 1\,G,$ and $4^3 = 1\,R$.

(a) Convert the $6\,R + 2\,G + 2\,C$ number into equivalent decimal number.

(b) Find the base 4 representations of a decimal number 8548_{10}.

1-15. Evidence shows that base 20 has historically been used for number systems. If the numbers are represented as 0, 1, 2, 3, 4, 5, 6, 7, 8, 9, A, B, C, D, E, F, G, H, I, J, then do the following:

(a) Convert 56180_{10} to base 20.

(b) Convert $9ABF_{20}$ to decimal numbers.

(c) Convert $D5HA.5_{20}$ to decimal numbers.

1-16. *In each of the following cases, determine the radix r:

(a) $(BEE)_r = (2699)_{10}$ (b) $(365)_r = (194)_{10}$

1-17. The following mathematical calculation is available in a written script of ancient age, wherein the base is unknown. The calculation indicates summation and multiplication of the unknown number system as presented below. Find the base of the number system.

$$(24 + 13) \times 2 = 134$$

1-18. Find the binary representations for each of the following BCD numbers:

    (a) 0010 1001 0111 0101   **(b)** 0001 1001 0010.0101 0100

1-19. *Represent the decimal numbers 715 and 354 in BCD.

1-20. *Internally in the computer, with few exceptions, all numerical computation is done using binary numbers. Input, however, often uses ASCII, which is formed by appending 011 to the left of a BCD code. Thus, an algorithm that directly converts a BCD integer to a binary integer is very useful. Here is one such algorithm:

1. Draw lines between the 4-bit decades in the BCD number.

2. Move the BCD number one bit to the right.

3. Subtract 0011 from each BCD decade containing a binary value > 0111.

4. Repeat steps 2 and 3 until the leftmost 1 in the BCD number has been moved out of the least significant decade position.

5. Read the binary result to the right of the least significant BCD decade.

    (a) Execute the algorithm for the BCD number 0111 1000.

    (b) Execute the algorithm for the BCD number 0011 1001 0111.

1-21. Internally in a computer, with few exceptions, all computation is done using binary numbers. Output, however, often uses ASCII, which is formed by appending 011 to the left of a BCD code. Thus, an algorithm that directly converts a binary integer to a BCD integer is very useful. Here is one such algorithm:

1. Draw lines to bound the expected BCD decades to the left of the binary number.

2. Move the binary number one bit to the left.

3. Add 0011 to each BCD decade containing a binary value > 0100.

4. Repeat steps 2 and 3 until the last bit in the binary number has been moved into the least significant BCD decade position.

5. Read the BCD result.

    (a) Execute the algorithm for the binary number 1111000.

    (b) Execute the algorithm for the binary number 01110010111.

1-22. How many ASCII codes are possible and how many ASCII characters are used? How an upper-case letter can be converted into lower-case?

1-23. Find the characters representing the following ASCII codes: 1001110 1101111 0101110 0110001 0101101. Represent the 8 bit binary codes for **(a)** even parity system and **(b)** odd parity system.

1-24. Represent the following sentence into ASCII code by maintaining the space and upper- and lower-case letters as given under double quotes: "Pro. No. 1-24".

1-25. *Show the bit configuration that represents the decimal number 255 in: **(a)** binary, **(b)** BCD, **(c)** ASCII, and **(d)** ASCII with odd parity.

1-26. What is the use of Unicode code points? How the compatibility with ASCII characters is maintained in UTF-8 format? Encode the U+00C3 in UTF-8.

1-27. **(a)** List the 7-bit binary number equivalents for 64 through 69 with a parity bit added in the rightmost position, giving odd parity to the overall 7-bit numbers. **(b)** Repeat for even parity.

1-28. Using the procedure given in Section 1-7, find the hexadecimal Gray code.

1-29. This problem concerns wind measurements made by the wireless weather station in Example 1-1. The wind direction is to be measured with a disk encoder like the one shown in Figure 1-6(b). **(a)** Assuming that the code 000 corresponds to N, list the Gray code values for each of the directions, S, E, W, NW, NE, SW, and SE. **(b)** Explain why the Gray code you have assigned avoids the reporting of major errors in wind direction.

1-30. Calculate the total number of bit changes in a one cycle of an 8-bit counter which is counting in binary number. If the counter is now used to count in Gray code, then what will be the total number of bit changes in one complete cycle? What is the advantage of lower number of bit changes?

2

COMBINATIONAL LOGIC CIRCUITS

In this chapter, we will begin our study of logic and computer design by describing logic gates and various means of representing the input/output relationships of logic circuits. In addition, we will learn the mathematical techniques for designing circuits from these gates and learn how to design cost-effective circuits. These techniques, which are fundamental to the design of almost all digital circuits, are based on Boolean algebra. One aspect of design is to avoid unnecessary circuitry and excess cost, a goal accomplished by a technique called optimization. Karnaugh maps provide a graphic method for enhancing understanding of logic design and optimization and solving small optimization problems for "two-level" circuits. Karnaugh maps, while applicable only to simple circuits, have much in common with advanced techniques that are used to create much more complex circuits. Another design constraint for logic is propagation delay, the amount of time that it takes for a change on the input of gate to result in a change on the output. Having completed our coverage of combinational optimization, we introduce the VHDL and Verilog hardware description languages (HDLs) for combinational circuits. The role of HDLs in digital design is discussed along with one of the primarily applications of HDLs as the input to automated synthesis tools. Coverage of general concepts and modeling of combinational circuits using VHDL and Verilog follows.

In terms of the digital design process and abstraction layers from Chapter 1, we will begin with the logic gate abstraction layer. There are two types of logic circuits, combinational and sequential. In a combinational circuit, the circuit output depends only upon the present inputs, whereas in a sequential circuit, the output depends upon present inputs as well as the sequence of past inputs. This chapter deals with combinational logic circuits and presents several methods for describing the input and output relationships of combinational logic gates, including Boolean equations, truth tables, schematics, and HDL. The chapter then describes manual methods of optimizing combinational logic circuits to reduce the number of logic gates that are required. While these manual optimization methods are only practical for small circuits

> and only for optimizing gate count, they illustrate one of the constraints involved in designing combinational logic. The methods also have many aspects in common with methods that are used on much larger circuits and other types of constraints.

2-1 BINARY LOGIC AND GATES

Digital circuits are hardware components that manipulate binary information. The circuits are implemented using transistors and interconnections in complex semi-conductor devices called *integrated circuits*. Each basic circuit is referred to as a *logic gate*. For simplicity in design, we model the transistor-based electronic circuits as logic gates. Thus, the designer need not be concerned with the internal electronics of the individual gates, but only with their external logic properties. Each gate performs a specific logical operation. The outputs of gates are applied to the inputs of other gates to form a digital circuit.

In order to describe the operational properties of digital circuits, we need to introduce a mathematical notation that specifies the operation of each gate and that can be used to analyze and design circuits. This binary logic system is one of a class of mathematical systems generally called *Boolean algebras* (after the English mathematician George Boole, who in 1854 published a book introducing the mathematical theory of logic). The specific Boolean algebra we will study is used to describe the interconnection of digital gates and to design logic circuits through the manipulation of Boolean expressions. We first introduce the concept of binary logic and show its relationship to digital gates and binary signals. We then present the properties of the Boolean algebra, together with other concepts and methods useful in designing logic circuits.

Binary Logic

Binary logic deals with binary variables, which take on two discrete values, and with the operations of mathematical logic applied to these variables. The two values the variables take may be called by different names, as mentioned in Section 1-1, but for our purpose, it is convenient to think in terms of binary values and assign 1 or 0 to each variable. In the first part of this book, variables are designated by letters of the alphabet, such as $A, B, C, X, Y,$ and Z. Later this notation will be expanded to include strings of letters, numbers, and special characters. Associated with the binary variables are three basic logical operations called AND, OR, and NOT:

1. **AND.** This operation is represented by a dot or by the absence of an operator. For example, $Z = X \cdot Y$ or $Z = XY$ is read "Z is equal to X AND Y." The logical operation AND is interpreted to mean that $Z = 1$ if and only if $X = 1$ and $Y = 1$—otherwise $Z = 0$. (Remember that X, Y, and Z are binary variables and can be equal to only 1 or 0.)

2. **OR.** This operation is represented by a plus symbol. For example, $Z = X + Y$ is read "Z is equal to X OR Y," meaning that $Z = 1$ if $X = 1$ or if $Y = 1$, or if both $X = 1$ and $Y = 1$. $Z = 0$ if and only if $X = 0$ and $Y = 0$.

3. **NOT.** This operation is represented by a bar over the variable. For example, $Z = \overline{X}$ is read "Z is equal to NOT X," meaning that Z is what X is not. In other words, if $X = 1$, then $Z = 0$—but if $X = 0$, then $Z = 1$. The NOT operation is also referred to as the *complement* operation, since it changes a 1 to 0 and a 0 to 1.

Binary logic resembles binary arithmetic, and the operations AND and OR have similarities to multiplication and addition, respectively. This is why the symbols used for AND and OR are the same as those used for multiplication and addition. However, binary logic should not be confused with binary arithmetic. One should realize that an arithmetic variable designates a number that may consist of many digits, whereas a logic variable is always either a 1 or a 0. The following equations define the logical OR operation:

$$0 + 0 = 0$$
$$0 + 1 = 1$$
$$1 + 0 = 1$$
$$1 + 1 = 1$$

These resemble binary addition, except for the last operation. In binary logic, we have $1 + 1 = 1$ (read "one OR one is equal to one"), but in binary arithmetic, we have $1 + 1 = 10$ (read "one plus one is equal to two"). To avoid ambiguity, the symbol $\vee$ is sometimes used for the OR operation instead of the $+$ symbol. But as long as arithmetic and logic operations are not mixed, each can use the $+$ symbol with its own independent meaning.

The next equations define the logical AND operation:

$$0 \cdot 0 = 0$$
$$0 \cdot 1 = 0$$
$$1 \cdot 0 = 0$$
$$1 \cdot 1 = 1$$

This operation is identical to binary multiplication, provided that we use only a single bit. Alternative symbols to the · for AND and + for OR, are symbols $\wedge$ and $\vee$, respectively, that represent conjunctive and disjunctive operations in propositional calculus.

For each combination of the values of binary variables such as X and Y, there is a value of Z specified by the definition of the logical operation. The definitions may be listed in compact form in a truth table. A *truth table* for an operation is a table of combinations of the binary variables showing the relationship between the values that the variables take on and the values of the result of the operation. The truth tables for the operations AND, OR, and NOT are shown in Table 2-1. The tables list

□ **TABLE 2-1**
Truth Tables for the Three Basic Logical Operations

AND			OR			NOT	
X	Y	Z = X · Y	X	Y	Z = X + Y	X	Z = X̄
0	0	0	0	0	0	0	1
0	1	0	0	1	1	1	0
1	0	0	1	0	1		
1	1	1	1	1	1		

all possible combinations of values for two variables and the results of the operation. They clearly demonstrate the definition of the three operations.

Logic Gates

Logic gates are electronic circuits that operate on one or more input signals to produce an output signal. Electrical signals such as voltages or currents exist throughout a digital system in either of two recognizable values. Voltage-operated circuits respond to two separate voltage ranges that represent a binary variable equal to logic 1 or logic 0, as illustrated in Figure 2-1. The input terminals of logic gates accept binary signals within the allowable range and respond at the output terminals with binary signals that fall within a specified range. The intermediate regions between the allowed ranges in the figure are crossed only during changes from 1 to 0 or from 0 to 1. These changes are called *transitions*, and the intermediate regions are called the *transition regions*.

The graphics symbols used to designate the three types of gates—AND, OR, and NOT—are shown in Figure 2-1(a). The gates are electronic circuits that produce the equivalents of logic-1 and logic-0 output signals in accordance with their respective truth tables if the equivalents of logic-1 and logic-0 input signals are applied. The two input signals X and Y to the AND and OR gates take on one of four possible combinations: 00, 01, 10, or 11. These input signals are shown as timing diagrams in

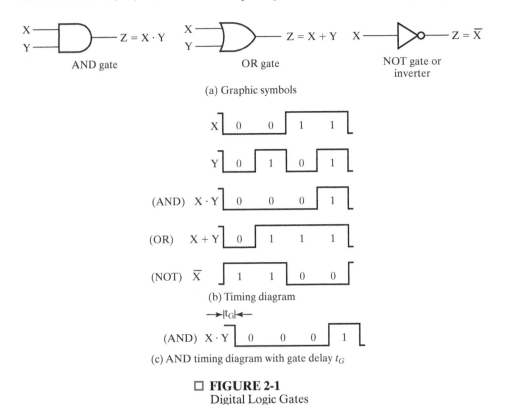

(a) Graphic symbols

(b) Timing diagram

(c) AND timing diagram with gate delay t_G

☐ **FIGURE 2-1**
Digital Logic Gates

Figure 2-1(b), together with the timing diagrams for the corresponding output signal for each type of gate. The horizontal axis of a *timing diagram* represents time, and the vertical axis shows a signal as it changes between the two possible voltage levels. The low level represents logic 0 and the high level represents logic 1. The AND gate responds with a logic-1 output signal when both input signals are logic 1. The OR gate responds with a logic-1 output signal if either input signal is logic 1. The NOT gate is more commonly referred to as an *inverter*. The reason for this name is apparent from the response in the timing diagram. The output logic signal is an inverted version of input logic signal X.

In addition to its function, each gate has another very important property called *gate delay*, the length of time it takes for an input change to result in the corresponding output change. Depending on the technology used to implement the gate, the length of time may depend on which of the inputs are changing. For example, for the AND gate shown in Figure 2-1(a), with both inputs equal to 1, the gate delay when input B changes to 0 may be longer than the gate delay when the input A changes to 0. Also, the gate delay when the output is changing from 0 to 1 may be longer than when the output is changing from 1 to 0, or vice versa. In the simplified model introduced here, these variations are ignored and the gate delay is assumed to have a single value, t_G. This value may be different for each gate type, number of inputs, and the underlying technology and circuit design of the gate. In Figure 2-1(c), the output of the AND gate is shown taking into consideration the AND gate delay, t_G. A change in the output waveform is shifted t_G time units later compared to the change in input X or Y that causes it. When gates are attached together to form logic circuits, the delays down each path from an input to an output add together. In Section 2-7, we will revisit gate delay and consider a more accurate model.

AND and OR gates may have more than two inputs. An AND gate with three inputs and an OR gate with six inputs are shown in Figure 2-2. The three-input AND gate responds with a logic-1 output if all three inputs are logic 1. The output is logic 0 if any input is logic 0. The six-input OR gate responds with a logic 1 if any input is logic 1; its output becomes a logic 0 only when all inputs are logic 0.

Since Boolean functions are expressed in terms of AND, OR, and NOT operations, it is a straightforward procedure to implement a Boolean function with AND, OR, and NOT gates. We find, however, that the possibility of considering gates with other logic operations is of considerable practical interest. Factors to be taken into consideration when constructing other types of gates are the feasibility and economy of implementing the gate with electronic components, the ability of the gate to implement Boolean functions alone or in conjunction with other gates, and the convenience of representing gate functions that are frequently used. In this section, we

(a) Three-input AND gate $F = ABC$

(b) Six-input OR gate $G = A + B + C + D + E + F$

□ **FIGURE 2-2**
Gates with More than Two Inputs

introduce these other gate types, which are used throughout the rest of the text. Specific techniques for incorporating these gate types in circuits are given in Section 3-2.

The graphics symbols and truth tables of the most commonly used logic-gate types are shown in Figure 2-3. Although the gates in Figure 2-3 are shown with just two binary input variables, X and Y, and one output binary variable, F, with the exception of the inverter, all may have more than two inputs. The distinctively shaped symbols shown, as well as rectangular symbols not shown, are specified in detail in the Institute of Electrical and Electronics Engineers' (IEEE) *Standard Graphic Symbols for Logic Functions* (IEEE Standard 91–1984). The AND, OR, and NOT gates were defined previously. The NOT circuit inverts the logic sense of a binary signal to produce the complement operation. Recall that this circuit is typically called an *inverter* rather than a NOT gate. The small circle at the output of the graphic symbol of an inverter is formally called a *negation indicator* and designates the logical complement. We informally refer to the negation indicator as a "bubble."

The NAND gate represents the complement of the AND operation, and the NOR gate represents the complement of the OR operation. Their respective names are abbreviations of NOT-AND and NOT-OR, respectively. The graphics symbols for the NAND gate and NOR gate consist of an AND symbol and an OR symbol, respectively, with a bubble on the output, denoting the complement operation. In contemporary integrated circuit technology, NAND and NOR gates are the natural primitive gate functions for the simplest and fastest electronic circuits. If we consider the inverter as a degenerate version of NAND and NOR gates with just one input, NAND gates alone or NOR gates alone can implement any Boolean function. Thus, these gate types are much more widely used than AND and OR gates in actual logic circuits. As a consequence, actual circuit implementations are often done in terms of these gate types.

A gate type that alone can be used to implement all possible Boolean functions is called a universal gate and is said to be "functionally complete." To show that the NAND gate is a universal gate, we need only show that the logical operations of AND, OR, and NOT can be obtained with NAND gates only. This is done in Figure 2-4. The complement operation obtained from a one-input NAND gate corresponds to a NOT gate. In fact, the one-input NAND is an invalid symbol and is replaced by the NOT symbol, as shown in the figure. The AND operation requires a NAND gate followed by a NOT gate. The NOT inverts the output of the NAND, giving an AND operation as the result. The OR operation is achieved using a NAND gate with NOTs on each input. As will be detailed in Section 2-2, when DeMorgan's theorem is applied, the inversions cancel, and an OR function results.

Two other gates that are commonly used are the exclusive-OR (XOR) and exclusive-NOR (XNOR) gates, which will be described in more detail in Section 2-6. The XOR gate shown in Figure 2-3 is similar to the OR gate, but excludes (has the value 0 for) the combination with both X and Y equal to 1. The graphics symbol for the XOR gate is similar to that for the OR gate, except for the additional curved line on the inputs. The exclusive-OR has the special symbol $\oplus$ to designate its operation. The exclusive-NOR is the complement of the exclusive-OR, as indicated by the

Name	Distinctive-Shape Graphics Symbol	Algebraic Equation	Truth Table
AND		$F = XY$	X Y | F 0 0 | 0 0 1 | 0 1 0 | 0 1 1 | 1
OR		$F = X + Y$	X Y | F 0 0 | 0 0 1 | 1 1 0 | 1 1 1 | 1
NOT (inverter)		$F = \overline{X}$	X | F 0 | 1 1 | 0
NAND		$F = \overline{X \cdot Y}$	X Y | F 0 0 | 1 0 1 | 1 1 0 | 1 1 1 | 0
NOR		$F = \overline{X + Y}$	X Y | F 0 0 | 1 0 1 | 0 1 0 | 0 1 1 | 0
Exclusive-OR (XOR)		$F = X\overline{Y} + \overline{X}Y$ $= X \oplus Y$	X Y | F 0 0 | 0 0 1 | 1 1 0 | 1 1 1 | 0
Exclusive-NOR (XNOR)		$F = XY + \overline{X}\overline{Y}$ $= \overline{X \oplus Y}$	X Y | F 0 0 | 1 0 1 | 0 1 0 | 0 1 1 | 1

□ **FIGURE 2-3**
Commonly Used Logic Gates

☐ **FIGURE 2-4**
Logical Operations with NAND Gates

bubble at the output of its graphics symbol. These gates indicate whether their two inputs are equal (XNOR) or not equal (XOR) to each other.

HDL Representations of Gates

While schematics using the basic logic gates are sufficient for describing small circuits, they are impractical for designing more complex digital systems. In contemporary computer systems design, HDL has become intrinsic to the design process. Consequently, we introduce HDLs early in the text. Initially, we justify such languages by describing their uses. We will then briefly discuss VHDL and Verilog®, the most popular of these languages. At the end of this chapter and in Chapters 3 and 4, we will introduce them both in detail, although, in any given course, we expect that only one of them will be covered.

HDLs resemble programming languages, but are specifically oriented to describing hardware structures and behavior. They differ markedly from typical programming languages in that they represent extensive parallel operation, whereas most programming languages represent serial operation. An obvious use for an HDL is to provide an alternative to schematics. When a language is used in this fashion, it is referred to as a *structural description*, in which the language describes an interconnection of components. Such a structural description, referred to as a *netlist*, can be used as input to logic simulation just as a schematic is used. For this application, models for each of the primitive blocks are required. If an HDL is used, then these models can also be written in the HDL, providing a more uniform, portable representation for simulation input. Our use of HDLs in this chapter will be mainly limited to structural models. But as we will show later in the book, HDLs can represent much more than low-level behavior. In contemporary digital design, HDL models at a high level of abstraction can be automatically synthesized into optimized, working hardware.

To provide an initial introduction to HDLs, we start with features aimed at representing structural models. Table 2-2 shows the built-in Verilog primitives for the

☐ **TABLE 2-2**
Verilog Primitives for Combinational Logic Gates

Gate primitive	Example instance
and	and (F, X, Y);
or	or (F, X, Y);
not	not (F, Y);
nand	nand (F, X, Y);
nor	nor (F, X, Y);
xor	xor (F, X, Y);
xnor	xnor (F, X, Y);

☐ **TABLE 2-3**
VHDL Predefined Logic Operators

VHDL logic operator	Example
not	F <= not X;
and	F <= X and Y;
or	F <= X or Y;
nand	F <= X nand Y;
nor	F <= X nor Y;
xor	F <= X xor Y;
xnor	F <= X xnor Y;

common logic gates from Figure 2-3. Each primitive declaration includes a list of signals that are its inputs and output. The first signal in the list is the output of the gate, and the remaining signals are the inputs. For the not gate, there can be only one input, but for the other gates, there can be two or more inputs. In Verilog, the gate primitives can be connected together to create structural models of logic circuits. VHDL does not have built-in logic gate primitives, but it does have logic operators that can be used to model the basic combinational gates, shown in Table 2-3. Verilog also has logic operators that can be used to model the basic combinational gates, shown in Table 2-4. Chapters 3 and 4 will show the necessary details to create fully simulation-ready models using these gate primitives and logic operators, but the reason for describing them at this point is to show that the HDLs provide an alternative for representing logic circuits. For small circuits, describing the input/output relationships with logic functions, truth tables, or schematics might be clear and feasible, but for larger, more complex circuits, HDLs are often more appropriate.

2-2 BOOLEAN ALGEBRA

The Boolean algebra we present is an algebra dealing with binary variables and logic operations. The variables are designated by letters of the alphabet, and the three basic logic operations are AND, OR, and NOT (complementation). A *Boolean expression* is an algebraic expression formed by using binary variables, the constants 0 and 1,

☐ **TABLE 2-4**
   Verilog Bitwise Logic Operators

Verilog operator symbol	Operator function	Example
~	Bitwise not	F = ~X;
&	Bitwise and	F = X & Y;
|	Bitwise or	F = X | Y;
^	Bitwise xor	F = X ^ Y;
~^, ^~	Bitwise xnor	F = X ~^ Y;

the logic operation symbols, and parentheses. A *Boolean function* can be described by a Boolean equation consisting of a binary variable identifying the function followed by an equals sign and a Boolean expression. Optionally, the function identifier is followed by parentheses enclosing a list of the function variables separated by commas. A *single-output Boolean function* is a mapping from each of the possible combinations of values 0 and 1 on the function variables to value 0 or 1. A *multiple-output Boolean function* is a mapping from each of the possible combinations of values 0 and 1 on the function variables to combinations of 0 and 1 on the function outputs.

EXAMPLE 2-1   Boolean Function Example–Power Windows

Consider an example Boolean equation representing electrical or electronic logic for control of the lowering of the driver's power window in a car.

$$L(D, X, A) = D\overline{X} + A$$

The window is raised or lowered by a motor driving a lever mechanism connected to the window. The function $L = 1$ means that the window motor is powered up to turn in the direction that lowers the window. $L = 0$ means the window motor is not powered up to turn in this direction. D is an output produced by pushing a panel switch on the inside of the driver's door. With $D = 1$, the lowering of the driver's window is requested, and with $D = 0$, this action is not requested. X is the output of a mechanical limit switch. $X = 1$ if the window is at a limit—in this case, in the fully down position. $X = 0$ if the window is not at its limit—i.e., not in the fully down position. $A = 1$ indicates automatic lowering of the window until it is in the fully down position. A is a signal generated by timing logic from D and X. Whenever D has been 1 for at least one-half second, A becomes 1 and remains at 1 until $X = 1$. If $D = 1$ for less than one-half second, $A = 0$. Thus, if the driver requests that the window be lowered for one-half second or longer, the window is to be lowered automatically to the fully down position.

  The two parts of the expression, $D\overline{X}$ and A, are called *terms* of the expression for L. The function L is equal to 1 if term $D\overline{X}$ is equal to 1 or if term A is equal to 1. Otherwise, L is equal to 0. The complement operation dictates that if $\overline{X} = 1$, then $X = 0$. Therefore, we can say that $L = 1$ if $D = 1$, and $X = 0$ or if $A = 1$. So what does the equation for L say if interpreted in words? It says that the window will be lowered if the window is not fully lowered ($X = 0$) and the switch D is being pushed ($D = 1$) or if the window is to be lowered automatically to fully down position ($A = 1$). ∎

    A Boolean equation expresses the logical relationship between binary variables. It is evaluated by determining the binary value of the expression for all possible combinations of values for the variables. A Boolean function can be represented by a truth table. A *truth table* for a function is a list of all combinations of 1s and 0s that can be assigned to the binary variables and a list that shows the value of the function for each binary combination. The truth tables for the logic operations given in Table 2-1 are special cases of truth tables for functions. The number of rows in a truth table is 2^n, where n is the number of variables in the function. The binary combinations for the truth table are the n-bit binary numbers that correspond to counting in decimal from 0 through $2^n - 1$. Table 2-5 shows the truth table for the function $L = D\overline{X} + A$. There are eight possible binary combinations that assign bits to the three variables D, X, and A. The column labeled L contains either 0 or 1 for each of these combinations. The table shows that the function L is equal to 1 if $D = 1$ and $X = 0$ or if $A = 1$. Otherwise, the function L is equal to 0.

    An algebraic expression for a Boolean function can be transformed into a circuit diagram composed of logic gates that implements the function. The logic circuit diagram for function L is shown in Figure 2-5, with the equivalent Verilog and VHDL models for the circuit shown in Figures 2-6 and 2-7. An inverter on input X generates the complement, $\overline{X}$. An AND gate operates on $\overline{X}$ and D, and an OR gate combines $D\overline{X}$ and A. In logic circuit diagrams, the variables of the function F are taken as the inputs of the circuit, and the binary variable F is taken as the output of the circuit. If the circuit has a single output, F is a single output function. If the circuit has multiple

□ **TABLE 2-5**
Truth Table for the Function $L = D\overline{X} + A$

D	X	A	L
0	0	0	0
0	0	1	1
0	1	0	0
0	1	1	1
1	0	0	1
1	0	1	1
1	1	0	0
1	1	1	1

□ **FIGURE 2-5**
Logic Circuit Diagram for $L = D\overline{X} + A$

```
module fig2_5 (L, D, X, A);
    input D, X, A;
    output L;
    wire X_n, t2;

    not (X_n, X);
    and (t2, D, X_n);
    or (L, t2, A);
endmodule
```

☐ **FIGURE 2-6**
Verilog Model for the Logic Circuit of Figure 2-5

```
library ieee, lcdf_vhdl;
use ieee.std_logic_1164.all,
lcdf_vhdl.func_prims.all;
entity fig2_5 is
  port (L: out std_logic;
  D, X, A: in std_logic);
end fig2_5;

architecture structural of fig2_5 is
 component NOT1
  port(in1: in std_logic;
    out1: out std_logic);
 end component;
 component AND2
  port(in1, in2: in std_logic;
    out1: out std_logic);
 end component;
 component OR2
  port(in1, in2: in std_logic;
    out1: out std_logic);
 end component;
signal X_n, t2: std_logic;

begin
    g0: NOT1 port map(X, X_n);
    g1: AND2 port map(D, X_n, t2);
    g3: OR2 port map(t2, A, L);
end structural;
```

☐ **FIGURE 2-7**
VHDL Model for the Logic Circuit of Figure 2-5

outputs, function F is a multiple output function with multiple variables and equations required to represent its outputs. Circuit gates are interconnected by wires that carry logic signals. Logic circuits of this type are called *combinational logic circuits*, since the variables are "combined" by the logical operations. This is in contrast to the sequential logic to be treated in Chapter 4, in which variables are stored over time as well as being combined.

There is only one way that a Boolean function can be represented in a truth table. However, when the function is in algebraic equation form, it can be expressed in a variety of ways. The particular expression used to represent the function dictates the interconnection of gates in the logic circuit diagram. By manipulating a Boolean expression according to Boolean algebraic rules, it is often possible to obtain a simpler expression for the same function. This simpler expression reduces both the number of gates in the circuit and the numbers of inputs to the gates. To see how this is done, we must first study the basic rules of Boolean algebra.

Basic Identities of Boolean Algebra

Table 2-6 lists the most basic identities of Boolean algebra. The notation is simplified by omitting the symbol for AND whenever doing so does not lead to confusion. The first nine identities show the relationship between a single variable X, its complement $\overline{X}$, and the binary constants 0 and 1. The next five identities, 10 through 14, have counterparts in ordinary algebra. The last three, 15 through 17, do not apply in ordinary algebra, but are useful in manipulating Boolean expressions.

The basic rules listed in the table have been arranged into two columns that demonstrate the property of duality of Boolean algebra. The *dual* of an algebraic expression is obtained by interchanging OR and AND operations and replacing 1s by 0s and 0s by 1s. An equation in one column of the table can be obtained from the corresponding equation in the other column by taking the dual of the expressions on both sides of the equals sign. For example, relation 2 is the dual of relation 1 because the OR has been replaced by an AND and the 0 by 1. It is important to note that most of the time the dual of an expression is not equal to the original expression, so that an expression usually cannot be replaced by its dual.

□ **TABLE 2-6**
   Basic Identities of Boolean Algebra

1.	$X + 0 = X$	2.	$X \cdot 1 = X$	
3.	$X + 1 = 1$	4.	$X \cdot 0 = 0$	
5.	$X + X = X$	6.	$X \cdot X = X$	
7.	$X + \overline{X} = 1$	8.	$X \cdot \overline{X} = 0$	
9.	$\overline{\overline{X}} = X$			
10.	$X + Y = Y + X$	11.	$XY = YX$	Commutative
12.	$X + (Y + Z) = (X + Y) + Z$	13.	$X(YZ) = (XY)Z$	Associative
14.	$X(Y + Z) = XY + XZ$	15.	$X + YZ = (X + Y)(X + Z)$	Distributive
16.	$\overline{X + Y} = \overline{X} \cdot \overline{Y}$	17.	$\overline{X \cdot Y} = \overline{X} + \overline{Y}$	DeMorgan's

The nine identities involving a single variable can be easily verified by substituting each of the two possible values for X. For example, to show that $X + 0 = X$, let $X = 0$ to obtain $0 + 0 = 0$, and then let $X = 1$ to obtain $1 + 0 = 1$. Both equations are true according to the definition of the OR logic operation. Any expression can be substituted for the variable X in all the Boolean equations listed in the table. Thus, by identity 3 and with $X = AB + C$, we obtain

$$AB + C + 1 = 1$$

Note that identity 9 states that double complementation restores the variable to its original value. Thus, if $X = 0$, then $\overline{X} = 1$ and $\overline{\overline{X}} = 0 = X$.

Identities 10 and 11, the commutative laws, state that the order in which the variables are written will not affect the result when using the OR and AND operations. Identities 12 and 13, the associative laws, state that the result of applying an operation over three variables is independent of the order that is taken, and therefore, the parentheses can be removed altogether, as follows:

$$X + (Y + Z) = (X + Y) + Z = X + Y + Z$$

$$X(YZ) = (XY)Z = XYZ$$

These two laws and the first distributive law, identity 14, are well known from ordinary algebra, so they should not pose any difficulty. The second distributive law, given by identity 15, is the dual of the ordinary distributive law and does not hold in ordinary algebra. As illustrated previously, each variable in an identity can be replaced by a Boolean expression, and the identity still holds. Thus, consider the expression $(A + B)(A + CD)$. Letting $X = A$, $Y = B$, and $Z = CD$, and applying the second distributive law, we obtain

$$(A + B)(A + CD) = A + BCD$$

The last two identities in Table 2-6,

$$\overline{X + Y} = \overline{X} \cdot \overline{Y} \text{ and } \overline{X \cdot Y} = \overline{X} + \overline{Y}$$

are referred to as DeMorgan's theorem. This is a very important theorem and is used to obtain the complement of an expression and of the corresponding function. DeMorgan's theorem can be illustrated by means of truth tables that assign all the possible binary values to X and Y. Table 2-7 shows two truth tables that verify the

☐ **TABLE 2-7**
Truth Tables to Verify DeMorgan's Theorem

(a) X	Y	X + Y	$\overline{X + Y}$	(b) X	Y	$\overline{X}$	$\overline{Y}$	$\overline{X} \cdot \overline{Y}$
0	0	0	1	0	0	1	1	1
0	1	1	0	0	1	1	0	0
1	0	1	0	1	0	0	1	0
1	1	1	0	1	1	0	0	0

first part of DeMorgan's theorem. In (a), we evaluate $\overline{X + Y}$ for all possible values of X and Y. This is done by first evaluating $X + Y$ and then taking its complement. In (b), we evaluate $\overline{X}$ and $\overline{Y}$ and then AND them together. The result is the same for the four binary combinations of X and Y, which verifies the identity of the equation.

Note the order in which the operations are performed when evaluating an expression. In part (b) of the table, the complement over a single variable is evaluated first, followed by the AND operation, just as in ordinary algebra with multiplication and addition. In part (a), the OR operation is evaluated first. Then, noting that the complement over an expression such as $X + Y$ is considered as specifying NOT $(X + Y)$, we evaluate the expression within the parentheses and take the complement of the result. It is customary to exclude the parentheses when complementing an expression, since a bar over the entire expression joins it together. Thus, $\overline{(X + Y)}$ is expressed as $\overline{X + Y}$ when designating the complement of $X + Y$.

DeMorgan's theorem can be extended to three or more variables. The general DeMorgan's theorem can be expressed as

$$\overline{X_1 + X_2 + \ldots + X_n} = \overline{X}_1 \overline{X}_2 \ldots \overline{X}_n$$

$$\overline{X_1 X_2 \ldots X_n} = \overline{X}_1 + \overline{X}_2 + \ldots + \overline{X}_n$$

Observe that the logic operation changes from OR to AND or from AND to OR. In addition, the complement is removed from the entire expression and placed instead over each variable. For example,

$$\overline{A + B + C + D} = \overline{A}\,\overline{B}\,\overline{C}\,\overline{D}$$

Algebraic Manipulation

Boolean algebra is a useful tool for simplifying digital circuits. Consider, for example, the Boolean function represented by

$$F = \overline{X}YZ + \overline{X}Y\overline{Z} + XZ$$

The implementation of this equation with logic gates is shown in Figure 2-8(a). Input variables X and Z are complemented with inverters to obtain $\overline{X}$ and $\overline{Z}$. The three terms in the expression are implemented with three AND gates. The OR gate forms the logical OR of the terms. Now consider a simplification of the expression for F by applying some of the identities listed in Table 2-6:

$$F = \overline{X}YZ + \overline{X}Y\overline{Z} + XZ$$

$$= \overline{X}Y(Z + \overline{Z}) + XZ \qquad \text{by identity 14}$$

$$= \overline{X}Y \cdot 1 + XZ \qquad \text{by identity 7}$$

$$= \overline{X}Y + XZ \qquad \text{by identity 2}$$

The expression is reduced to only two terms and can be implemented with gates as shown in Figure 2-8(b). It is obvious that the circuit in (b) is simpler than the one in (a) yet, both implement the same function. It is possible to use a truth table to verify that the two implementations are equivalent. This is shown in Table 2-8. As

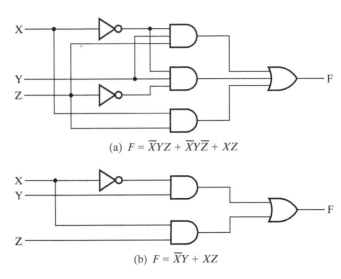

(a) $F = \overline{X}YZ + \overline{X}Y\overline{Z} + XZ$

(b) $F = \overline{X}Y + XZ$

□ **FIGURE 2-8**
Implementation of Boolean Function with Gates

□ **TABLE 2-8**
Truth Table for Boolean Function

X	Y	Z	(a) F	(b) F
0	0	0	0	0
0	0	1	0	0
0	1	0	1	1
0	1	1	1	1
1	0	0	0	0
1	0	1	1	1
1	1	0	0	0
1	1	1	1	1

expressed in Figure 2-8(a), the function is equal to 1 if $X = 0$, $Y = 1$, and $Z = 1$; if $X = 0$, $Y = 1$, and $Z = 0$; or if X and Z are both 1. This produces the four 1s for F in part (a) of the table. As expressed in Figure 2-8(b), the function is equal to 1 if $X = 0$ and $Y = 1$ or if $X = 1$ and $Z = 1$. This produces the same four 1s in part (b) of the table. Since both expressions produce the same truth table, they are equivalent. Therefore, the two circuits have the same output for all possible binary combinations of the three input variables. Each circuit implements the same function, but the one with fewer gates and/or fewer gate inputs is preferable because it requires fewer components.

When a Boolean equation is implemented with logic gates, each term requires a gate, and each variable within the term designates an input to the gate. We define a *literal* as a single variable within a term that may or may not be complemented. The expression for the function in Figure 2-8(a) has three terms and eight literals; the one in Figure 2-8(b) has two terms and four literals. By reducing the number of terms, the number of literals, or both in a Boolean expression, it is often possible to obtain a simpler circuit. Boolean algebra is applied to reduce an expression for the purpose of obtaining a simpler circuit. For highly complex functions, finding the best expression based on counts of terms and literals is very difficult, even by the use of computer programs. Certain methods, however, for reducing expressions are often included in computer tools for synthesizing logic circuits. These methods can obtain good, if not the best, solutions. The only manual method for the general case is a cut-and-try procedure employing the basic relations and other manipulations that become familiar with use. The following examples use identities from Table 2-6 to illustrate a few of the possibilities:

1. $X + XY = X \cdot 1 + XY = X(1 + Y) = X \cdot 1 = X$

2. $XY + X\overline{Y} = X(Y + \overline{Y}) = X \cdot 1 = X$

3. $X + \overline{X}Y = (X + \overline{X})(X + Y) = 1 \cdot (X + Y) = X + Y$

Note that the intermediate steps $X = X \cdot 1$ and $X \cdot 1 = X$ are often omitted because of their rudimentary nature. The relationship $1 + Y = 1$ is useful for eliminating redundant terms, as is done with the term XY in this same equation. The relation $Y + \overline{Y} = 1$ is useful for combining two terms, as is done in equation 2. The two terms being combined must be identical except for one variable, and that variable must be complemented in one term and not complemented in the other. Equation 3 is simplified by means of the second distributive law (identity 15 in Table 2-6). The following are three more examples of simplifying Boolean expressions:

4. $X(X + Y) = X \cdot X + X \cdot Y = X + XY = X(1 + Y) = X \cdot 1 = X$

5. $(X + Y)(X + \overline{Y}) = X + Y\overline{Y} = X + 0 = X$

6. $X(\overline{X} + Y) = X\overline{X} + XY = 0 + XY = XY$

The six equalities represented by the initial and final expressions are theorems of Boolean algebra proved by the application of the identities from Table 2-6. These theorems can be used along with the identities in Table 2-6 to prove additional results and to assist in performing simplification.

Theorems 4 through 6 are the duals of equations 1 through 3. Remember that the dual of an expression is obtained by changing AND to OR and OR to AND throughout (and 1s to 0s and 0s to 1s if they appear in the expression). The *duality principle* of Boolean algebra states that a Boolean equation remains valid if we take the dual of the expressions on both sides of the equals sign. Therefore, equations 4, 5, and 6 can be obtained by taking the dual of equations 1, 2, and 3, respectively.

Along with the results just given in equations 1 through 6, the following *consensus theorem* is useful when simplifying Boolean expressions:

$$XY + \overline{X}Z + YZ = XY + \overline{X}Z$$

The theorem shows that the third term, YZ, is redundant and can be eliminated. Note that Y and Z are associated with X and $\overline{X}$ in the first two terms and appear together in the term that is eliminated. The proof of the consensus theorem is obtained by first ANDing YZ with $(X + \overline{X}) = 1$ and proceeds as follows:

$$XY + \overline{X}Z + YZ = XY + \overline{X}Z + YZ(X + \overline{X})$$
$$= XY + \overline{X}Z + XYZ + \overline{X}YZ$$
$$= XY + XYZ + \overline{X}Z + \overline{X}YZ$$
$$= XY(1 + Z) + \overline{X}Z(1 + Y)$$
$$= XY + \overline{X}Z$$

The dual of the consensus theorem is

$$(X + Y)(\overline{X} + Z)(Y + Z) = (X + Y)(\overline{X} + Z)$$

The following example shows how the consensus theorem can be applied in manipulating a Boolean expression:

$$(A + B)(\overline{A} + C) = A\overline{A} + AC + \overline{A}B + BC$$
$$= AC + \overline{A}B + BC$$
$$= AC + \overline{A}B$$

Note that $A\overline{A} = 0$ and $0 + AC = AC$. The redundant term eliminated in the last step by the consensus theorem is BC.

Complement of a Function

The complement representation for a function F, $\overline{F}$, is obtained from an interchange of 1s to 0s and 0s to 1s for the values of F in the truth table. The complement of a function can be derived algebraically by applying DeMorgan's theorem. The generalized form of this theorem states that the complement of an expression is obtained by interchanging AND and OR operations and complementing each variable and constant, as shown in Example 2-2.

EXAMPLE 2-2 Complementing Functions

Find the complement of each of the functions represented by the equations $F_1 = \overline{X}Y\overline{Z} + \overline{X}\,\overline{Y}Z$ and $F_2 = X(\overline{Y}\,\overline{Z} + YZ)$. Applying DeMorgan's theorem as many times as necessary, we obtain the complements as follows:

$$\overline{F}_1 = \overline{\overline{X}Y\overline{Z} + \overline{X}\,\overline{Y}Z} = (\overline{\overline{X}Y\overline{Z}}) \cdot (\overline{\overline{X}\,\overline{Y}Z})$$
$$= (X + \overline{Y} + Z)(X + Y + \overline{Z})$$
$$\overline{F}_2 = \overline{X(\overline{Y}\,\overline{Z} + YZ)} = \overline{X} + \overline{(\overline{Y}\,\overline{Z} + YZ)}$$
$$= \overline{X} + \overline{\overline{Y}\,\overline{Z}} \cdot \overline{YZ}$$
$$= \overline{X} + (Y + Z)(\overline{Y} + \overline{Z})$$

A simpler method for deriving the complement of a function is to take the dual of the function equation and complement each literal. This method follows from the generalization of DeMorgan's theorem. Remember that the dual of an expression is obtained by interchanging AND and OR operations and 1s and 0s. To avoid confusion in handling complex functions, adding parentheses around terms before taking the dual is helpful, as illustrated in the next example. ■

EXAMPLE 2-3   Complementing Functions by Using Duals

Find the complements of the functions in Example 2-2 by taking the duals of their equations and complementing each literal.

We begin with

$$F_1 = \overline{X}Y\overline{Z} + \overline{X}\,\overline{Y}Z = (\overline{X}Y\overline{Z}) + (\overline{X}\,\overline{Y}Z)$$

The dual of F_1 is

$$(\overline{X} + Y + \overline{Z})(\overline{X} + \overline{Y} + Z)$$

Complementing each literal, we have

$$(X + \overline{Y} + Z)(X + Y + \overline{Z}) = \overline{F}_1$$

Now,

$$F_2 = X(\overline{Y}\,\overline{Z} + YZ) = X((\overline{Y}\,\overline{Z}) + (YZ))$$

The dual of F_2 is

$$X + (\overline{Y} + \overline{Z})(Y + Z)$$

Complementing each literal yields

$$\overline{X} + (Y + Z)(\overline{Y} + \overline{Z}) = \overline{F}_2$$ ■

2-3   STANDARD FORMS

A Boolean function expressed algebraically can be written in a variety of ways. There are, however, specific ways of writing algebraic equations that are considered to be standard forms. The standard forms facilitate the simplification procedures for Boolean expressions and, in some cases, may result in more desirable expressions for implementing logic circuits.

The standard forms contain *product terms* and *sum terms*. An example of a product term is $X\overline{Y}Z$. This is a logical product consisting of an AND operation among three literals. An example of a sum term is $X + Y + \overline{Z}$. This is a logical sum consisting of an OR operation among the literals. In Boolean algebra, the words "product" and "sum" do not imply arithmetic operations—instead, they specify the logical operations AND and OR, respectively.

Minterms and Maxterms

A truth table defines a Boolean function. An algebraic expression for the function can be derived from the table by finding a logical sum of product terms for which the function assumes the binary value 1. A product term in which all the variables appear exactly once, either complemented or uncomplemented, is called a *minterm*. Its characteristic property is that it represents exactly one combination of binary variable values in the truth table. It has the value 1 for that combination and 0 for all others. There are 2^n distinct minterms for n variables. The four minterms for the two variables X and Y are $\overline{X}\,\overline{Y}$, $\overline{X}Y$, $X\overline{Y}$, and XY. The eight minterms for the three variables X, Y, and Z are listed in Table 2-9. The binary numbers from 000 to 111 are listed under the variables. For each binary combination, there is a related minterm. Each minterm is a product term of exactly n literals, where n is the number of variables. In this example, $n = 3$. A literal is a complemented variable if the corresponding bit of the related binary combination is 0 and is an uncomplemented variable if it is 1. A symbol m_j for each minterm is also shown in the table, where the subscript j denotes the decimal equivalent of the binary combination corresponding to the minterm. This list of minterms for any given n variables can be formed in a similar manner from a list of the binary numbers from 0 through $2^n - 1$. In addition, the truth table for each minterm is given in the right half of the table. These truth tables clearly show that each minterm is 1 for the corresponding binary combination and 0 for all other combinations. Such truth tables will be helpful later in using minterms to form Boolean expressions.

A sum term that contains all the variables in complemented or uncomplemented form is called a *maxterm*. Again, it is possible to formulate 2^n maxterms with n variables. The eight maxterms for three variables are listed in Table 2-10. Each maxterm is a logical sum of the three variables, with each variable being complemented if the corresponding bit of the binary number is 1 and uncomplemented if it is 0. The symbol for a maxterm is M_j, where j denotes the decimal equivalent of the binary combination corresponding to the maxterm. In the right half of the table, the truth table for each maxterm is given. Note that the value of the maxterm is 0 for the corresponding combination and 1 for all other combinations. It is now clear where the terms "minterm" and "maxterm" come from: a minterm is a function, not equal to 0, having the minimum number of 1s in its truth table; a maxterm is a function, not equal to 1, having the maximum of 1s in its truth table. Note from Table 2-9

☐ **TABLE 2-9**
Minterms for Three Variables

X	Y	Z	Product Term	Symbol	m_0	m_1	m_2	m_3	m_4	m_5	m_6	m_7
0	0	0	$\overline{X}\,\overline{Y}\,\overline{Z}$	m_0	1	0	0	0	0	0	0	0
0	0	1	$\overline{X}\,\overline{Y}Z$	m_1	0	1	0	0	0	0	0	0
0	1	0	$\overline{X}Y\overline{Z}$	m_2	0	0	1	0	0	0	0	0
0	1	1	$\overline{X}YZ$	m_3	0	0	0	1	0	0	0	0
1	0	0	$X\overline{Y}\,\overline{Z}$	m_4	0	0	0	0	1	0	0	0
1	0	1	$X\overline{Y}Z$	m_5	0	0	0	0	0	1	0	0
1	1	0	$XY\overline{Z}$	m_6	0	0	0	0	0	0	1	0
1	1	1	XYZ	m_7	0	0	0	0	0	0	0	1

and Table 2-10 that a minterm and maxterm with the same subscript are the comple-ments of each other; that is, $M_j = \overline{m_j}$ and $m_j = \overline{M_j}$. For example, for $j = 3$, we have

$$M_3 = X + \overline{Y} + \overline{Z} + = \overline{\overline{X}Y Z} = \overline{m_3}$$

A Boolean function can be represented algebraically from a given truth table by forming the logical sum of all the minterms that produce a 1 in the function. This expression is called a *sum of minterms*. Consider the Boolean function F in Table 2-11(a). The function is equal to 1 for each of the following binary combinations of the variables X, Y, and Z : 000, 010, 101 and 111. These combinations correspond to minterms 0, 2, 5, and 7. By examining Table 2-11 and the truth tables for these min-terms in Table 2-9, it is evident that the function F can be expressed algebraically as the logical sum of the stated minterms:

$$F = \overline{X}\,\overline{Y}\overline{Z} + \overline{X}Y\overline{Z} + X\overline{Y}Z + XYZ = m_0 + m_2 + m_5 + m_7$$

This can be further abbreviated by listing only the decimal subscripts of the minterms:

$$F(X, Y, Z) = \Sigma m(0, 2, 5, 7)$$

□ **TABLE 2-10**
Maxterms for Three Variables

X	Y	Z	Sum Term	Symbol	M_0	M_1	M_2	M_3	M_4	M_5	M_6	M_7
0	0	0	$X + Y + Z$	M_0	0	1	1	1	1	1	1	1
0	0	1	$X + Y + \overline{Z}$	M_1	1	0	1	1	1	1	1	1
0	1	0	$X + \overline{Y} + Z$	M_2	1	1	0	1	1	1	1	1
0	1	1	$X + \overline{Y} + \overline{Z}$	M_3	1	1	1	0	1	1	1	1
1	0	0	$\overline{X} + Y + Z$	M_4	1	1	1	1	0	1	1	1
1	0	1	$\overline{X} + Y + \overline{Z}$	M_5	1	1	1	1	1	0	1	1
1	1	0	$\overline{X} + \overline{Y} + Z$	M_6	1	1	1	1	1	1	0	1
1	1	1	$\overline{X} + \overline{Y} + \overline{Z}$	M_7	1	1	1	1	1	1	1	0

□ **TABLE 2-11**
Boolean Functions of Three Variables

(a) X	Y	Z	F	$\overline{F}$	(b) X	Y	Z	E
0	0	0	1	0	0	0	0	1
0	0	1	0	1	0	0	1	1
0	1	0	1	0	0	1	0	1
0	1	1	0	1	0	1	1	0
1	0	0	0	1	1	0	0	1
1	0	1	1	0	1	0	1	1
1	1	0	0	1	1	1	0	0
1	1	1	1	0	1	1	1	0

The symbol Σ stands for the logical sum (Boolean OR) of the minterms. The numbers following it represent the minterms of the function. The letters in parentheses following F form a list of the variables in the order taken when the minterms are converted to product terms.

Now consider the complement of a Boolean function. The binary values of $\overline{F}$ in Table 2-11(a) are obtained by changing 1s to 0s and 0s to 1s in the values of F. Taking the logical sum of minterms of $\overline{F}$, we obtain

$$\overline{F}(X,Y,Z) = \overline{X}\,\overline{Y}Z + \overline{X}YZ + X\overline{Y}\,\overline{Z} + XY\overline{Z} = m_1 + m_3 + m_4 + m_6$$

or, in abbreviated form,

$$\overline{F}(X, Y, Z) = \Sigma m(1, 3, 4, 6)$$

Note that the minterm numbers for $\overline{F}$ are the ones missing from the list of the minterm numbers of F. We now take the complement of $\overline{F}$ to obtain F:

$$F = \overline{m_1 + m_3 + m_4 + m_6} = \overline{m_1} \cdot \overline{m_3} \cdot \overline{m_4} \cdot \overline{m_6}$$

$$= M_1 \cdot M_3 \cdot M_4 \cdot M_6 \text{ (since } \overline{m_j} = M_j\text{)}$$

$$= (X + Y + \overline{Z})(X + \overline{Y} + \overline{Z})(\overline{X} + Y + Z)(\overline{X} + \overline{Y} + Z)$$

This shows the procedure for expressing a Boolean function as a *product of maxterms*. The abbreviated form for this product is

$$F(X, Y, Z) = \Pi M(1, 3, 4, 6)$$

where the symbol Π denotes the logical product (Boolean AND) of the maxterms whose numbers are listed in parentheses. Note that the decimal numbers included in the product of maxterms will always be the same as the minterm list of the complemented function, such as (1, 3, 4, 6) in the foregoing example. Maxterms are seldom used directly when dealing with Boolean functions, since we can always replace them with the minterm list of $\overline{F}$.

The following is a summary of the most important properties of minterms:

1. There are 2^n minterms for n Boolean variables. These minterms can be generated from the binary numbers from 0 to $2^n - 1$.

2. Any Boolean function can be expressed as a logical sum of minterms.

3. The complement of a function contains those minterms not included in the original function.

4. A function that includes all the 2^n minterms is equal to logic 1.

A function that is not in the sum-of-minterms form can be converted to that form by means of a truth table, since the truth table always specifies the minterms of the function. Consider, for example, the Boolean function

$$E = \overline{Y} + \overline{X}\,\overline{Z}$$

The expression is not in sum-of-minterms form, because each term does not contain all three variables X, Y, and Z. The truth table for this function is listed in Table 2-11(b).

From the table, we obtain the minterms of the function:

$$E(X, Y, Z) = \Sigma m(0, 1, 2, 4, 5)$$

The minterms for the complement of E are given by

$$\overline{E}(X, Y, Z) = \Sigma m(3, 6, 7)$$

Note that the total number of minterms in E and $\overline{E}$ is equal to eight, since the function has three variables, and three variables produce a total of eight minterms. With four variables, there will be a total of 16 minterms, and for two variables, there will be four minterms. An example of a function that includes all the minterms is

$$G(X, Y) = \Sigma m(0, 1, 2, 3) = 1$$

Since G is a function of two variables and contains all four minterms, it is always equal to logic 1.

Sum of Products

The sum-of-minterms form is a standard algebraic expression that is obtained directly from a truth table. The expression so obtained contains the maximum number of literals in each term and usually has more product terms than necessary. This is because, by definition, each minterm must include all the variables of the function, complemented or uncomplemented. Once the sum of minterms is obtained from the truth table, the next step is to try to simplify the expression to see whether it is possible to reduce the number of product terms and the number of literals in the terms. The result is a simplified expression in *sum-of-products* form. This is an alternative standard form of expression that contains product terms with up to n literals. An example of a Boolean function expressed as a sum of products is

$$F = \overline{Y} + \overline{X}Y\overline{Z} + XY$$

The expression has three product terms, the first with one literal, the second with three literals, and the third with two literals.

The logic diagram for a sum-of-products form consists of a group of AND gates followed by a single OR gate, as shown in Figure 2-9. Each product term requires an AND gate, except for a term with a single literal. The logical sum is formed with an OR gate that has single literals and the outputs of the AND gates as inputs. Often,

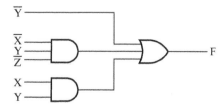

☐ **FIGURE 2-9**
Sum-of-Products Implementation

we assumed that the input variables are directly available in their complemented and uncomplemented forms, so inverters are not included in the diagram. The AND gates followed by the OR gate form a circuit configuration referred to as a *two-level implementation* or *two-level circuit*.

If an expression is not in sum-of-products-form, it can be converted to the standard form by means of the distributive laws. Consider the expression

$$F = AB + C(D + E)$$

This is not in sum-of-products form, because the term $D + E$ is part of a product, not a single literal. The expression can be converted to a sum of products by applying the appropriate distributive law as follows:

$$F = AB + C(D + E) = AB + CD + CE$$

The function F is implemented in a nonstandard form in Figure 2-10(a). This requires two AND gates and two OR gates. There are three levels of gating in the circuit. F is implemented in sum-of-products form in Figure 2-10(b). This circuit requires three AND gates and an OR gate and uses two levels of gating. The decision as to whether to use a two-level or multiple-level (three levels or more) implementation is complex. Among the issues involved are the number of gates, number of gate inputs, and the amount of delay between the time the input values are set and the time the resulting output values appear. Two-level implementations are the natural form for certain implementation technologies, as we will see in Chapter 5.

Product of Sums

Another standard form of expressing Boolean functions algebraically is the *product of sums*. This form is obtained by forming a logical product of sum terms. Each logical sum term may have any number of distinct literals. An example of a function expressed in product-of-sums form is

$$F = X(\overline{Y} + Z)(X + Y + \overline{Z})$$

This expression has sum terms of one, two, and three literals. The sum terms perform an OR operation, and the product is an AND operation.

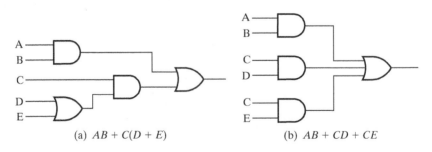

(a) $AB + C(D + E)$ (b) $AB + CD + CE$

☐ **FIGURE 2-10**
Three-Level and Two-Level Implementation

□ **FIGURE 2-11**
Product-of-Sums Implementation

The gate structure of the product-of-sums expression consists of a group of OR gates for the sum terms (except for a single literal term), followed by an AND gate. This is shown in Figure 2-11 for the preceding function F. As with the sum of products, this standard type of expression results in a two-level gating structure.

2-4 TWO-LEVEL CIRCUIT OPTIMIZATION

The complexity of a logic circuit that implements a Boolean function is directly related to the algebraic expression from which the function is implemented. Although the truth-table representation of a function is unique, when expressed algebraically, the function appears in many different forms. Boolean expressions may be simplified by algebraic manipulation, as discussed in Section 2-2. However, this procedure of simplification is awkward, because it lacks specific rules to predict each succeeding step in the manipulative process and it is difficult to determine whether the simplest expression has been achieved. By contrast, the map method provides a straightforward procedure for optimizing Boolean functions of up to four variables. Maps for five and six variables can be drawn as well, but are more cumbersome to use. The map is also known as the *Karnaugh map*, or *K-map*. The map is a diagram made up of squares, with each square representing one row of a truth table, or correspondingly, one minterm of a single output function. Since any Boolean function can be expressed as a sum of minterms, it follows that a Boolean function is recognized graphically in the map by those squares for which the function has value 1, or correspondingly, whose minterms are included in the function. From a more complex view, the map presents a visual diagram of all possible ways a function may be expressed in a standard form. Among these ways are the optimum sum-of-products standard forms for the function. The optimized expressions produced by the map are always in sum-of-products or product-of-sums form. Thus, maps handle optimization for two-level implementations, but do not apply directly to possible simpler implementations for the general case with three or more levels. Initially, this section covers sum-of-products optimization and, later, applies it to performing product-of-sums optimization.

Cost Criteria

In the prior section, counting literals and terms was mentioned as a way of measuring the simplicity of a logic circuit. We introduce two cost criteria to formalize this concept.

The first criterion is *literal cost*, the number of literal appearances in a Boolean expression corresponding exactly to the logic diagram. For example, for the circuits in Figure 2-10, the corresponding Boolean expressions are

$$F = AB + C(D + E) \text{ and } F = AB + CD + CE$$

There are five literal appearances in the first equation and six in the second, so the first equation is the simplest in terms of literal cost. Literal cost has the advantage that it is very simple to evaluate by counting literal appearances. It does not, however, represent circuit complexity accurately in all cases, even for the comparison of different implementations of the same logic function. The following Boolean equations, both for function G, illustrate this situation:

$$G = ABCD + \overline{A}\,\overline{B}\,\overline{C}\overline{D} \text{ and } G = (\overline{A} + B)(\overline{B} + C)(\overline{C} + D)(\overline{D} + A)$$

The implementations represented by these equations both have a literal cost of eight. But, the first equation has two terms and the second has four. This suggests that the first equation has a lower cost than the second.

To capture the difference illustrated, we define *gate-input cost* as the number of inputs to the gates in the implementation corresponding exactly to the given equation or equations. This cost can be determined easily from the logic diagram by simply counting the total number of inputs to the gates in the logic diagram. For sum-of-products or product-of-sums equations, it can be found from the equation by finding the sum of

1. all literal appearances,
2. the number of terms excluding terms that consist only of a single literal, and, optionally,
3. the number of distinct complemented single literals.

In (1), all gate inputs from outside the circuit are represented. In (2), all gate inputs within the circuit, except for those to inverters, are represented and in (3), inverters needed to complement the input variables are counted in the event that complemented input variables are not provided. For the two preceding equations, excluding the count from (3), the respective gate-input counts are $8 + 2 = 10$ and $8 + 4 = 12$. Including the count from (3), that of input inverters, the respective counts are 14 and 16. So the first equation for G has a lower gate-input cost, even though the literal costs are equal.

Gate-input cost is currently a good measure for contemporary logic implementations, since it is proportional to the number of transistors and wires used in implementing a logic circuit. Representation of gate inputs becomes particularly important in measuring cost for circuits with more than two levels. Typically, as the number of levels increases, literal cost represents a smaller proportion of the actual circuit cost, since more and more gates have no inputs from outside the circuit itself. On the Companion Website, we introduce complex gate types for which evaluation of the gate-input cost from an equation is invalid, since the correspondence between the AND, OR, and NOT operations in the equation and the gates in the circuit can no longer be established. In such cases, as well as for equation forms more complex than sum-of-products and product-of-sums, the gate-input count must be determined directly from the implementation.

Regardless of the cost criteria used, we see later that the simplest expression is not necessarily unique. It is sometimes possible to find two or more expressions that satisfy the cost criterion applied. In that case, either solution is satisfactory from the cost standpoint.

Map Structures

We will consider maps for two, three, and four variables as shown in Figure 2-12. The number of squares in each map is equal to the number of minterms in the corresponding function. In our discussion of minterms, we defined a minterm m_i to go with the row of the truth table with i in binary as the variable values. This use of i to

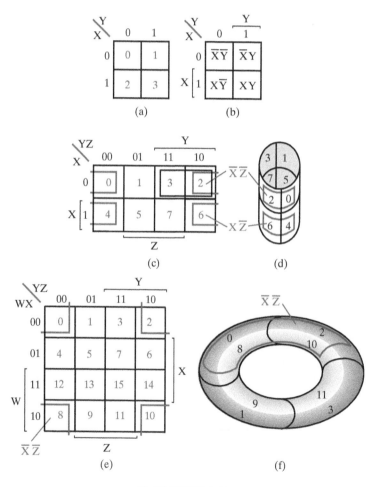

☐ **FIGURE 2-12**
Map Structures

represent the minterm m_i is carried over to the cells of the maps, each of which corresponds to a minterm. For two, three, and four variables, there are 4, 8, and 16 squares, respectively. Each of the maps is labeled in two ways: 1) with variables at the upper left for the columns and the rows and with a binary combination of those variables for each column and each row, and 2) with single variable labels at the edges of the map applied by a bracket to single or double rows and columns. Each location of a variable label aligns with the region of the map for which the variable has value 1. The region for which the variable has value 0 is implicitly labeled with the complement of the variable. Only one of these two schemes is required to completely label a map, but both are shown to allow selection of the one that works best for a given user.

Beginning with the binary combination scheme, we note that the binary combinations across the top and down the left side of a map take the form of a Gray code as introduced in Section 1-7. The use of the Gray code is appropriate because it represents the adjacency of binary combinations and of the corresponding minterms that is the foundation of K-maps. Two binary combinations are said to be *adjacent* if they differ in the value of exactly one variable. Two product terms (including minterms) are *adjacent* if they differ in one and only one literal which appears uncomplemented in one and complemented in the other. For example, the combinations $(X, Y, Z) = 011$ and 010 are adjacent, since they differ only in the value of variable Z. Further, the minterms $\overline{X}YZ$ and $\overline{X}Y\overline{Z}$ are adjacent, since they have identical literal appearances except for Z, which appears uncomplemented and complemented. The reason for the use of a Gray code on K-maps is that any two squares which share a common edge correspond to a pair of adjacent binary combinations and adjacent minterms. This correspondence can be used to perform simplification of product terms for a given function on a K-map. This simplification is based on the Boolean algebraic theorem:

$$AB + A\overline{B} = A$$

Applying this to the example with $A = \overline{X}Y$ and $B = Z$,

$$(\overline{X}Y)Z + (\overline{X}Y)\overline{Z} = \overline{X}Y$$

Looking at the K-map in Figure 2-12(c), we see that the two corresponding squares are located at $(X, Y, Z) = 011$ (3) and 010 (2), which are in row 0 and columns 11 and 10, respectively. Note that these two squares are adjacent (share an edge) and can be combined, as indicated by the black rectangle in Figure 2-12(c). This rectangle on the K-map contains both 0 and 1 for Z, and so no longer depends on Z, and can be read off as $\overline{X}Y$. This demonstrates that whenever we have two squares sharing edges that are minterms of a function, these squares can be combined to form a product term with one less variable.

For the 3- and 4-variable K-maps, there is one more issue to be addressed with respect to the adjacency concept. For a 3-variable K-map, suppose we consider the minterms 0 and 2 in Figure 2-12(c). These two minterms do not share an edge, and hence do not appear to be adjacent. However, these two minterms are $\overline{X}\,\overline{Y}\,\overline{Z}$ and $\overline{X}\,Y\,\overline{Z}$, which by definition are adjacent. In order to recognize this adjacency on the K-map, we need to consider the left and right borders of the map to be a shared edge. Geometrically, this can be accomplished by forming a cylinder from the map so that the squares touching the left and right borders actually have a shared edge! A view of this cylinder appears in Figure 2-12(d). Here minterms m_0 and m_2 share an edge and, from the K-map, are adjacent. Likewise, m_4 and m_6 share an edge on the K-map and are adjacent. The two rectangles resulting from these adjacencies are shown in Figure 2-12(c) and 2-12(d) in blue.

The 4-variable K-map in Figure 2-12(e) can likewise be formed into a cylinder. This demonstrates four adjacencies, m_0 and m_2, m_4 and m_6, m_{12} and m_{14}, and m_8 and m_{10}. The minterms m_0 and m_8, $\overline{W}\,\overline{X}\,\overline{Y}\,\overline{Z}$ and $W\,\overline{X}\,\overline{Y}\,\overline{Z}$, are adjacent, suggesting that the top border of the map should be a shared edge with the bottom border. This can be accomplished by taking the cylinder formed from the map and bending it, joining these two borders. This results in the torus (doughnut shape) in Figure 2-12(f). The additional resulting adjacencies identifiable on the map are m_1 and m_9, m_3 and m_{11}, and m_2 and m_{10}.

Unfortunately, the cylinder and the torus are not convenient to use, but they can help us remember the locations of shared edges. These edges are at the left and right border pair for the flat 3-variable map and at the left and right border pair and the top and bottom border pair for 4-variable K-maps, respectively. The use of flat maps will require the use of pairs of split rectangles lying across the border pairs.

One final detail is the placing of a given function F on a map. Suppose that the function F is given as a truth table with the row designated by decimal i corresponding to the binary input values equivalent to i. Based on the binary combinations on the left and top edges of the K-map combined in order, we can designate each cell of the map by the same i. This will permit easy transfer of the 0 and 1 values of F from the truth table onto the K-map. The values of i for this purpose are shown on the three maps in Figure 2-12. It is a good idea to determine how to fill in the values of i quickly by noting the order of the values of i in a row depends on the Gray code value order for the columns and the ordering of the rows of i values depends on the Gray code value order for the rows. For example, for the 4-variable map, the rows-of-columns order of the i values is: 0, 1, 3, 2, 4, 5, 7, 6, 12, 13, 15, 14, 8, 9, 11, 10. The rows-of-columns order of the i values for 2-variable and 3-variable maps are the first four values and the first eight values from this sequence. These values can also be used for sum of minterm expressions defined using the abbreviated Σ notation. Note that the positioning of the i values is dependent upon the placement of the variables in order from lower left side to middle right side to right top and middle bottom for a 4-variable map. For 2- and 3-variable maps, the order is the same with the nonexistent "middle" positions skipped. Any variation from this ordering will give a different map structure.

Two-Variable Maps

There are four basic steps for using a K-map. Initially, we present each of these steps using a 2-variable function $F(A, B)$ as an example.

The first step is to enter the function on the K-map. The function may be in the form of a truth table, the Σm shorthand notation for a sum of minterms, or a sum-of-products expression. The truth table for $F(A, B)$ is given in Table 2-12. For each row in which the function F has value 1, the values of A and B can be read to

☐ **TABLE 2-12**
Two-Variable Function F(A, B)

A	B	F
0	0	1
0	1	1
1	0	0
1	1	1

determine where to place a 1 on the map. For example, the function has value 1 for the combination $A = 0$ and $B = 0$. Thus, a 1 is placed in the upper left square of the K-map in Figure 2-13(a) corresponding to $A = 0$ and $B = 0$. This operation is repeated for rows $(0, 1)$ and $(1, 1)$ in the truth table to complete the entry of F in the map.

If the decimal subscripts for the minterms have been added to the truth table and entered on the map as discussed previously, a much faster approach to entering the function on the map is available. The subscripts for the minterms of the function are those corresponding to the rows for which the function is a 1. So a 1 is simply entered in squares 0, 1, and 3 of the K-map. For these two entry methods, as well as others, we assume that each remaining square contains a 0, but do not actually enter 0s in the K-map.

The Σm notation for F in the truth table is $F(A, B) = \Sigma m(0, 1, 3)$, which can be entered on the K-map simply by placing 1 in each of the squares 0, 1, and 3. Alternatively, a sum-of-products expression such as $F = \overline{A} + AB$ can be given as a specification. This can be converted to minterms and entered on the K-map. More simply, the region of the K-map corresponding to each of the product terms can be identified and filled with 1s. Since AB is a minterm, we can simply place a 1 in square 3. For $\overline{A}$, we note that the region is that identified as "not" A on the K-map and consists of squares 0 and 1. So $\overline{A}$ can be entered by placing a 1 in each of these two squares. In general, this last process becomes easier once we have mastered the concept of rectangles on a K-map, as discussed next.

The second step is to identify collections of squares on the map representing product terms to be considered for the simplified expression. We call such objects *rectangles*, since their shape is that of a rectangle (including, of course, a square).

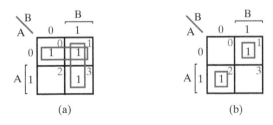

(a)   (b)

☐ **FIGURE 2-13**
Two-Variable K-Map Examples

Rectangles that correspond to product terms are restricted to contain numbers of squares that are powers of 2, such as 1, 2, 4, and 8. Also, this implies that the length of a side of any rectangle is a power of 2. Our goal is to find the fewest such rectangles that include or cover all of the squares marked with 1s. This will give the fewest product terms and the least input cost for summing the product terms. Any rectangle we are planning to use should be as large as possible in order to include as many 1s as possible. Also, a larger rectangle gives a lower input cost for the corresponding product term.

For the example, there are two largest rectangles. One consists of squares 1 and 0, the other of squares 3 and 1. Squares 1 and 0 correspond to minterms $\overline{A}B$ and $\overline{A}\,\overline{B}$, which can be combined to form rectangle $\overline{A}$. Squares 3 and 1 correspond to minterms AB and $\overline{A}B$, which can be combined to form rectangle B.

The third step is to determine if any of the rectangles we have generated is not needed to cover all of the 1s on the K-map. In the example, we can see that rectangle $\overline{A}$ is required to cover minterm 0 and rectangle B is required to cover minterm 3. In general, a rectangle is not required if it can be deleted and all of the 1s on the map are covered by the remaining rectangles. If there are choices as to which rectangle of two having unequal size to remove, the largest one should remain.

The final step is to read off the sum-of-products expression, determining the corresponding product terms for the required rectangles in the map. In the example, we can read off the corresponding product terms by using the rectangles shown and the variable labels on the map boundary as $\overline{A}$ and B, respectively. This gives a sum-of-products expression for F as:

$$F = \overline{A} + B$$

EXAMPLE 2-4   Another 2-Variable Map Example

The function $G(A, B) = \Sigma m(1, 2)$ is shown on the 2-variable K-map in Figure 2-13(b). Looking at the map, we find the two rectangles are simply the minterms 1 and 2. From the map, ■

$$G(A, B) = \overline{A}B + A\overline{B}$$

From Figure 2-13(a) and 2-13(b), we find that 2-variable maps contain: (1) 1 × 1 rectangles which correspond to minterms and (2) 2 × 1 rectangles consisting of a pair of adjacent minterms. A 1 × 1 rectangle can appear on any square of the map and a 2 × 1 rectangle can appear either horizontally or vertically on the map, each in one of two positions. Note that a 2 × 2 rectangle covers the entire map and corresponds to the function $F = 1$.

Three-Variable Maps

We introduce simplification on 3-variable maps by using two examples followed by a discussion of the new concepts involved beyond those required for 2-variable maps.

□ **FIGURE 2-14**
Three-Variable K-Maps for Examples 2-5 through 2-7

EXAMPLE 2-5 Three-Variable Map Simplification 1

Simplify the Boolean function

$$F(A, B, C) = \Sigma m(0, 1, 2, 3, 4, 5)$$

This function has been entered on the K-map shown in Figure 2-14(a), where squares 0 through 5 are marked with 1s. In the map, the two largest rectangles each enclose four squares containing 1s. Note that two squares, 0 and 1, lie in both of the rectangles. Since these two rectangles include all of the 1s in the map and neither can be removed, the logical sum of the corresponding two product terms gives the optimized expression for F:

$$F = \overline{A} + \overline{B}$$

To illustrate algebraically how a 4×4 rectangle such as $\overline{B}$ arises, consider the two adjacent black rectangles $A\overline{B}$ and $\overline{A}\,\overline{B}$ connected by two pairs of adjacent minterms. These can be combined based on the theorem $XY + X\overline{Y} = X$ with $X = \overline{B}$ and $Y = A$ to obtain $\overline{B}$. ∎

EXAMPLE 2-6 Three-Variable Map Simplification 2

Simplify the Boolean function

$$G(A, B, C) = \Sigma m(0, 2, 4, 5, 6)$$

This function has been entered on the K-map shown in Figure 2-14(b), where squares listed are marked with 1s. In some cases, two squares in the map are adjacent and form a rectangle of size two, even though they do not touch each other. For example, in Figure 2-14(b) and 2-12(d), m_0 is adjacent to m_2 because the minterms differ by one variable. This can be readily verified algebraically:

$$m_0 + m_2 = \overline{A}\,\overline{B}\,\overline{C} + \overline{A}B\overline{C} = \overline{A}\,\overline{C}(\overline{B} + B) = \overline{A}\,\overline{C}$$

This rectangle is represented in black in Figure 2-14(b) and in blue in Figure 2-12(d) on a cylinder where the adjacency relationship is apparent. Likewise, a rectangle is shown in both figures for squares 4 and 6 which corresponds to $A\overline{C}$. From the prior example, it is apparent that these two rectangles can be combined to give a larger rectangle $\overline{C}$ which covers squares 0, 2, 4, and 6. An additional rectangle is required to cover square 5. The largest such rectangle covers squares 4 and 5. It can be read from the K-map as $A\overline{B}$. The resulting simplified function is

$$G(A, B) = A\overline{B} + \overline{C}$$ ■

From Figures 2-14(a) and 2-14(b), we find that 3-variable maps can contain all of the rectangles contained in a 2-variable map plus: (1) 2×2 rectangles, (2) 1×4 rectangles, (3) 2×1 "split rectangles" at the left and right edges, and a 2×2 split rectangle at the left and right edges. Note that a 2×4 rectangle covers the entire map and corresponds to the function $G = 1$.

EXAMPLE 2-7   Three-Variable Map Simplification 3

Simplify the Boolean function

$$H(A, B, C) = \Sigma m(1, 3, 4, 5, 6)$$

This function has been entered on the K-map shown in Figure 2-14(c), where squares listed are marked with 1s. In this example, we intentionally set the goal of finding all of the largest rectangles in order to emphasize step 3 of simplification, which has not been a significant step in earlier examples. Progressing from the upper center, we find the rectangles corresponding to the following pairs of squares: $(3, 1), (1, 5), (5, 4)$, $(4, 6)$. Can any of these rectangles be removed and still have all squares covered? Since only $(3, 1)$ covers 3, it cannot be removed. The same holds for $(4, 6)$ which covers square 6. After these are included, the only square that remains uncovered is 5, which permits either $(1, 5)$ or $(5, 4)$, but not both, to be removed. Assuming that $(5, 4)$ remains, the result can be read from the map as

$$H(A, B, C) = \overline{A}C + A\overline{B} + A\overline{C}$$ ■

EXAMPLE 2-8   Four-Variable Map Simplification 1

Simplify the Boolean function

$$F(A, B, C, D) = \Sigma m(0, 1, 2, 4, 5, 6, 8, 9, 10, 12, 13)$$

The minterms of the function are marked with 1s in the K-map shown in Figure 2-15. Eight squares in the two left columns are combined to form a rectangle for the one literal term, $\overline{C}$. The remaining three 1s cannot be combined to give a single simplified product term—rather, they must be combined as two split 2×2 rectangles. The top two 1s on the right are combined with the top two 1s on the left to give the term $\overline{A}\,\overline{D}$. Note again that it is permissible to use the same square more than once. We are now left with a square marked with a 1 in the fourth row and fourth column (minterm 1010). Instead of taking this square alone, which will give a term with four literals, we combine it with squares already used to form a rectangle of four squares on the four corners, giving the term $\overline{B}\,\overline{D}$. This rectangle is represented in Figure 2-15 and in Figure 2-12(e) on a torus, where the adjacency relationships between the four squares are apparent. The optimized expression is the logical sum of the three terms:

$$F = \overline{C} + \overline{A}\,\overline{D} + \overline{B}\,\overline{D}$$ ■

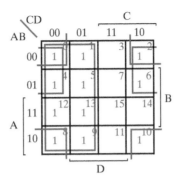

☐ **FIGURE 2-15**
Four-Variable K-Map for Example 2-8

EXAMPLE 2-9 Four-Variable Map Simplification 2

Simplify the Boolean function

$$G(A, B, C, D) = \overline{A}\,\overline{C}\overline{D} + \overline{A}D + \overline{B}C + CD + A\overline{B}\overline{D}$$

This function has four variables: A, B, C, and D. It is expressed in a fairly complex sum-of-products form. In order to enter G on a K-map, we will actually enter the regions corresponding to the product terms onto the map, fill the regions with 1s, and then copy the 1s onto a new map for solution. The area in the map covered by the function is shown in Figure 2-16(a). $\overline{A}\,\overline{C}\overline{D}$ places 1s on squares 0 and 4. $\overline{A}D$ adds 1s to squares 1, 3, 5, and 7. $\overline{B}C$ adds new 1s to squares 2, 10, and 11. CD adds a new 1 to square 15 and $A\,\overline{B}\overline{D}$ adds the final 1 to square 8. The resulting function

$$G(A, B, C, D) = \Sigma m(0, 1, 2, 3, 4, 5, 7, 8, 10, 11, 15)$$

is placed on the map in Figure 2-16(b). It is a good idea to check if the 4-corner rectangle $\overline{B}\overline{D}$ is present and required. It is present, is required to cover square 8, and also covers squares 0, 2, and 10. With these squares covered, it is easy to see that just two

(a) K-map for original function G   (b) K-map for simplified function G

☐ **FIGURE 2-16**
Four-Variable K-Map for Example 2-9

rectangles, $\overline{A}\,\overline{C}$ and CD, cover all of the remaining uncovered squares. We can read off the resulting function as:

$$G = \overline{B}\,\overline{D} + \overline{A}\,\overline{C} + CD$$

Note that this function is much simpler than the original sum-of-products given.   ■

2-5   MAP MANIPULATION

When combining squares in a map, it is necessary to ensure that all the minterms of the function are included. At the same time, we need to minimize the number of terms in the optimized function by avoiding any redundant terms whose minterms are already included in other terms. In this section, we consider a procedure that assists in the recognition of useful patterns in the map. Other topics to be covered are the optimization of products of sums and the optimization of incompletely specified functions.

Essential Prime Implicants

The procedure for combining squares in a map may be made more systematic if we introduce the terms "implicant," "prime implicant," and "essential prime implicant." A product term is an *implicant* of a function if the function has the value 1 for all minterms of the product term. Clearly, all rectangles on a map made up of squares containing 1s correspond to implicants. If the removal of any literal from an implicant P results in a product term that is not an implicant of the function, then P is a *prime implicant*. On a map for an n-variable function, the set of prime implicants corresponds to the set of all rectangles made up of 2^m squares containing 1s ($m = 0, 1, ..., n$), with each rectangle containing as many squares as possible.

   If a minterm of a function is included in only one prime implicant, that prime implicant is said to be *essential*. Thus, if a square containing a 1 is in only one rectangle representing a prime implicant, then that prime implicant is essential. In Figure 2-14(c), the terms $\overline{A}\,C$ and $A\,\overline{C}$ are essential prime implicants, and the terms $A\,\overline{B}$ and $\overline{B}\,C$ are *nonessential prime implicants*.

   The prime implicants of a function can be obtained from a map of the function as all possible maximum collections of 2^m squares containing 1s ($m = 0, 1, ..., n$) that constitute rectangles. This means that a single 1 on a map represents a prime implicant if it is not adjacent to any other 1s. Two adjacent 1s form a rectangle representing a prime implicant, provided that they are not within a rectangle of four or more squares containing 1s. Four 1s form a rectangle representing a prime implicant if they are not within a rectangle of eight or more squares containing 1s, and so on. Each essential prime implicant contains at least one square that is not contained in any other prime implicant.

   The systematic procedure for finding the optimized expression from the map requires that we first determine all prime implicants. Then, the optimized expression is obtained from the logical sum of all the essential prime implicants, plus other prime implicants needed to include remaining minterms not included in the essential prime implicants. This procedure will be clarified by examples.

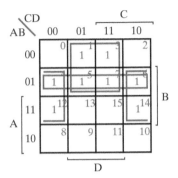

☐ **FIGURE 2-17**
Prime Implicants for Example 2-10: $\overline{A}\,D$, $B\,\overline{D}$, and $\overline{A}\,B$

EXAMPLE 2-10   Simplification Using Prime Implicants

Consider the map of Figure 2-17. There are three ways that we can combine four squares into rectangles. The product terms obtained from these combinations are the prime implicants of the function, $\overline{A}\,D$, $B\,\overline{D}$ and $\overline{A}\,B$. The terms $\overline{A}\,D$ and $B\,\overline{D}$ are essential prime implicants, but $\overline{A}\,B$ is not essential. This is because minterms 1 and 3 are included only in the term $\overline{A}\,D$, and minterms 12 and 14 are included only in the term $B\,\overline{D}$. But minterms 4, 5, 6, and 7 are each included in two prime implicants, one of which is $\overline{A}\,B$, so the term $\overline{A}\,B$ is not an essential prime implicant. In fact, once the essential prime implicants are chosen, the term $\overline{A}\,B$ is not needed, because all the minterms are already included in the two essential prime implicants. The optimized expression for the function of Figure 2-17 is

$$F = \overline{A}\,D + B\,\overline{D}$$ ■

EXAMPLE 2-11   Simplification Via Essential and Nonessential Prime Implicants

A second example is shown in Figure 2-18. The function plotted in part (a) has seven minterms. If we try to combine squares, we will find that there are six prime impli-

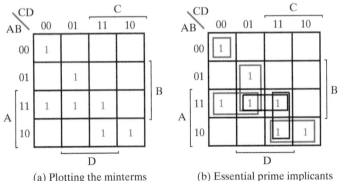

(a) Plotting the minterms   (b) Essential prime implicants

☐ **FIGURE 2-18**
Simplification with Prime Implicants in Example 2-11

cants. In order to obtain a minimum number of terms for the function, we must first determine the prime implicants that are essential. As shown in blue in part (b) of the figure, the function has four essential prime implicants. The product term $\overline{A}\,\overline{B}\,\overline{C}\,\overline{D}$ is essential because it is the only prime implicant that includes minterm 0. Similarly, the product terms $B\overline{C}D$, $AB\overline{C}$, and $A\overline{B}C$ are essential prime implicants because they are the only ones that include minterms 5, 12, and 10, respectively. Minterm 15 is included in two nonessential prime implicants. The optimized expression for the function consists of the logical sum of the four essential prime implicants and one prime implicant that includes minterm 15:

$$F = \overline{A}\,\overline{B}\,\overline{C}\,\overline{D} + B\overline{C}D + AB\overline{C} + A\overline{B}C + \begin{pmatrix} A\,C\,D \\ \text{or} \\ A\,B\,D \end{pmatrix} \quad \blacksquare$$

The identification of essential prime implicants in the map provides an additional tool which shows the terms that must absolutely appear in every sum-of-products expression for a function and provides a partial structure for a more systematic method for choosing patterns of prime implicants.

Nonessential Prime Implicants

Beyond using all essential prime implicants, the following rule can be applied to include the remaining minterms of the function in nonessential prime implicants:

Selection Rule: Minimize the overlap among prime implicants as much as possible. In particular, in the final solution, make sure that each prime implicant selected includes at least one minterm not included in any other prime implicant selected.

In most cases, this results in a simplified, although not necessarily optimum, sum-of-products expression. The use of the selection rule is illustrated in the next example.

EXAMPLE 2-12 Simplifying a Function Using the Selection Rule

Find a simplified sum-of-products form for $(0, 1, 2, 4, 5, 10, 11, 13, 15)$.

The map for F is given in Figure 2-19, with all prime implicants shown. $\overline{A}\,\overline{C}$ is the only essential prime implicant. Using the preceding selection rule, we can choose the remaining prime implicants for the sum-of-products form in the order indicated by the numbers. Note how the prime implicants 1 and 2 are selected in order to include minterms without overlapping. Prime implicant 3 ($\overline{A}\,\overline{B}\,D$) and prime implicant $\overline{B}\,C\overline{D}$ both include the one remaining minterm 0010, and prime implicant 3 is arbitrarily selected to include the minterm and complete the sum-of-products expression:

$$F(A, B, C, D) = \overline{A}\,\overline{C} + ABD + A\overline{B}C + \overline{A}\,\overline{B}\,D$$

The prime implicants not used are shown in black in Figure 2-19. ■

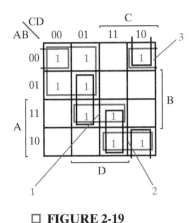

☐ **FIGURE 2-19**
Map for Example 2-12

Product-of-Sums Optimization

The optimized Boolean functions derived from the maps in all of the previous examples were expressed in sum-of-products form. With only minor modification, the product-of-sums form can be obtained.

The procedure for obtaining an optimized expression in product-of-sums form follows from the properties of Boolean functions. The 1s placed in the squares of the map represent the minterms of the function. The minterms not included in the function belong to the complement of the function. From this, we see that the complement of a function is represented in the map by the squares not marked by 1s. If we mark the empty squares with 0s and combine them into valid rectangles, we obtain an optimized expression of the complement of the function, $\overline{F}$. We then take the complement of $\overline{F}$ to obtain F as a product of sums. This is done by taking the dual and complementing each literal, as in Example 2-13.

EXAMPLE 2-13   **Simplifying a Product-of-Sums Form**

Simplify the following Boolean function in product-of-sums form:

$$F(A, B, C, D) = \Sigma m(0, 1, 2, 5, 8, 9, 10)$$

The 1s marked in the map of Figure 2-20 represent the minterms of the function. The squares marked with 0s represent the minterms not included in F and therefore denote the complement of F. Combining the squares marked with 0s, we obtain the optimized complemented function

$$\overline{F} = AB + CD + B\overline{D}$$

Taking the dual and complementing each literal gives the complement of $\overline{F}$. This is F in product-of-sums form:

$$F = (\overline{A} + \overline{B})(\overline{C} + \overline{D})(\overline{B} + D)$$

■

□ **FIGURE 2-20**
Map for Example 2-13

The previous example shows the procedure for obtaining the product-of-sums optimization when the function is originally expressed as a sum of minterms. The procedure is also valid when the function is originally expressed as a product of maxterms or a product of sums. Remember that the maxterm numbers are the same as the minterm numbers of the complemented function, so 0s are entered in the map for the maxterms or for the complement of the function. To enter a function expressed as a product of sums into the map, we take the complement of the function and, from it, find the squares to be marked with 0s. For example, the function

$$F = (\overline{A} + \overline{B} + C)(B + D)$$

can be plotted in the map by first obtaining its complement,

$$\overline{F} = AB\overline{C} + \overline{B}\,\overline{D}$$

and then marking 0s in the squares representing the minterms of $\overline{F}$. The remaining squares are marked with 1s. Then, combining the 1s gives the optimized expression in sum-of-products form. Combining the 0s and then complementing gives the optimized expression in product-of-sums form. Thus, for any function plotted on the map, we can derive the optimized function in either one of the two standard forms.

Don't-Care Conditions

The minterms of a Boolean function specify all combinations of variable values for which the function is equal to 1. The function is assumed to be equal to 0 for the rest of the minterms. This assumption, however, is not always valid, since there are applications in which the function is not specified for certain variable value combinations. There are two cases in which this occurs. In the first case, the input combinations never occur. As an example, the four-bit binary code for the decimal digits has six combinations that are not used and not expected to occur. In the second case, the input combinations are expected to occur, but we do not care what the outputs are in response to these combinations. In both cases, the outputs are said to be unspecified for the input combinations. Functions that have unspecified outputs for some input combinations are called *incompletely specified functions.* In most applications, we simply do not care what value is assumed by the function for the unspecified minterms. For this reason, it is customary to call the unspecified minterms of a function *don't-care conditions.* These conditions can be used on a map to provide further simplification of the function.

It should be realized that a don't-care minterm cannot be marked with a 1 on the map, because that would require that the function always be a 1 for such a minterm. Likewise, putting a 0 in the square requires the function to be 0. To distinguish the don't-care condition from 1s and 0s, an X is used. Thus, an X inside a square in the map indicates that we do not care whether the value of 0 or 1 is assigned to the function for the particular minterm.

In choosing adjacent squares to simplify the function in a map, the don't-care minterms may be used. When simplifying function F using the 1s, we can choose to include those don't-care minterms that give the simplest prime implicants for F. When simplifying function $\overline{F}$ using the 0s, we can choose to include those don't-care minterms that give the simplest prime implicants for $\overline{F}$, irrespective of those included in the prime implicants for F. In both cases, whether or not the don't-care minterms are included in the terms in the final expression is irrelevant. The handling of don't-care conditions is illustrated in the next example.

EXAMPLE 2-14   Simplification with Don't-Care Conditions

To clarify the procedure for handling the don't-care conditions, consider the following incompletely specified function F that has three don't-care minterms d:

$$F(A, B, C, D) = \Sigma m(1, 3, 7, 11, 15)$$

$$d(A, B, C, D) = \Sigma m(0, 2, 5)$$

The minterms of F are the variable combinations that make the function equal to 1. The minterms of d are the don't-care minterms. The map optimization is shown in Figure 2-21. The minterms of F are marked by 1s, those of d are marked by Xs, and the remaining squares are filled with 0s. To get the simplified function in sum-of-products form, we must include all five 1s in the map, but we may or may not include any of the Xs, depending on what yields the simplest expression for the function. The term CD includes the four minterms in the third column. The remaining minterm in square 0001 can be combined with square 0011 to give a three-literal term. However, by including one or two adjacent Xs, we can combine four squares into a rectangle to give a two-literal term. In part (a) of the figure, don't-care minterms 0 and 2 are included with the 1s, which results in the simplified function

$$F = CD + \overline{A}\,\overline{B}$$

In part (b), don't-care minterm 5 is included with the 1s, and the simplified function now is

$$F = CD + \overline{A}D$$

The two expressions represent two functions that are algebraically unequal. Both include the specified minterms of the original incompletely specified function, but

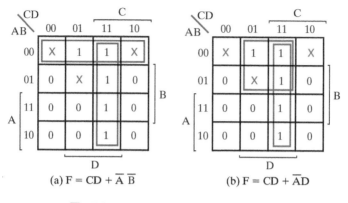

(a) $F = CD + \overline{A}\,\overline{B}$ (b) $F = CD + \overline{A}D$

□ **FIGURE 2-21**
Example with Don't-Care Conditions

each includes different don't-care minterms. As far as the incompletely specified function is concerned, both expressions are acceptable. The only difference is in the value of *F* for the unspecified minterms.

It is also possible to obtain an optimized product-of-sums expression for the function of Figure 2-21. In this case, the way to combine the 0s is to include don't-care minterms 0 and 2 with the 0s, giving the optimized complemented function

$$\overline{F} = \overline{D} + A\overline{C}$$

Taking the complement of $\overline{F}$ gives the optimized expression in product-of-sums form:

$$F = D(\overline{A} + C)$$ ■

The foregoing example shows that the don't-care minterms in the map are initially considered as representing both 0 and 1. The 0 or 1 value that is eventually assigned depends on the optimization process. Due to this process, the optimized function will have a 0 or 1 value for each minterm of the original function, including those that were initially don't cares. Thus, although the outputs in the initial specification may contain Xs, the outputs in a particular implementation of the specification are only 0s and 1s.

MORE OPTIMIZATION This supplement gives a procedure for selecting prime implicants that guarantees an optimum solution. In addition, it presents a symbolic method for performing prime-implicant generation and a tabular method for prime-implicant selection. The supplement also discusses how finding the true two-level optimum solution for large circuits is impractical due to the difficulty of generating all of the prime implicants and selecting from a large number of possible prime-implicant solutions. The supplement describes a computer algorithm that generally achieves near-optimum two-level solutions for large circuits much more quickly than using the optimum approach.

2-6 EXCLUSIVE-OR OPERATOR AND GATES

In addition to the exclusive-OR gate shown in Figure 2-3, there is an exclusive-OR operator with its own algebraic identities. The exclusive-OR (XOR), denoted by $\oplus$, is a logical operation that performs the function

$$X \oplus Y = X\overline{Y} + \overline{X}Y$$

It is equal to 1 if exactly one input variable is equal to 1. The exclusive-NOR, also known as the *equivalence*, is the complement of the exclusive-OR and is expressed by the function

$$\overline{X \oplus Y} = XY + \overline{X}\,\overline{Y}$$

It is equal to 1 if both X and Y are equal to 1 or if both are equal to 0. The two functions can be shown to be the complement of each other, either by means of a truth table or, as follows, by algebraic manipulation:

$$\overline{X \oplus Y} = \overline{X\overline{Y} + \overline{X}Y} = (\overline{X} + Y)(X + \overline{Y}) = XY + \overline{X}\,\overline{Y}$$

The following identities apply to the exclusive-OR operation:

$$X \oplus 0 = X \qquad\qquad X \oplus 1 = \overline{X}$$

$$X \oplus X = 0 \qquad\qquad X \oplus \overline{X} = 1$$

$$X \oplus \overline{Y} = \overline{X \oplus Y} \qquad \overline{X} \oplus Y = \overline{X \oplus Y}$$

Any of these identities can be verified by using a truth table or by replacing the $\oplus$ operation by its equivalent Boolean expression. It can also be shown that the exclusive-OR operation is both commutative and associative—that is,

$$A \oplus B = B \oplus A$$

$$(A \oplus B) \oplus C = A \oplus (B \oplus C) = A \oplus B \oplus C$$

This means that the two inputs to an exclusive-OR gate can be interchanged without affecting the operation. It also means that we can evaluate a 3-variable exclusive-OR operation in any order, and for this reason, exclusive-ORs with three or more variables can be expressed without parentheses.

A two-input exclusive-OR function may be constructed with conventional gates. Two NOT gates, two AND gates, and an OR gate are used. The associativity of the exclusive-OR operator suggests the possibility of exclusive-OR gates with more than two inputs. The exclusive-OR concept for more than two variables, however, is replaced by the odd function to be discussed next. Thus, there is no symbol for exclusive-OR for more than two inputs. By duality, the exclusive-NOR is replaced by the even function and has no symbol for more than two inputs.

Odd Function

The exclusive-OR operation with three or more variables can be converted into an ordinary Boolean function by replacing the $\oplus$ symbol with its equivalent Boolean expression. In particular, the 3-variable case can be converted to a Boolean expression as follows:

$$X \oplus Y \oplus Z = (X\overline{Y} + \overline{X}Y)\overline{Z} + (XY + \overline{X}\,\overline{Y})Z$$

$$= X\overline{Y}\overline{Z} + \overline{X}Y\overline{Z} + \overline{X}\,\overline{Y}Z + XYZ$$

The Boolean expression clearly indicates that the 3-variable exclusive-OR is equal to 1 if only one variable is equal to 1 or if all three variables are equal to 1. Hence, whereas in the 2-variable function only one variable need be equal to 1, with three or more variables an odd number of variables must be equal to 1. As a consequence, the multiple-variable exclusive-OR operation is defined as the *odd function*. In fact, strictly speaking, this is the correct name for the $\oplus$ operation with three or more variables; the name "exclusive-OR" is applicable to the case with only two variables.

The definition of the odd function can be clarified by plotting the function on a map. Figure 2-22(a) shows the map for the 3-variable odd function. The four minterms of the function differ from each other in at least two literals and hence cannot be adjacent on the map. These minterms are said to be *distance two* from each other. The odd function is identified from the four minterms whose binary values have an odd number of 1s. The 4-variable case is shown in Figure 2-22(b). The eight minterms

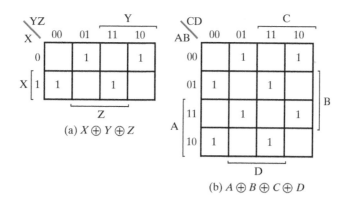

□ **FIGURE 2-22**
Maps for Multiple-Variable Odd Functions

□ **FIGURE 2-23**
Multiple-Input Odd Functions

marked with 1s in the map constitute the odd function. Note the characteristic pattern of the distance between the 1s in the map. It should be mentioned that the minterms not marked with 1s in the map have an even number of 1s and constitute the complement of the odd function, called the *even function*. The odd function is implemented by means of two-input exclusive-OR gates, as shown in Figure 2-23. The even function is obtained by replacing the output gate with an exclusive-NOR gate.

2-7   GATE PROPAGATION DELAY

As mentioned in Section 2-1, an important property of logic gates is *propagation delay*. Propagation delay is the time required for a change in value of a signal to propagate from input to output. The operating speed of a circuit is inversely related to the longest propagation delays through the gates of the circuit. The operating speed of a circuit is usually a critical design constraint. In many cases, operating speed can be the most important design constraint.

The determination of propagation delay is illustrated in Figure 2-24. Three propagation delay parameters are defined. The *high-to-low propagation time* t_{PHL} is the delay measured from the reference voltage on the input IN to the reference voltage on the output OUT, with the output voltage going from H to L. The reference voltage we are using is the 50 percent point, halfway between the minimum and the maximum values of the voltage signals; other reference voltages may be used, depending on the logic family. The *low-to-high propagation time* t_{PLH} is the delay measured from the reference voltage on the input voltage IN to the reference voltage on the output voltage OUT, with the output voltage going from L to H. We define the *propagation delay* t_{pd} as the maximum of these two delays. The reason we have chosen the maximum value is that we will be most concerned with finding the longest time for a signal to propagate from inputs to outputs. Otherwise, the definitions given for t_{pd} may be inconsistent, depending on the use of the data. Manufacturers usually specify the maximum and typical values for both t_{PHL} and t_{PLH} or for t_{pd} for their products.

Two different models, transport delay and inertial delay, are employed in modeling gates during simulation. For *transport delay*, the change in an output in response to the change of an input occurs after a specified propagation delay. *Inertial delay* is similar to transport delay, except that if the input changes cause the output to change twice in an interval less than the *rejection time*, then the first of the two output changes does not occur. The rejection time is a specified value no larger than the propagation delay and is often equal to the propagation delay. An AND gate modeled with both a transport delay and an inertial delay is illustrated in Figure 2-25. To help visualize the delay behavior, we have also given the AND output with no delay. A colored bar on this waveform shows a 2 ns propagation delay time after each input change, and a smaller black bar shows a rejection time of 1 ns. The output modeled with the transport delay is identical to that for no delay, except that it is shifted to the right by 2 ns. For the inertial delay, the waveform is likewise shifted. To define the waveform for the delayed output, we will call each change in a waveform an *edge*. To determine whether a particular edge appears in the ID output, it must be determined whether a second edge occurs in the ND output before the end of the rejection time

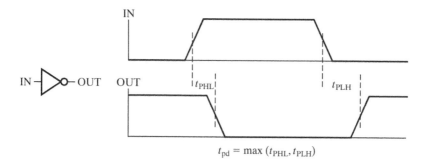

$$t_{pd} = \max (t_{PHL}, t_{PLH})$$

□ **FIGURE 2-24**
Propagation Delay for an Inverter

for the edge in question, and whether the edge will result in a change in the ID output. Since edge b occurs before the end of the rejection time for edge a in the ND output, edge a does not appear in the ID output. Since edge b does not change the state of ID, it is ignored. Since edge d occurs at the rejection time after edge c in the ND output, edge c does appear. Edge e, however, occurs within the rejection time after edge d, so edge d does not appear. Since edge c appeared and edge d did not appear, edge e does not cause a change.

Next, we want to consider further the components that make up the gate delay within a circuit environment. The gate itself has some fixed inherent delay. Because it represents capacitance driven, however, the actual fan-out of the gate, in terms of standard loads, discussed in Chapter 5, also affects the propagation delay of the gate. But depending upon the loading of the gate by the inputs of the logic attached to its output, the overall delay of the gate may be significantly larger than the inherent gate delay. Thus, a simple expression for propagation delay can be given by a formula

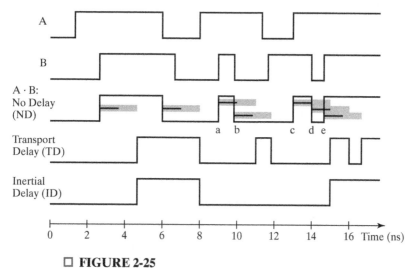

□ **FIGURE 2-25**
Examples of Behavior of Transport and Inertial Delays

or table that considers a fixed delay plus a delay per standard load times the number of standard loads driven by the output as shown in the example that follows.

EXAMPLE 2-15   Calculation of Gate Delay Based on Fan-Out

A 4-input NAND gate output is attached to the inputs of the following gates with the given number of standard loads representing their inputs:

  4-input NOR gate—0.80 standard load
  3-input NAND gate—1.00 standard load, and
  inverter—1.00 standard load.

The formula for the delay of the 4-input NAND gate is

$$t_{pd} = 0.07 + 0.021 \times \text{SL ns}$$

where SL is the sum of the standard loads driven by the gate.

  Ignoring the wiring delay, the delay projected for the NAND gate as loaded is

$$t_{pd} = 0.07 + 0.021 \times (0.80 + 1.00 + 1.00) = 0.129 \text{ ns}$$

In modern high-speed circuits, the portion of the gate delay due to wiring capacitance is often significant. While ignoring such delay is unwise, it is difficult to evaluate, since it depends on the layout of the wires in the integrated circuit. Nevertheless, since we do not have this information or a method to obtain a good estimate of it, we ignore this delay component here. ■

2-8   HDLs Overview

Designing complex systems and integrated circuits would not be feasible without the use of *computer-aided design (CAD)* tools. *Schematic capture* tools support the drawing of blocks and interconnections at all levels of the hierarchy. At the level of primitives and functional blocks, *libraries* of graphics symbols are provided. Schematic capture tools support the construction of a hierarchy by permitting the generation of symbols for hierarchical blocks and the replication of symbols for reuse.

  The primitive blocks and the functional block symbols from libraries have associated models that allow the behavior and the timing of the hierarchical blocks and the entire circuit to be verified. This verification is performed by applying inputs to the blocks or circuit and using a *logic simulator* to determine the outputs.

  The primitive blocks from libraries can also have associated data, such as physical area information and delay parameters, that can be used by *logic synthesizers* to optimize designs being generated automatically from HDL specifications.

  As we briefly described in Section 2-1, while schematics and Boolean equations are adequate for small circuits, HDLs have become crucial to the modern design process required for developing large, complex circuits. HDLs resemble software programming languages, but they have particular features to describe hardware structures and behavior. They differ from typical programming languages by representing the parallel operations performed by hardware, whereas most programming languages represent serial operations.

As we will show in the remainder of this chapter and in Chapters 3 and 4, the power of an HDL becomes more apparent when it is used to represent more than just schematic information. It can represent Boolean equations, truth tables, and complex operations such as arithmetic. Thus, in top-down design, a very high-level description of an entire system can be precisely specified using an HDL. As a part of the design process, this high-level description can then be refined and partitioned into lower-level descriptions. Ultimately, a final description in terms of primitive components and functional blocks can be obtained as the result of the design process. Note that all of these descriptions can be simulated. Since they represent the same system in terms of function, but not necessarily timing, they should respond by giving the same logic values for the same applied inputs. This vital simulation property supports design verification and is one of the principal reasons for the use of HDLs.

A final major reason for increased use of HDLs is logic synthesis. An HDL description of a system can be written at an intermediate level referred to as a register transfer language (RTL) level. A logic synthesis tool with an accompanying library of components can convert such a description into an interconnection of primitive components that implements the circuit. This replacement of the manual logic design process makes the design of complex logic much more efficient. Logic synthesis transforms an RTL description of a circuit in an HDL into an optimized netlist representing storage elements and combinational logic. The optimizations involved are more complex than those presented previously in this chapter, but they share many of the same underlying concepts. Subsequent to logic optimization, this netlist may be transformed by using physical design tools into an actual integrated circuit layout or field programmable gate array (FPGA). The logic synthesis tool takes care of a large portion of the details of a design and allows designers to explore the trade-offs between design constraints that are essential to advanced designs.

Currently, VHDL and Verilog are widely used, standard hardware design languages. The language standards are defined, approved, and published by the Institute of Electrical and Electronics Engineers (IEEE). All implementations of these languages must obey their respective standard. This standardization gives HDLs another advantage over schematics. HDLs are portable across computer-aided design tools, whereas schematic capture tools are typically unique to a particular vendor. In addition to the standard languages, a number of major companies have their own internal languages, often developed long before the standard languages and incorporating features unique to their particular products.

Regardless of the HDL, a typical procedure is used in employing an HDL description as simulation input. The steps in the procedure are analysis, elaboration, and initialization, followed finally by the simulation. Analysis and elaboration are typically performed by a compiler similar to those for programming languages. *Analysis* checks the description for violations of the syntax and semantic rules for the HDL and produces an intermediate representation of the design. *Elaboration* traverses the design hierarchy represented by the description; in this process, the design hierarchy is flattened to an interconnection of modules that are described only by their behaviors. The end result of the analysis and elaboration performed by the compiler is a simulation model of the original HDL description. This model is then passed to the simulator for execution. *Initialization* sets all of the variables in the simulation model to specified or default values. *Simulation* executes the simulation model in either batch or interactive mode with inputs specified by the user.

Because fairly complex hardware can be described efficiently in an HDL, a special HDL structure called a *testbench* may be used. The testbench is a description that includes the design to be tested, typically referred to as the Device Under Test (DUT). The testbench describes a collection of hardware and software functions that apply inputs to the DUT and analyze the outputs for correctness. This approach bypasses the need to provide separate inputs to the simulator and to analyze, often manually, the simulator outputs. Construction of a testbench provides a uniform verification mechanism that can be used at multiple levels in the top-down design process for verification of correct function of the design.

Logic Synthesis

As indicated earlier, the availability of logic synthesis tools is one of the driving forces behind the growing use of HDLs. Logic synthesis transforms an RTL description of a circuit in an HDL into an optimized netlist representing storage elements and combinational logic. Subsequently, this netlist may be transformed by using physical design tools into an actual integrated circuit layout. This layout serves as the basis for integrated circuit manufacture. The logic synthesis tool takes care of a large portion of the details of a design and allows exploration of the cost/performance trade-offs essential to advanced designs.

Figure 2-26 shows a simple high-level flow of the steps involved in logic synthesis. The user provides an HDL description of the circuit to be designed as well as

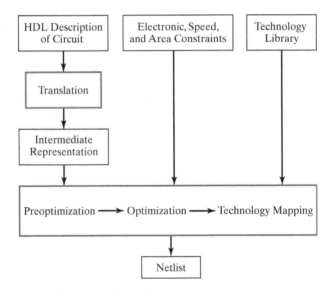

☐ **FIGURE 2-26**
High-Level Flow for Logic Synthesis Tool

various constraints or bounds on the design. Electrical constraints include allow-able gate fan-outs and output loading restrictions. Area and speed constraints direct the optimization steps of the synthesis. Area constraints typically give the maxi-mum permissible area that a circuit is allowed to occupy within the integrated circuit.

Alternatively, a general directive may be given which specifies that area is to be minimized. Speed constraints are typically maximum allowable values for the delay on various paths in the circuit. Alternatively, a general directive may be given to maximize speed. Area and speed both translate into the cost of a circuit. A fast circuit will typically have larger area and thus cost more to manufacture. A circuit that need not operate fast can be optimized for area, and, relatively speak-ing, costs less to manufacture. In some sophisticated synthesis tools, power con-sumption can also be used as a constraint. Additional information used by a synthesis tool is a *technology library* that describes the primitive blocks available for use in the netlist as well as their physical parameters necessary for delay com-putations. The latter information is essential in meeting constraints and perform-ing optimization.

The first major step in the synthesis process in Figure 2-26 is a translation of the HDL description into an intermediate form. The translation result may be an inter-connection of generic gates and storage elements, not taken from the technology library. It may also be in an alternate form that represents clusters of logic and the interconnections between the clusters.

The second major step in the synthesis process is optimization. A preoptimiza-tion step may be used to simplify the intermediate form. For example, logic that is identical in the intermediate form may be shared. Next is the optimization, in which the intermediate form is processed to attempt to meet the constraints specified. Typically, two-level and multiple-level optimization are performed. Optimization is followed by *technology mapping*, which replaces AND gates, OR gates, and inverters with gates from the technology library. In order to evaluate area and speed parame-ters associated with these gates, additional information from the technology library is used. In sophisticated synthesis tools, further optimization may be applied during technology mapping in order to improve the likelihood of meeting the constraints on the design. Optimization can be a very complex, time-consuming process for large circuits. Many optimization passes may be necessary to achieve the desired results or to demonstrate that constraints are difficult, if not impossible, to meet. The designer may need to modify the constraints or the HDL in order to achieve a satisfactory design. Modification of the HDL may include manual design of some portions of the logic in order to achieve the design goals.

The output of the optimization/technology mapping processes is typically a netlist corresponding to a schematic diagram made up of storage elements, gates, and other combinational logic functional blocks. This output serves as input to phys-ical design tools that physically place the logic elements and route the interconnec-tions between them to produce the layout of the circuit for manufacture. In the case of programmable parts, such as field-programmable gate arrays as discussed in Chapter 5, an analog to the physical design tools produces the binary information used to program the logic within the parts.

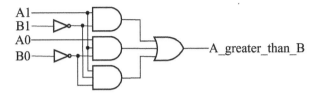

☐ **FIGURE 2-27**
Gate level schematic for a two-bit greater-than comparator circuit

2-9 HDL Representations—VHDL

Since an HDL is used for describing and designing hardware, it is very important to keep the underlying hardware in mind as you write in the language. This is particularly critical if your language description is to be synthesized. For example, if you ignore the hardware that will be generated, it is very easy to specify a large complex gate structure by using an inefficient HDL description when a much simpler structure using only a few gates is all that is needed. For this reason, we initially emphasize description of detailed hardware with VHDL, and proceed to more abstract, higher-level descriptions later.

Selected examples in this chapter are useful for introducing VHDL as an alternative means for representing detailed digital circuits. Initially, we show structural VHDL descriptions that replace the schematic for the two-bit greater-than comparator circuit given in Figure 2-27. This example illustrates many of the fundamental concepts of VHDL. We then present higher-level behavioral VHDL descriptions for these circuits that further illustrate fundamental VHDL concepts.

EXAMPLE 2-16 **Structural VHDL for a Two-Bit Greater-Than Comparator Circuit**

Figure 2-28 shows a VHDL description for the two-bit greater-than comparator circuit from Figure 2-27. This example will be used to demonstrate a number of general VHDL features as well as structural description of circuits.

The text between two dashes – – and the end of the line is interpreted as a *comment*. So the description in Figure 2-28 begins with a two-line comment identifying the description and its relationship to Figure 2-27. To assist in discussion of this description, comments providing line numbers have been added on the right. As a language, VHDL has a syntax that describes precisely the valid constructs that can be used in the language. This example will illustrate many aspects of the syntax. In particular, note the use of semicolons, commas, and colons in the description.

Initially, we skip lines 3 and 4 of the description to focus on the overall structure. Line 6 begins the declaration of an *entity*, which is the fundamental unit of a VHDL design. In VHDL, just as for a symbol in a schematic, we need to give the design a name and to define its inputs and outputs. This is the function of the *entity declaration*. **Entity** and **is** are keywords in VHDL. Keywords, which we show in bold type, have a special meaning and cannot be used to name objects such as entities, inputs, outputs

```
-- Two-bit greater-than circuit : Structural VHDL Description      --  1
-- (See Figure 2-27 for logic diagram)                            --  2
library ieee, lcdf_vhdl;                                          --  3
use ieee.std_logic_1164.all, lcdf_vhdl.func_prims.all;           --  4
                                                                 --  5
entity comparator_greater_than_structural is                     --  6
  port (A: in std_logic_vector(1 downto 0);                      --  7
    B: in std_logic_vector(1  downto 0);                         --  8
    A_greater_than_B: out std_logic);                            --  9
end comparator_greater_than_structural;                          -- 10
                                                                 -- 11
architecture structural of comparator_greater_than_structural is -- 12
                                                                 -- 13
  component NOT1                                                  -- 14
   port(in1: in std_logic;                                       -- 15
     out1: out std_logic);                                       -- 16
  end component;                                                  -- 17
  component AND2                                                  -- 18
   port(in1, in2: in std_logic;                                  -- 19
     out1: out std_logic);                                       -- 20
  end component;                                                  -- 21
  component AND3                                                  -- 22
   port(in1, in2, in3: in std_logic;                             -- 23
     out1: out std_logic);                                       -- 24
  end component;                                                  -- 25
  component OR3                                                   -- 26
   port(in1, in2, in3 : in std_logic;                            -- 27
     out1: out std_logic);                                       -- 28
  end component;                                                  -- 29
signal B1_n, B0_n, and0_out, and1_out, and2_out: std_logic;      -- 30
begin                                                             -- 31
  inv_0: NOT1 port map (in1 => B(0), out1 => B0_n);              -- 32
  inv_1: NOT1 port map (B(1), B1_n);                             -- 33
  and_0: AND2 port map (A(1), B1_n, and0_out);                   -- 34
  and_1: AND3 port map (A(1), A(0), B0_n, and1_out);             -- 35
  and_2: AND3 port map (A(0), B1_n, B0_n, and2_out);             -- 36
  or0: OR3 port map (and0_out,and1_out,and2_out, A_greater_than_B); -- 37
end structural;                                                   -- 38
```

□ **FIGURE 2-28**
Structural VHDL Description of Two-Bit Greater-Than Comparator Circuit

or signals. Statement **entity** `comparator_greater_than_structural` **is** declares that a design exists with the name `comparator_greater_than_struc-tural`. VHDL is case insensitive (i.e., names and keywords are not distinguished by the use of uppercase or lowercase letters). `COMPARATOR_greater_than_Structural` is the same as `comparator_Greater_than_structural` and `comparator_greater_than_Structural`.

Next, a *port declaration* in lines 7 through 9 is used to define the inputs and outputs just as we would do for a symbol in a schematic. For the example design, there are two input signals: `A` and `B`. The fact that these are inputs is denoted by the mode **in**. Likewise, `A_greater_than_B` is denoted as an output by the mode **out**. In VHDL is a strongly typed language, so the type of the inputs and output must be declared. In the case of the output, the type is `std_logic`, which represents *standard logic*. This type declaration specifies the values that may appear on the inputs and the outputs, as well as the operations that may be applied to the signals. Standard logic, among its nine values, includes the usual binary values 0 and 1 and two additional values `X` and `U`. `X` represents an unknown value, `U` an uninitalized value. We have chosen to use standard logic, which includes these values, since these values are used by typical simulation tools.

The inputs `A` and `B` illustrate another VHDL concept, `std_logic_vectors`. The inputs are each two bits wide, so they are specified as type `std_logic_vector` instead of individual `std_logic` signals. In specifying vectors, we use an index. Since `A` consists of two input signals numbered 0 and 1, with 1 being the most significant (leftmost) bit, the index for `A` is 1 down to 0. The components of this vector are `A(1)` and `A(0)`. `B` likewise consists of two signals numbered 1 and 0, so its index is also 1 down to 0. Beginning at line 32, note how the signals within `std_logic_vectors` are referred to by giving the signal name and the index in parentheses. Also, if one wishes to have the larger index for a vector appear last, VHDL uses a somewhat different notational approach. For example, `signal N: std_logic_vector (0 to 3)` defines the first (leftmost) bit in signal `N` as `N(0)` and the last (rightmost) signal in `N` as `N(3)`. It is also possible to refer to subvectors (e.g., `N(1 to 2)`, which refers to `N(1)` and `N(2)`, would be the center two signals in `N`).

In order to use the types `std_logic` and `std_logic_vector`, it is necessary to define the values and the operations. For convenience, a *package* consisting of pre-compiled VHDL code is employed. Packages are usually stored in a directory referred to as a *library*, which is shared by some or all of the tool users. For `std_logic`, the basic package is `ieee.std_logic_1164`. This package defines the values and basic logic operators for types `std_ulogic` and `std_logic`. In order to use `std_logic`, we include line 3 to call up the **library** of packages called `ieee` and include line 4 containing `ieee.std_logic_1164.all` to indicate we want to use **all** of the package `std_logic_1164` from the `ieee` library. An additional library, `lcdf_vhdl`, contains a package called `func_prims` made up of basic logic gates, latches, and flip-flops described using VHDL, of which we use **all**. Library `lcdf_vhdl` is available in ASCII for copying from the Companion Website for the text. Note that the statements in lines 3 and 4 are tied to the entity that follows. If another entity is included in the same file, which also uses type `std_logic` and the elements from `func_prims`, the library and use statements must be repeated prior to that entity declaration.

The entity declaration ends with keyword **end** followed by the entity name. Thus far, we have discussed the equivalent of a schematic symbol in VHDL for the circuit.

STRUCTURAL DESCRIPTION   Next, we want to specify the function of the circuit. A particular representation of the function of an entity is called the *architecture* of the entity. Thus, the contents of line 12 declare a VHDL architecture named structural for the entity comparator_greater_than_structural to exist. The details of the architecture follow. In this case, we use a *structural description* that is equivalent to the schematic for the circuit given in Figure 2-27.

First, we declare the gate types we are going to use as components of our description in lines 15 through 29. Since we are building this architecture from gates, we declare an inverter called NOT1, a 2-input AND gate called AND2, a 3-input AND gate called AND3, and a 3-input OR gate called OR3 as *components*. These gate types are VHDL descriptions in package func_prims that contain the entity and architecture for each of the gates. The name and the port declaration for a component must be identical to those for the underlying entity. For NOT1, port gives the input name in1 and the output name out1. The component declaration for AND2 gives input names in1 and in2, and output name out1. Similarly, the component declarations for AND3 and OR3 give input names in1, in2, and in3, and output name out1.

Next, before specifying the interconnection of the gates, which is equivalent to a circuit netlist, we must name all of the nets in the circuit. The inputs and outputs already have names. The internal nets are the outputs of the two inverters and of the three AND gates in Figure 2-27. These output nets are declared as *signals* of type std_logic. Not_B1 and not_B0 are the signals for the two inverter outputs and and0_out, and1_out, and and2_out are the signals for the three AND gate outputs. Likewise, all of the inputs and outputs declared as ports are signals. In VHDL, there are both signals and variables. Variables are evaluated instantaneously. In contrast, signals are evaluated at some future point in time. This time may be physical time, such as 2 ns from the current time, or may be what is called *delta time*, in which a signal is evaluated one delta time from the current time. Delta time is viewed as an infinitesimal amount of time. Some time delay in evaluation of signals is essential to the internal operation of the typical digital simulator and, of course, based on the delay of gates, is realistic in performing simulations of circuits. For simplicity, we will typically be simulating circuits for correct function, not for performance or delay problems. For such functional simulation, it is easiest to let the delays default to delta times. Thus, no delay will be explicit in our VHDL descriptions of circuits, although delays may appear in test benches.

Following the declaration of the internal signals, the main body of the architecture starts with the keyword **begin**. The circuit described consists of two inverters, one 2-input AND gate, two 3-input AND gates, and one 3-input OR gate. Line 32 gives the label inv_0 to the first inverter and indicates that the inverter is component NOT1. Next is a **port map**, which maps the input and output of the inverter to the signals to which they are connected. This particular form of port map uses => with the port of the gate on the left and the signal to which it is connected on the right. For example, the input of inverter inv_0 is B(0) and the output is not_B0.

Lines 33 through 37 give the remaining five gates and the signals connected to their inputs and outputs. These five gates use an alternative method to specify the port maps for the logic gates. Instead of explicitly giving the component input and output names, we assume that these names are in the port map in the same order as given for the component. We can then implicitly specify the signals attached to these names by listing the signals in same order as the names. For example, in line 33, B(1) is connected to the input and not_B1 is connected to the output. The architecture is completed with the keyword **end** followed by its name structural. ∎

DATAFLOW DESCRIPTION   A dataflow description describes a circuit in terms of function rather than structure and is made up of concurrent assignment statements or their equivalent. Concurrent assignment statements are executed concurrently (i.e., in parallel) whenever one of the values on the right-hand side of the statement changes. For example, whenever a change occurs in a value on the right-hand side of a Boolean equation, the left-hand side is evaluated. The use of dataflow descriptions made up of Boolean equations is illustrated in Example 2-17.

EXAMPLE 2-17   Dataflow VHDL for a Two-Bit Greater-Than Comparator Circuit

Figure 2-29 shows a dataflow VHDL description for the two-bit greater-than comparator circuit from Figure 2-27. This example will be used to demonstrate a dataflow description made up of Boolean equations. The library, use, and entity statements

```
-- Two-bit greater-than circuit : Dataflow VHDL Description      -- 1
-- (See Figure 2-27 for logic diagram)                           -- 2
library ieee;                                                    -- 3
use ieee.std_logic_1164.all;                                     -- 4
                                                                 -- 5
entity comparator_greater_than_dataflow is                       -- 6
  port (A: in std_logic_vector(1 downto 0);                      -- 7
    B: in std_logic_vector(1 downto 0);                          -- 8
    A_greater_than_B: out std_logic);                            -- 9
end comparator_greater_than_dataflow;                            -- 10
                                                                 -- 11
architecture dataflow of comparator_greater_than_dataflow is     -- 12
signal B1_n, B0_n, and0_out, and1_out, and2_out: std_logic;      -- 13
begin                                                            -- 14
  B1_n <= not B(1);                                              -- 15
  B0_n <= not B(0);                                              -- 16
  and0_out <= A(1) and B1_n;                                     -- 17
  and1_out <= A(1) and A(0) and B0_n;                            -- 18
  and2_out <= A(0) and B1_n and B0_n;                            -- 19
  A_greater_than_B <= and0_out or and1_out or and2_out;          -- 20
end dataflow;                                                    -- 21
```

☐ **FIGURE 2-29**
Dataflow VHDL Description of Two-Bit Greater-Than Comparator Circuit

are identical to those in Figure 2-28, so they are not repeated here. The dataflow description begins in line 15. The signals B0_n and B1_n are defined by signal assignments that apply the **not** operation to the input signal B(0) and B(1), respectively. In line 17, B1_n and A(1) are combined with an **and** operator to form and0_out. The signals and1_out, and2_out, and A_greater_than_B are similarly defined in lines 18 through 20, with A_greater_than_B using the **or** operator. Note that this dataflow description is much simpler than the structural description in Figure 2-28.

The order of execution of the assignment statements does not depend upon the order of their appearance in the model description, but rather on the order of changes of signals on the right-hand side of the assignment statements. Thus the description in Figure 2-29 would have exactly the same behavior even if the assignment statements were listed in some other order, e.g., if line 15 and line 20 were interchanged. ∎

BEHAVIORAL DESCRIPTION Dataflow models using concurrent assignments are considered to be behavioral descriptions, because they describe the function of the circuit without describing its structure. As will be shown in Chapter 4, VHDL also provides ways to describe behavior using statements that execute sequentially within a process, known as algorithmic modeling. But even with dataflow modeling using concurrent assignments, VHDL provides ways to describe circuits more abstractly than the logic level.

EXAMPLE 2-18   VHDL for a Two-Bit Greater-Than Comparator Using When-Else

In Figure 2-30, instead of using Boolean equation-like statements in the architecture to describe the multiplexer, we use a *when-else* statement. This model of the circuit

```
-- Two-bit greater-than circuit : Conditional VHDL Description     --  1
-- using when-else(See Figure 2-27 for logic diagram)             --  2
library ieee;                                                     --  3
use ieee.std_logic_1164.all;                                      --  4
                                                                  --  5
entity comparator_greater_than_behavioral is                     --  6
  port (A: in std_logic_vector(1 downto 0);                      --  7
    B: in std_logic_vector(1 downto 0);                          --  8
    A_greater_than_B: out std_logic);                            --  9
end comparator_greater_than_behavioral;                          -- 10
                                                                  -- 11
architecture when_else of comparator_greater_than_behavioral is  -- 12
begin                                                            -- 13
  A_greater_than_B <= '1' when (A > B) else                      -- 14
            '0';                                                 -- 15
end when_else;                                                   -- 16
```

☐ **FIGURE 2-30**
Dataflow VHDL Description of Two-Bit Greater-Than Comparator Using *When-Else*

describes the behavior of the circuit (i.e., the output is a 1 when $A > B$ and 0 otherwise) using the desired mathematical operation of the circuit rather than Boolean logic. Whenever either A or B changes, the *when* condition is re-evaluated and the value is assigned accordingly. ■

Example 2-19 **VHDL for a Two-Bit Greater-Than Comparator Using** *With-Select*

With-select is a variation on *when-else* as illustrated for the model shown in Figure 2-31. The expression, the value of which is to be used for the decision, follows **with** and precedes **select**. The values for the expression that causes the alternative assignments then follow **when** with each of the assignment-value pairs separated by commas. In the example, A is the signal, the value of which determines the value selected for A_greater_than_B. For this example, A is used to select a function of B that represents the proper output. When $A = $ "00," 0 is assigned to the output because the function is 0 for all combinations of B. When

```
-- Two-bit greater-than circuit : Conditional VHDL Description      -- 1
-- using with-select(See Figure 2-27 for logic diagram)            -- 2
library ieee;                                                       -- 3
use ieee.std_logic_1164.all, ieee.std_logic_unsigned .all;         -- 4
                                                                   -- 5
entity comparator_greater_than_behavioral2 is                      -- 6
  port (A: in std_logic_vector(1 downto 0);                        -- 7
    B: in std_logic_vector(1 downto 0);                            -- 8
    A_greater_than_B: out std_logic);                              -- 9
end comparator_greater_than_behavioral2;                           -- 10
                                                                   -- 11
architecture with_select of comparator_greater_than_behavioral2 is -- 12
begin                                                              -- 13
 with A select                                                     -- 14
 A_greater_than_B <= '0' when "00",                                -- 15
              B(0) nor B(1) when "01",                             -- 16
              not B(1) when "10",                                  -- 17
              B(0) nand B(1) when "11",                            -- 18
              'X' when others;                                     -- 19
end with_select;                                                   -- 20
```

☐ **FIGURE 2-31**
Conditional Dataflow VHDL Description of Two-Bit Greater-Than Comparator Using *With-Select*

A = "01," the output should only be 1 when B = "00," which is the NOR function of the two bits of B. When A = "10," the output is a 1 when $B(1)$ is 0 and 0 when $B(1)$ is 1, so the function assigned is the inverse of $B(1)$. When A = "11," the output is a 1 except for when B = "11," which is the NAND function of the two bits of B. Finally, 'X' is assigned to the output **when others**, where **others** represents the standard logic combinations not already specified, i.e., when one of the bits of A is neither a 0 nor a 1, such as U.

This example is somewhat contrived for this particular circuit, resulting in a description that is less straightforward than the previous versions. However, this example illustrates an approach with the conditional operator that is often useful when a set of conditions is used to select between several functions. We will see examples of these types of selection circuits in later chapters, particularly in Chapter 3 with multiplexers and Chapter 6 with register transfers.

Note that *when-else* permits decisions on multiple distinct signals. For example, a model could have a first **when** conditioned on one signal, with another **when** in the **else** part that is conditioned on a different signal, and so on. In contrast, the *with-select* can depend on only a single Boolean condition (e.g., either the first signal or the second one, but not both). Also, for typical synthesis tools, *when-else* usually results in a more complex logical structure than *with-select* because *when-else* depends upon multiple conditions.   ■

TESTBENCHES   As briefly described in Section 2-8, a testbench is an HDL model whose purpose is to test another model, often called the Device Under Test (DUT), by applying stimuli to the inputs. More complex testbenches will also analyze the output of the DUT for correctness. Figure 2-32 shows a simple VHDL testbench for the structural two-bit greater-than comparator circuit. The testbench has several aspects that are common to testbenches. First, the entity declaration does not have any input or output ports (lines 5–6). Second, the architecture for the testbench declares the component for the DUT (lines 11–15) and then instantiates the DUT (line 17). The architecture also declares the signals that will be connected to the inputs and outputs of the DUT (lines 9–10). Finally, the architecture applies combinations of inputs to the DUT to test it under various conditions (lines 18–29). The input values are applied using a process named tb, where a process is a block of statements that are executed sequentially. The tb process in this testbench starts at the beginning of the simulation, and assigns values to the inputs of the DUT, waiting 10 ns of simulation time between assignments, and then halting by waiting forever. The process in this example uses only a few combinations of inputs for the sake of clarity, although it does test all three conditions for the relationship between A and B ($A < B, A = B$, and $A > B$). Processes will be described in more detail in Chapter 4, where a richer set of sequential statements that can be used in a process will be introduced.

This completes our introduction to VHDL for combinational circuits. We will continue with more on VHDL by presenting additional features of the language to describe more complex circuits in Chapters 3 and 4.

```
-- Testbench for VHDL two-bit greater-than comparator        -- 1
library ieee;                                                -- 2
use ieee.std_logic_1164.all, ieee.std_logic_unsigned.all;    -- 3
                                                             -- 4
entity greater_testbench is                                  -- 5
end greater_testbench;                                       -- 6
                                                             -- 7
architecture testbench of greater_testbench is               -- 8
signal A, B: std_logic_vector (1 downto 0);                  -- 9
signal struct_out: std_logic;                                -- 10
component comparator_greater_than_structural is              -- 11
   port (A: in std_logic_vector(1 downto 0);                 -- 12
   B: in std_logic_vector(1 downto 0);                       -- 13
   A_greater_than_B: out std_logic);                         -- 14
end component;                                                -- 15
begin                                                        -- 16
u1: comparator_greater_than_structural port map(A,B, struct_out);  -- 17
tb: process                                                  -- 18
begin                                                        -- 19
 A <= "10";                                                  -- 20
 B <= "00";                                                  -- 21
 wait for 10 ns;                                             -- 22
 B <= "01";                                                  -- 23
 wait for 10 ns;                                             -- 24
 B <= "10";                                                  -- 25
 wait for 10 ns;                                             -- 26
 B <= "11";                                                  -- 27
 wait; -- halt the process                                   -- 28
end process;                                                 -- 29
end testbench;                                               -- 30
```

☐ **FIGURE 2-32**
Testbench for the Structural Model of the Two-Bit Greater-Than Comparator

2-10 HDL Representations—Verilog

Since an HDL is used for describing and designing hardware, it is very important to keep the underlying hardware in mind as you write in the language. This is particularly critical if your language description is to be synthesized. For example, if you ignore the hardware that will be generated, it is very easy to specify a large complex gate structure by using an inefficient HDL description, when a much simpler structure using only a few gates is all that is needed. For this reason, initially, we emphasize describing detailed hardware with Verilog, and finishing with more abstract, higher-level descriptions.

Selected examples in this chapter are useful for introducing Verilog as an alternative means for representing detailed digital circuits. First, we show a structural Verilog description in Figure 2-33 that replaces the schematic for the

```
// Two-bit greater-than circuit: Verilog structural model        //  1
// See Figure 2-27 for logic diagram                             //  2
module comparator_greater_than_structural(A, B, A_greater_than_B); //  3
 input [1:0] A, B;                                               //  4
 output A_greater_than_B;                                        //  5
 wire B0_n, B1_n, and0_out, and1_out, and2_out;                 //  6
  not                                                           //  7
   inv0(B0_n,  B[0]),  inv1(B1_n,  B[1]);                       //  8
  and                                                           //  9
   and0(and0_out,  A[1],  B1_n),                                // 10
   and1(and1_out,  A[1],  A[0],  B0_n),                         // 11
   and2(and2_out,  A[0],  B1_n,  B0_n);                         // 12
  or                                                            // 13
   or0(A_greater_than_B,  and0_out,  and1_out,  and2_out);      // 14
endmodule                                                       // 15
```

□ **FIGURE 2-33**
Structural Verilog Description of Two-Bit Greater-Than Circuit

two-bit greater-than comparator. This example illustrates many of the fundamental concepts of Verilog. We then present higher-level behavioral Verilog descriptions for these circuits that further illustrate Verilog concepts.

EXAMPLE 2-20   Structural Verilog for a Two-Bit Greater-Than Circuit

The Verilog description for the two-bit greater-than circuit from Figure 2-27 is given in Figure 2-33. This description will be used to introduce a number of general Verilog features, as well as to illustrate structural circuit description.

The text between two slashes / / and the end of a line as shown in lines 1 and 2 of Figure 2-33 is interpreted as a comment. For multiline comments, there is an alternative notation using a / and *:

```
/* Two-bit greater-than circuit: Verilog structural model
  See  Figure 2-27  for logic diagram */
```

To assist in discussion of the Verilog description, comments providing line numbers have been added on the right. As a language, Verilog has a syntax that describes precisely the valid constructs that can be used in the language. This example will illustrate many aspects of the syntax. In particular, note the use of commas and colons in the description. Commas ($,$) are typically used to separate elements of a list and semicolons ($;$) are used to terminate Verilog statements.

Line 3 begins the declaration of a **module**, which is the fundamental building block of a Verilog design. The remainder of the description defines the module, ending in line 15 with **endmodule**. Note that there is no ; after **endmodule**. Just as for a symbol in a schematic, we need to give the design a name and to define its inputs and outputs. This is the function of the *module statement* in line 3 and the *input* and *output declarations* that follow. The words **module**, **input**, and **output** are keywords in Verilog. Keywords, which we show in bold type, have a special meaning and cannot be used as names of objects such as modules, inputs, outputs, or wires. The statement **module** comparator_greater_than_structural declares that a design or design part exists with the name comparator_greater_than_structural. Further, Verilog names are case sensitive (i.e., names are distinguished by the use of uppercase or lowercase letters). COMPARATOR_greater_than_Structural, Comparator_greater_than_structural, and comparator_greater_than_Structural are all distinct names.

Just as we would do for a symbol in a schematic, we give the names of the decoder inputs and outputs in the module statement. Next, an *input declaration* is used to define which of the names in the module statement are inputs. For the example design, there are two input signals, *A* and *B*. The fact that these are inputs is denoted by the keyword **input**. Similarly, an *output declaration* is used to define the output. The signal A_greater_than_B is denoted as an output by the keyword **output**.

Inputs and outputs as well as other binary signal types in Verilog can take on one of four values. The two obvious values are 0 and 1. Added are x to represent unknown values and z to represent high-impedance values on the outputs of 3-state logic. Verilog also has strength values that, when combined with the four values given, provide 120 possible signal states. Strength values are used in electronic circuit modeling, however, so will not be considered here.

The inputs *A* and *B* also illustrate the Verilog concept of a vector. In line 4, instead of specifying *A* and *B* as single bit wires, they are specified as multiple-bit wires called *vectors*. The bits of a vector are named by a range of integers. This range is given by maximum and minimum values. By specifying these two values, we specify the width of the vector and the names of each of its bits. The line **input** [1:0] A, B indicates that *A* and *B* are each a vector with a width of two, with the most significant (leftmost) bit numbered 1 and least significant (rightmost) bit numbered 0. The components of *A* are $A[1]$ and $A[0]$. Once a vector has been declared, then the entire vector or its subcomponents can be referenced. For example, *A* refers to the two bits of *A*, and $A[1]$ refers to the most significant bit of *A*. These types of references are used in specifying the output and inputs in instances of the gates in lines 8 and lines 9 through 12. Also, Verilog permits the larger index for a vector to appear last. For example, input [0:3] N defines an input port *N* as a vector with four bits, where the most significant (leftmost) bit is numbered 0 and the least significant (rightmost) bit is numbered 3.

STRUCTURAL DESCRIPTION   Next, we want to specify the function of the decoder. In this case, we use a *structural description* that is equivalent to the circuit schematic given in Figure 2-27. Note that the schematic is made up of gates. Verilog provides 14 primitive gates as keywords. Of these, we are interested in eight for now: **buf**, **not**, **and**, **or**, **nand**, **nor**, **xor**, and **xnor**. **buf** and **not** have single inputs, and all other gate types may have from two to any integer number of inputs. **buf** is a buffer, which has the function $z = x$, with x as the input and z as the output. It is as an amplifier of electronic signals that can be used to provide greater fan-out or smaller delays. **xor** is the exclusive-OR gate and **xnor** is the exclusive-NOR gate, the complement of the exclusive-OR. In our example, we will use just three gate types, **not**, **and**, and **or** as shown in lines 7 through 14 of Figure 2-33.

Before specifying the interconnection of the gates, which is the same as a circuit netlist, we need to name all of the nets in the circuit. The inputs and outputs already have names. The internal nets are the outputs of the two inverters and of the three AND gates in Figure 2-27. In line 6, these nets are declared as *wires* by use of the keyword **wire**. Names B0_n and B1_n are used for the inverter outputs and and0_out, and1_out, and and2_out for the outputs of the AND gates. In Verilog, **wire** is the default net type. Notably, **input** and **output** ports have the default type **wire**.

Following the declaration of the internal signals, the circuit described contains two inverters, one 2-input AND gate, two 3-input AND gates, and one 3-input OR gate. A statement consists of a gate type followed by a list of instances of that gate type separated by commas. Each instance consists of a gate name and, enclosed in parentheses, the gate output and inputs separated by commas, with the output given first. The first statement begins on line 7 with the **not** gate type. Following is inverter inv0 with B0_n as the output and B0 as the input. To complete the statement, inv1 is similarly described. Lines 9 through 14 give the remaining four gates and the signals connected to their outputs and inputs, respectively. For example, in line 12, an instance of a 3-input AND gate named and2 is defined. It has output and2_out and inputs A[0], B1_n, and B0_n. The module is completed with the keyword **endmodule**. ■

DATAFLOW DESCRIPTION   A dataflow description describes a circuit in terms of function rather than structure and is made up of concurrent assignment statements or their equivalent. Concurrent assignment statements are executed concurrently (i.e., in parallel) whenever one of the values on the right-hand side of the statement changes. For example, whenever a change occurs in a value on the right-hand side of a Boolean equation, the left-hand side is evaluated. The use of dataflow descriptions made up of Boolean equations is illustrated in Example 2-21.

EXAMPLE 2-21   Dataflow Verilog for a Two-Bit Greater-Than Comparator

In Figure 2-34, a dataflow Verilog description is given for the two-bit greater-than comparator. This particular dataflow description uses the assignment statement consisting of the keyword **assign** followed, in this case, by a Boolean equation. In such equations, we use the bitwise Boolean operators given in Table 2-4. In line 7 of Figure 2-34, B1_n is assigned the inverse of B[1] using the ~ operator. In line 9, A[1] and B1_n are ANDed together with an & operator. This AND combination is assigned to the output and0_out. The wires and1_out and and2_out are similarly defined in lines 10 and 11. The output A_greater_than_B is assigned using the OR operator | on wires and0_out, and1_out, and and2_out on line 12.

The order of execution of the assignment statements does not depend upon the order of their appearance in the model description, but rather on the order of changes of signals on the right-hand side of the assignment statements. Thus the description in Figure 2-34 would have exactly the same behavior even if the assignment statements were listed in some other order, e.g., if lines 7 and 12 were interchanged. ■

```
// Two-bit greater-than circuit: Dataflow model                    //  1
// See Figure 2-27 for logic diagram                              //  2
module comparator_greater_than_dataflow(A, B, A_greater_than_B);  //  3
 input [1:0] A, B;                                                //  4
 output A_greater_than_B;                                         //  5
 wire B1_n, B0_n, and0_out, and1_out, and2_out;                  //  6
 assign B1_n = ~B[1];                                            //  7
 assign B0_n = ~B[0];                                            //  8
 assign and0_out = A[1] & B1_n;                                  //  9
 assign and1_out = A[1] & A[0] & B0_n;                           // 10
 assign and2_out = A[0] & B1_n & B0_n;                           // 11
 assign A_greater_than_B = and0_out | and1_out | and2_out;       // 12
endmodule                                                         // 13
```

☐ **FIGURE 2-34**
Dataflow Verilog Description of Two-Bit Greater-Than Comparator

BEHAVIORAL DESCRIPTION   Dataflow models using concurrent assignments are considered to be behavioral descriptions, because they describe the function of the circuit without describing its structure. As will be shown in Chapter 4, Verilog also provides ways to describe behavior using statements that execute sequentially within a process, known as algorithmic modeling. But even with dataflow modeling using concurrent assignments, Verilog provides ways to describe circuits at levels higher than the logic level.

EXAMPLE 2-22   Verilog for a Two-Bit Greater-Than Comparator Using Conditional Operator

The description in Figure 2-35 implements the circuit's function by using a conditional operator ? : in line 6. If the logical value within the parentheses before the ? is true, then the value before the : is assigned to signal that is the target of the assignment, in this case, A_greater_than_B. If the logical value is false, then the value after the : is assigned. The value 1'b1 represents a constant. The first 1 specifies that the constant contains one digit, 'b that the constant is given in binary, and 1 gives the constant value. In this case, if the condition $A > B$ is true, then A_greater_than_B is assigned the value 1'b1; otherwise, A_greater_than_B is assigned the value 1'b0.   ■

```
// Two-bit greater-than circuit: Conditional model          // 1
// See Figure 2-27 for logic diagram                        // 2
module comparator_greater_than_conditional2(A, B, A_greater_than_B);  // 3
 input [1:0] A, B;                                          // 4
 output A_greater_than_B;                                   // 5
 assign A_greater_than_B = (A > B)? 1'b1 :                  // 6
     1'b0;                                                  // 7
endmodule                                                   // 8
```

□ **FIGURE 2-35**
Conditional Dataflow Verilog Description of Two-Bit Greater-Than Circuit

EXAMPLE 2-23   Verilog for a Two-Bit Greater-Than Circuit Using Behavioral Model

As a more extended example of the conditional operator, another form of dataflow description using a conditional operator is shown in Figure 2-36. The logical equality operator is denoted by =. Suppose we consider condition A = 2'b00. 2'b00 represents a constant. The 2 specifies that the constant contains two digits, b that the constant is given in binary, and 00 gives the constant value. Thus, the expression has value true if vector A is equal to 00; otherwise, it is false. If the expression is true, then 1'b0 is assigned to A_greater_than_B. If the expression is false, then the next expression containing a ? is evaluated, and so on. In this case, for a condition to be evaluated, all conditions preceding it must evaluate to false. If none of the decisions evaluate to true, then the default value 1'bx is assigned to A_greater_than_B. Recall that default value x represents unknown.

This example is somewhat contrived for this particular circuit, resulting in a description that is less straightforward than the previous versions. However, this example illustrates an approach with the conditional operator that is often useful when a set of conditions is used to select between several functions. We will see

```
// Two-bit greater-than circuit: Conditional model           // 1
// See Figure 2-27 for logic diagram                         // 2
module comparator_greater_than_conditional(A, B, A_greater_than_B);   // 3
 input [1:0] A, B;                                           // 4
 output A_greater_than_B;                                    // 5
 assign A_greater_than_B = (A == 2'b00)? 1'b0 :              // 6
                (A == 2'b01)? ~(B[1]|B[0]):                  // 7
                (A == 2'b10)? ~B[1] :                        // 8
                (A == 2'b11)? ~(B[1]&B[0]):                  // 9
                1'bx;                                        // 10
 endmodule                                                   // 11
```

☐ **FIGURE 2-36**
Conditional Dataflow Verilog Description of Two-Bit Greater-Than Circuit
Using Combinations

examples of these types of selection circuits in later chapters, particularly in Chapter 3 with multiplexers and Chapter 6 with register transfers. ■

EXAMPLE 2-24   Verilog for a Two-Bit Greater-Than Circuit Using a Behavioral Description

As a final example of the two-bit greater-than circuit, Figure 2-37 is a description that describes the behavior of the circuit at a much higher level of abstraction than Boolean equations. This description simply uses single statement with the > mathematical operator to implement the desired function. ■

TESTBENCHES   As briefly described in Section 2-8, a testbench is an HDL model whose purpose is to test another model, often called the Device Under Test (DUT), by applying stimuli to the inputs. More complex testbenches will also analyze the output of the DUT for correctness. Figure 2-38 shows a simple Verilog testbench for the structural two-bit greater-than comparator circuit. The testbench has several aspects that are common to testbenches. First, the module declaration does not have any

```
// Two-bit greater-than circuit: Behavioral model           // 1
// See Figure 2-27 for logic diagram                         // 2
module comparator_greater_than_behavioral(A, B, A_greater_than_B);   // 3
 input [1:0] A, B;                                           // 4
 output A_greater_than_B;                                    // 5
 assign A_greater_than_B = A > B;                            // 6
endmodule                                                    // 7
```

☐ **FIGURE 2-37**
Behavioral Verilog Description of Two-Bit Greater-Than Circuit

```
// Testbench for Verilog two-bit greater-than comparator        // 1
module comparator_testbench_verilog();                          // 2
 reg [1:0] A, B;                                                 // 3
 wire struct_out;                                                // 4
 comparator_greater_than_structural U1(A, B, struct_out);       // 5
 initial                                                         // 6
 begin                                                           // 7
  A = 2'b10;                                                     // 8
  B = 2'b00;                                                     // 9
  #10;                                                           // 10
  B = 2'b01;                                                     // 11
  #10;                                                           // 12
  B = 2'b10;                                                     // 13
  #10;                                                           // 14
  B = 2'b11;                                                     // 15
 end                                                             // 16
endmodule                                                        // 17
```

□ **FIGURE 2-38**
Testbench for the Structural Model of the Two-Bit Greater-Than Comparator

input or output ports (line 2). Second, the testbench declares the registers (variables) and wires that will be connected to the inputs and outputs of the DUT (lines 3–4) and instantiates the DUT (line 5). Finally, the testbench applies combinations of inputs to the DUT to test it under various conditions (lines 6–16). The input values are applied using a process, which is a block of statements that are executed sequentially. Because the values for A and B are assigned as variables in a process rather than with continuous assignments, A and B must be declared as type `reg` rather than as type `wire` (line 3). The process in this testbench runs once at the beginning of the simulation because of the keyword `initial` (line 6), and assigns values to the inputs of the DUT, waiting 10 time units of simulation time between assignments. In Verilog, delays are specified with a number sign (#) followed by a real number. The process in this example uses only a few combinations of inputs for the sake of clarity, although it does test all three conditions for the relationship between A and B ($A < B$, $A = B$, and $A > B$). Processes will be described in more detail in Chapter 4, where a richer set of sequential statements that can be used in a process will be introduced.

This completes our introduction to Verilog for combinational circuits. We will continue with more on Verilog by presenting additional features of the language for describing more complex circuits in Chapters 3 and 4.

2-11 CHAPTER SUMMARY

The logic operations AND, OR, and NOT define the input/output relationships of logic components called gates, from which digital systems are implemented. A Boolean algebra defined in terms of these operations provides a tool for manipulating Boolean functions in designing digital logic circuits. Minterm and maxterm standard forms correspond directly to truth tables for functions. These standard forms can be manipulated into sum-of-products and product-of-sums forms, which correspond to two-level gate circuits. Two cost measures to be minimized in optimizing a circuit are the number of input literals to the circuit and the total number of inputs to the gates in the circuit. K-maps with two to four variables are an effective alternative to algebraic manipulation in optimizing small circuits. These maps can be used to optimize sum-of-products forms, product-of-sums forms, and incompletely specified functions with don't-care conditions.

The primitive operations AND and OR are not directly implemented by primitive logic elements in the most popular logic family. Thus, NAND and NOR primitives that implement these families were introduced and used to implement circuits. A more complex primitive, the exclusive-OR, and its complement, the exclusive-NOR, were presented along with their mathematical properties.

Gate propagation delays were discussed. Propagation delay determines the speed of the overall digital circuit, and thus is a major design constraint.

Finally, the chapter provided a general introduction to HDLs and introduced two languages, VHDL and Verilog. Combinational circuits were used to illustrate structural and behavioral level descriptions for the two languages.

REFERENCES

1. BOOLE, G. *An Investigation of the Laws of Thought.* New York: Dover, 1854.

2. DIETMEYER, D. L. *Logic Design of Digital Systems*, 3rd ed. Boston: Allyn & Bacon, 1988.

3. GAJSKI, D. D. *Principles of Digital Design.* Upper Saddle River, NJ: Prentice Hall, 1997.

4. *IEEE Standard Graphic Symbols for Logic Functions* (includes IEEE Std 91a–1991 Supplement and IEEE Std 91–1984). New York: The Institute of Electrical and Electronics Engineers, 1991.

5. KARNAUGH, M. "A Map Method for Synthesis of Combinational Logic Circuits," *Transactions of AIEE, Communication and Electronics*, 72, part I (November 1953), 593–99.

6. MANO, M. M. *Digital Design*, 3rd ed. Upper Saddle River, NJ: Prentice Hall, 2002.

7. WAKERLY, J. F. *Digital Design: Principles and Practices*, 4th ed. Upper Saddle River, NJ: Pearson Prentice Hall, 2004.

PROBLEMS

The plus (+) indicates a more advanced problem and the asterisk (*) indicates that a solution is available on the Companion Website for the text.

2-1. *Demonstrate by means of truth tables the validity of the following identities:

(a) DeMorgan's theorem for three variables: $\overline{XYZ} = \overline{X} + \overline{Y} + \overline{Z}$

(b) The second distributive law: $X + YZ = (X + Y)(X + Z)$

(c) $\overline{X}Y + \overline{Y}Z + X\overline{Z} = X\overline{Y} + Y\overline{Z} + \overline{X}Z$

2-2. *Prove the identity of each of the following Boolean equations, using algebraic manipulation:

(a) $\overline{X}\,\overline{Y} + \overline{X}Y + XY = \overline{X} + Y$

(b) $\overline{A}B + \overline{B}\,\overline{C} + AB + \overline{B}C = 1$

(c) $Y + \overline{X}Z + X\overline{Y} = X + Y + Z$

(d) $\overline{X}\,\overline{Y} + \overline{Y}Z + XZ + XY + Y\overline{Z} = \overline{X}\,\overline{Y} + XZ + Y\overline{Z}$

2-3. +Prove the identity of each of the following Boolean equations, using algebraic manipulation:

(a) $AB\overline{C} + B\overline{C}\,\overline{D} + BC + \overline{C}D = B + \overline{C}D$

(b) $WY + \overline{W}Y\overline{Z} + WXZ + \overline{W}X\overline{Y} = WY + \overline{W}X\overline{Z} + \overline{X}Y\overline{Z} + X\overline{Y}Z$

(c) $A\overline{D} + \overline{A}B + \overline{C}D + \overline{B}C = (\overline{A} + \overline{B} + \overline{C} + \overline{D})(A + B + C + D)$

2-4. +Given that $A \cdot B = 0$ and $A + B = 1$, use algebraic manipulation to prove that

$$(A + C) \cdot (\overline{A} + B) \cdot (B + C) = B \cdot C$$

2-5. +A specific Boolean algebra with just two elements 0 and 1 has been used in this chapter. Other Boolean algebras can be defined with more than two elements by using elements that correspond to binary strings. These algebras form the mathematical foundation for bitwise logical operations that we will study in Chapter 6. Suppose that the strings are each a nibble (half of a byte) of four bits. Then there are 2^4, or 16, elements in the algebra, where an element I is the four-bit nibble in binary corresponding to I in decimal. Based on bitwise application of the two-element Boolean algebra, define each of the following for the new algebra so that the Boolean identities hold:

(a) The OR operation $A + B$ for any two elements A and B

(b) The AND operation $A \cdot B$ for any two elements A and B

(c) The element that acts as the 0 for the algebra

(d) The element that acts as the 1 for the algebra

(e) For any element A, the element $\overline{A}$.

2-6. Simplify the following Boolean expressions to expressions containing a minimum number of literals.

(a) $\overline{W}\overline{X}Y + \overline{W}\overline{Y} + \overline{X}YZ + \overline{W}\overline{X}Y$

(b) $(W + X)(\overline{W} + Y + \overline{X})$

(c) $\overline{X}YZ + XYZ + \overline{X}Y\overline{Z} + XZ$

(d) $(\overline{W + X + Y})(X + \overline{Y})$

(e) $WX\overline{Y} + X\overline{Y}\overline{Z} + XY + \overline{Y}Z + \overline{W}XY$

2-7. *Reduce the following Boolean expressions to the indicated number of literals:

(a) $\overline{X}\,\overline{Y} + XYZ + \overline{X}Y$ to three literals

(b) $X + Y(Z + \overline{X + Z})$ to two literals

(c) $\overline{W}X(\overline{Z} + \overline{Y}Z) + X(W + \overline{W}YZ)$ to one literal

(d) $(AB + \overline{A}\,\overline{B})(\overline{C}\,\overline{D} + CD) + \overline{AC}$ to four literals

2-8. Apply DeMorgan's theorem to express the function

$$F = X\overline{Y} + WX + W\overline{Y}$$

(a) with only OR and complement operations.

(b) with only AND and complement operations.

(c) with only NAND and complement operations.

2-9. *Find the complement of the following expressions:

(a) $A\overline{B} + \overline{A}B$

(b) $(\overline{V}W + X)Y + \overline{Z}$

(c) $WX(\overline{Y}Z + Y\overline{Z}) + \overline{W}\,\overline{X}(\overline{Y} + Z)(Y + \overline{Z})$

(d) $(A + \overline{B} + C)(\overline{A}\,\overline{B} + C)(A + \overline{B}\,\overline{C})$

2-10. *Obtain the truth table of the following functions, and express each function in sum-of-minterms and product-of-maxterms form:

(a) $(XY + Z)(Y + XZ)$

(b) $(\overline{A} + B)(\overline{B} + C)$

(c) $WX\overline{Y} + WX\overline{Z} + WXZ + \overline{Y}\overline{Z}$

2-11. For the Boolean functions E and F, as given in the following truth table:

X	Y	Z	F	E
0	0	0	0	0
0	0	1	0	1
0	1	0	0	0
0	1	1	1	1
1	0	0	1	0
1	0	1	1	0
1	1	0	1	1
1	1	1	1	1

(a) List the minterms and maxterms of each function.

(b) List the maxterms of $\overline{F}$ and $\overline{E}$

(c) List the minterms of $E + F$ and $E \cdot F$.

(d) Express E and F in sum-of-minterms algebraic form.

(e) Simplify $E \cdot F$ to expressions with a minimum of literals.

2-12. *Convert the following expressions into sum-of-products and product-of-sums forms:

(a) $(AB + C)(B + \overline{C}D)$

(b) $\overline{X} + X(X + \overline{Y})(Y + \overline{Z})$

(c) $(A + B\overline{C} + CD)(\overline{B} + EF)$

2-13. Draw the logic diagram for the following Boolean expressions. The diagram should correspond exactly to the equation. Assume that the complements of the inputs are not available.

(a) $\overline{A}\,\overline{B}\,\overline{C} + AB + AC$

(b) $X(Y\overline{Z} + \overline{Y}Z) + \overline{W}(Y + \overline{X}Z)$

(c) $AC(\overline{B} + D) + \overline{A}C(\overline{B} + D) + BC(\overline{A} + \overline{D})$

2-14. Optimize the following Boolean functions by means of a 3-variable map:

(a) $F(A, B, C) = \Sigma m(3, 4, 5, 6, 7)$

(b) $F(A, B, C) = \Sigma m(1, 3, 6, 7)$

(c) $F(A, B, C) = \Sigma m(3, 6, 7)$

(d) $F(A, B, C) = \Sigma m(1, 3, 4, 5, 6, 7)$

2-15. *Optimize the following Boolean expressions using a map:

(a) $\overline{X}\overline{Z} + Y\overline{Z} + XYZ$

(b) $\overline{A}B + \overline{B}C + \overline{A}\,\overline{B}\,\overline{C}$

(c) $\overline{A}\overline{B} + A\overline{C} + \overline{B}C + \overline{A}B\overline{C}$

2-16. Optimize the following Boolean functions by means of a 4-variable map:

(a) $F(A, B, C, D) = \Sigma m(3, 4, 5, 6, 7, 12, 13)$

(b) $F(A, B, C, D) = \Sigma m(4, 6, 7, 12, 13)$

(c) $F(A, B, C, D) = \Sigma m(0, 1, 4, 5, 6, 7, 12, 13)$

(d) $F(A, B, C, D) = \Sigma m(1, 3, 4, 5, 6, 7)$

2-17. Optimize the following Boolean functions, using a map:

(a) $F(A, B, C, D) = \Sigma m(0, 1, 4, 5, 8, 9, 12, 13, 15)$

(b) $F(A, B, C, D) = \Sigma m(4, 6, 7, 12, 13)$

2-18. *Find the minterms of the following expressions by first plotting each expression on a map:

(a) $XY + XZ + \overline{X}YZ$

(b) $XZ + \overline{W}X\overline{Y} + WXY + \overline{W}YZ + W\overline{Y}Z$

(c) $\overline{B}\,\overline{D} + ABD + \overline{A}BC$

2-19. *Find all the prime implicants for the following Boolean functions, and determine which are essential:

(a) $F(W, X, Y, Z) = \Sigma m\ (0, 2, 5, 7, 8, 10, 12, 13, 14, 15)$

(b) $F(A, B, C, D) = \Sigma m\ (0, 2, 3, 5, 7, 8, 10, 11, 14, 15)$

(c) $F(A, B, C, D) = \Sigma m\ (1, 3, 4, 5, 9, 10, 11, 12, 13, 14, 15)$

2-20. Optimize the following Boolean functions by finding all prime implicants and essential prime implicants and applying the selection rule:

(a) $F(A, B, C, D) = \Sigma m(0, 1, 5, 6, 7, 11, 12, 13, 15)$

(b) $F(A, B, C, D) = \Sigma m(1, 3, 5, 7, 13, 15)$

(c) $F(A, B, C, D) = \Sigma m(0, 2, 4, 8, 10, 12, 13, 15)$

2-21. Optimize the following Boolean functions in product-of-sums form:

(a) $F(A, B, C, D) = \Sigma m(1, 2, 3, 5, 6, 7, 13, 14, 15)$

(b) $F(A, B, C, D) = \Sigma m(0, 1, 2, 3, 6, 8, 9, 10, 11, 14)$

2-22. *Optimize the following expressions in (1) sum-of-products and (2) product-of-sums forms:

(a) $A\bar{C} + \bar{B}D + \bar{A}CD + ABCD$

(b) $(\bar{A} + \bar{B} + \bar{D})(A + \bar{B} + \bar{C})(\bar{A} + B + \bar{D})(B + \bar{C} + \bar{D})$

(c) $(\bar{A} + \bar{B} + D)(\bar{A} + \bar{D})(A + B + \bar{D})(A + \bar{B} + C + D)$

2-23. Optimize the following functions that are given in maxterms into (1) product-of-sums and (2) sum-of-products forms:

(a) $F(A, B, C, D) = \Pi M(2, 5, 6, 7, 8, 9, 10, 11, 14)$

(b) $F(A, B, C, D) = \Pi M(5, 7, 9, 11)$

2-24. Optimize the following Boolean functions F together with the don't-care conditions d in sum-of-products form:

(a) $F(A, B, C, D) = \Sigma m(2, 3, 4, 6, 8, 10, 12, 13, 14), d(A, B, C, D) = \Sigma m(0, 1, 15)$

(b) $F(A, B, C, D) = \Pi M(5, 7, 13, 15), d(A, B, C, D) = \Sigma m(9, 11)$

(c) $F(A, B, C, D) = \Pi M(10, 13, 14, 15), d(A, B, C, D) = \Sigma m(0, 3, 4, 7, 12)$

2-25. *Optimize the following Boolean functions F together with the don't-care conditions d. Find all prime implicants and essential prime implicants, and apply the selection rule.

(a) $F(A, B, C) = \Sigma m(3, 5, 6), d(A, B, C) = \Sigma m(0, 7)$

(b) $F(W, X, Y, Z) = \Sigma m(0, 2, 4, 5, 8, 14, 15), d(W, X, Y, Z) = \Sigma m(7, 10, 13)$

(c) $F(A, B, C, D) = \Sigma m(4, 6, 7, 8, 12, 15),$
$d(A, B, C, D) = \Sigma m(2, 3, 5, 10, 11, 14)$

2-26. Optimize the following Boolean functions F together with the don't-care conditions d in (1) product-of-sums and (2) sum-of-products forms.

(a) $F(A, B, C, D) = \Sigma m(0, 1, 4, 5, 6, 11, 15),$
$d(A, B, C, D) = \Sigma m(7, 8, 9, 12)$

(b) $F(A, B, C, D) = \Pi m(2, 3, 7, 8, 10, 12),$
$d(A, B, C, D) = \Sigma m(0, 9, 13, 14)$

2-27. *Prove that the dual of the exclusive-OR is also its complement.

2-28. Implement the following Boolean function with exclusive-OR and AND gates, using a minimum number of gate inputs:

$$F(A, B, C, D) = AB\bar{C}D + A\bar{D} + \bar{A}D$$

2-29. *The NOR gates in Figure 2-39 have propagation delay $t_{pd} = 0.073$ ns and the inverter has a propagation delay $t_{pd} = 0.048$ ns. What is the propagation delay of the longest path through the circuit?

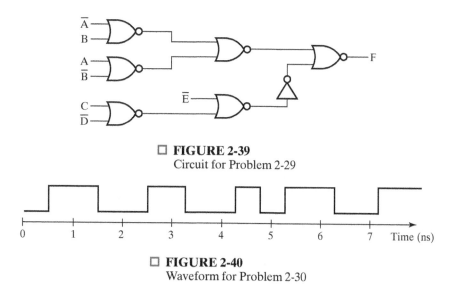

□ **FIGURE 2-39**
Circuit for Problem 2-29

□ **FIGURE 2-40**
Waveform for Problem 2-30

2-30. The waveform in Figure 2-40 is applied to an inverter. Find the output of the inverter, assuming that

(a) It has no delay.

(b) It has a transport delay of 0.06 ns.

(c) It has an inertial delay of 0.06 ns with a rejection time of 0.04 ns.

2-31. Assume that t_{pd} is the *average* of t_{PHL} and t_{PLH}. Find the delay from each input to the output in Figure 2-41 by

(a) Finding t_{PHL} and t_{PLH} for each path, assuming $t_{PHL} = 0.20$ ns and $t_{PLH} = 0.36$ ns for each gate. From these values, find t_{pd} for each path.

(b) Using $t_{pd} = 0.28$ ns for each gate.

(c) Compare your answers from parts (a) and (b) and discuss any differences.

2-32. The rejection time for inertial delays is required to be less than or equal to the propagation delay. In terms of the discussion of the example in Figure 2-25, why is this condition necessary to determine the delayed output?

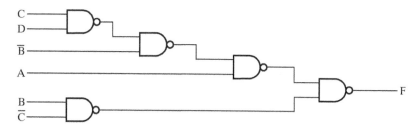

□ **FIGURE 2-41**
Circuit for Problem 2-31

2-33. +For a given gate, $t_{PHL} = 0.05$ ns and $t_{PLH} = 0.10$ ns. Suppose that an inertial delay model is to be developed from this information for typical gate-delay behavior.

  (a) Assuming a positive output pulse (LHL), what would the propagation delay and rejection time be?

  (b) Discuss the applicability of the parameters in (a) assuming a negative output pulse (HLH).

All HDL files for circuits referred to in the remaining problems are available in ASCII form for simulation and editing on the Companion Website for the text. A VHDL or Verilog compiler/simulator is necessary for the problems or portions of problems requesting simulation. Descriptions can still be written, however, for many problems without using compilation or simulation.

```
-- Combinational Circuit 1: Structural VHDL Description
library ieee, lcdf_vhdl;
use ieee.std_logic_1164.all, lcdf_vhdl.func_prims.all;
   entity comb_ckt_1 is
   port(x1, x2, x3, x4 : in std_logic;
        f : out std_logic);
end comb_ckt_1;

architecture structural_1 of comb_ckt_1 is
  component NOT1
    port(in1: in std_logic;
         out1: out std_logic);
  end component;
  component AND2
    port(in1, in2 : in std_logic;
         out1: out std_logic);
  end component;
  component OR3
    port(in1, in2, in3 : in std_logic;
         out1: out std_logic);
  end component;
  signal n1, n2, n3, n4, n5, n6 : std_logic;
  begin
    g0: NOT1 port map (in1 => x1, out1 => n1);
    g1: NOT1 port map (in1 => n3, out1 => n4);
    g2: AND2 port map (in1 => x2, in2 => n1,
                       out1 => n2);
    g3: AND2 port map (in1 => x2, in2 => x3,
                       out1 => n3);
    g4: AND2 port map (in1 => x3, in2 => x4,
                       out1 => n5);
    g5: AND2 port map (in1 => x1, in2 => n4,
                       out1 => n6);
    g6: OR3 port map (in1 => n2, in2 => n5,
                      in3 => n6, out1 => f);
  end structural_1;
```

□ **FIGURE 2-42**
VHDL for Problem 2-34

2-34. *Find a logic diagram that corresponds to the VHDL structural description in Figure 2-42. Note that complemented inputs are not available.

2-35. Using Figure 2-28 as a framework, write a structural VHDL description of the circuit in Figure 2-43. Replace *X*, *Y*, and *Z* with X (2:0). Consult package `func_prims` in library `lcdf_vhdl` for information on the various gate components. Compile `func_prims` and your VHDL model, and simulate your VHDL model for all eight possible input combinations to verify your description's correctness.

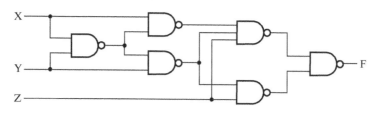

□ **FIGURE 2-43**
Circuit for Problem 2-35, 2-38, 2-41, and 2-43

2-36. Using Figure 2-28 as a framework, write a structural VHDL description of the circuit in Figure 2-44. Consult package `func_prims` in library `lcdf_vhdl` for information on the various gate components. Compile `func_prims` and your VHDL model, and simulate your VHDL model for all 16 possible input combinations to verify your description's correctness.

2-37. Find a logic diagram representing minimum two-level logic needed to implement the VHDL dataflow description in Figure 2-45. Note that complemented inputs are available.

2-38. *Write a dataflow VHDL description for the circuit in Figure 2-43 by using the Boolean equation for the output *F*.

2-39. *Find a logic diagram that corresponds to the Verilog structural description in Figure 2-46. Note that complemented inputs are not available.

□ **FIGURE 2-44**
Circuit for Problems 2–36 and 2-40

```
-- Combinational Circuit 2: Dataflow VHDL Description
library ieee;
use ieee.std_logic_1164.all;
entity comb_ckt_2 is
  port(a, b, c, d, a_n, b_n, c_n, d_n: in std_logic;
        f, g : out std_logic);
-- a_n, b_n, . . . are complements of a, b, . . . , respectively.

end comb_ckt_2;
architecture dataflow_1 of comb_ckt_2 is
begin
    f <= b and (a or (a_n and c)) or (b_n and c and d_n);
    g <= b and (c or (a_n and c_n) or (c_n and d_n));
end dataflow_1;
```

☐ **FIGURE 2-45**
VHDL for Problem 2–37

```
// Combinational Circuit 1: Structural Verilog Description
module comb_ckt_1(x1, x2, x3, x4, f);
  input x1, x2, x3, x4;
  output f;

  wire n1, n2, n3, n4, n5, n6;
  not
    go(n1, x1),
    g1(n4, n3);
  and
    g2(n2, x2, n1),
    g3(n3, x2, x3),
    g4(n5, x3, x4),);
    g5(n6, x1, n4),);
  or
    g6(f, n2, n5, n6),
endmodule
```

☐ **FIGURE 2-46**
Verilog for Problems 2–39 and 2-41

2-40. Using Figure 2-33 as a framework, write a structural Verilog description of the circuit in Figure 2-44. Compile and simulate your Verilog model for all 16 possible input combinations to verify your description's correctness.

2-41. Using Figure 2-46 as a framework, write a structural Verilog description of the circuit in Figure 2-43. Replace *X*, *Y*, and *Z* with **input** [2:0] X. Compile and simulate your Verilog model for all eight possible input combinations to verify your description's correctness.

2-42. Find a logic diagram representing minimum 2-level logic needed to implement the Verilog dataflow description in Figure 2-47. Note that complemented inputs are available.

2-43. *Write a dataflow Verilog description for the circuit in Figure 2-43 by using the Boolean equation for the output *F* and using Figure 2-34 as a model.

```
// Combinational Circuit 2: Dataflow Verilog Description
module comb_ckt_1 (a, b, c, d, a_n, b_n, c_n, d_n, f, g);
// a_n, b_n, . . . are complements of a, b, . . . , respectively.
   input a, b, c, d, a_n, b_n, c_n, d_n;
   output f, g;

   assign f = b & (a |(a_n & c)) | (b_n & c & d_n);
   assign g = b & (c | (a_n & c_n) | (c_n & d_n));
endmodule
```

□ **FIGURE 2-47**
Verilog for Problem 2–42

3

COMBINATIONAL LOGIC DESIGN

In this chapter, we continue our study of the design of combinational circuits. The chapter begins by describing a hierarchical approach to design, where the desired functionality is broken into smaller, less complex pieces that can be designed individually and then connected together to form the final circuit. We learn about a number of common functions and the corresponding fundamental circuits that are very useful in designing larger digital circuits. The fundamental, reusable circuits, which we call *functional blocks*, implement functions of a single variable, decoders, encoders, code converters, and multiplexers. The chapter then covers a special class of functional blocks that perform arithmetic operations. It introduces the concept of iterative circuits made up of arrays of combinational cells and describes blocks designed as iterative arrays for performing addition, covering both addition and subtraction. The simplicity of these arithmetic circuits comes from using complement representations for numbers and complement-based arithmetic. We also introduce circuit contraction, which permits us to design new functional blocks from existing ones. Contraction involves application of value fixing to the inputs of existing blocks and simplification of the resulting circuits. These circuits perform operations such as incrementing a number, decrementing a number, or multiplying a number by a constant. Many of these new functional blocks will be used to construct sequential functional blocks in Chapter 6.

The various concepts in this chapter are pervasive in the design of the generic computer in the diagram at the beginning of Chapter 1. Combinational logic is a mainstay in all of the digital components. Multiplexers are very important for selecting data in the processor, in memory, and on I/O boards. Decoders are used for selecting boards attached to the input—output bus and to decode instructions to determine the operations performed in the processor. Encoders are used in a number of components, such as the keyboard. Functional blocks are widely used, so concepts from this chapter apply across all of the digital components of the generic computer, including memories. In the generic computer diagram at the beginning of Chapter 1, adders, adder-subtractors,

> and other arithmetic circuits are used in the processor. Incrementers and decrementers are used widely in other components as well, so concepts from this chapter apply across most components of the generic computer.

3-1 BEGINNING HIERARCHICAL DESIGN

As briefly described in Chapter 1, the procedure for designing a digital system is to:

1. specify the desired behavior,
2. formulate the relationship between the inputs and outputs of the system, usually in terms of Boolean equations or a truth table,
3. optimize the representation of the logical behavior to minimize the number of logic gates required, as illustrated by the Karnaugh map procedure introduced in Chapter 2,
4. map the optimized logic to the available implementation technology, such as the logic gates from Chapter 2 or the functional blocks described in this chapter, and
5. verify the correctness of the final design in meeting the specifications.

The focus in this chapter is on the first four steps of the design procedure for combinational logic, from specifying the system to mapping the logic to the available implementation technology. But in actual design practice, the last step of verifying the correctness of the design typically is a considerable part of the effort creating the design. While an in-depth treatment of verification is beyond the scope of an introductory text such as this one, we should keep in mind that making sure that the design meets the specification is an important step that is often a bottleneck in the product design cycle. Small designs can be verified manually by finding the Boolean logic equations for the design and confirming that the truth table for them matches the specification. Larger designs are verified using simulation as well as more advanced techniques. If the circuit does not meet its specification, then it is incorrect. As a consequence, verification plays a vital role in preventing incorrect circuit designs from being manufactured and used.

For complex digital systems, rather than applying the design process above to the whole system, a typical method for designing them is to use a "divide-and-conquer" approach called *hierarchical design*. The resulting related symbols and schematics constitute a *hierarchy* representing the circuit designed. In order to deal with circuit complexity, the circuit is broken up into pieces we call *blocks*, and the above design procedure is used to design the blocks. The blocks are then interconnected to form the circuit. The functions of these blocks and their interfaces are carefully defined, so that the circuit formed by interconnecting the blocks obeys the initial circuit specification. If a block is still too large and complex to be designed as a single entity, it can be broken into smaller blocks. This process can be repeated as necessary. Note that since we are working primarily with logic circuits, we use the term "circuit" in this discussion, but the ideas apply equally well to the "systems" covered in later chapters.

Example 3-1 illustrates a very simple use of hierarchical design to "divide and conquer" a circuit that has eight inputs. This number of inputs makes the truth table cumbersome and K-maps impossible. Thus, direct application of the basic combinational design approach, as used in Chapter 2, is difficult.

EXAMPLE 3-1   Design of a 4-Bit Equality Comparator

SPECIFICATION: An equality comparator is a circuit that compares two binary vectors to determine whether they are equal or not. The inputs to this specific circuit consist of two vectors: $A(3:0)$ and $B(3:0)$. Vector A consists of four bits, $A(3), A(2), A(1),$ and $A(0)$, with $A(3)$ as the most significant bit. Vector B has a similar description with B replaced by A. The output of the circuit is a single-bit variable E. Output E is equal to 1 if vectors A and B are equal and equal to 0 if vectors A and B are unequal.

FORMULATION: The formulation attempts to bypass the use of a truth table due to its size. In order for A and B to be equal, the bit values in each of the respective positions, 3 down to 0, of A and B must be equal. If all of the bit positions for A and B contain equal values in every position, then $E = 1$—otherwise, $E = 0$. Intuitively, we can see from this formulation of the problem that the circuit can be developed as a simple 2-level hierarchy with the complete circuit at the top level and five circuits at the bottom level. Since comparison of a bit from A and the corresponding bit from B must be done in each of the bit positions, we can decompose the problem into four 1-bit comparison circuits MX and an additional circuit ME that combines the four comparison-circuit outputs to obtain E. A logic diagram of the hierarchy showing the interconnection of the five blocks is shown in Figure 3-1(a).

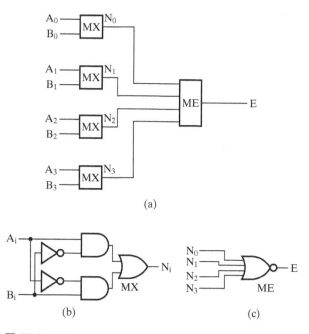

□ **FIGURE 3-1**
Hierarchical Diagram for a 4-Bit Equality Comparator

OPTIMIZATION: For bit position i, we define the circuit output N_i to be 0 if A_i and B_i have the same values and $N_i = 1$ if A_i and B_i have different values. Thus, the MX circuit can be described by the equation

$$N_i = \overline{A_i}B_i + A_i\overline{B_i}$$

which has the circuit diagram shown in Figure 3-1(b). By using hierarchy, we can employ four copies of this circuit, one for each of the four bits of A and B. Output $E = 1$ only if all of the N_i values are 0. This can be described by the equation

$$E = \overline{N_0 + N_1 + N_2 + N_3}$$

and has the diagram given in Figure 3-1(c). Both of the circuits given are optimum two-level circuits. These two circuit diagrams plus the block diagram in Figure 3-1(a) represent the hierarchical design of the circuit. The actual circuit is obtained by replacing the respective blocks in Figure 3-1(a) by copies of the two circuits shown in Figures 3-1(b) and (c).

The structure of the hierarchy for the 4-bit equality comparator can be represented without the interconnections by starting with the top block for the overall circuit and, below each block, connecting those blocks or primitives from which the block is constructed. Using this representation, the hierarchy for the 4-bit equality comparator circuit is shown in Figure 3-2(a). Note that the resulting structure has the form of a tree with the root at the top. The "leaves" of the tree are the gates, in this case 21 of them. In order to provide a more compact representation of the hierarchy, we can reuse blocks, as shown in Figure 3-2(b). This diagram corresponds to blocks used in Figure 3-1, with only one copy of each distinct block shown. These diagrams and the circuits in Figure 3-1 are helpful in illustrating a number of useful concepts associated with hierarchies and hierarchical blocks. ∎

First of all, a hierarchy reduces the complexity required to represent the schematic diagram of a circuit. For example, in Figure 3-2(a), 21 gates appear. This means that if the circuit were designed directly in terms of gates, the schematic for the

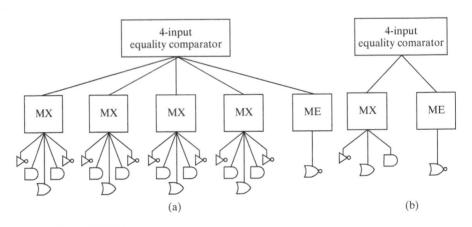

(a)   (b)

☐ **FIGURE 3-2**
Diagrams Representing the Structure of the Hierarchy for Figure 3-1

circuit would consist of 21 interconnected gate symbols, in contrast to just 11 symbols used to describe the circuit implementation as a hierarchy in Figure 3-1. Thus, a hierarchy gives a simplified representation of a complex circuit.

Second, the hierarchy ends at a set of "leaves" in Figure 3-2. In this case, the leaves consist of AND gates, OR gates, inverters, and a NOR gate. Since the gates are electronic circuits, and we are interested here only in designing the logic, these gates are commonly called *primitive blocks*. These are *predefined* rudimentary blocks that have a symbol, but no logic schematic. In general, more complex structures that likewise have symbols, but no logic schematics, are also predefined blocks. Instead of schematics, their function can be defined by a program or description that can serve as a model. For example, in the hierarchy depicted in Figure 3-1, the MX blocks could have been considered as predefined exclusive-OR gates consisting of electronic circuits. In such a case, the diagram describing the internal logic for MX exclusive-OR blocks in Figure 3-1(b) would not be necessary. The hierarchical representations in Figure 3-1(b) and 3-2(a) would then end with the exclusive-OR blocks. In any hierarchy, the "leaves" consist of predefined blocks, some of which may be primitives.

A third very important property that results from hierarchical design is the *reuse* of blocks, as illustrated in Figures 3-2(a) and (b). In part (a), there are four copies of the 2-input MX block. In part (b), there is only one copy of the 2-input MX block. This represents the fact that the designer has to design only one 2-input MX block and can use this design four times in the 4-bit equality comparator circuit. In general, suppose that at various levels of a hierarchy, the blocks used are carefully defined in such a manner that many of them are identical. A prerequisite for being able to achieve this goal is a fundamental property of the circuit called *regularity*. A *regular circuit* has a function that permits it to be constructed from copies of a reasonably small set of distinct blocks. An *irregular circuit* has a function with no such property. Clearly the regularity for any given function is a matter of degree. For a given repeated block, only one design is necessary. This design can be used everywhere the block is required. The appearance of a block within a design is called an *instance* of the block and its use is called an *instantiation*. The block is *reusable* in the sense that it can be used in multiple places in the circuit design and, possibly, in the design of other circuits as well. This concept greatly reduces the design effort required for complex circuits. Note that, in the implementation of the actual circuit, separate hardware has to be provided for each instance of the block, as represented in Figure 3-2(a). The reuse, as represented in Figure 3-2(b), is confined to the schematics that need to be designed, not to the actual hardware implementation. The ratio of the number of primitives in the final circuit to the total number of blocks in a hierarchical diagram including primitives is a measure of regularity. A larger ratio represents higher regularity; for example, for the 4-bit comparator as in Figure 3-1, this ratio is 21/11.

A complex digital system may contain millions of interconnected gates. A single very-large-scale integrated (VLSI) processor circuit often contains hundreds of millions of gates. With such complexity, the interconnected gates appear to be an incomprehensible maze. Such complex systems or circuits are not designed manually simply by interconnecting gates one at a time.

In this chapter we focus on predefined, reusable blocks that typically lie at the lower levels of logic design hierarchies. These are blocks of intermediate size that provide basic functions used in digital design. They allow designers to do much of the design process above the primitive block, i.e., gate level. We refer to these particular blocks as *functional blocks*. Thus, a functional block is a predefined collection of interconnected gates. Many of these functional blocks have been available for decades as medium-scale integrated (MSI) circuits that were interconnected to form larger circuits or systems. Similar blocks are now, in computer-aided design tool libraries, used for designing larger integrated circuits. These functional blocks provide a catalog of digital components that are widely used in the design and implementation of integrated circuits for computers and digital systems.

3-2 TECHNOLOGY MAPPING

Before we begin our discussion of functional blocks, it will be helpful if we first discuss *technology mapping*, where a logic diagram or netlist is transformed into a new diagram or netlist using available technology components. In this section, we introduce NAND and NOR gate cells and consider mapping AND, OR, NOT descriptions to one or the other of these two technologies. In currently available transistor technologies, NAND and NOR gates are smaller and faster than AND and OR gates. As we described in Chapter 2, the NAND and NOR functions are both functionally complete, so any Boolean function can be implemented using only one or the other. Later in this chapter, we will show how to implement logic functions by mapping them onto more complex functional blocks. In Chapter 5, technology mapping to programmable implementation technologies is covered.

 ADVANCED TECHNOLOGY MAPPING   Technology mapping using collections of cell types including multiple gate types is covered in this supplement on the Companion Web Site for the text.

A NAND technology consists of a collection of cell types, each of which includes a NAND gate with a fixed number of inputs. The cells have numerous properties, as described in Chapter 5. Because of these properties, there may be more than one cell type with a given number of inputs n. For simplicity, we will assume that there are four cell types, based on the number of inputs, n, for $n = 1, 2, 3$, and 4. We will call these four cell types Inverter ($n = 1$), 2NAND, 3NAND, and 4NAND, respectively.

A convenient way to implement a Boolean function with NAND gates is to begin with the optimized logic diagram of the circuit consisting of AND and OR gates and inverters. Next, the function is converted to NAND logic by converting the logic diagram to NAND gates and inverters. The same conversion applies for NOR gate cells.

Given an optimized circuit that consists of AND gates, OR gates, and inverters, the following procedure produces a circuit using NAND (or NOR) gates with unrestricted gate fan-in:

1. Replace each AND and OR gate with the NAND (NOR) gate and inverter equivalent circuits shown in Figures 3-3(a) and (b).

2. Cancel all inverter pairs.

3. Without changing the logic function, (a) "push" all inverters lying between (i) either a circuit input or a driving NAND (NOR) gate output and (ii) the driven NAND (NOR) gate inputs toward the driven NAND (NOR) gate inputs. Cancel pairs of inverters in series whenever possible during this step. (b) Replace inverters in parallel with a single inverter that drives all of the outputs of the parallel inverters. (c) Repeat (a) and (b) until there is at most one inverter between the circuit input or driving NAND (NOR) gate output and the attached NAND (NOR) gate inputs.

In Figure 3-3(c), the rule for pushing an inverter through a "dot" is illustrated. The inverter on the input line to the dot is replaced with inverters on each of the

(a) Mapping to NAND gates

(b) Mapping to NOR gates

(c) Pushing an inverter through a "dot"

(d) Canceling inverter pairs

□ **FIGURE 3-3**
Mapping of AND Gates, OR Gates, and Inverters to
NAND Gates, NOR Gates, and Inverters

output lines from the dot. The cancelation of pairs of inverters in Figure 3-3(d) is based on the Boolean algebraic identity

$$\overline{\overline{X}} = X$$

The next example illustrates this procedure for NAND gates.

EXAMPLE 3-2 Implementation with NAND Gates

Implement the following optimized function with NAND gates:

$$F = AB + \overline{(AB)}C + (\overline{AB})\overline{D} + E$$

The AND, OR, inverter implementation is given in Figure 3-4(a). In Figure 3-4(b), step 1 of the procedure has been applied, replacing each AND gate and OR gate with its equivalent circuit using NAND gates and inverters from Figure 3-3(a). Labels appear on dots and inverters to assist in the explanation. In step 2, the inverter pairs (1, 2) and (3, 4), cancel, giving direct connections between the corresponding NAND gates in Figure 3-4(d). As shown in Figure 3-4(c), inverter 5 is pushed through X and cancels with inverters 6 and 7, respectively. This gives direct connections between the corresponding NAND gates in Figure 3-4(d). No further steps can be applied, since inverters 8 and 9 cannot be paired with other inverters and must remain in the final mapped circuit in Figure 3-4(d). The next example illustrates this procedure for NOR gates.

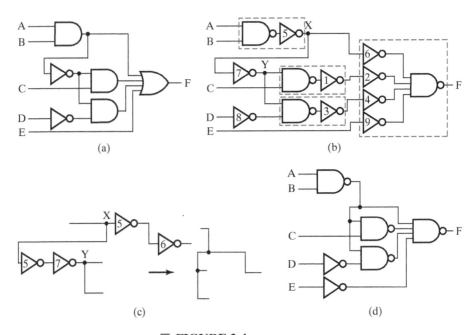

(a)

(b)

(c)

(d)

□ **FIGURE 3-4**
Solution to Example 3-2

EXAMPLE 3-3 Implementation with NOR Gates

Implement the same optimized Boolean function used in Example 3-2 with NOR gates:

$$F = AB + \overline{(AB)}C + \overline{(AB)}\overline{D} + E$$

The AND, OR, inverter implementation is given in Figure 3-5(a). In Figure 3-5(b), step 1 of the procedure has been applied, replacing each AND gate and OR gate with its equivalent circuit using NOR gates and inverters from Figure 3-3(b). Labels appear on dots and inverters to assist in the explanation. In step 2, inverter 1 can be pushed through dot X to cancel with inverters 2 and 3, respectively. The pair of inverters on the D input line cancel as well. The single inverters on input lines A, B, and C and output line F must remain, giving the final mapped circuit that appears in Figure 3-5(c).

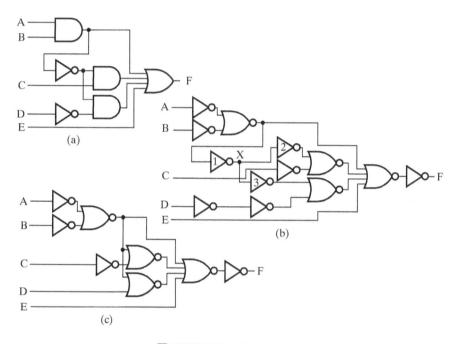

(a)

(b)

(c)

□ **FIGURE 3-5**

Solution to Example 3-3

In Example 3-2 the gate-input cost of the mapped circuit is 12, and in Example 3-3 the gate-input cost is 14, so the NAND implementation is less costly. Also, the NAND implementation involves a maximum of three gates in series while the NOR implementation has a maximum of five gates in series. With equal gate delays assumed, the shorter series of gates in the NAND circuit gives a maximum delay from an input change to a corresponding output change about 0.6 times as long as that for the NOR circuit. So, in this particular case, the NAND circuit is superior to the NOR circuit in both cost and delay.

The result of a technology mapping is clearly influenced by the initial circuit or equation forms prior to mapping. For example, mapping to NANDs for a circuit with an OR gate at the output produces a NAND gate at the output. Mapping to NORs for the same circuit produces an inverter driven by a NOR gate at the output. Because of these results, the sum of products is viewed as more natural for NANDs and the product of sums, which eliminates the output inverter, as more natural for NORs. Nevertheless, the choice should be based on which form gives the best over-all implementation in terms of whatever optimization criteria are being applied. ■

3-3 COMBINATIONAL FUNCTIONAL BLOCKS

Earlier, we defined and illustrated combinational circuits and their design. In this section, we define specific combinational functions and corresponding combinational circuits, referred to as *functional blocks*. In some cases, we will go through the design process for obtaining a circuit from the function, while in other cases, we will simply present the function and an implementation of it. These functions have special impor-tance in digital design. In the past, the functional blocks were manufactured as small- and medium-scale integrated circuits. Today, in very-large-scale integrated (VLSI) circuits, functional blocks are used to design circuits with many such blocks. Combina-tional functions and their implementations are fundamental to the understanding of VLSI circuits. By using a hierarchy, we typically construct circuits as instances of these functions or the associated functional blocks as well as logic design at the gate level.

Large-scale and very-large-scale integrated circuits are almost always sequen-tial circuits, as detailed beginning in Chapter 4. The functions and functional blocks discussed in this chapter are combinational. However, they are often combined with storage elements to form sequential circuits, as shown in Figure 3-6. Inputs to the combinational circuit can come from both the external environment and the storage elements. Outputs from the combinational circuit go to both the external environ-ment and the storage elements. In later chapters, we use the combinational functions and blocks defined here, with storage elements to form sequential circuits that per-form very useful functions. Further, the functions and blocks defined here serve as a basis for describing and understanding both combinational and sequential circuits using hardware description languages.

3-4 RUDIMENTARY LOGIC FUNCTIONS

Value fixing, transferring, inverting, and enabling are among the most elementary of combinational logic functions. The first two operations, value fixing and transferring, do not involve any Boolean operators. They use only variables and constants. As a

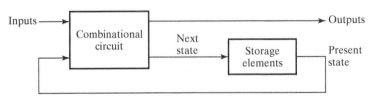

☐ **FIGURE 3-6**
Block Diagram of a Sequential Circuit

□ **TABLE 3-1**
Functions of One Variable

X	F = 0	F = X	F = $\overline{X}$	F = 1
0	0	0	1	1
1	0	1	0	1

consequence, logic gates are not involved in the implementation of these operations. Inverting involves only one logic gate per variable, and enabling involves one or two logic gates per variable.

Value-Fixing, Transferring, and Inverting

If a single-bit function depends on a single variable X, four different functions are possible. Table 3-1 gives the truth tables for these functions. The first and last columns of the table assign either constant value 0 or constant value 1 to the function, thus performing *value fixing*. In the second column, the function is simply the input variable X, thus *transferring* X from input to output. In the third column, the function is $\overline{X}$, thus *inverting* input X to become output $\overline{X}$.

The implementations for these four functions are given in Figure 3-7. Value fixing is implemented by connecting a constant 0 or constant 1 to output F, as shown in Figure 3-7(a). Figure 3-7(b) shows alternative representations used in logic schematics. For the positive logic convention, constant 0 is represented by the electrical ground symbol and constant 1 by a power-supply voltage symbol. The latter symbol is labeled with either V_{CC} or V_{DD}. Transferring is implemented by a simple wire connecting X to F as in Figure 3-7(c). Finally, inverting is represented by an inverter which forms $F = \overline{X}$ from input X, as shown in Figure 3-7(d).

Multiple-Bit Functions

The functions defined so far can be applied to multiple bits on a bitwise basis. We can think of these multiple-bit functions as vectors of single-bit functions. For example, suppose that we have four functions, F_3, F_2, F_1, and F_0, that make up a four-bit function F. We can order the four functions with F_3 as the most significant bit and F_0 the

□ **FIGURE 3-7**
Implementation of Functions of a Single Variable X

☐ **FIGURE 3-8**
Implementation of Multibit Rudimentary Functions

least significant bit, providing the vector $F = (F_3, F_2, F_1, F_0)$. Suppose that F consists of rudimentary functions $F_3 = 0$, $F_2 = 1$, $F_1 = A$, and $F_0 = \overline{A}$. Then we can write F as the vector $(0, 1, A, \overline{A})$. For $A = 0$, $F = (0, 1, 0, 1)$ and for $A = 1$, $F = (0, 1, 1, 0)$. This multiple-bit function can be referred to as $F(3:0)$ or simply as F and is implemented in Figure 3-8(a). For convenience in schematics, we often represent a set of multiple, related wires by using a single line of greater thickness with a slash, across the line. An integer giving the number of wires represented accompanies the slash as shown in Figure 3-8(b). In order to connect the values $0, 1, X$, and $\overline{X}$ to the appropriate bits of F, we break F up into four wires, each labeled with the bit of F. Also, in the process of transferring, we may wish to use only a subset of the elements in F—for example, F_2 and F_1. The notation for the bits of F can be used for this purpose, as shown in Figure 3-8(c). In Figure 3-8(d), a more complex case illustrates the use of F_3, F_1, F_0 at a destination. Note that since F_3, F_1, and F_0 are not all together, we cannot use the range notation $F(3:0)$ to denote this subvector. Instead, we must use a combination of two subvectors, $F(3), F(1:0)$, denoted by subscripts $3, 1:0$. The actual notation used for vectors and subvectors varies among the schematic drawing tools or HDL tools available. Figure 3-8 illustrates just one approach. For a specific tool, the documentation should be consulted.

Value fixing, transferring, and inverting have a variety of applications in logic design. Value fixing involves replacing one or more variables with constant values 1 and 0. Value fixing may be permanent or temporary. In permanent value fixing, the value can never be changed. In temporary value fixing, the values can be changed, often by mechanisms somewhat different from those employed in ordinary logical operation. A major application of fixed and temporary value fixing is in programmable logic devices. Any logic function that is within the capacity of the programmable device can be implemented by fixing a set of values, as illustrated in the next example.

EXAMPLE 3-4   Lecture-Hall Lighting Control Using Value Fixing

The Problem: The design of a part of the control for the lighting of a lecture hall specifies that the switches that control the normal lights be programmable. There are to be three different modes of operation for the two switches. Switch P is on the podium in the front of the hall and switch R is adjacent to a door at the rear of the lecture hall. H (house lights) is 1 for the house lights on and 0 for the house lights off. The light control for house lights can be programmed to be in one of three modes, M_0, M_1, or M_2, defined as:

> M_0: Either switch P or switch R turns the house lights on and off.
> M_1: Only the podium switch P turns the house lights on and off.
> M_2: Only the rear switch R turns the house lights on and off.

The Solution: The truth tables for $H(P, R)$ as a function of programming modes M_0, M_1, and M_2 are given in Table 3-2. The functions for M_1 and M_2 are straightforward, but the function for M_0 needs more thought. This function must permit the changing of one out of the two switches P or R to change the output. A parity function has this property, and the parity function for two inputs is the exclusive OR, the function entered into Table 3-2 for M_0. The goal is to find a circuit that will implement the three programming modes and provide the output $H(P, R)$.

The circuit chosen for a value-fixing implementation is shown in Figure 3-9(a); later in this chapter, this standard circuit is referred to as a 4–to–1 multiplexer. A condensed truth table is given for this circuit in Figure 3-9(b). P and R are input variables, as are I_0 through I_3. Values 0 and 1 can be assigned to I_0 through I_3 depending upon the desired function for each mode. Note that H is actually a function of six variables, giving a fully expanded truth table containing 64 rows and seven columns. But, by putting I_0 through I_3 in the output column, we considerably reduce the size of the table. The equation for the output H for this truth table is

$$H(P, R, I_0, I_1, I_2, I_3) = \overline{P}\,\overline{R}I_0 + \overline{P}RI_1 + P\overline{R}I_2 + PRI_3$$

By fixing the values of I_0 through I_3, we can implement any function $H(P, R)$. As shown in Table 3-2, we can implement the function for M_0, $H = \overline{P}R + P\overline{R}$ by using $I_0 = 0, I_1 = 1, I_2 = 1$, and $I_3 = 0$. We can implement the function for M_1, $H = P$ by using $I_0 = 0, I_1 = 0, I_2 = 1$, and $I_3 = 1$, and $M_2, H = R$ by using $I_0 = 0, I_1 = 1, I_2 = 0$, and $I_3 = 1$. Any one of these functions can be implemented permanently, or all can be implemented temporarily by fixing $I_0 = 0$, and using I_1, I_2, and I_3 as variables with values as assigned above for each of the three modes. The final circuit with $I_0 = 0$ and the programming table after I_0 has been fixed at 0 are shown in Figures 3-9(c) and (d), respectively.

□ **TABLE 3-2**
Function Implementation by Value Fixing

Mode:		M_0	M_1	M_2
P	R	$H = \overline{P}R + P\overline{R}$	$H = P$	$H = R$
0	0	0	0	0
0	1	1	0	1
1	0	1	1	0
1	1	0	1	1

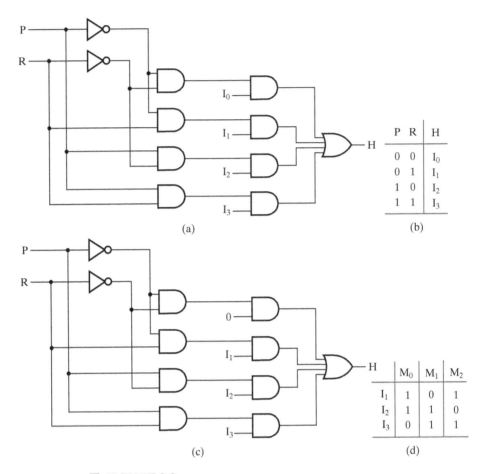

☐ **FIGURE 3-9**
Implementation of Three Functions by Using Value Fixing ■

Enabling

In general, enabling permits an input signal to pass through to an output. In addition to replacing the input signal with the Hi-Z state, which will be discussed in Section 6-8, disabling also can replace the input signal with a fixed output value, either 0 or 1. The additional input signal, often called *ENABLE* or *EN*, is required to determine whether the output is enabled or not. For example, if *EN* is 1, the input X reaches the output (enabled), but if *EN* is 0, the output is fixed at 0 (disabled). For this case, with the disabled value at 0, the input signal is ANDed with the *EN* signal, as shown in Figure 3-10(a). If the disabled value is 1, then the input signal X is ORed with the complement of the *EN* signal, as shown in Figure 3-10(b). In this case, if *EN* = 1, a 0 is applied to the OR gate, and the input X on the other OR gate, input reaches the output, but if *EN* = 0 , a 1 is applied to the OR gate, which blocks the passage of input X to the output. It is also possible for each of the circuits in Figure 3-10 to be modified to invert the *EN* input, so that *EN* = 0 enables X to reach the output and *EN* = 1 blocks X.

(a)

(b)

☐ **FIGURE 3-10**
Enabling Circuits

 EXAMPLE 3-5 Car Electrical Control Using Enabling

The Problem: In most automobiles, the lights, radio, and power windows operate only if the ignition switch is turned on. In this case, the ignition switch acts as an "enabling" signal. Suppose that we model this automotive subsystem using the following variables and definitions:

Ignition switch IG: Value 0 if off and value 1 if on
Light switch LS: Value 0 if off and value 1 if on
Radio switch RS: Value 0 if off and value 1 if on
Power window switch WS: Value 0 if off and value 1 if on
Lights L: Value 0 if off and value 1 if on
Radio R: Value 0 if off and value 1 if on
Power windows W: Value 0 if off and value 1 if on

The Solution: Table 3-3 contains the condensed truth table for the operation of this automobile subsystem. Note that when the ignition switch IS is off (0), all of the controlled accessories are off (0) regardless of their switch settings. This is indicated by the first row of the table. With the use of Xs, this condensed truth table with just nine rows represents the same information as the usual 16-row truth table. Whereas Xs in output columns represent don't-care conditions, Xs in input

☐ **TABLE 3-3**
Truth Table For Enabling Application

Input Switches				Accessory Control		
IS	LS	RS	WS	L	R	W
0	X	X	X	0	0	0
1	0	0	0	0	0	0
1	0	0	1	0	0	1
1	0	1	0	0	1	0
1	0	1	1	0	1	1
1	1	0	0	1	0	0
1	1	0	1	1	0	1
1	1	1	0	1	1	0
1	1	1	1	1	1	1

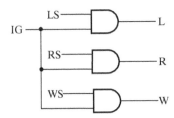

☐ **FIGURE 3-11**
Car Electrical Control Using Enabling

columns are used to represent product terms that are not minterms. For example, 0XXX represents the product term $\overline{IS}$. Just as with minterms, each variable is complemented if the corresponding bit in the input combination from the table is 0 and is not complemented if the bit is 1. If the corresponding bit in the input combination is an X, then the variable does not appear in the product term. When the ignition switch *IS* is on (1), then the accessories are controlled by their respective switches. When IS is off (0), all accessories are off. So *IS* replaces the normal values of the outputs *L*, *R*, and *W* with a fixed value 0 and meets the definition of an *ENABLE* signal. The resulting circuit is given in Figure 3-11. ■

3-5 Decoding

In digital computers, discrete quantities of information are represented by binary codes. An *n*-bit binary code is capable of representing up to 2^n distinct elements of coded information. Decoding is the conversion of an *n*-bit input code to an *m*-bit output code with $n \leq m \leq 2^n$, such that each valid input code word produces a unique output code. Decoding is performed by a *decoder*, a combinational circuit with an *n*-bit binary code applied to its inputs and an *m*-bit binary code appearing at the outputs. The decoder may have unused bit combinations on its inputs for which no corresponding *m*-bit code appears at the outputs. Among all of the specialized functions defined here, decoding is the most important, since this function and the corresponding functional blocks are incorporated into many of the other functions and functional blocks defined here.

In this section, the functional blocks that implement decoding are called *n*–to–*m*-line decoders, where $m \leq 2^n$. Their purpose is to generate the 2^n (or fewer) minterms from the *n* input variables. For $n = 1$ and $m = 2$, we obtain the 1–to–2–line decoding function with input *A* and outputs D_0 and D_1. The truth table for this decoding function is given in Figure 3-12(a). If $A = 0$, then $D_0 = 1$ and $D_1 = 0$. If $A = 1$, then $D_0 = 0$ and $D_1 = 1$. From this truth table, $D_0 = \overline{A}$ and $D_1 = A$, giving the circuit shown in Figure 3-12(b).

A second decoding function for $n = 2$ and $m = 4$ with the truth table given in Figure 3-13(a) better illustrates the general nature of decoders. This table has 2-variable minterms as its outputs, with each row containing one output value equal to 1 and three output values equal to 0. Output D_i is equal to 1 whenever the two input values on A_1 and A_0 are the binary code for the number *i*. As a consequence, the circuit implements the four possible minterms of two variables, one minterm for

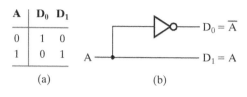

A	D_0	D_1
0	1	0
1	0	1

(a)   (b)

□ **FIGURE 3-12**
A 1–to–2-Line Decoder

each output. In the logic diagram in Figure 3-13(b), each minterm is implemented by a 2-input AND gate. These AND gates are connected to two 1–to–2-line decoders, one for each of the lines driving the AND gate inputs.

Large decoders can be constructed by simply implementing each minterm function using a single AND gate with more inputs. Unfortunately, as decoders become larger, this approach gives a high gate-input cost. In this section, we give a procedure that uses design hierarchy and collections of AND gates to construct any decoder with n inputs and 2^n outputs. The resulting decoder has the same or a lower gate-input cost than the one constructed by simply enlarging each AND gate.

To construct a 3–to–8-line decoder ($n = 3$), we can use a 2–to–4-line decoder and a 1–to–2-line decoder feeding eight 2-input AND gates to form the minterms. Hierarchically, the 2–to–4-line decoder can be implemented using two 1–to–2-line decoders feeding four 2-input AND gates, as observed in Figure 3-13. The resulting structure is shown in Figure 3-14.

The general procedure is as follows:

1. Let $k = n$.

2. If k is even, divide k by 2 to obtain $k/2$. Use 2^k AND gates driven by two decoders of output size $2^{k/2}$. If k is odd, obtain $(k + 1)/2$ and $(k - 1)/2$. Use 2^k AND

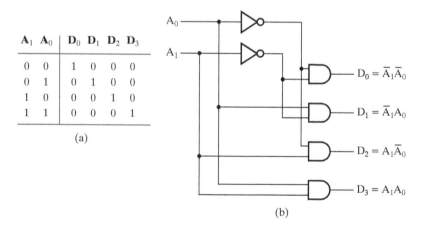

A_1	A_0	D_0	D_1	D_2	D_3
0	0	1	0	0	0
0	1	0	1	0	0
1	0	0	0	1	0
1	1	0	0	0	1

(a)

$D_0 = \overline{A}_1\overline{A}_0$

$D_1 = \overline{A}_1 A_0$

$D_2 = A_1\overline{A}_0$

$D_3 = A_1 A_0$

(b)

□ **FIGURE 3-13**
A 2–to–4-Line Decoder

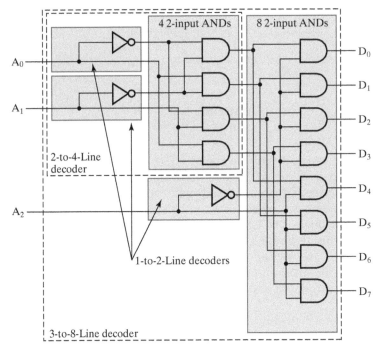

□ **FIGURE 3-14**
A 3–to–8-Line Decoder

gates driven by a decoder of output size $2^{(k+1)/2}$ and a decoder of output size $2^{(k-1)/2}$.

3. For each decoder resulting from step 2, repeat step 2 with k equal to the values obtained in step 2 until $k = 1$. For $k = 1$, use a 1–to–2 decoder.

EXAMPLE 3-6   6–to–64-Line Decoder

For a 6–to–64-line decoder ($k = n = 6$), in the first execution of step 2, 64 2-input AND gates are driven by two decoders of output size $2^3 = 8$ (i.e., by two 3–to–8-line decoders). In the second execution of step 2, $k = 3$. Since k is odd, the result is $(k + 1)/2 = 2$ and $(k - 1)/2 = 1$. Eight 2-input AND gates are driven by a decoder of output size $2^2 = 4$ and by a decoder of output size $2^1 = 2$ (i.e., by a 2–to–4-line decoder and by a 1–to–2-line decoder, respectively). Finally, on the next execution of step 2, $k = 2$, giving four 2-input AND gates driven by two decoders with output size 2 (i.e., by two 1–to–2-line decoders). Since all decoders have been expanded, the algorithm terminates with step 3 at this point. The resulting structure is shown in Figure 3-15. This structure has a gate input cost of $6 + 2 (2 \times 4) + 2 (2 \times 8) + 2 \times 64 = 182$. If a single AND gate for each minterm was used, the resulting gate-input cost would be $6 + (6 \times 64) = 390$, so a substantial gate-input cost reduction has been achieved. ■

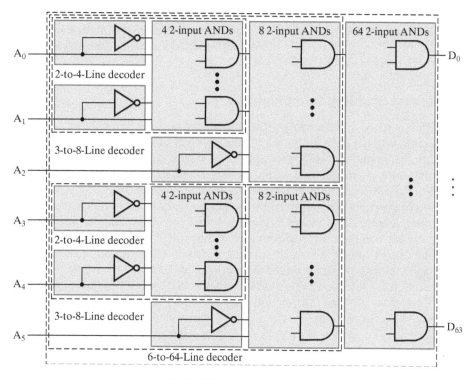

□ **FIGURE 3-15**
A 6–to–64–Line Decoder

As an alternative expansion situation, suppose that multiple decoders are needed and that the decoders have common input variables. In this case, instead of implementing separate decoders, parts of the decoders can be shared. For example, suppose that three decoders d_a, d_b, and d_c are functions of input variables as follows:

d_a (A, B, C, D)
d_b (A, B, C, E)
d_c (C, D, E, F)

A 3–to–8-line decoder for A, B, and C can be shared between d_a and d_b. A 2–to–4-line decoder for C and D can be shared between d_a and d_c. A 2–to–4-line decoder for C and E can be shared between d_b and d_c. If we implemented all of this sharing, we would have C entering three different decoders and the circuit would be redundant. To use C just once in shared decoders larger than 1 to 2, we can consider the following distinct cases:

1. (A, B) shared by d_a and d_b, and (C, D) shared by d_a and d_c,

2. (A, B) shared by d_a and d_b, and (C, E) shared by d_b and d_c, or

3. (A, B, C) shared by d_a and d_b.

Since cases 1 and 2 will clearly have the same costs, we will compare the cost of cases 1 and 3. For case 1, the costs of functions d_a, d_b, and d_c are reduced by the cost of two 2–to–4-line decoders (exclusive of inverters) or 16 gate inputs. For case 3, the costs for functions d_a and d_b are reduced by one 3–to–8–line decoder (exclusive of inverters) or 24 gate inputs. So case 3 should be implemented. Formalization of this procedure into an algorithm is beyond our current scope, so only this illustration of the approach is given.

Decoder and Enabling Combinations

The function, n–to–m–line decoding with enabling, can be implemented by attaching m enabling circuits to the decoder outputs. Then, m copies of the enabling signal EN are attached to the enable control inputs of the enabling circuits. For $n = 2$ and $m = 4$, the resulting 2–to–4–line decoder with enable is shown in Figure 3-16, along with its truth table. For $EN = 0$, all of the outputs of the decoder are 0. For $EN = 1$, one of the outputs of the decode, determined by the value on (A_1, A_0), is 1 and all others are 0. If the decoder is controlling a set of lights, then with $EN = 0$, all lights are off, and with $EN = 1$, exactly one light is on, with the other three off. For large decoders $(n \geq 4)$, the gate-input cost can be reduced by placing the enable circuits on the inputs to the decoder and their complements rather than on each of the decoder outputs.

In Section 3-7, selection using multiplexers will be covered. The inverse of selection is *distribution*, in which information received from a single line is transmitted to one of 2^n possible output lines. The circuit which implements such distribution is called a *demultiplexer*. The specific output to which the input signal is transmitted is controlled by the bit combination on n selection lines. The 2–to–4–line decoder with enable in Figure 3-16 is an implementation of a 1–to–4–line demultiplexer. For the demultiplexer, input EN provides the data, while the other inputs act as the selection variables. Although the two circuits have different applications, their logic diagrams are exactly the same. For this reason, a decoder with enable input is referred to as a decoder/demultiplexer. The data input EN has a path to all four outputs, but the input information is directed to only one of the outputs, as specified by the two selection lines A_1 and A_0. For example, if $(A_1, A_0) = 10$, output D_2 has the value applied to input EN, while

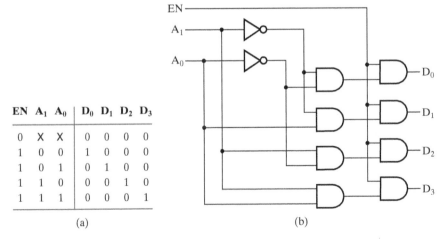

EN	A_1	A_0	D_0	D_1	D_2	D_3
0	X	X	0	0	0	0
1	0	0	1	0	0	0
1	0	1	0	1	0	0
1	1	0	0	0	1	0
1	1	1	0	0	0	1

(a)   (b)

☐ **FIGURE 3-16**
A 2–to–4–Line Decoder with Enable

all other outputs remain inactive at logic 0. If the decoder is controlling a set of four lights, with $(A_1, A_0) = 10$ and EN periodically changing between 1 and 0, the light controlled by D_2 flashes on and off and all other lights are off.

The next several examples illustrate using VHDL and Verilog to describe the behavior of decoders, providing additional instances of structural and dataflow modeling in each language with the language constructs initially introduced in Chapter 2.

EXAMPLE 3-7   VHDL Models for a 2–to–4-Line Decoder

Figure 3-17 shows a structural VHDL description for the 2–to–4-line decoder circuit from Figure 3-16. The model uses the library of basic gates `lcdf_vhdl` available from the Companion Website for the text as described in Chapter 2.

Figure 3-18 shows a dataflow VHDL description for the 2–to–4-line decoder circuit from Figure 3-16. Note that this dataflow description is much simpler than the structural description in Figure 3-17, which is often the case. The library, use, and entity statements are identical to those in Figure 3-16, so they are not repeated here. ▪

```
-- 2-to-4-Line Decoder with Enable: Structural VHDL Description    -- 1
-- (See Figure 3-16 for logic diagram)                            -- 2
library ieee, lcdf_vhdl;                                          -- 3
use ieee.std_logic_1164.all, lcdf_vhdl.func_prims.all;           -- 4
entity decoder_2_to_4_w_enable is                                -- 5
  port (EN, A0, A1: in std_logic;                                -- 6
      D0, D1, D2, D3: out std_logic);                            -- 7
end decoder_2_to_4_w_enable;                                     -- 8
                                                                 -- 9
architecture structural_1 of decoder_2_to_4_w_enable is          -- 10
  component NOT1                                                 -- 11
    port (in1: in std_logic;                                    -- 12
        out1: out std_logic);                                   -- 13
  end component;                                                 -- 14
  component AND2                                                 -- 15
    port (in1, in2: in std_logic;                               -- 16
        out1: out std_logic);                                   -- 17
  end component;                                                 -- 18
  signal A0_n, A1_n, N0, N1, N2, N3: std_logic;                 -- 19
  begin                                                         -- 20
    g0: NOT1 port map (in1 => A0, out1 => A0_n);                -- 21
    g1: NOT1 port map (in1 => A1, out1 => A1_n);                -- 22
    g2: AND2  port map  (in1 => A0_n, in2 => A1_n, out1 => N0); -- 23
    g3: AND2  port map  (in1 => A0, in2 => A1_n, out1 => N1);   -- 24
    g4: AND2  port map  (in1 => A0_n, in2 => A1, out1 => N2);   -- 25
    g5: AND2  port map  (in1 => A0, in2 => A1, out1 => N3);     -- 26
    g6: AND2  port map  (in1 => EN, in2 => N0, out1 => D0);     -- 27
    g7: AND2  port map  (in1 => EN, in2 => N1, out1 => D1);     -- 28
    g8: AND2  port map  (in1 => EN, in2 => N2, out1 => D2);     -- 29
    g9: AND2  port map  (in1 => EN, in2 => N3, out1 => D3);     -- 30
end structural_1;                                                -- 31
```

□ **FIGURE 3-17**
Structural VHDL Description of 2–to–4-Line Decoder

```
-- 2-to-4-Line Decoder: Dataflow VHDL Description          -- 1
-- (See Figure 3-16 for logic diagram)                     -- 2
-- Use library, use, and entity entries from 2_to_4_decoder_st;   -- 3
                                                           -- 4
architecture dataflow_1 of decoder_2_to_4_w_enable is      -- 5
                                                           -- 6
signal A0_n, A1_n: std_logic;                              -- 7
begin                                                      -- 8
   A0_n <= not A0;                                         -- 9
   A1_n <= not A1;                                         -- 10
   D0 <= A0_n and A1_n and EN;                             -- 11
   D1 <= A0 and A1_n and EN;                               -- 12
   D2 <= A0_n and A1 and EN;                               -- 13
   D3 <= A0 and A1 and EN;                                 -- 14
end dataflow_1;                                            -- 15
```

☐ **FIGURE 3-18**
Dataflow VHDL Description of 2–to–4-Line Decoder

EXAMPLE 3-8   Verilog Models for a 2–to–4-Line Decoder

A structural Verilog description for the 2-to-4-line decoder circuit from Figure 3-16 is given in Figure 3-19. In Figure 3-20, a dataflow description is given for the 2–to–4-line decoder. This particular dataflow description uses an assignment statement followed by a Boolean equation. ■

```
// 2-to-4-Line Decoder with Enable: Structural Verilog Desc.   // 1
// (See Figure 3-16 for logic diagram)                         // 2
module decoder_2_to_4_st_v (EN, A0, A1, D0, D1, D2, D3);        // 3
   input EN, A0, A1;                                           // 4
   output D0, D1, D2, D3;                                      // 5
                                                               // 6
   wire A0_n, A1_n, N0, N1, N2, N3;                            // 7
   not                                                         // 8
     g0(A0_n, A0),                                             // 9
     g1(A1_n, A1);                                             // 10
   and                                                         // 11
     g3(N0, A0_n, A1_n),                                       // 12
     g4(N1, A0, A1_n),                                         // 13
     g5(N2, A0_n, A1),                                         // 14
     g6(N3, A0, A1),                                           // 15
     g7(D0, N0, EN),                                           // 16
     g8(D1, N1, EN),                                           // 17
     g9(D2, N2, EN),                                           // 18
     g10(D3, N3, EN);                                          // 19
endmodule                                                      // 20
```

☐ **FIGURE 3-19**
Structural Verilog Description of 2–to–4-Line Decoder

```
// 2-to-4-Line Decoder with Enable: Dataflow Verilog Desc.       // 1
// (See Example 3-16 for logic diagram)                          // 2
module decoder_2_to_4_df_v(EN, A0, A1, D0, D1, D2, D3);          // 3
   input EN, A0, A1;                                             // 4
   output D0, D1, D2, D3;                                        // 5
                                                                 // 6
   assign D0 = EN & ~A1 & ~A0;                                   // 7
   assign D1 = EN & ~A1 & A0;                                    // 8
   assign D2 = EN & A1 & ~A0;                                    // 9
   assign D3 = EN & A1 & A0;                                     // 10
                                                                 // 11
endmodule                                                        // 12
```

□ **FIGURE 3-20**
Dataflow Verilog Description of 2–to–4-Line Decoder

Decoder-Based Combinational Circuits

A decoder provides the 2^n minterms of n input variables. Since any Boolean function can be expressed as a sum of minterms, one can use a decoder to generate the minterms and combine them with an external OR gate to form a sum-of-minterms implementation. In this way, any combinational circuit with n inputs and m outputs can be implemented with an n–to–2^n-line decoder and m OR gates.

The procedure for implementing a combinational circuit by means of a decoder and OR gates requires that the Boolean functions be expressed as a sum of minterms. This form can be obtained from the truth table or by plotting each function on a K-map. A decoder is chosen or designed that generates all the minterms of the input variables. The inputs to each OR gate are selected as the appropriate minterm outputs according to the list of minterms of each function. This process is shown in the next example.

EXAMPLE 3-9   Decoder and OR-Gate Implementation of a Binary Adder Bit

In Chapter 1, we considered binary addition. The sum bit output S and the carry bit output C for a bit position in the addition are given in terms of the two bits being added, X and Y, and the incoming carry from the right, Z, in Table 3-4.

From this truth table, we obtain the functions for the combinational circuit in sum-of-minterms form:

$$S(X, Y, Z) = \Sigma m(1, 2, 4, 7)$$

$$C(X, Y, Z) = \Sigma m(3, 5, 6, 7)$$

Since there are three inputs and a total of eight minterms, we need a 3–to–8-line decoder. The implementation is shown in Figure 3-21. The decoder generates all eight minterms for inputs X, Y, and Z. The OR gate for output S forms the logical sum of minterms 1, 2, 4, and 7. The OR gate for output C forms the logical sum of minterms 3, 5, 6, and 7. Minterm 0 is not used.   ■

☐ **TABLE 3-4**
Truth Table for 1-Bit Binary Adder

X	Y	Z	C	S
0	0	0	0	0
0	0	1	0	1
0	1	0	0	1
0	1	1	1	0
1	0	0	0	1
1	0	1	1	0
1	1	0	1	0
1	1	1	1	1

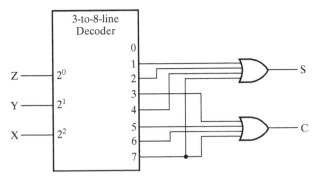

☐ **FIGURE 3-21**
Implementing a Binary Adder Using a Decoder

A function with a long list of minterms requires an OR gate with a large number of inputs. A function having a list of k minterms can be expressed in its complement form with $2^n - k$ minterms. If the number of minterms in a function F is greater than $\overline{F}$, then the complement of F, $\overline{F}$, can be expressed with fewer minterms. In such a case, it is advantageous to use a NOR gate instead of an OR gate. The OR portion of the NOR gate produces the logical sum of the minterms of $\overline{F}$. The output bubble of the NOR gate complements this sum and generates the normal output F.

The decoder method can be used to implement any combinational circuit. However, this implementation must be compared with other possible implementations to determine the best solution. The decoder method may provide the best solution, particularly if the combinational circuit has many outputs based on the same inputs and each output function is expressed with a small number of minterms.

□ **TABLE 3-5**
   Truth Table for Octal-to-Binary Encoder

Inputs								Outputs		
D_7	D_6	D_5	D_4	D_3	D_2	D_1	D_0	A_2	A_1	A_0
0	0	0	0	0	0	0	1	0	0	0
0	0	0	0	0	0	1	0	0	0	1
0	0	0	0	0	1	0	0	0	1	0
0	0	0	0	1	0	0	0	0	1	1
0	0	0	1	0	0	0	0	1	0	0
0	0	1	0	0	0	0	0	1	0	1
0	1	0	0	0	0	0	0	1	1	0
1	0	0	0	0	0	0	0	1	1	1

3-6 ENCODING

An encoder is a digital function that performs the inverse operation of a decoder. An encoder has 2^n (or fewer) input lines and n output lines. The output lines generate the binary code corresponding to the input value. An example of an encoder is the octal-to-binary encoder whose truth table is given in Table 3-5. This encoder has eight inputs, one for each of the octal digits, and three outputs that generate the corresponding binary number. It is assumed that only one input has a value of 1 at any given time, so that the table has only eight rows with specified output values. For the remaining 56 rows, all of the outputs are don't cares.

From the truth table, we can observe that A_i is 1 for the columns in which D_j is 1 only if subscript j has a binary representation with a 1 in the ith position. For example, output $A_0 = 1$ if the input is 1 or 3 or 5 or 7. Since all of these values are odd, they have a 1 in the 0 position of their binary representation. This approach can be used to find the truth table. From the table, the encoder can be implemented with n OR gates, one for each output variable A_i. Each OR gate combines the input variables D_j having a 1 in the rows for which A_i has value 1. For the 8–to–3-line encoder, the resulting output equations are

$$A_0 = D_1 + D_3 + D_5 + D_7$$

$$A_1 = D_2 + D_3 + D_6 + D_7$$

$$A_2 = D_4 + D_5 + D_6 + D_7$$

which can be implemented with three 4-input OR gates.

The encoder just defined has the limitation that only one input can be active at any given time: if two inputs are active simultaneously, the output produces an incorrect combination. For example, if D_3 and D_6 are 1 simultaneously, the output of the encoder will be 111, because all the three outputs are equal to 1. This represents neither a binary 3 nor a binary 6. To resolve this ambiguity, some encoder circuits must establish an input priority to ensure that only one input is encoded. If we establish a higher priority for inputs with higher subscript numbers, and if both D_3 and D_6 are 1 at the same time, the output will be 110, because D_6 has higher priority than D_3. Another ambiguity in the octal-to-binary encoder is that an output of all 0s is generated when all the inputs are 0, but this output is the same as when D_0 is equal to 1. This discrepancy can be resolved by providing a separate output to indicate that at least one input is equal to 1.

Priority Encoder

A priority encoder is a combinational circuit that implements a priority function. As mentioned in the preceding paragraph, the operation of the priority encoder is such that if two or more inputs are equal to 1 at the same time, the input having the highest priority takes precedence. The truth table for a four-input priority encoder is given in Table 3-6. With the use of Xs, this condensed truth table with just five rows represents the same information as the usual 16-row truth table. Whereas Xs in output columns represent don't-care conditions, Xs in input columns are used to represent product terms that are not minterms. For example, 001X represents the product term $\overline{D}_3 \overline{D}_2 D_1$. Just as with minterms, each variable is complemented if the corresponding bit in the input combination from the table is 0 and is not complemented if the bit is 1. If the corresponding bit in the input combination is an X, then the variable does not appear in the product term. Thus, for 001X, the variable D_0, corresponding to the position of the X, does not appear in $\overline{D}_3 \overline{D}_2 D_1$.

The number of rows of a full truth table represented by a row in the condensed table is 2^p, where p is the number of Xs in the row. For example, in Table 3-6, 1XXX represents $2^3 = 8$ truth-table rows, all having the same value for all outputs. In forming a condensed truth table, we must include each minterm in at least one of the rows in the sense that the minterm can be obtained by filling in 1s and 0s for the Xs. Also, a minterm must never be included in more than one row such that the rows in which it appears have one or more conflicting output values.

We form Table 3-6 as follows: Input D_3 has the highest priority; so, regardless of the values of the other inputs, when this input is 1, the output for $A_1 A_0$ is 11 (binary 3). From this we obtain the last row of the table. D_2 has the next priority level. The output is 10 if $D_2 = 1$, provided that $D_3 = 0$, regardless of the values of the lower-priority inputs. From this, we obtain the fourth row of the table. The output for D_1 is generated only if all inputs with higher priority are 0, and so on down the priority levels. From this, we obtain the remaining rows of the table. The valid output designated by V is set to 1 only when one or more of the inputs are equal to 1. If all inputs

□ **TABLE 3-6**
Truth Table of Priority Encoder

Inputs				Outputs		
D_3	D_2	D_1	D_0	A_1	A_0	V
0	0	0	0	X	X	0
0	0	0	1	0	0	1
0	0	1	X	0	1	1
0	1	X	X	1	0	1
1	X	X	X	1	1	1

are 0, V is equal to 0, and the other two outputs of the circuit are not used and are specified as don't-care conditions in the output part of the table.

The maps for simplifying outputs A_1 and A_0 are shown in Figure 3-22. The minterms for the two functions are derived from Table 3-6. The output values in the table can be transferred directly to the maps by placing them in the squares covered by the corresponding product term represented in the table. The optimized equation for each function is listed under the map for the function. The equation for output V is an OR function of all the input variables. The priority encoder is implemented in Figure 3-23 according to the following Boolean functions:

$$A_0 = D_3 + D_1\overline{D}_2$$
$$A_1 = D_2 + D_3$$
$$V = D_0 + D_1 + D_2 + D_3$$

Encoder Expansion

Thus far, we have considered only small encoders. Encoders can be expanded to larger numbers of inputs by expanding OR gates. In the implementation of

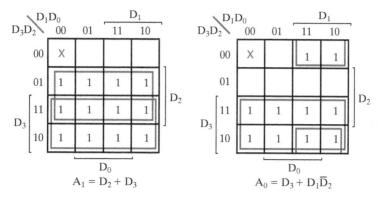

☐ **FIGURE 3-22**
Maps for Priority Encoder

☐ **FIGURE 3-23**
Logic Diagram of a 4-Input Priority Encoder

decoders, the use of multiple-level circuits with OR gates beyond the output levels shared in implementing the more significant bits in the output codes reduces the gate input cost as n increases for $n \geq 5$. For $n \geq 3$, multiple-level circuits result from technology mapping anyway, due to limited gate fan-in. Designing multiple-level circuits with shared gates reduces the cost of the encoders after technology mapping.

3-7 SELECTING

Selection of information to be used in a computer is a very important function, not only in communicating between the parts of the system, but also within the parts as well. Circuits that perform selection typically have a set of inputs from which selections are made, a single output, and a set of control lines for making the selection. First, we consider selection using multiplexers; then we briefly examine selection circuits implemented by using three-state drivers.

Multiplexers

A multiplexer is a combinational circuit that selects binary information from one of many input lines and directs the information to a single output line. The selection of a particular input line is controlled by a set of input variables, called *selection inputs*.

Normally, there are 2^n input lines and n selection inputs whose bit combinations determine which input is selected. We begin with $n = 1$, a 2–to–1-line multiplexer. This function has two information inputs, I_0 and I_1, and a single select input S. The truth table for the circuit is given in Table 3-7. Examining the table, if the select input $S = 0$, the output of the multiplexer takes on the values of I_0, and, if input $S = 1$, the output of the multiplexer takes on the values of I_1. Thus, S selects either input I_0 or input I_1 to appear at output Y. From this discussion, we can see that the equation for the 2–to–1-line multiplexer output Y is

$$Y = \overline{S}I_0 + SI_1$$

□ **TABLE 3-7**
Truth Table for 2–to–1-Line Multiplexer

S	I_0	I_1	Y
0	0	0	0
0	0	1	0
0	1	0	1
0	1	1	1
1	0	0	0
1	0	1	1
1	1	0	0
1	1	1	1

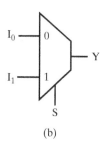

(a) (b)

□ **FIGURE 3-24**
(a) Single-Bit 2–to–1-Line Multiplexer; (b) common Symbol for a Multiplexer

This same equation can be obtained by using a 3-variable K-map. As shown in Figure 3-24(a), the implementation of the preceding equation can be decomposed into a 1–to–2-line decoder, two enabling circuits, and a 2-input OR gate. A common symbol for a 2-to-1 multiplexer is shown in Figure 3-24(b), with a trapezoid signifying the selection of the output on the short parallel side from among the 2^n information inputs on the long parallel side.

Suppose that we wish to design a 4–to–1-line multiplexer. In this case, the function Y depends on four inputs I_0, I_1, I_2, and I_3 and two select inputs S_1 and S_0. By placing the values of I_0 through I_3 in the Y column, we can form Table 3-8, a condensed truth table for this multiplexer. In this table, the information variables do not appear as input columns of the table but appear in the output column. Each row represents multiple rows of the full truth table. In Table 3-8, the row 00 I_0 represents all rows in which $(S_1, S_0) = 00$. For $I_0 = 1$ it gives $Y = 1$, and for $I_0 = 0$ it gives $Y = 0$. Since there are six variables, and only S_1 and S_0 are fixed, this single row represents 16 rows of the corresponding full truth table. From the table, we can write the equation for Y as

$$Y = \overline{S}_1\overline{S}_0I_0 + \overline{S}_1S_0I_1 + S_1\overline{S}_0I_2 + S_1S_0I_3$$

If this equation is implemented directly, two inverters, four 3-input AND gates, and a 4-input OR gate are required, giving a gate-input cost of 18. A different implementation can be obtained by factoring the AND terms to give

$$Y = (\overline{S}_1\overline{S}_0)I_0 + (\overline{S}_1S_0)I_1 + (S_1\overline{S}_0)I_2 + (S_1S_0)I_3$$

□ **TABLE 3-8**
Condensed Truth Table for 4-to-1-Line Multiplexer

S_1	S_0	Y
0	0	I_0
0	1	I_1
1	0	I_2
1	1	I_3

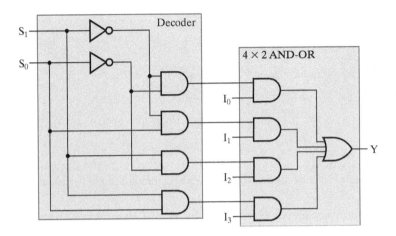

□ **FIGURE 3-25**
A Single-Bit 4–to–1-Line Multiplexer

This implementation can be constructed by combining a 2–to–4-line decoder, four AND gates used as enabling circuits, and a 4-input OR gate, as shown in Figure 3-25. We will refer to the combination of AND gates and OR gates as an $m \times 2$ AND-OR, where m is the number of AND gates and 2 is the number of inputs to the AND gates. This resulting circuit has a gate input cost of 22, which is more costly. Nevertheless, it provides a structural basis for constructing larger n–to–2^n-line multiplexers by expansion.

A multiplexer is also called a *data selector*, since it selects one of many information inputs and steers the binary information to the output line. The term "multiplexer" is often abbreviated as "MUX."

Multiplexers can be expanded by considering vectors of input bits for larger values of n. Expansion is based upon the circuit structure given in Figure 3-24(a), consisting of a decoder, enabling circuits, and an OR gate. Multiplexer design is illustrated in Examples 3-10 and 3-11.

EXAMPLE 3-10   64–to–1-Line Multiplexer

A multiplexer is to be designed for $n = 6$. This will require a 6–to–64-line decoder as given in Figure 3-15, and a 64×2 AND-OR gate. The resulting structure is shown in Figure 3-26. This structure has a gate-input cost of $182 + 128 + 64 = 374$.

In contrast, if the decoder and the enabling circuit were replaced by inverters plus 7-input AND gates, the gate-input cost would be $6 + 448 + 64 = 518$. For single-bit multiplexers such as this one, combining the AND gate generating D_i with the AND gate driven by D_i into a single 3-input AND gate for every $i = 0$ through 63 reduces the gate-input cost to 310. For multiple-bit multiplexers, this

□ **FIGURE 3-26**
A 64–to–1-Line Multiplexer

reduction to 3-input ANDs cannot be performed without replicating the output ANDs of the decoders. As a result, in almost all cases, the original structure has a lower gate-input cost. The next example illustrates the expansion to a multiple-bit multiplexer. ∎

EXAMPLE 3-11   4–to–1-Line Quad Multiplexer

A quad 4–to–1-line multiplexer, which has two selection inputs and each information input replaced by a vector of four inputs, is to be designed. Since the information inputs are a vector, the output Y also becomes a four-element vector. The implementation for this multiplexer requires a 2–to–4-line decoder, as given in Figure 3-13, and four 4×2 AND-OR gates. The resulting structure is shown in Figure 3-27. This structure has a gate-input cost of $10 + 32 + 16 = 58$. In contrast, if four 4-input multiplexers implemented with 3-input gates were placed side by side, the gate-input cost would be 76. So, by sharing the decoder, we reduced the gate-input cost.

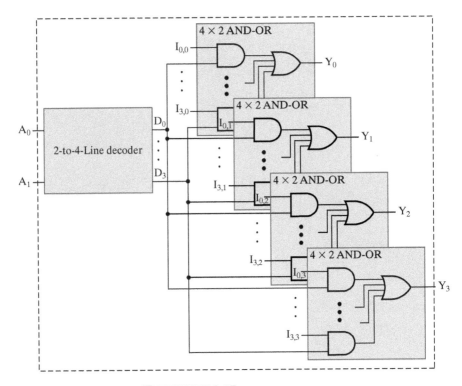

☐ **FIGURE 3-27**
A Quad 4–to–1-Line Multiplexer ■

The next several examples illustrate using VHDL and Verilog to describe the behavior of multiplexers, providing additional instances of structural and dataflow modeling in each language with the language constructs initially introduced in Chapter 2.

EXAMPLE 3-12   VHDL Models for a 4-to-1 Multiplexer

In Figure 3-28 shows a structural description of the 4–to–1-line multiplexer from Figure 3-25. This model illustrates two VHDL concepts introduced in Chapter 2: std_logic_vector and an alternative approach to mapping ports.

The architecture in Figure 3-29, instead of using Boolean equation-like statements to describe the multiplexer, uses a *when-else* statement. This statement is a representation of the function table given as Table 3-8. When S takes on a particular binary value, then a particular input I(i) is assigned to output Y. When the value on S is 00, then Y is assigned I (0). Otherwise, the **else** is invoked so that when the value on S is 01, then Y is assigned I (1), and so on. In standard logic, each of the bits can take on 9 different values. So the pair of bits for S can take on 81 possible values, only 4 of which have been specified so far. In order to define Y for the remaining 77 values, the final

```
-- 4-to-1-Line Multiplexer: Structural VHDL Description        -- 1
-- (See Figure 3-25 for logic diagram)                         -- 2
library ieee, lcdf_vhdl;                                        -- 3
use ieee.std_logic_1164.all, lcdf_vhdl.func_prims.all;         -- 4
entity multiplexer_4_to_1_st is                                -- 5
  port (S: in std_logic_vector(0 to 1);                        -- 6
        I: in std_logic_vector(0 to 3);                        -- 7
        Y: out std_logic);                                     -- 8
end multiplexer_4_to_1_st;                                     -- 9
                                                               --10
architecture structural_2 of multiplexer_4_to_1_st is          --11
  component NOT1                                               --12
    port(in1: in std_logic;                                    --13
         out1: out std_logic);                                 --14
  end component;                                               --15
  component AND2                                               --16
    port(in1, in2: in std_logic;                               --17
         out1: out std_logic);                                 --18
  end component;                                               --19
  component OR4                                                --20
    port(in1, in2, in3, in4: in std_logic;                     --21
         out1: out std_logic);                                 --22
  end component;                                               --23
  signal S_n: std_logic_vector(0 to 1);                        --24
  signal D, N: std_logic_vector(0 to 3);                       --25
  begin                                                        --26
    g0: NOT1 port map (S(0), S_n(0));                          --27
    g1: NOT1 port map (S(1), S_n(1));                          --28
    g2: AND2 port map (S_n(1), S_n(0), D(0));                  --29
    g3: AND2 port map (S_n(1), S(0), D(1));                    --30
    g4: AND2 port map (S(1), S_n(0), D(2));                    --31
    g5: AND2 port map (S(1), S(0), D(3));                      --32
    g6: AND2 port map (D(0), I(0), N(0));                      --33
    g7: AND2 port map (D(1), I(1), N(1));                      --34
    g8: AND2 port map (D(2), I(2), N(2));                      --35
    g9: AND2 port map (D(3), I(3), N(3));                      --36
    g10: OR4 port map (N(0), N(1), N(2), N(3), Y);             --37
  end structural_2;                                            --38
```

□ **FIGURE 3-28**
Structural VHDL Description of 4–to–1-Line Multiplexer

else followed by X (unknown) is given. This assigns the value X to Y if any of these 77 values occurs on S. However, this output value occurs only in simulation, since Y will always take on a 0 or 1 value in an actual circuit.

Figure 3-30 provides an alternative implementation using *with-select* for the 4–to–1-line multiplexer. The expression, the value of which is to be used for the decision, follows **with** and precedes **select**. The values for the expression that causes the alternative assignments then follow **when** with each of the assignment-value

```
-- 4-to-1-Line Mux: Conditional Dataflow VHDL Description    -- 1
-- Using When-Else (See Table 3-8 for function table)        -- 2
library ieee;                                                -- 3
use ieee.std_logic_1164.all;                                 -- 4
entity multiplexer_4_to_1_we is                              -- 5
   port (S : in std_logic_vector(1 downto 0);                -- 6
         I : in std_logic_vector(3 downto 0);                -- 7
         Y : out std_logic);                                 -- 8
end multiplexer_4_to_1_we;                                   -- 9
                                                             -- 10
architecture function_table of multiplexer_4_to_1_we is     -- 11
begin                                                        -- 12
   Y <= I(0) when S = "00" else                              -- 13
        I(1) when S = "01" else                              -- 14
        I(2) when S = "10" else                              -- 15
        I(3) when S = "11" else                              -- 16
        'X';                                                 -- 17
end function_table;                                          -- 18
```

☐ **FIGURE 3-29**
Conditional Dataflow VHDL Description of 4–to–1-Line Multiplexer Using When-Else

```
--4-to-1-Line Mux: Conditional Dataflow VHDL Description     -- 1
Using with Select (See Table 3-8 for function table)        -- 2
library ieee;                                                -- 3
use ieee.std_logic_1164.all;                                 -- 4
entity multiplexer_4_to_1_ws is                              -- 5
   port (S : in std_logic_vector(1 downto 0);                -- 6
         I : in std_logic_vector(3 downto 0);                -- 7
         Y : out std_logic);                                 -- 8
end multiplexer_4_to_1_ws;                                   -- 9
                                                             -- 10
architecture function_table_ws of multiplexer_4_to_1_ws is  -- 11
begin                                                        -- 12
   with S select                                             -- 13
      Y <= I(0) when "00",                                   -- 14
           I(1) when "01",                                   -- 15
           I(2) when "10",                                   -- 16
           I(3) when "11",                                   -- 17
           'X'when others;                                   -- 18
end function_table_ws;                                       -- 19
```

☐ **FIGURE 3-30**
Conditional Dataflow VHDL Description of 4–to–1-Line Multiplexer Using With-Select

pairs separated by commas. In the example, S is the signal, the value of which determines the value selected for Y. When S = "00", I(0) is assigned to Y. When S = "01", I(1) is assigned to Y and so on. 'X' is assigned to Y **when others**, where **others** represents the 77 standard logic combinations not already specified.

These last two models provide examples of the difference between when-else and with-select that was noted in Chapter 2: when-else permits decisions on multiple distinct signals, while with-select can depend on only one signal. For example, for the demultiplexer in Figure 3-16, the first **when** can be conditioned on input EN with the subsequent **when**'s conditioned on input S. In contrast, the with-select can depend on only a single Boolean condition (e.g., either EN or S, but not both). Also, as noted previously in Chapter 2, for typical synthesis tools, when-else usually results in a more complex logical structure, since each of the decisions depends not only on the condition currently being evaluated, but also on all prior decisions as well. As a consequence, the structure that is synthesized takes into account this priority order, replacing the 4×2 AND-OR by a chain of four 2-to-1 multiplexers. In contrast, there is no direct dependency between the decisions made in with-select. With-select produces a decoder and the 4×2 AND-OR gate. ■

EXAMPLE 3-13   Verilog Models for a 4–to–1-Line Multiplexer

In Figure 3-31, the structural description of the 4–to–1-line multiplexer from Figure 3-25 illustrates the Verilog concept of a vector that was introduced in Chapter 2. Rather than

```
// 4-to-1-Line Multiplexer: Structural Verilog Description    //  1
// (See Figure 3-25 for logic diagram)                        //  2
module multiplexer_4_to_1_st_v(S, I, Y);                      //  3
   input [1:0] S;                                             //  4
   input [3:0] I;                                             //  5
   output Y;                                                  //  6
                                                              //  7
   wire [1:0] not_S;                                          //  8
   wire [0:3] D, N;                                           //  9
                                                              // 10
not                                                           // 11
   gn0(not_S[0], S[0]),                                       // 12
   gn1(not_S[1], S[1]);                                       // 13
                                                              // 14
and                                                           // 15
   g0(D[0], not_S[1], not_S[0]),                              // 16
   g1(D[1], not_S[1], S[0]),                                  // 17
   g2(D[2], S[1], not_S[0]),                                  // 18
   g3(D[3], S[1], S[0]);                                      // 19
   g0(N[0], D[0], I[0]),                                      // 20
   g1(N[1], D[1], I[1]),                                      // 21
   g2(N[2], D[2], I[2]),                                      // 22
   g3(N[3], D[3], I[3]);                                      // 23
                                                              // 24
or go(Y, N[0], N[1], N[2], N[3]);                             // 25
                                                              // 26
endmodule                                                     // 27
```

□ **FIGURE 3-31**
Structural Verilog Description of 4–to–1-Line Multiplexer

specifying each wire as a single bit, the wires are specified as multiple-bit vectors where each individual wire can be accessed using the vector name and the number of the individual wire within the vector range.

Figure 3-32 shows a Verilog dataflow model using single Boolean equation for *Y* to describe the multiplexer. This equation is in sum-of-products form with & for AND and | for OR. Components of the S and I vectors are used as its variables.

The Verilog model in Figure 3-33 resembles the function table given as Table 3-8 by using a conditional operator on binary combinations. If the logical value within the parentheses is true, then the value before the : is assigned to the independent variable, in this case, Y. If the logical value is false, then the value after the: is assigned. Suppose we consider condition S == 2'b00, where == is the logical equality operator. As introduced in Chapter 2, 2'b00 is Verilog's representation of a constant, representing a two-bit binary constant with a value of 00.

```
// 4-to-1-Line Multiplexer: Dataflow Verilog Description
// (See Figure 3-25 for logic diagram)
module multiplexer_4_to_1_df_v(S, I, Y);
   input [1:0] S;
   input [3:0] I;
   output Y;

   assign Y = (~ S[1] & ~ S[0] & I[0])| (~ S[1] & S[0] & I[1])
            | (S[1] & ~ S[0] & I[2]) | (S[1] & S[0] & I[3]);
endmodule
```

☐ **FIGURE 3-32**
Dataflow Verilog Description of 4–to–1-Line Multiplexer Using a Boolean Equation

```
// 4-to-1 Line Multiplexer: Dataflow Verilog Description
// (See Table 3-8 for function table)
module  multiplexer_4_to_1_cf_v(S, I, Y);
   input [1:0] S;
   input [3:0] I;
   output Y;

   assign Y =   (S == 2'b00) ? I[0] :
                (S == 2'b01) ? I[1] :
                (S == 2'b10) ? I[2] :
                (S == 2'b11) ? I[3] : 1'bx ;
endmodule
```

☐ **FIGURE 3-33**
Conditional Dataflow Verilog Description of 4–to–1-Line Multiplexer Using Combinations

```
// 4-to-1-Line Multiplexer: Dataflow Verilog Description
// (See Table 3-8 for function table)
module multiplexer_4_to_1_tf_v(S, I, Y);
    input [1:0] S;
    input [3:0] I;
    output Y;

    assign Y = S[1] ? (S[0] ? I[3] : I[2]) :
                      (S[0] ? I[1] : I[0]);
endmodule
```

□ **FIGURE 3-34**

Conditional Dataflow Verilog Description of 4–to–1-Line
Multiplexer Using Binary Decisions

Thus, the expression has value true if vector S is equal to 00; otherwise, it is false.
If the expression is true, then I[0] is assigned to Y. If the expression is false, then
the next expression containing a ? is evaluated, and so on. In this example, for a
condition to be evaluated, all conditions preceding it must evaluate to false. If
none of the conditions evaluate to true, then the default value 1'bx (unknown) is
assigned to Y.

The final form of a Verilog dataflow description for the multiplexer is shown in
Figure 3-34. It is based on conditional operators used to form a decision tree, which
corresponds to a factored Boolean expression. In this case, if S[1] is 1, then S[0] is
evaluated to determine whether Y is assigned I[3] or assigned I[2]. If S[1] is 0,
then S[0] is evaluated to determine whether Y is assigned I[1] or I[0]. For a regular structure such as a multiplexer, this approach, based on two-way (binary) decisions, gives a simple dataflow expression. ■

EXAMPLE 3-14   Security System Sensor Selection using Multiplexers

The Problem: A home security system has 15 sensors that detect open doors and windows. Each sensor produces a digital signal 0 when the window or door is closed and 1
when the window or door is open. The control for the security system is a microcontroller with eight digital input/output bits available. Each bit can be programmed to be
either an input or an output. Design a logic circuit that repeatedly checks each of the
15 sensor values by connecting the sensor output to a microcontroller input/output
that is programmed to be an input. The parts list for the design consists of the following
multiplexer parts: 1) a single 8–to–1-line multiplexer, 2) a dual 4–to–1-line multiplexer,
and 3) a quad 2–to–1-line multiplexer. Any number of each part is available. The design
is to minimize the number of parts and also minimize the number of microcontroller
input/outputs used. Microcontroller input/outputs programmed as outputs are to be
used to control the select inputs on the multiplexers.

The Solution: Some of the sensors can be connected to multiplexer inputs and
some directly to microcontroller inputs. One possible solution that minimizes the number of multiplexers is to use two 8–to–1 multiplexers, each connected to a

microcontroller input. The two multiplexers handle 16 sensors and require three microcontroller outputs as selection inputs. Since there are 15 sensor outputs, the unused 16th multiplexer input can be attached to 0. The number of microcontroller input/outputs used is $3 + 2 = 5$. Use of any of the other multiplexer types will increase the number of microcontroller inputs used and decrease the number of microcontroller outputs used. The increase in inputs, however, is always greater than the decrease in outputs. So the initial solution is best in terms of microcontroller input/outputs used. ■

Multiplexer-Based Combinational Circuits

Earlier in this section, we learned that a decoder combined with an $m \times 2$ AND-OR gate implements a multiplexer. The decoder in the multiplexer generates the minterms of the selection inputs. The AND-OR gate provides enabling circuits that determine whether the minterms are "attached" to the OR gate with the information inputs (I_i) used as the enabling signals. If the I_i input is a 1, then minterm m_i is attached to the OR gate, and, if the I_i input is a 0, then minterm m_i is replaced by a 0. Value fixing applied to the I inputs provides a method for implementing a Boolean function of n variables with a multiplexer having n selection inputs and 2^n data inputs, one for each minterm. Further, an m-output function can be implemented by using value fixing on a multiplexer with m-bit information vectors instead of the individual I bits, as illustrated by the next example.

EXAMPLE 3-15 Multiplexer Implementation of a Binary-Adder Bit

The values for S and C from the 1-bit binary adder truth table given in Table 3-4 can be generated by using value fixing on the information inputs of a multiplexer.

□ **FIGURE 3-35**
Implementing a 1-Bit Binary Adder with a Dual 8–to–1-Line Multiplexer

Since there are three selection inputs and a total of eight minterms, we need a dual 8–to–1–line multiplexer for implementing the two outputs, S and C. The implementation based on the truth table is shown in Figure 3-35. Each pair of values, such as $(0, 1)$ on $(I_{1,1}, I_{1,0})$, is taken directly from the corresponding row of the last two truth-table columns. ■

A more efficient method implements a Boolean function of n variables with a multiplexer that has only $n - 1$ selection inputs. The first $n - 1$ variables of the function are connected to the selection inputs of the multiplexer. The remaining variable of the function is used for the information inputs. If the final variable is Z, each data input of the multiplexer will be either Z, $\bar{Z}$, 1, or 0. The function can be implemented by attaching implementations of the four rudimentary functions from Table 3-1 to the information inputs to the multiplexer. The next example demonstrates this procedure.

EXAMPLE 3-16   Alternative Multiplexer Implementation of a Binary Adder Bit

This function can be implemented with a dual 4–to–1–line multiplexer, as shown in Figure 3-36. The design procedure can be illustrated by considering the sum S. The two variables X and Y are applied to the selection lines in that order; X is connected to the S_1 input, and Y is connected to the S_0 input. The values for the data input lines are determined from the truth table of the function. When $(X, Y) = 00$, the output S is equal to Z, because $S = 0$ when $Z = 0$ and $S = 1$ when $Z = 1$. This requires that the variable Z be applied to information input I_{00}. The operation of the multiplexer is such that, when $(X, Y) = 00$, information input I_{00} has a path to the output that makes S equal to Z. In a similar fashion, we can determine the required input to lines I_{10}, I_{20}, and I_{30} from the value of S when $(X, Y) = 01, 10$, and 11, respectively. A similar approach can be used to determine the values for I_{01}, I_{11}, I_{21}, and I_{31}. ■

☐ **FIGURE 3-36**
Implementing a 1-Bit Binary Adder with a Dual 4–to–1–Line Multiplexer

The general procedure for implementing any Boolean function of n variables with a multiplexer with $n - 1$ selection inputs and 2^{n-1} data inputs follows from the preceding example. The Boolean function is first listed in a truth table. The first $n - 1$ variables in the table are applied to the selection inputs of the multiplexer. For each combination of the selection variables, we evaluate the output as a function of the last variable. This function can be 0, 1, the variable, or the complement of the variable. These values are then applied to the appropriate data inputs. This process is illustrated in the next example.

EXAMPLE 3-17   Multiplexer Implementation of 4-Variable Function

As a second example, consider the implementation of the following Boolean function:

$$F(A, B, C, D) = \Sigma m(1, 3, 4, 11, 12, 13, 14, 15)$$

This function is implemented with an 8×1 multiplexer as shown in Figure 3-37. To obtain a correct result, the variables in the truth table are connected to selection inputs S_2, S_1, and S_0 in the order in which they appear in the table (i.e., such that A is connected to S_2, B is connected to S_1, and C is connected to S_0, respectively). The values for the data inputs are determined from the truth table. The information line number is determined from the binary combination of A, B, and C. For example,

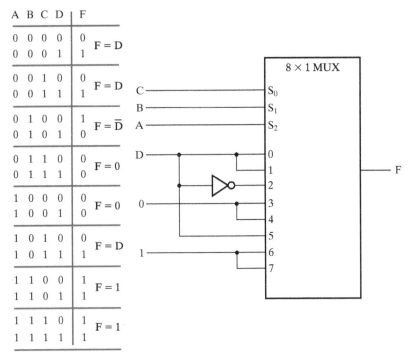

☐ **FIGURE 3-37**
Implementing a Four-Input Function with a Multiplexer

when $(A, B, C) = 101$, the truth table shows that $F = D$, so the input variable D is applied to information input I_5. The binary constants 0 and 1 correspond to two fixed signal values. Recall from Section 3-6 that, in a logic schematic, these constant values are replaced by the ground and power symbols, as shown in Figure 3-7. ■

The next example provides a comparison between implementing a combinational circuit using logic gates, decoders, or multiplexers.

EXAMPLE 3-18   Design of a BCD–to–Seven-Segment Decoder

SPECIFICATION: Digital readouts found in many consumer electronic products such as alarm clocks often use light-emitting diodes (LEDs). Each digit of the readout is formed from seven LED segments, each of which can be illuminated by a digital signal. A BCD–to–seven-segment decoder is a combinational circuit that accepts a decimal digit in BCD and generates the appropriate outputs for the segments of the display for that decimal digit. The seven outputs of the decoder (a, b, c, d, e, f, g) select the corresponding segments in the display, as shown in Figure 3-38(a). The numeric designations chosen to represent the decimal digits are shown in Figure 3-38(b). The BCD–to–seven-segment decoder has four inputs, A, B, C, and D, for the BCD digit and seven outputs, a through g, for controlling the segments.

FORMULATION: The truth table of the combinational circuit is listed in Table 3-9. On the basis of Figure 3-38(b), each BCD digit illuminates the proper segments for the decimal display. For example, BCD 0011 corresponds to decimal 3, which is displayed as segments a, b, c, d, and g. The truth table assumes that a logic 1 signal illuminates the segment and a logic 0 signal turns the segment off. Some seven-segment displays operate in reverse fashion and are illuminated by a logic 0 signal. For these displays, the seven outputs must be complemented. The six binary combinations 1010 through 1111 have no meaning in BCD. In the previous example, we assigned these combinations to don't-care conditions. If we do the same here, the design will most likely produce some arbitrary and meaningless displays for the unused combinations. As long as these combinations do not occur, we can use that approach to reduce the complexity of the converter. A safer choice, turning off all the segments when any one of the unused input combinations occurs, avoids any spurious displays if any of the combinations occurs, but increases the converter complexity. This choice can be accomplished by assigning all 0s to minterms 10 through 15.

(a) Segment designation   (b) Numeric designation for display

□ **FIGURE 3-38**
Seven-Segment Display

☐ **TABLE 3-9**
Truth Table for BCD–to–Seven-Segment Decoder

A	B	C	D	a	b	c	d	e	f	g

BCD Input				Seven-Segment Decoder						
A	B	C	D	a	b	c	d	e	f	g
0	0	0	0	1	1	1	1	1	1	0
0	0	0	1	0	1	1	0	0	0	0
0	0	1	0	1	1	0	1	1	0	1
0	0	1	1	1	1	1	1	0	0	1
0	1	0	0	0	1	1	0	0	1	1
0	1	0	1	1	0	1	1	0	1	1
0	1	1	0	1	0	1	1	1	1	1
0	1	1	1	1	1	1	0	0	0	0
1	0	0	0	1	1	1	1	1	1	1
1	0	0	1	1	1	1	1	0	1	1
All other inputs				0	0	0	0	0	0	0

OPTIMIZATION: For implementing the function using logic gates, the information from the truth table can be transferred into seven K-maps, from which the initial optimized output functions can be derived. The plotting of the seven functions in map form is left as an exercise. One possible way of simplifying the seven functions results in the following Boolean functions:

$$a = \overline{A}C + \overline{A}BD + \overline{B}\,\overline{C}\,\overline{D} + A\overline{B}\,\overline{C}$$

$$b = \overline{A}\,\overline{B} + \overline{A}\,\overline{C}\,\overline{D} + \overline{A}CD + A\overline{B}\,\overline{C}$$

$$c = \overline{A}B + \overline{A}D + \overline{B}\,\overline{C}\,\overline{D} + A\overline{B}\,\overline{C}$$

$$d = \overline{A}C\overline{D} + \overline{A}\,\overline{B}C + \overline{B}\,\overline{C}\,\overline{D} + A\overline{B}\,\overline{C} + \overline{A}BC\overline{D}$$

$$e = \overline{A}C\overline{D} + \overline{B}\,\overline{C}\,\overline{D}$$

$$f = \overline{A}B\overline{C} + \overline{A}\,\overline{C}\,\overline{D} + \overline{A}B\overline{D} + A\overline{B}\,\overline{C}$$

$$g = \overline{A}C\overline{D} + \overline{A}\,\overline{B}C + \overline{A}B\overline{C} + A\overline{B}\,\overline{C}$$

Independent implementation of these seven functions requires 27 AND gates and 7 OR gates. However, by sharing the six product terms common to the different output expressions, the number of AND gates can be reduced to 14 along with a substantial savings in gate-input cost. For example, the term $\overline{B}\,\overline{C}\,\overline{D}$ occurs in a, c, d, and e. The output of the AND gate that implements this product term goes directly to the inputs of the OR gates in all four functions. For this function, we stop optimization with the two-level circuit and shared AND gates, realizing that it might be possible to reduce the gate-input cost even further by applying multiple-level optimization.

In general, the total number of gates can be reduced in a multiple-output combinational circuit by using common terms of the output functions. The maps of the output functions may help us find the common terms by finding identical implicants from two or more maps. Some of the common terms may not be prime implicants of the individual functions. The designer must be inventive and combine squares in the maps in such a way as to create common terms. This can be done more formally by using a procedure for simplifying multiple-output functions. The prime implicants are defined not only for each individual function, but also for all possible combinations of the output functions. These prime implicants are formed by using the AND operator on every possible nonempty subset of the output functions and finding the prime implicants of each of the results. Using this entire set of prime implicants, we can employ a formal selection process to find the optimum two-level multiple-output circuit. Such a procedure is implemented in various forms in logic optimization software and is used to obtain the equations.

The circuit can also be implemented using a decoder or multiplexers rather than only logic gates. One 4-to-16 decoder along with seven OR gates (one for each function for the segments on the display) is all that is required—however, in practice, OR gates with more than four inputs are not practical, so more gates would be required. In sum-of-minterms form, the inputs to each of the seven OR gates would be:

$$a(A, B, C, D) = \Sigma m(0, 2, 3, 5, 6, 7, 8, 9)$$

$$b(A, B, C, D) = \Sigma m(0, 1, 2, 3, 4, 7, 8, 9)$$

$$c(A, B, C, D) = \Sigma m(0, 1, 3, 4, 5, 6, 7, 8, 9)$$

$$d(A, B, C, D) = \Sigma m(0, 2, 3, 5, 6, 8, 9)$$

$$e(A, B, C, D) = \Sigma m(0, 2, 6, 8)$$

$$f(A, B, C, D) = \Sigma m(0, 4, 5, 6, 8, 9)$$

$$g(A, B, C, D) = \Sigma m(2, 3, 4, 5, 6, 8, 9)$$

For a multiplexer implementation, seven 8-to-1 multiplexers are required, one for each function for the segments on the display. Alternatively, a 7-bit wide 8-to-1 multiplexer could be used. With the select inputs S_2 connected to A, S_1 connected to B, and S_0 connected to C, then the data inputs to the seven multiplexers would be as shown in Table 3-10. ■

3-8 ITERATIVE COMBINATIONAL CIRCUITS

The remainder of this chapter focuses on functional blocks for arithmetic. The arithmetic functional blocks are typically designed to operate on binary input vectors and produce binary output vectors. Further, the function implemented often requires that the same subfunction be applied to each bit position. Thus, a functional block can be designed for the subfunction and then used repetitively for each bit position of the overall arithmetic block being designed. There will often be one or more connections to pass values between adjacent bit positions. These internal variables are inputs or outputs of the subfunctions, but are not

□ **TABLE 3-10**
Inputs to Multiplexers to Implement Seven-Segment-Display decoder

Select Inputs	Multiplexer Data Inputs for Each Output Function						
$S_2 S_1 S_0$	a	b	c	d	e	f	g
000	$\overline{D}$	1	1	$\overline{D}$	$\overline{D}$	$\overline{D}$	0
001	1	1	D	1	$\overline{D}$	0	1
010	D	$\overline{D}$	1	D	0	1	1
011	1	D	1	$\overline{D}$	$\overline{D}$	$\overline{D}$	$\overline{D}$
100	1	1	1	1	$\overline{D}$	1	1
101	0	0	0	0	0	0	0
110	0	0	0	0	0	0	0
111	0	0	0	0	0	0	0

accessible outside the overall arithmetic block. The subfunction blocks are referred to as *cells* and the overall implementation is an *array of cells*. The cells in
the array are often, but not always, identical. Due to the repetitive nature of the
circuit and the association of a vector index with each of the circuit cells, the overall functional block is referred to as an *iterative array*. Iterative arrays, a special
case of hierarchical circuits, are useful in handling vectors of bits—for example, a
circuit that adds two 32-bit binary integers. At a minimum, such a circuit has 64
inputs and 32 outputs. As a consequence, beginning with truth tables and writing
equations for the entire circuit is out of the question. Since iterative circuits are
based on repetitive cells, the design process is considerably simplified by a basic
structure that guides the design.

A block diagram for an iterative circuit that operates on two *n*-input vectors
and produces an *n*-output vector is shown in Figure 3-39. In this case, there are two
lateral connections between each pair of cells in the array, one from left to right and
the other from right to left. Also, optional connections, indicated by dashed lines,
exist at the right and left ends of the array. An arbitrary array employs as many lateral connections as needed for a particular design. The definition of the functions
associated with such connections is very important in the design of the array and its

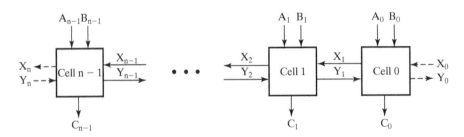

□ **FIGURE 3-39**
Block Diagram of an Iterative Circuit

cell. In particular, the number of connections used and their functions can affect both the cost and speed of an iterative circuit.

In the next section, we will define cells for performing addition in individual bit positions and then define a binary adder as an iterative array of cells.

3-9 BINARY ADDERS

An arithmetic circuit is a combinational circuit that performs arithmetic operations such as addition, subtraction, multiplication, and division with binary numbers or with decimal numbers in a binary code. We will develop arithmetic circuits by means of hierarchical, iterative design. We begin at the lowest level by finding a circuit that performs the addition of two binary digits. This simple addition consists of four possible elementary operations: $0 + 0 = 0, 0 + 1 = 1, 1 + 0 = 1$, and $1 + 1 = 10$ The first three operations produce a sum requiring a one-bit representation, but when both the augend and addend are equal to 1, the binary sum requires two bits. Because of this case, the result is always represented by two bits, the carry and the sum. The carry obtained from the addition of two bits is added to the next-higher-order pair of significant bits. A combinational circuit that performs the addition of two bits is called a *half adder*. One that performs the addition of three bits (two significant bits and a previous carry) is called a *full adder*. The names of the circuits stem from the fact that two half adders can be employed to implement a full adder. The half adder and the full adder are basic arithmetic blocks with which other arithmetic circuits are designed.

Half Adder

A half adder is an arithmetic circuit that generates the sum of two binary digits. The circuit has two inputs and two outputs. The input variables are the augend and addend bits to be added, and the output variables produce the sum and carry. We assign the symbols X and Y to the two inputs and S (for "sum") and C (for "carry") to the outputs. The truth table for the half adder is listed in Table 3-11. The C output is 1 only when both inputs are 1. The S output represents the least significant bit of the sum. The Boolean functions for the two outputs, easily obtained from the truth table, are

$$S = \overline{X}Y + X\overline{Y} = X \oplus Y$$

$$C = XY$$

□ **TABLE 3-11**
Truth Table of Half Adder

Inputs		Outputs	
X	Y	C	S
0	0	0	0
0	1	0	1
1	0	0	1
1	1	1	0

☐ **FIGURE 3-40**
Logic Diagram of Half Adder

The half adder can be implemented with one exclusive-OR gate and one AND gate, as shown in Figure 3-40.

Full Adder

A full adder is a combinational circuit that forms the arithmetic sum of three input bits. Besides the three inputs, it has two outputs. Two of the input variables, denoted by X and Y, represent the two significant bits to be added. The third input, Z, represents the carry from the previous lower significant position. Two outputs are necessary because the arithmetic sum of three bits ranges in value from 0 to 3, and binary 2 and 3 need two digits for their representation. Again, the two outputs are designated by the symbols S for "sum" and C for "carry"; the binary variable S gives the value of the bit of the sum, and the binary variable C gives the output carry. The truth table of the full adder is listed in Table 3-12. The values for the outputs are determined from the arithmetic sum of the three input bits. When all the input bits are 0, the outputs are 0. The S output is equal to 1 when only one input is equal to 1 or when all three inputs are equal to 1. The C output is a carry of 1 if two or three inputs are equal to 1. The maps for the two outputs of the full adder are shown in Figure 3-41. The simplified sum-of-product functions for the two outputs are

$$S = \overline{X}\,\overline{Y}Z + \overline{X}Y\overline{Z} + X\overline{Y}\,\overline{Z} + XYZ$$

$$C = XY + XZ + YZ$$

The two-level implementation requires seven AND gates and two OR gates. However, the map for output S is recognized as an odd function, as discussed in

☐ **TABLE 3-12**
Truth Table of Full Adder

Inputs			Outputs	
X	Y	Z	C	S
0	0	0	0	0
0	0	1	0	1
0	1	0	0	1
0	1	1	1	0
1	0	0	0	1
1	0	1	1	0
1	1	0	1	0
1	1	1	1	1

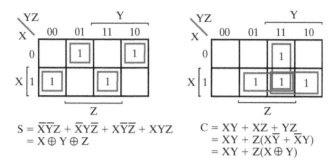

$$S = \overline{X}\overline{Y}Z + \overline{X}Y\overline{Z} + X\overline{Y}\overline{Z} + XYZ$$
$$= X \oplus Y \oplus Z$$

$$C = XY + XZ + YZ$$
$$= XY + Z(X\overline{Y} + \overline{X}Y)$$
$$= XY + Z(X \oplus Y)$$

□ **FIGURE 3-41**
Maps for Full Adder

Section 2-6. Furthermore, the C output function can be manipulated to include the exclusive-OR of X and Y. The Boolean functions for the full adder in terms of exclusive-OR operations can then be expressed as

$$S = (X \oplus Y) \oplus Z$$
$$C = XY + Z(X \oplus Y)$$

The logic diagram for this multiple-level implementation is shown in Figure 3-42. It consists of two half adders and an OR gate.

Binary Ripple Carry Adder

A parallel binary adder is a digital circuit that produces the arithmetic sum of two binary numbers using only combinational logic. The parallel adder uses n full adders in parallel, with all input bits applied simultaneously to produce the sum.

The full adders are connected in cascade, with the carry output from one full adder connected to the carry input of the next full adder. Since a 1 carry may appear near the least significant bit of the adder and yet propagate through many full

□ **FIGURE 3-42**
Logic Diagram of Full Adder

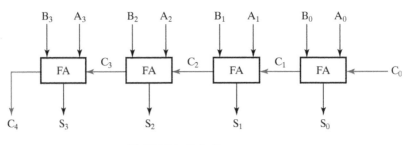

□ **FIGURE 3-43**
4-Bit Ripple Carry Adder

adders to the most significant bit, just as a wave ripples outward from a pebble dropped in a pond, the parallel adder is referred to as a *ripple carry adder*. Figure 3-43 shows the interconnection of four full-adder blocks to form a 4-bit ripple carry adder. The augend bits of A and the addend bits of B are designated by subscripts in increasing order from right to left, with subscript 0 denoting the least significant bit. The carries are connected in a chain through the full adders. The input carry to the parallel adder is C_0, and the output carry is C_4. An n-bit ripple carry adder requires n full adders, with each output carry connected to the input carry of the next-higher-order full adder. For example, consider the two binary numbers $A = 1011$ and $B = 0011$. Their sum, $S = 1110$, is formed with a 4-bit ripple carry adder as follows:

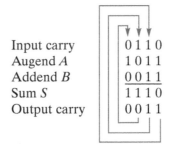

Input carry	0 1 1 0
Augend A	1 0 1 1
Addend B	0 0 1 1
Sum S	1 1 1 0
Output carry	0 0 1 1

The input carry in the least significant position is 0. Each full adder receives the corresponding bits of A and B and the input carry, and generates the sum bit for S and the output carry. The output carry in each position is the input carry of the next-higher-order position, as indicated by the blue lines.

The 4-bit adder is a typical example of a digital component that can be used as a building block. It can be used in many applications involving arithmetic operations. Observe that the design of this circuit by the usual method would require a truth table with 512 entries, since there are nine inputs to the circuit. By cascading the four instances of the known full adders, it is possible to obtain a simple and straightforward implementation without directly solving this larger problem. This is an example of the power of iterative circuits and circuit reuse in design.

3-10 BINARY SUBTRACTION

In Chapter 1, we briefly examined the subtraction of unsigned binary numbers. Although beginning texts cover only signed-number addition and subtraction, to the complete exclusion of the unsigned alternative, unsigned-number arithmetic plays an important role in computation and computer hardware design. It is used in floating-point units, in signed-magnitude addition and subtraction algorithms, and in extending the precision of fixed-point numbers. For these reasons, we will treat unsigned-number addition and subtraction here. We also, however, choose to treat it first so that we can clearly justify, in terms of hardware cost, an approach that otherwise appears bizarre and often is accepted on faith, namely, the use of complement representations in arithmetic.

In Section 1-4, subtraction is performed by comparing the subtrahend with the minuend and subtracting the smaller from the larger. The use of a method containing this comparison operation results in inefficient and costly circuitry. As an alternative, we can simply subtract the subtrahend from the minuend. Using the same numbers as in a subtraction example from Section 1-4, we have

Borrows into:	11100
Minuend:	10011
Subtrahend:	−1100110
Difference:	10101
Correct Difference:	− 01011

If no borrow occurs into the most significant position, then we know that the subtrahend is not larger than the minuend and that the result is positive and correct. If a borrow does occur into the most significant position, as indicated in blue, then we know that the subtrahend is larger than the minuend. The result must then be negative, and so we need to correct its magnitude. We can do this by examining the result of the calculation when a borrow occurs:

$$M - N + 2^n$$

Note that the added 2^n represents the value of the borrow into the most significant position. Instead of this result, the desired magnitude is $N - M$. This can be obtained by subtracting the preceding formula from 2^n:

$$2^n - (M - N + 2^n) = N - M$$

In the previous example, $100000 - 10101 = 01011$, which is the correct magnitude.

In general, the subtraction of two n-digit numbers, $M - N$, in base 2 can be done as follows:

1. Subtract the subtrahend N from the minuend M.

2. If no end borrow occurs, then $M \geq N$, and the result is nonnegative and correct.

3. If an end borrow occurs, then $N > M$, and the difference, $M - N + 2^n$, is subtracted from 2^n, and a minus sign is appended to the result.

Subtraction of a binary number from 2^n to obtain an n-digit result is called taking the *2s complement* of the number. So in step 3, we are taking the 2s complement of the difference $M - N + 2^n$. Use of the 2s complement in subtraction is illustrated by the following example.

EXAMPLE 3-19   Unsigned Binary Subtraction by 2s Complement Subtract

Perform the binary subtraction $01100100 - 10010110$. We have

Borrows into:	10011110
Minuend:	01100100
Subtrahend:	-10010110
Initial Result:	11001110

The end borrow of 1 implies correction:

2^8	100000000
$-$Initial Result:	-11001110
Final Result:	-00110010 ▪

To perform subtraction using this method requires a subtractor for the initial subtraction. In addition, when necessary, either the subtractor must be used a second time to perform the correction, or a separate 2s complementer circuit must be provided. So, thus far, we require a subtractor, an adder, and possibly a 2s complementer to perform both addition and subtraction. The block diagram for a 4-bit adder–subtractor using these functional blocks is shown in Figure 3-44. The inputs are applied to both the adder and the subtractor, so both operations are performed in parallel. If an end borrow value of 1 occurs in the subtraction, then the selective 2s complementer receives a value of 1 on its *complement* input. This circuit then takes the 2s complement of the output of the subtractor. If the end borrow has value of 0, the selective 2s complementer passes the output of the subtractor through unchanged. If subtraction is the operation, then a 1 is applied to S of the multiplexer that selects the output of the complementer. If addition is the operation, then a 0 is applied to S, thereby selecting the output of the adder.

As we will see, this circuit is more complex than necessary. To reduce the amount of hardware, we would like to share logic between the adder and the subtractor. This can also be done using the notion of the complement. So before considering the combined adder–subtractor further, we will take a more careful look at complements.

Complements

There are two types of complements for each base-r system: the *radix complement*, which we saw earlier for base 2, and the *diminished radix complement*. The first is referred to as the *r's complement* and the second as the *$(r - 1)$'s complement*. When the value of the base r is substituted in the names, the two types are referred to as the

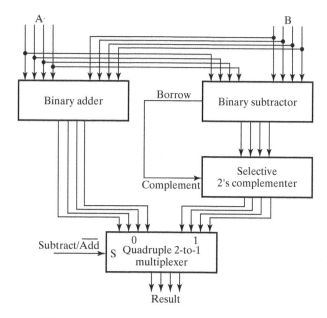

□ **FIGURE 3-44**
Block Diagram of Binary Adder–Subtractor

2s and 1s complements for binary numbers and the 10s and 9s complements for decimal numbers, respectively. Since our interest for the present is in binary numbers and operations, we will deal with only 1s and 2s complements.

Given a number N in binary having n digits, the *1s complement of N* is defined as $(2^n - 1) - N$. 2^n is represented by a binary number that consists of a 1 followed by n 0s. $2^n - 1$ is a binary number represented by n 1s. For example, if $n = 4$, we have $2^4 = (10000)_2$ and $2^4 - 1 = (1111)_2$. Thus, the 1s complement of a binary number is obtained by subtracting each digit from 1. When subtracting binary digits from 1, we can have either $1 - 0 = 1$ or $1 - 1 = 0$, which causes the original bit to change from 0 to 1 or from 1 to 0, respectively. Therefore, the 1s complement of a binary number is formed by changing all 1s to 0s and all 0s to 1s—that is, applying the NOT or complement operation to each of the bits. Following are two numerical examples:

The 1s complement of 1011001 is 0100110.
The 1s complement of 0001111 is 1110000.

In similar fashion, the 9s complement of a decimal number, the 7s complement of an octal number, and the 15s complement of a hexadecimal number are obtained by subtracting each digit from 9, 7, and F (decimal 15), respectively.

Given an n-digit number N in binary, the *2s complement of N* is defined as $2^n - N$ for $N \neq 0$ and 0 for $N = 0$. The reason for the special case of $N = 0$ is that the result must have n bits, and subtraction of 0 from 2^n gives an $(n + 1)$-bit result, $100 \ldots 0$. This special case is achieved by using only an n-bit subtractor or otherwise dropping the 1 in the extra position. Comparing with the 1s complement, we note that the 2s complement can be obtained by adding 1 to the 1s complement, since

$2^n - N = \{[(2^n - 1) - N] + 1\}$. For example, the 2s complement of binary 101100 is $010011 + 1 = 010100$ and is obtained by adding 1 to the 1s complement value. Again, for $N = 0$, the result of this addition is 0, achieved by ignoring the carry out of the most significant position of the addition. These concepts hold for other bases as well. As we will see later, they are very useful in simplifying 2s complement and subtraction hardware.

Also, the 2s complement can be formed by leaving all least significant 0s and the first 1 unchanged and then replacing 1s with 0s and 0s with 1s in all other higher significant bits. Thus, the 2s complement of 1101100 is 0010100 and is obtained by leaving the two low-order 0s and the first 1 unchanged and then replacing 1s with 0s and 0s with 1s in the other four most significant bits. In other bases, the first nonzero digit is subtracted from the base r, and the remaining digits to the left are replaced with $r - 1$ minus their values.

It is also worth mentioning that the complement of the complement restores the number to its original value. To see this, note that the 2s complement of N is $2^n - N$, and the complement of the complement is $2^n - (2^n - N) = N$, giving back the original number.

Subtraction Using 2s Complement

Earlier, we expressed a desire to simplify hardware by sharing adder and subtractor logic. Armed with complements, we are prepared to define a binary subtraction procedure that uses addition and the corresponding complement logic. The subtraction of two n-digit unsigned numbers, $M - N$, in binary can be done as follows:

1. Add the 2s complement of the subtrahend N to the minuend M. This performs $M + (2^n - N) = M - N + 2^n$.

2. If $M \geq N$, the sum produces an end carry, 2^n. Discard the end carry, leaving result $M - N$.

3. If $M < N$, the sum does not produce an end carry, since it is equal to $2^n - (N - M)$, the 2s complement of $N - M$. Perform a correction, taking the 2s complement of the sum and placing a minus sign in front to obtain the result $-(N - M)$.

The examples that follow further illustrate the foregoing procedure. Note that, although we are dealing with unsigned numbers, there is no way to get an unsigned result for the case in step 3. When working with paper and pencil, we recognize, by the absence of the end carry, that the answer must be changed to a negative number. If the minus sign for the result is to be preserved, it must be stored separately from the corrected n-bit result.

EXAMPLE 3-20   Unsigned Binary Subtraction by 2s Complement Addition

Given the two binary numbers $X = 1010100$ and $Y = 1000011$, perform the subtraction $X - Y$ and $Y - X$ using 2s complement operations. We have

$$X = \quad 1010100$$

$$\text{2s complement of } Y = \quad 0111101$$

$$\text{Sum} = \quad 10010001$$

$$\text{Discard end carry } 2^7 = \quad -\underline{10000000}$$

$$\textit{Answer: } X - Y = \quad 0010001$$

$$Y = \quad 1000011$$

$$\text{2s complement of } X = \quad \underline{0101100}$$

$$\text{Sum} = \quad 1101111$$

There is no end carry.
Answer: $Y - X = -(\text{2s complement of } 1101111) = -0010001$. ■

While subtraction of unsigned numbers also can be done by means of the 1s complement, it is little used in modern designs, so will not be covered here.

3-11 BINARY ADDER-SUBTRACTORS

Using the 2s complement, we have eliminated the subtraction operation and need only the complementer and an adder. When performing a subtraction we complement the subtrahend N, and when performing an addition we do not complement N. These operations can be accomplished by using a selective complementer and adder interconnected to form an adder–subtractor. We have used 2s complement, since it is most prevalent in modern systems. The 2s complement can be obtained by taking the 1s complement and adding 1 to the least significant bit. The 1s complement can be implemented easily with inverter circuits, and we can add 1 to the sum by making the input carry of the parallel adder equal to 1. Thus, by using 1s complement and an unused adder input, the 2s complement is obtained inexpensively. In 2s complement subtraction, as a correction step after adding, we complement the result and append a minus sign if an end carry does not occur. The correction operation is performed by using either the adder–subtractor a second time with $M = 0$ or a selective complementer as in Figure 3-44.

The circuit for subtracting $A - B$ consists of a parallel adder as shown in Figure 3-43, with inverters placed between each B terminal and the corresponding full-adder input. The input carry C_0 must be equal to 1. The operation that is performed becomes A plus the 1s complement of B plus 1. This is equal to A plus the 2s complement of B. For unsigned numbers, it gives $A - B$ if $A \geq B$ or the 2s complement of $B - A$ if $A < B$.

The addition and subtraction operations can be combined into one circuit with one common binary adder. This is done by including an exclusive-OR gate with each

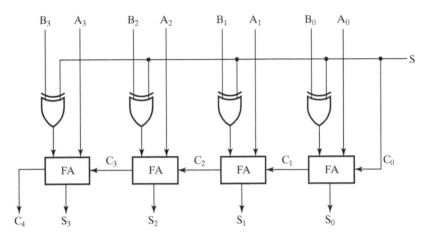

☐ **FIGURE 3-45**
Adder-Subtractor Circuit

full adder. A 4-bit adder–subtractor circuit is shown in Figure 3-45. Input S controls the operation. When $S = 0$ the circuit is an adder, and when $S = 1$ the circuit becomes a subtractor. Each exclusive-OR gate receives input S and one of the inputs of B, B_i. When $S = 0$, we have $B_i \oplus 0$. If the full adders receive the value of B, and the input carry is 0, the circuit performs A plus B. When $S = 1$, we have $B_i \oplus 1 = \overline{B_i}$ and $C_0 = 1$. In this case, the circuit performs the operation A plus the 2s complement of B.

Signed Binary Numbers

In the previous section, we dealt with the addition and subtraction of unsigned numbers. We will now extend this approach to signed numbers, including a further use of complements that eliminates the correction step.

Positive integers and the number zero can be represented as unsigned numbers. To represent negative integers, we need a notation for negative values. In ordinary arithmetic, a negative number is indicated by a minus sign and a positive number by a plus sign. Because of hardware limitations, computers must represent everything with 1s and 0s, including the sign of a number. As a consequence, it is customary to represent the sign with a bit placed in the most significant position of an n-bit number. The convention is to make the sign bit 0 for positive numbers and 1 for negative numbers.

It is important to realize that both signed and unsigned binary numbers consist of a string of bits when represented in a computer. The user determines whether the number is signed or unsigned. If the binary number is signed, then the leftmost bit represents the sign and the rest of the bits represent the number. If the binary number is assumed to be unsigned, then the leftmost bit is the most significant bit of the number. For example, the string of bits 01001 can be considered as 9 (unsigned binary) or +9 (signed binary), because the leftmost bit is 0. Similarly, the string of bits 11001 represents the binary equivalent of 25 when considered as an unsigned number or -9 when considered as a signed number. The latter is because the 1 in the leftmost position designates a minus sign and the remaining four bits represent binary 9. Usually, there is no confusion in identifying the bits because the type of number representation is known in advance. The representation of signed numbers just discussed is referred to as the *signed-magnitude* system. In this system, the number consists of a magnitude and a symbol ($+$ or $-$) or a bit (0 or 1) indicating the sign. This is the representation of signed numbers used in ordinary arithmetic.

In implementing signed-magnitude addition and subtraction for n-bit numbers, the single sign bit in the leftmost position and the $n - 1$ magnitude bits are processed separately. The magnitude bits are processed as unsigned binary numbers. Thus, subtraction involves the correction step. To avoid this step, we use a different system for representing negative numbers, referred to as a *signed-complement* system. In this system, a negative number is represented by its complement. While the signed-magnitude system negates a number by changing its sign, the signed-complement system negates a number by taking its complement. Since positive numbers always start with 0 (representing a plus sign) in the leftmost position, their complements will always start with a 1, indicating a negative number. The signed-complement system can use either the 1s or the 2s complement, but the latter is the most common. As an example, consider the number 9, represented in binary with eight bits. $+9$ is represented with a sign bit of 0 in the leftmost position, followed by the binary equivalent of 9, to give 00001001. Note that all eight bits must have a value, and therefore, 0s are inserted between the sign bit and the first 1. Although there is only one way to represent $+9$, we have two different ways to represent -9 using eight bits:

In signed-magnitude representation: 10001001
In signed 2s complement representation: 11110111

In signed magnitude, -9 is obtained from $+9$ by changing the sign bit in the leftmost position from 0 to 1. The signed 2s complement representation of -9 is obtained by taking the 2s complement of the positive number, including the 0 sign bit.

Table 3-13 lists all possible 4-bit signed binary numbers in two representations. The equivalent decimal number is also shown. Note that the positive numbers in both representations are identical and have 0 in the leftmost position. The signed 2s complement system has only one representation for 0, which is always positive. The signed-magnitude system has a positive 0 and a negative 0, which is something not encountered in ordinary arithmetic. Note that both negative numbers have a 1 in the leftmost bit position; this is the way we distinguish them from positive numbers. With four bits, we can represent 16 binary numbers. In the signed-magnitude representation, there are seven positive numbers and seven negative numbers, and two signed zeros. In the 2s complement representation, there are seven positive numbers, one zero, and eight negative numbers.

The signed-magnitude system is used in ordinary arithmetic, but is awkward when employed in computer arithmetic due to the separate handling of the sign and the correction step required for subtraction. Therefore, the signed complement is normally used. The following discussion of signed binary arithmetic deals exclusively

□ **TABLE 3-13**
Signed Binary Numbers

Decimal	Signed 2s Complement	Signed Magnitude
+ 7	0111	0111
+ 6	0110	0110
+ 5	0101	0101
+ 4	0100	0100
+ 3	0011	0011
+ 2	0010	0010
+ 1	0001	0001
+ 0	0000	0000
− 0	—	1000
− 1	1111	1001
− 2	1110	1010
− 3	1101	1011
− 4	1100	1100
− 5	1011	1101
− 6	1010	1110
− 7	1001	1111
− 8	1000	—

with the signed 2s complement representation of negative numbers, because it prevails in actual use.

Signed Binary Addition and Subtraction

The addition of two numbers, $M + N$, in the signed-magnitude system follows the rules of ordinary arithmetic: If the signs are the same, we add the two magnitudes and give the sum the sign of M. If the signs are different, we subtract the magnitude of N from the magnitude of M. The absence or presence of an end borrow then determines the sign of the result, based on the sign of M, and determines whether or not a 2s complement correction is performed. For example, since the signs are different, (00011001) + (10100101) causes 0100101 to be subtracted from 0011001. The result is 1110100, and an end borrow of 1 occurs. The end borrow indicates that the magnitude of M is smaller than that of N. So the sign of the result is opposite to that of M and is therefore a minus. The end borrow indicates that the magnitude of the result, 1110100, must be corrected by taking its 2s complement. Combining the sign and the corrected magnitude of the result, we obtain 1 0001100.

In contrast to this signed-magnitude case, the rule for adding numbers in the signed 2s complement system does not require comparison or subtraction, but only addition. The procedure is simple and can be stated as follows for binary numbers:

The addition of two signed binary numbers with negative numbers represented in signed 2s complement form is obtained from the addition of the two numbers, including their sign bits. A carry out of the sign bit position is discarded.

Numerical examples of signed binary addition are given in Example 3-21. Note that negative numbers will already be in 2s complement form and that the sum obtained after the addition, if negative, is left in that same form.

EXAMPLE 3-21   Signed Binary Addition Using 2s Complement

$+6$	00000110	-6	11111010	$+6$	00000110	-6	11111010
$+13$	00001101	$+13$	00001101	-13	11110011	-13	11110011
$+19$	00010011	$+7$	00000111	-7	11111001	-19	11101101

In each of the four cases, the operation performed is addition, including the sign bits. Any carry out of the sign bit position is discarded, and negative results are automatically in 2s complement form. ■

The complement form for representing negative numbers is unfamiliar to people accustomed to the signed-magnitude system. To determine the value of a negative number in signed 2s complement, it is necessary to convert the number to a positive number in order to put it in a more familiar form. For example, the signed binary number 11111001 is negative, because the leftmost bit is 1. Its 2s complement is 00000111, which is the binary equivalent of +7. We therefore recognize the original number to be equal to -7.

The subtraction of two signed binary numbers when negative numbers are in 2s complement form is very simple and can be stated as follows:

Take the 2s complement of the subtrahend (including the sign bit) and add it to the minuend (including the sign bit). A carry out of the sign bit position is discarded.

This procedure stems from the fact that a subtraction operation can be changed to an addition operation if the sign of the subtrahend is changed. That is,

$$(\pm A) - (+B) = (\pm A) + (-B)$$

$$(\pm A) - (-B) = (\pm A) + (+B)$$

But changing a positive number to a negative number is easily done by taking its 2s complement. The reverse is also true, because the complement of a negative number that is already in complement form produces the corresponding positive number. Numerical examples are shown in Example 3-22.

EXAMPLE 3-22   Signed Binary Subtraction Using 2s Complement

-6	11111010	11111010	$+6$	00000110	00000110
$-(-13)$	$-$ 11110011	$+$ 00001101	$-(-13)$	$-$ 11110011	$+$ 00001101
$+7$		00000111	$+19$		00010011

The end carry is discarded. ■

It is worth noting that binary numbers in the signed-complement system are added and subtracted by the same basic addition and subtraction rules as are unsigned numbers. Therefore, computers need only one common hardware circuit to handle both types of arithmetic. The user or programmer must interpret the results of such addition or subtraction differently, depending on whether it is assumed that the numbers are signed or unsigned. Thus, the same adder–subtractor designed for unsigned numbers can be used for signed numbers. If the signed numbers are in 2s complement representation, then the circuit in Figure 3-45 can be used.

EXAMPLE 3-23   Electronic Scale Feature

Often goods or materials must be placed in a container to be weighed. These three definitions apply to the use of a container in weighing:

> *Gross Weight*—Weight of the container plus its contents.
> *Tare Weight*—Weight of the empty container.
> *Net Weight*—Weight of the contents only.

The Problem: For a particular electronic scale, a feature that permits the net weight to be displayed is activated by the following sequence of actions:

1) Place the empty container on the scale.
2) Press the TARE button to indicate that the current weight is the weight of the empty container.
3) Add the contents to be weighed to the container (measure the gross weight).
4) Read the net weight from the scale indicator.

Assuming that the container weight (tare weight) is stored by the scale,

> **(a)** What arithmetic logic is required?
> **(b)** How many bits are required for the operands, assuming the gross weight capacity of the scale is 2200 grams with one gram as the smallest unit?

The Solution: (a) The scale is measuring the gross weight. The displayed result is the net weight. So a subtractor is needed to form:

$$\text{Net Weight} = \text{Gross Weight} - \text{(stored)} \text{Tare Weight}$$

Since the container plus its contents always weighs at least as much as the container only, for this application the result must always be nonnegative. If, on the other hand, the user makes use of this feature to find the differences in the weight of two objects, then a negative result is possible. In the design of the actual scale, this negative result is properly taken into account in the display logic.

(b) Assuming that the weights and the subtraction are in binary, 12 bits are required to represent 2200 grams. If the weights and the subtraction are represented in BCD, then $2 + 3 \times 4 = 14$ bits are required.   ■

Overflow

To obtain a correct answer when adding and subtracting, we must ensure that the result has a sufficient number of bits to accommodate the sum. If we start with two n-bit numbers, and the sum occupies $n + 1$ bits, we say that an *overflow* occurs. This is true for binary or decimal numbers, whether signed or unsigned. When one performs addition with paper and pencil, an overflow is not a problem, since we are not limited by the width of the page. We just add another 0 to a positive number and another 1 to a negative number, in the most significant position, to extend them to $n + 1$ bits and then perform the addition. Overflow is a problem in computers because the number of bits that hold a number is fixed, and a result that exceeds the number of bits cannot be accommodated. For this reason, computers detect and can signal the occurrence of an overflow. The overflow condition may be handled automatically by interrupting the execution of the program and taking special action. An alternative is to monitor for overflow conditions using software.

The detection of an overflow after the addition of two binary numbers depends on whether the numbers are considered to be signed or unsigned. When two unsigned numbers are added, an overflow is detected from the end carry out of the most significant position. In unsigned subtraction, the magnitude of the result is always equal to or smaller than the larger of the original numbers, making overflow impossible. In the case of signed 2s complement numbers, the most significant bit always represents the sign. When two signed numbers are added, the sign bit is treated as a part of the number, and an end carry of 1 does not necessarily indicate an overflow.

With signed numbers, an overflow cannot occur for an addition if one number is positive and the other is negative: Adding a positive number to a negative number produces a result whose magnitude is equal to or smaller than the larger of the original numbers. An overflow may occur if the two numbers added are both positive or both negative. To see how this can happen, consider the following 2s complement example: Two signed numbers, +70 and +80, are stored in two 8-bit registers. The range of binary numbers, expressed in decimal, that each register can accommodate is from +127 to −128. Since the sum of the two stored numbers is +150, it exceeds the capacity of an 8-bit register. This is also true for −70 and −80. These two additions, together with the two most significant carry bit values, are as follows:

Carries:	01	Carries:	10
+70	01000110	−70	10111010
+80	01010000	−80	10110000
+150	10010110	−150	01101010

Note that the 8-bit result that should have been positive has a negative sign bit and that the 8-bit result that should have been negative has a positive sign bit. If, however, the carry out of the sign bit position is taken as the sign bit of the result, then the 9-bit answer so obtained will be correct. But since there is no position in the result for the ninth bit, we say that an overflow has occurred.

An overflow condition can be detected by observing the carry into the sign bit position and the carry out of the sign bit position. If these two carries are not equal, an overflow has occurred. This is indicated in the 2s complement example just completed, where the two carries are explicitly shown. If the two carries are applied to an

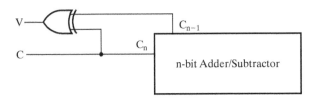

☐ **FIGURE 3-46**
Overflow Detection Logic for Addition and
Subtraction

exclusive-OR gate, an overflow is detected when the output of the gate is equal to 1. For this method to work correctly for 2s complement, it is necessary either to apply the 1s complement of the subtrahend to the adder and add 1 or to have overflow detection on the circuit that forms the 2s complement as well as on the adder. This condition is due to overflow when complementing the maximum negative number.

Simple logic that provides overflow detection is shown in Figure 3-46. If the numbers are considered unsigned, then the C output being equal to 1 detects a carry (an overflow) for an addition and indicates that no correction step is required for a subtraction. C being equal to 0 detects no carry (no overflow) for an addition and indicates that a correction step is required for a subtraction.

If the numbers are considered signed, then the output V is used to detect an overflow. If $V = 0$ after a signed addition or subtraction, it indicates that no overflow has occurred and the result is correct. If $V = 1$, then the result of the operation contains $n + 1$ bits, but only the rightmost n of those bits fit in the n-bit result, so an overflow has occurred. The $(n + 1)$th bit is the actual sign, but it cannot occupy the sign bit position in the result.

MULTIPLIERS AND DIVIDERS A supplement that discusses the design of multipliers and dividers is available on the Companion Website for the text.

HDL Models of Adders

Thus far, all of the HDL descriptions used have contained only a single entity (VHDL) or module (Verilog). Descriptions that represent circuits using hierarchies have multiple entities, one for each distinct element of the hierarchy, as shown in the next example.

EXAMPLE 3-24   Hierarchical VHDL for a 4-Bit Ripple Carry Adder

The example in Figures 3-47 and 3-48 uses three entities to build a hierarchical description of a 4-bit ripple carry adder. The style used for the architectures will be a mix of structural and dataflow description. The three entities are a half adder, a full adder that uses half adders, and the 4-bit adder itself. The architecture of `half_adder` consists of two dataflow assignments, one for s and one for c. The architecture of `full_adder` uses `half_adder` as a component. In addition, three internal signals,

```
-- 4-bit Adder: Hierarchical Dataflow/Structural
-- (See Figures 3-42 and 3-43 for logic diagrams)
library ieee;
use ieee.std_logic_1164.all;
entity half_adder is
  port (x, y : in std_logic;
        s, c : out std_logic);
end half_adder;

architecture dataflow_3 of half_adder is
  begin
    s <= x xor y;
    c <= x and y;
end dataflow_3;

library ieee;
use ieee.std_logic_1164.all;
entity full_adder is
  port (x, y, z : in std_logic;
        s, c : out std_logic);
end full_adder;

architecture struc_dataflow_3 of full_adder is
  component half_adder
    port (x, y : in std_logic;
          s, c : out std_logic);
  end component;
  signal hs, hc, tc: std_logic;
  begin
    HA1: half_adder
      port map  (x, y, hs, hc);
    HA2: half_adder
      port map (hs, z, s, tc);
    c <= tc or hc;
end struc_dataflow_3;

library ieee;
use ieee.std_logic_1164.all;
entity adder_4 is
  port(B, A : in std_logic_vector(3 downto 0);
       C0 : in std_logic;
        S : out std_logic_vector(3 downto 0);
       C4: out std_logic);
end adder_4;
```

□ **FIGURE 3-47**
Hierarchical Structural/Dataflow Description of 4-Bit Full Adder

```
architecture structural_4 of adder_4 is
  component full_adder
    port(x, y, z : in std_logic;
         s, c: out std_logic);
  end component;
  signal C: std_logic_vector (4 downto 0);
  begin
    Bit0: full_adder
     port map (B(0), A(0), C(0), S(0), C(1));
    Bit1: full_adder
     port map (B(1), A(1), C(1), S(1), C(2));
    Bit2: full_adder
     port map (B(2), A(2), C(2), S(2), C(3));
    Bit3: full_adder
     port map (B(3), A(3), C(3), S(3), C(4));
    C(0) <= C0;
    C4 <= C(4);
end structural 4;
```

☐ **FIGURE 3-48**
Hierarchical Structural/Dataflow Description of 4-Bit Full
Adder (continued)

hs, hc, and tc, are declared. These signals are applied to two half adders and are also used in one dataflow assignment to construct the full adder in Figure 3-42. In the adder_4 entity, four full-adder components are simply connected together using the signals given in Figure 3-43.

Note that C0 and C4 are an input and an output, respectively, but C(0) through C(4) are internal signals (i.e., neither inputs nor outputs). C(0) is assigned C0 and C4 is assigned C(4). The use of C(0) and C(4) separately from C0 and C4 is not essential here, but is useful to illustrate a VHDL constraint. Suppose we wanted to add overflow detection to the adder as shown in Figure 3-46. If C(4) is not defined separately, then one might attempt to write

$$v <= C(3) \quad \textbf{xor} \quad C4$$

In VHDL, this is incorrect. An output cannot be used as an internal signal. Thus, it is necessary to define an internal signal to use in place of C4 (e.g., C(4)) giving

$$v <= C(3) \quad \textbf{xor} \quad C(4)$$ ■

Behavioral Description

The 4-bit adder provides an opportunity to illustrate description of circuits at levels higher than the logic level. Such levels of description are referred to as the behavioral level or the register transfer level. We will specifically study register transfers in Chapter 6. Without studying register transfers, however, we can still show a behavioral-level description.

EXAMPLE 3-25   Behavioral VHDL for a 4-Bit Ripple Carry Adder

A behavioral description for the 4-bit adder is given in Figure 3-49. In the architecture of the entity `adder_4_b`, the addition logic is described by a single statement using $+$ and &. The $+$ represents addition and the & represents an operation called *concatenation*. A concatenation operator combines two signals into a single signal having its number of bits equal to the sum of the number of bits in the original signals. In the example, `'0'` & `A` represents the signal vector

$$\texttt{'0'A(3)A(2)A(1)A(0)}$$

with $1 + 4 = 5$ signals. Note that `'0'`, which appears on the left in the concatenation expression, appears on the left in the signal listing. The inputs to the addition are all converted to 5-bit quantities for consistency, since the output including C4 is five bits. This conversion is not essential, but is a safe approach.

Since $+$ cannot be performed on the `std_logic` type, we need an additional package to define addition for the `std_logic` type. In this case, we are using `std_logic_arith`, a package present in the `ieee` library. Further, we wish to specifically define the addition to be unsigned, so we use the unsigned extension. Also, concatenation in VHDL cannot be used on the left side of an assignment statement. To obtain `C4` and `S` as the result of the addition, a 5-bit signal sum is declared. The signal sum is assigned the result of the addition including the carry out. Following are two additional assignment statements which split sum into outputs `C4` and `S`.

```
-- 4-bit Adder: Behavioral Description
library ieee;
use ieee.std_logic_1164.all;
use ieee.std_logic_unsigned.all;

entity adder_4_b is
   port(B, A : in std_logic_vector(3 downto 0);
        C0 : in std_logic;
        S : out std_logic_vector(3 downto 0);
        C4: out std_logic);
end adder_4_b;

architecture behavioral of adder_4_b is
signal sum: std_logic_vector (4 downto 0);
begin
   sum <= ('0' & A) + ('0' & B) + ("0000" & C0);
   C4 <= sum(4);
   S <= sum(3 downto 0);
end behavioral;
```

□ **FIGURE 3-49**
Behavioral Description of 4-Bit Adder

EXAMPLE 3-26   Hierarchical Verilog for a 4-Bit Ripple Carry Adder

The description in Figure 3-50 uses three modules to represent a hierarchical design for a 4-bit ripple carry adder. The style used for the modules will be a mix of structural and dataflow description. The three modules are a half adder, a full adder built around half adders, and the 4-bit adder itself.

The half_adder module consists of two dataflow assignments, one for s and one for c. The full_adder module uses the half_adder as a component as in Figure 3-42. In the full_adder, three internal wires, hs, hc, and tc, are declared. Inputs, outputs, and these wire names are applied to the two half adders, and tc and hc are ORed to form carry c. Note that the same names can be used on

```verilog
// 4-bit Adder: Hierarchical Dataflow/Structural
// (See Figures 3-42 and 3-43 for logic diagrams)

module half_adder_v(x, y, s, c);
   input x, y;
   output s, c;

   assign s = x ^ y;
   assign c = x & y;

endmodule

module full_adder_v(x, y, z, s, c);
   input x, y, z;
   output s, c;

   wire hs, hc, tc;

   half_adder_v HA1(x, y, hs, hc),
                HA2(hs, z, s, tc);
   assign c = tc | hc;

endmodule

module adder_4_v(B, A, C0, S, C4);
   input [3:0] B, A;
   input C0;
   output [3:0] S;
   output C4;

   wire [3:1] C;

   full_adder_v Bit0(B[0], A[0], C0, S[0], C[1]),
                Bit1(B[1], A[1], C[1], S[1], C[2]),
                Bit2(B[2], A[2], C[2], S[2], C[3]),
                Bit3(B[3], A[3], C[3], S[3], C4);

endmodule
```

☐ **FIGURE 3-50**
Hierarchical Dataflow/Structural Verilog Description of 4-Bit Adder

different modules (e.g., x, y, s, and c are used in both the `half_adder` and `full_adder`).

In the `adder_4` module, four full adders are simply connected together using the signals given in Figure 3-43. Note that C0 and C4 are an input and an output, respectively, but C(3) through C(1) are internal signals (i.e., neither inputs nor outputs). ■

EXAMPLE 3-27 Behavioral Verilog for a 4-Bit Ripple Carry Adder

Figure 3-51 shows the Verilog description for the 4-bit adder. In module adder_4_b_v, the addition logic is described by a single statement using + and { }. The + represents addition and the { } represents an operation called *concatenation*. The operation + performed on wire data types is unsigned. Concatenation combines two signals into a single signal having its number of bits equal to the sum of the number of bits in the original signals. In the example, {C4, S} represents the signal vector

$$C4 \quad S[3] \quad S[2] \quad S[1] \quad S[0]$$

with $1 + 4 = 5$ signals. Note that C4, which appears on the left in the concatenation expression, appears on the left in the signal listing. ■

```
        // 4-bit Adder: Behavioral Verilog Description

        module adder_4_b_v(A, B, C0, S, C4);
           input[3:0] A, B;
           input C0;
           output[3:0] S;
           output C4;

           assign {C4, S} = A + B + C0;
        endmodule
```

□ **FIGURE 3-51**
Behavioral Description of Four-Bit Full Adder Using Verilog

3-12 OTHER ARITHMETIC FUNCTIONS

Other arithmetic functions beyond $+$, $-$, $\times$ and $\div$, are quite important. Among these are incrementing, decrementing, multiplication and division by a constant, greater-than comparison, and less-than comparison. Each can be implemented for multiple-bit operands by using an iterative array of 1-bit cells. Instead of using these basic approaches, a combination of rudimentary functions and a new technique called contraction is used. Contraction begins with a circuit such as a binary adder or a binary multiplier. This approach simplifies design by converting existing circuits into useful, less complicated ones instead of designing the latter circuits directly.

Contraction

Value fixing, transferring, and inverting on inputs can be combined with function blocks to implement new functions. We can implement new functions by using similar techniques on a given circuit or on its equations and then contracting it for a specific application to a simpler circuit. We will call the procedure *contraction*. The goal of contraction is to accomplish the design of a logic circuit or functional block by using results from past designs. It can be applied by the designer in designing a target circuit or can be applied by logic synthesis tools to simplify an initial circuit with value fixing, transferring, and inverting on its inputs in order to obtain a target circuit. In both cases, contraction can also be applied to circuit outputs that are unused, to simplify a source circuit to a target circuit. First, we illustrate contraction by using Boolean equations.

EXAMPLE 3-28   Contraction of Full-Adder Equations

The circuit Add1 to be designed is to form the sum S_i and carry C_{i+1} for the single bit addition $A_i + 1 + C_i$. This addition is a special case with $B_i = 1$ of the addition performed by a full adder, $A_i + B_i + C_i$. Thus, equations for the new circuit can be obtained by taking the full-adder equations,

$$S_i = A_i \oplus B_i \oplus C_i$$

$$C_{i+1} = A_i B_i + A_i C_i + B_i C_i$$

setting $B_i = 1$, and simplifying the results, to obtain

$$S_i = A_i \oplus 1 \oplus C_i = \overline{A_i \oplus C_i}$$

$$C_{i+1} = A_i \cdot 1 + A_i C_i + 1 \cdot C_i = A_i + C_i$$

Suppose that this Add1 circuit is used in place of each of the four full adders in a 4-bit ripple carry adder. Instead of $S = A + B + C_0$, the computation being performed is $S = A + 1111 + C_0$. In 2s complement, this computation is $S = A - 1 + C_0$. If $C_0 = 0$, this implements the *decrement* operation $S = A - 1$, using considerably less logic than for a 4-bit addition or subtraction. ■

Contraction can be applied to equations, as done here, or directly on circuit diagrams with rudimentary functions applied to function-block inputs. In order to successfully apply contraction, the desired function must obtainable from the initial circuit by application of rudimentary functions on its inputs. Next we consider contraction based on unused outputs.

Placing an unknown value, X, on the output of a circuit means that output will not be used. Thus, the output gate and any other gates that drive only that output gate can be removed. The rules for contracting equations with Xs on one or more outputs are as follows:

1. Delete all equations with Xs on the circuit outputs.

2. If an intermediate variable does not appear in any remaining equation, delete its equation.

3. If an input variable does not appear in any remaining equation, delete it.

4. Repeat 2 and 3 until no new deletions are possible.

The rules for contracting a logic diagram with Xs on one or more outputs are as follows:

1. Beginning at the outputs, delete all gates with Xs on their outputs and place Xs on their input wires.

2. If all input wires driven by a gate are labeled with Xs, delete the gate and place Xs on its inputs.

3. If all input wires driven by an external input are labeled with Xs, delete the input.

4. Repeat steps 2 and 3 until no new deletions are possible.

In the next subsection, contraction of a logic diagram is illustrated for the increment operation.

Incrementing

Incrementing means adding a fixed value to an arithmetic variable, most often a fixed value of 1. An n-bit *incrementer* that performs the operation $A + 1$ can be obtained by using a binary adder that performs the operation $A + B$ with $B = 0 \ldots 01$. The use of $n = 3$ is large enough to determine the incrementer logic to construct the circuit needed for an n-bit incrementer.

Figure 3-52 (a) shows a 3-bit adder with the inputs fixed to represent the computation $A + 1$ and with the output from the most significant carry bit C_3 fixed at value X. Operand $B = 001$ and the incoming carry $C_0 = 0$, so that $A + 001 + 0$ is computed. Alternatively, $B = 000$ and incoming carry $C_0 = 1$ could have been used.

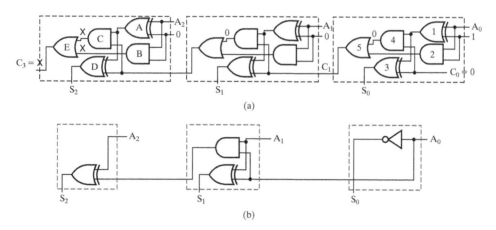

□ **FIGURE 3-52**
Contraction of Adder to Incrementer

Based on value fixing, there are three distinct contraction cases for the cells in the adder:

1. The least significant cell on the right with $B_0 = 1$ and $C_0 = 0$,

2. The typical cell in the middle with $B_1 = 0$, and

3. The most significant cell on the left with $B_2 = 0$ and $C_3 = $ X.

For the right cell, the output of gate 1 becomes $\overline{A}_0$, so it can be replaced by an inverter. The output of gate 2 becomes A_0, so it can be replaced by a wire connected to A_0. Applying $\overline{A}_0$ and 0 to gate 3, it can be replaced by a wire, connecting A_0 to the output S_0. The output of gate 4 is 0, so it can be replaced with a 0 value. Applying this 0 and A_0 from gate 2 to gate 5, gate 5 can be replaced by a wire connecting A_0 to C_1. The resulting circuit is shown as the right cell in Figure 3-52(b).

Applying the same technique to the typical cell with $B_1 = 0$ yields

$$S_1 = A_1 \oplus C_1$$
$$C_2 = A_1 C_1$$

giving the circuit shown as the middle cell in Figure 3-52(b).

For the left cell with $B_2 = 0$ and $C_3 = $ X, the effects of X are propagated first to save effort. Since gate E has X on its output, it is removed and Xs are placed on its two inputs. Since all gates driven by gates B and C have Xs on their inputs, they can be removed and Xs placed on their inputs. Gates A and D cannot be removed, since each is driving a gate without an X on its input. Gate A, however, becomes a wire, since $X \oplus 0 = X$. The resulting circuit is shown as the left cell in Figure 3-52(b).

For an incrementer with $n > 3$ bits, the least significant incrementer cell is used in position 0, the typical cell in positions 1 through $n - 2$, and the most significant cell in position $n - 1$. In this example, the rightmost cell in position 1 is contracted, but, if desired, it could be replaced with the cell in position 2 with $B_0 = 0$ and $C_0 = 1$. Likewise, the output C_3 could be generated, but not used. In both cases, logic cost and power efficiency are sacrificed to make all of the cells identical.

Decrementing

Decrementing is the addition of a fixed negative value to an arithmetic variable — most often, a fixed value of -1. A decrementer has already been designed in Example 3-28. Alternatively, a decrementer could be designed by using an adder–subtractor as a starting circuit and applying $B = 0 \ldots 01$, and selecting the subtraction operation by setting S to 1. Beginning with an adder–subtractor, we can also use contraction to design a circuit that increments for $S = 0$ and decrements for $S = 1$ by applying $B = 0 \ldots 01$, and letting S remain a variable. In this case, the result is a cell of the complexity of a full adder in the typical bit positions.

Multiplication by Constants

In Figure 3-53(a), a multiplier with a 3-bit multiplier and a 4-bit multiplicand is shown with constant values applied to the multiplier. (The design of this multiplier is explained in the supplement Multipliers and Dividers on the Companion Website.)

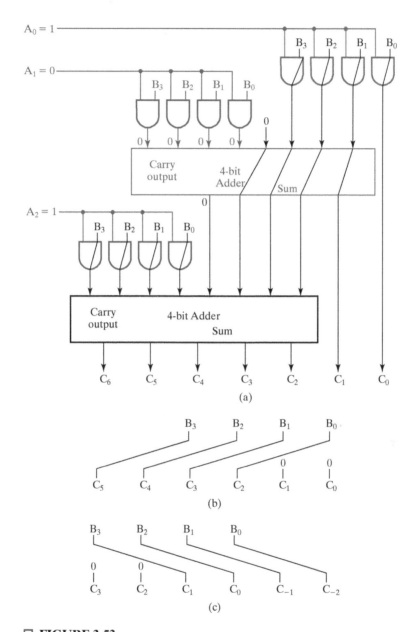

□ **FIGURE 3-53**
Contractions of Multiplier: (a) for $101 \times B$, (b) for $100 \times B$, and (c)
for $B \div 100$

Constants applied to the multiplier inputs have the following effects. If the multiplier
value for a particular bit position is 1, then the multiplicand will be applied to an adder.
If the value for a particular bit position is 0, then 0 will be applied to an adder and the
adder will be reduced by contraction to wires producing its right inputs plus a carry of
0 on its outputs. In both cases, the AND gates will be removed. In Figure 3-53(a), the

multiplier has been set to 101. The end result of the contraction of this circuit is a circuit that conveys the two least significant bits of B to the outputs C_1 and C_0. The circuit adds the two most significant bits of B to B, with the result shifted two positions to the left applied to product outputs C_6 through C_2.

An important special case occurs when the constant equals 2^i (i.e., for multiplication $2^i \times B$). In this case, only one 1 appears in the multiplier and all logic is eliminated from the circuit, resulting in only wires. In this case, for the 1 in position i, the result is B followed by i 0s. The functional block that results is simply a combination of skewed transfers and value fixing to 0. The function of this block is called a *left shift by i bit positions with zero fill*. *Zero fill* refers to the addition of 0s to the right of (or to the left of) an operand such as B. Shifting is a very important operation applied to both numerical and nonnumerical data. The contraction resulting from a multiplication by 2^2 (i.e., a left shift of two bit positions) is shown in Figure 3-53(b).

Division by Constants

Our discussion of division by constants will be restricted to division by powers of 2 (i.e., by 2^i in binary). Since multiplication by 2^i results in addition of i 0s to the right of the multiplicand, by analogy, division by 2^i results in removal of the i least significant bits of the dividend. The remaining bits are the quotient, and the bits discarded are the remainder. The function of this block is called a *right shift by i bit positions*. Just as for left shifting, right shifting is likewise a very important operation. The function block for division by 2^2 (i.e., right shifting by two bit positions) is shown in Figure 3-53(c).

Zero Fill and Extension

Zero fill, as defined previously for multiplication by a constant, can also be used to increase the number of bits in an operand. For example, suppose that a byte 01101011 is to be used as an input to a circuit that requires an input of 16 bits. One possible way of producing the 16-bit input is to zero-fill with eight 0s on the left to produce 0000000001101011. Another is to zero-fill on the right to produce 0110101100000000. The former approach would be appropriate for operations such as addition or subtraction. The latter approach could be used to produce a low-precision 16-bit multiplication result in which the byte represents the most significant eight bits of the actual product with the lower byte of the product discarded.

In contrast to zero fill, *sign extension* is used to increase the number of bits in an operand represented by using a complement representation for signed numbers. If the operand is positive, then bits can be added on the left by extending the sign of the number (0 for positive and 1 for negative). Byte 01101011, which represents 107 in decimal, extended to 16 bits becomes 0000000001101011. Byte 10010101, which in 2s complement represents −107, extended to 16 bits becomes 1111111110010101. The reason for using sign extension is to preserve the complement representation for signed numbers. For example, if 10010101 were extended with 0s, the magnitude represented would be very large, and further, the leftmost bit, which should be a 1 for a minus sign, would be incorrect in the 2s complement representation.

 DECIMAL ARITHMETIC The supplement that discusses decimal arithmetic functions and circuit implementations is available on the Companion Website for the text.

3-13 CHAPTER SUMMARY

This chapter dealt with functional blocks, combinational circuits that are frequently used to design larger circuits. Rudimentary circuits that implement functions of a single variable were introduced. The design of decoders that activate one of a number of output lines in response to an input code was covered. Encoders, the inverse of decoders, generated a code associated with the active line from a set of lines. The design of multiplexers that select from data applied at the inputs and present it at the output was illustrated.

The design of combinational logic circuits using decoders and multiplexers, was covered. In combination with OR gates, decoders provide a simple min term-based approach to implementing combinational circuits. Procedures were given for using an n-to-1-line multiplexer or a single inverter and an $(n - 1)$-to-1-line multiplexer to implement any n-input Boolean function.

This chapter also introduced common combinational circuits for performing arithmetic functions. The implementation of binary adders was treated in detail. The subtraction of unsigned binary numbers using 2s complement was presented, as was the representation of signed binary numbers and their addition and subtraction. The adder–subtractor, developed for unsigned binary, was found to apply directly to the addition and subtraction of signed 2s complement numbers as well.

REFERENCES

1. *High-Speed CMOS Logic Data Book*. Dallas: Texas Instruments, 1989.
2. *IEEE Standard VHDL Language Reference Manual* (ANSI/IEEE Std 1076-1993; revision of IEEE Std 1076-1987). New York: The Institute of Electrical and Electronics Engineers, 1994.
3. *IEEE Standard Description Language Based on the Verilog Hardware Description Language* (IEEE Std 1364-1995). New York: The Institute of Electrical and Electronics Engineers, 1995.
4. MANO, M. M. *Digital Design*, 3rd ed. Englewood Cliffs, NJ: Prentice Hall, 2002.
5. THOMAS, D. and P. Moorby. *The Verilog Hardware Description Language*, 5th ed. New York: Springer, 2002.
6. WAKERLY, J. F. *Digital Design: Principles and Practices*, 4th ed. Upper Saddle River, NJ: Pearson Prentice Hall, 2006.
7. YALAMANCHILI, S. *VHDL Starter's Guide*, 2nd ed. Upper Saddle River, NJ: Pearson Prentice Hall, 2005.

PROBLEMS

The plus (+) indicates a more advanced problem and the asterisk (*) indicates that a solution is available on the text website.

3-1. A majority function has an output value of 1 if there are more 1s than 0s on its inputs. The output is 0 otherwise. Design a four-input majority function.

3-2. *Find a function to detect an error in the representation of a decimal digit in BCD. In other words, write an equation with value 1 when the inputs are any one of the six unused bit combinations in the BCD code, and value 0 otherwise.

3-3. Design a binary code–to–BCD code converter that gives output code 1111 for all invalid input combinations. Assume that the binary code sequence for decimal numbers 0 through 9 is 0000, 0001, 0010, 0011, 0100, 0101, 0110, 0111, 1000, and 1001. All other input combinations should be considered to be invalid.

3-4. A simple well-known game, tic-tac-toe, is played on a three-by-three grid of squares by two players. The players alternate turns. Each player chooses a square and places a mark in a square. (One player uses X and the other O.) The first player with three marks in a row, in a column, or on a diagonal wins the game. A logic circuit is to be designed for an electronic tic-tac-toe that indicates the presence of a winning pattern. The circuit output W is a 1 if a winning pattern is present and a 0 if a winning pattern is not present. For each of the nine squares, there are two signals, X_i and O_i. Two copies of the circuit are used, one for Xs and one for Os. *Hint:* Form a condensed truth table for $W(X_1, X_2, \ldots, X_9)$.

(a) Design the X circuit for the following pattern of signals for the squares:

$$X_1\ X_2\ X_3$$
$$X_4\ X_5\ X_6$$
$$X_7\ X_8\ X_9$$

(b) Minimize the W output for the X circuit as much as possible, using Boolean algebra.

3-5. Repeat Problem 3-4 for 4×4 tic-tac-toe, which is played on a four-by-four grid. Assume that the numbering pattern is left to right and top to bottom, as in Problem 3-4.

3-6. A low-voltage lighting system is to use a binary logic control for a particular light. This light lies at the intersection point of a T-shaped hallway. There is a switch for this light at each of the three endpoints of the T. These switches have binary outputs 0 and 1 depending on their position and are named X_1, X_2, and X_3. The light is controlled by a buffer driving a thyristor, an electronic part that can switch power-circuit current. When Z, the input to the buffer, is 1, the light is ON, and when Z is 0, the light is OFF. You are to find a function $Z = F(X_1, X_2, X_3)$ so that if any one of the switches is changed, the value of Z changes, turning the light ON or OFF.

3-7. +A traffic light control at a simple intersection uses a binary counter to produce the following sequence of combinations on lines $A, B, C,$ and D: 0000, 0001, 0011, 0010, 0110, 0111, 0101, 0100, 1100, 1101, 1111, 1110, 1010, 1011, 1001, 1000. After 1000, the sequence repeats, beginning again with 0000, forever. Each combination is present for 5 seconds before the next one appears. These lines drive combinational logic with outputs to lamps RNS (red − north/south), YNS (yellow − north/south), GNS (green − north/south), REW (red − east/west), YEW (yellow − east/west), and GEW (green − east/west). The lamp controlled by each output is ON for a 1 applied and OFF for a 0 applied. For a given direction, assume that green is on for 30 seconds, yellow for 5 seconds, and red for 45 seconds. (The red intervals overlap for 5 seconds.) Divide the 80 seconds available for the cycle through the 16 combinations into 16 intervals and determine which lamps should be lit in each interval based on expected driver behavior. Assume that, for interval 0000, a change has just occurred and that GNS = 1, REW = 1, and all other outputs are 0. Design the logic to produce the six outputs using AND and OR gates and inverters.

3-8. Design a combinational circuit that accepts a 3-bit number and generates a 4-bit binary number output equal to double of the input number.

3-9. +Design a combinational circuit that accepts a 4-bit number and generates a 3-bit binary number output that approximates the square root of the number. For example, if the square root is 3.5 or larger, give a result of 4. If the square root is < 3.5 and ≥ 2.5, give a result of 3.

3-10. Design a circuit with a 3-bit input A, B, and C, in the form of Gray code, that produces a 3-bit output $0_0, 0_1,$ and 0_2 in binary form. For example, if the Gray code inputs are 001 and 011, then the circuit will produce 001 and 010, respectively.

3-11. A traffic metering system for controlling the release of traffic from an entrance ramp onto a superhighway has the following specifications for a part of its controller. There are three parallel metering lanes, each with its own stop (red)–go (green) light. One of these lanes, the car pool lane, is given priority for a green light over the other two lanes. Otherwise, a "round robin" scheme in which the green lights alternate is used for the other two (left and right) lanes. The part of the controller that determines which light is to be green (rather than red) is to be designed. The specifications for the controller follow:

Inputs

PS	Car pool lane sensor (car present − 1; car absent − 0)
LS	Left lane sensor (car present − 1; car absent − 0)
RS	Right lane sensor (car present − 1; car absent − 0)
RR	Round robin signal (select left − 1; select right − 0)

Outputs

PL	Car pool lane light (green − 1; red − 0)
LL	Left lane light (green − 1; red − 0)
RL	Right lane light (green − 1; red − 0)

Operation

1. If there is a car in the car pool lane, PL is 1.

2. If there are no cars in the car pool lane and the right lane, and there is a car in the left lane, LL is 1.

3. If there are no cars in the car pool lane and in the left lane, and there is a car in the right lane, RL is 1.

4. If there is no car in the car pool lane, there are cars in both the left and right lanes, and RR is 1, then LL $= 1$.

5. If there is no car in the car pool lane, there are cars in both the left and right lanes, and RR is 0, then RL $= 1$.

6. If any PL, LL, or RL is not specified to be 1 above, then it has value 0.

(a) Find the truth table for the controller part.

(b) Find a minimum multiple-level gate implementation with minimum gate-input cost using AND gates, OR gates, and inverters.

 3-12. Complete the design of the BCD–to–seven-segment decoder by performing the following steps:

(a) Plot the seven maps for each of the outputs for the BCD–to–seven-segment decoder specified in Table 3-9.

(b) Simplify the seven output functions in sum-of-products form, and determine the total number of gate inputs that will be needed to implement the decoder.

(c) Verify that the seven output functions listed in the text give a valid simplification. Compare the number of gate inputs with that obtained in part (b) and explain the difference.

3-13. Design a circuit to implement the following pair of Boolean equations:

$$F_0 = Z(XY + \bar{Y}\bar{X} + \bar{Z}(X\bar{Y} + \bar{X}Y)$$
$$F_1 = \bar{W}(X\bar{Y} + \bar{X}Y) + W(XY + \bar{Y}\bar{X})$$

To simplify drawing the schematic, the circuit is to use a hierarchy based on the factoring shown in the equation. Three instances (copies) of a single hierarchical circuit component made up of two AND gates, an OR gate, and an inverter are to be used. Draw the logic diagram for the hierarchical component and for the overall circuit diagram using a symbol for the hierarchical component.

3-14. A hierarchical component with the function is to be used along with inverters to implement the following equation:

$$F_0 = \bar{Z}(X\bar{Y} + \bar{X}Y) + Z(XY + \bar{X}\bar{Y})$$
$$F_1 = \bar{X}(\bar{W}Z + \bar{Z}W) + X(WZ + \bar{W}\bar{Z})$$

The overall circuit can be obtained by using Shannon's expansion theorem,

$$F = \overline{X} \cdot F_0(X) + X \cdot F_1(X)$$

where F_0 is F evaluated with variable $X = 0$ and F_0 is F evaluated with variable $X = 1$. This expansion F can be implemented with function H by letting $Y = F_0$ and $Z = F_1$. The expansion theorem can then be applied to each of F_0 and F_1 using a variable in each, preferably one that appears in both true and complemented form. The process can then be repeated until all F_i's are single literals or constants. For F_1, use $X = A$ to find G_0 and G_1 and then use $X = B$ for F_1 and F_1. Draw the top-level diagram for G using H as a hierarchical component.

3-15. +A NAND gate with eight inputs is required. For each of the following cases, minimize the number of gates used in the multiple-level result:

(a) Design the 8-input NAND gate using 2-input NAND gates and NOT gates.

(b) Design the 8-input NAND gate using 2-input NAND gates, 2-input NOR gates, and NOT gates only if needed.

(c) Compare the number of gates used in (a) and (b).

3-16. Perform technology mapping to NAND gates for the circuit in Figure 3-54. Use cell types selected from: Inverter ($n = 1$), 2NAND, 3NAND, and 4NAND, as defined at the beginning of Section 3-2.

3-17. Repeat Problem 3-16, using NOR gate cell types selected from: Inverter ($n = 1$), 2NOR, 3NOR, and 4NOR, each defined in the same manner as the corresponding four NAND cell types at the beginning of Section 3-2.

□ **FIGURE 3-54**
Circuit for Problems 3-16 and 3-17

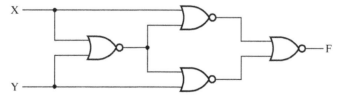

□ **FIGURE 3-55**
Circuit for Problem 3-20

☐ **FIGURE 3-56**
Circuit for Problems 3-21 and 3-22

3-18. **(a)** Repeat Problem 3-16 for the Boolean equations for the segments *a* and *c* of the BCD to seven-segment decoder from Example 3-18. Share common terms where possible.

(b) Repeat part (a) using only Inverter ($n = 1$) and 2NAND cell types.

3-19. **(a)** Repeat Problem 3-18, mapping to NOR gate cell types as in Problem 3-17. Share common terms where possible.

(b) Repeat part (a) using only Inverter ($n = 1$) and 2NOR cell types.

3-20. By using manual methods, verify that the circuit of Figure 3-55 generates the exclusive-NOR function.

3-21. The logic diagram for a 74HC138 MSI CMOS circuit is given in Figure 3-56. Find the Boolean function for each of the outputs. Describe the circuit function carefully.

3-22. Do Problem 3-21 by using logic simulation to find the output waveforms of the circuit or a partial truth-table listing, rather than finding Boolean functions.

3-23. **(a)** Use logic simulation to verify that the circuits described in Example 3-18 implement the BCD–to–seven-segment converter correctly.

(b) Design the converter assuming that the unused input combinations (minterms 10–15) can be don't cares rather than 0s. Simulate your design and compare it to your simulation from part (a).

3-24. *(a) Draw an implementation diagram for a constant vector function $F = (F_7, F_6, F_5, F_4, F_3, F_2, F_1, F_0) = (1,0,0,1,0,1,1,0)$ using the ground and power symbols in Figure 3-7(b).

(b) Draw an implementation diagram for a rudimentary vector function $G = (G_7, G_6, G_5, G_4, G_3, G_2, G_1, G_0) = (A, \overline{A}, 0, 1, \overline{A}, A, 1, 1)$ using inputs $1, 0, A,$ and $\overline{A}$.

3-25. **(a)** Draw an implementation diagram for rudimentary vector function $F = (F_7, F_6, F_5, F_4, F_3, F_2, F_1, F_0) = (A, \overline{A}, 1, \overline{A}, A, 0, 1, \overline{A})$, using the ground and power symbols in Figure 3-7(b) and the wire and inverter in Figures 3-7(c) and (d).

(b) Draw an implementation diagram for rudimentary vector function $G = (G_7, G_6, G_5, G_4, G_3, G_2, G_1, G_0) = (\overline{F}_0, \overline{F}_1, F_3, \overline{F}_2, 1, 0, 0, 1)$, using the ground and power symbols and components of vector F.

3-26. **(a)** Draw an implementation diagram for the vector $G = (G_0, G_1, G_2, G_3, G_4, G_5, G_6, G_7) = (F_4, F_5, F_6, F_7, F_0, F_2, F_1, F_3)$

(b) Draw a simple implementation for the rudimentary vector $H = (H_7, H_6, H_5, H_4, H_3, H_2, H_1, H_0) = (F_0, F_1, G_3, G_2, G_1, G_0, F_3, F_4)$

3-27. A home security system has a master switch that is used to enable an alarm, lights, video cameras, and a call to local police in the event one or more of six sets of sensors detects an intrusion. In addition there are separate switches to enable and disable the alarm, lights, and the call to local police. The inputs, outputs, and operation of the enabling logic are specified as follows:

Inputs

$S_i, i = 0, 1, 2, 3, 4, 5$: signals from six sensor sets ($0 =$ intrusion detected, $1 =$ no intrusion detected)

M: master switch ($0 =$ security system enabled, $1 =$ security system disabled)

A: alarm switch ($0 =$ alarm disabled, $1 =$ alarm enabled)

L: light switch ($0 =$ lights disabled, $1 =$ lights enabled)

P: police switch ($0 =$ police call disabled, $1 =$ police call enabled)

Outputs

A: alarm ($0 =$ alarm on, $1 =$ alarm off)

L: lights ($0 =$ lights on, $1 =$ lights off)

V: video cameras ($0 =$ video cameras off, $1 =$ video cameras on)

C: call to police ($0 =$ call off, $1 =$ call on)

Operation

If one or more of the sets of sensors detect an intrusion and the security system is enabled, then outputs activate based on the outputs of the remaining switches. Otherwise, all outputs are disabled.

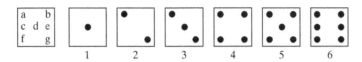

☐ **FIGURE 3-57**
Patterns for Dice for Problem 3-32

Find a minimum-gate-input cost realization of the enabling logic using AND and OR gates and inverters.

3-28. Design a 3–to–8-line decoder using two 2–to–4-line decoders and eight 2-input AND gates.

3-29. Design a 4–to–16-line decoder with enable using two 3–to–8-line decoders with enable and two AND gates and one OR gate.

3-30. *Design a 5–to–32-line decoder using a 3–to–8-line decoder, a 2–to–4-line decoder, and 32 2-input AND gates.

3-31. A special 4–to–16-line decoder is to be designed. The input codes used are in BCD format, i.e., from 000 to 1001. For a given code applied, the output D_i, with i equal to the decimal equivalent of the code, is 1 and all other outputs are 0. Design the decoder with a 3–to–8-line decoder, using AND gates and a NOT gate.

3-32. An electronic game uses an array of seven LEDs (light-emitting diodes) to display the results of a random roll of a die. A decoder is to be designed to illuminate the appropriate diodes for the display of each of the six die values. The desired display patterns are shown in Figure 3-57.

  (a) Use a 3–to–8-line decoder and OR gates to map the 3-bit combinations on inputs X_2, X_1, and X_0 for values 1 through 6 to the outputs a through g. Input combinations 000 and 111 are don't-cares.

  (b) Note that for the six die sides, only certain combinations of dots occur. For example, dot pattern $A = \{d\}$ and dot pattern $B = \{a, g\}$ can be used for representing input values 1, 2, and 3 as $\{A\}$, $\{B\}$, and $\{A, B\}$. Define four dot patterns A, B, C, and D, sets of which can provide all six output patterns. Design a minimized custom decoder that has inputs X_2, X_1, and X_0 and outputs A, B, C, and D, and compare its gate-input cost to that of the 3-to-8 decoder and OR gates in part (a).

3-33. Draw the detailed logic diagram of a 2–to–4-line decoder using only NAND gates. Include an enable input.

3-34. To provide uphill running and walking, an exercise treadmill has a grade feature that can be set from 0.0% to 15.0% in increments of 0.1%. (The grade in percent is the slope expressed as a percentage. For example, a slope of 0.10 is a grade of 10%.) The treadmill has a 10 high by 20 wide LCD dot array showing a plot of the grade versus time. This problem concerns only the vertical dimension of the display.

To define the vertical position of the LCD dot to be illuminated for the current grade, the 151 different grade values (0.0 to 15.0) need to be translated into ten different dot positions, $P0$ to $P9$. The translation of intervals of inputs to output values is represented as follows: [(0.0,1.4),0], [(1.5,2.9),1], [(3.0,4.4),2], [(4.5,5.9),3], [(6.0,7.4),4], [(7.5,8.9),5], [(9.0,10.4),6], [(10.5,11.9),7], [(12.0,13.4),8], and [(13.5,15.0),9]. The grade values are represented by a pair of values consisting of a 4-bit binary value 0 through 15 followed by a 4-bit BCD value 0 through 9. For example, 10.6 is represented by (10, 6) [1010, 0110]. Design a special decoder with eight inputs and ten outputs to perform this translation. Hint: Use two subcircuits, a 4–to–16-line decoder with the binary value as inputs and $D0$ through $D15$ as outputs, and a circuit which determines whether the BCD input value is greater than or equal to 5 (0101) with output $GE5$. Add additional logic to form outputs $P0$ through $P9$ from $D0$ through $D15$ and $GE5$. For example:

$$P_4 = D_6 + D_7 \cdot \overline{GE5} \text{ and}$$

$$P_5 = D_7 \cdot GE5 + D_8$$

3-35. *Design a 4-input priority encoder with inputs and outputs as in Table 3-6, but with the truth table representing the case in which input D_0 has the highest priority and input D_3 the lowest priority.

3-36. Derive the truth table of a decimal-to-binary priority encoder. There are 10 inputs I_1 through I_9 and outputs A_3 through A_0 and V. Input I_9 has the highest priority.

3-37. **(a)** Design a 4–to–1-line multiplexer using a 2–to–4-line decoder and a four 2-input AND gates and one 4-input OR gate.

(b) Repeat part (a) using three 2–to–1-line multiplexers.

3-38. Design an 8–to–1-line multiplexer using a 3–to–8-line decoder and an 8 × 2 AND gate and one OR gate.

3-39. Design a dual 8–to–1-line multiplexer using a 3–to–8-line decoder and a 2-to-1 line multiplexer with a line selection input.

3-40. Construct a 10–to–1-line multiplexer with two 3–to–8-line decoders, a 2–to–1-line multiplexer, and a 2-input AND-OR-NOT gate for the BCD input from 0000 to 1001.

3-41. Construct a 32–to–1-line multiplexer with two 3–to–8 decoders and one 4-to-1 line single multiplexer along with two input AND-OR gates. The decoders should be connected and inputs labeled so that the selection codes 00000 through 11111 can be applied.

3-42. *Construct a 15–to–1-line multiplexer with two 8–to–1-line multiplexers. Interconnect the two multiplexers and label the inputs such that any added logic required to have selection codes 0000 through 1110 is minimized.

3-43. Rearrange the condensed truth table for the circuit of Figure 3-16, and verify that the circuit can function as a demultiplexer.

3-44. A combinational circuit is defined by the following three Boolean functions:

$$F_1 = \overline{X}Y\overline{Z} + \overline{X}\overline{Y}Z + X\overline{Y}\overline{Z}$$
$$F_2 = \overline{X}\overline{Y}\overline{Z} + YZ$$
$$F_3 = YZ + XY$$
$$F_4 = \overline{X}Y + XY\overline{Z}$$

Design the circuit with a decoder and external OR gates.

3-45. The rear lights of a car are to be controlled by digital logic. There is a single lamp in each of the rear lights.

Inputs

LT	left turn switch—causes blinking of left side lamp
RT	right turn switch—causes blinking of right side lamp
EM	emergency flasher switch—causes blinking of both lamps
BR	brake applied switch—causes both lamps to be on
BL	blinking signal with 1 Hz frequency

Outputs

LR	power control for left rear lamp
RR	power control for right rear lamp

(a) Write the equations for LR and RR. Assume that BR overrides EM and that LT and RT override BR.

(b) Implement each function LR (BL, BR, EM, LT) and RR (BL, BR, EM, RT) with a 4–to–16-line decoder and external OR gates.

3-46. Implement the following Boolean function with an 8–to–1-line multiplexer and a single inverter with variable D as its input:

$$F(A, B, C, D) = \Sigma m(0, 2, 3, 5, 6, 9, 10, 13)$$

3-47. *Implement the Boolean function

$$F(A, B, C, D) = \Sigma m(1, 3, 4, 11, 12, 13, 14, 15)$$

with a 4–to–1-line multiplexer and external gates. Connect inputs A and B to the selection lines. The input requirements for the four data lines will be a function of the variables C and D. The values of these variables are obtained by expressing F as a function of C and D for each of the four cases when $AB = 00, 01, 10,$ and 11. These functions must be implemented with external gates.

3-48. Solve Problem 3-47 using two 3–to–8-line decoders with enables, an inverter, and OR gates with a maximum fan-in of 4.

3-49. Design a combinational circuit that forms the 2-bit binary sum S_1S_0 of two 2-bit numbers X_1X_0 and Y_1Y_0 and can produce a carry output C. Design the

☐ **FIGURE 3-58**
Circuit for Problems 3-50, 3-65, and 3-69

entire circuit with the help of three half adder circuit implementing each of the three outputs with XOR-AND and OR gates.

3-50. *The logic diagram of the first stage of a 4-bit adder, as implemented in integrated circuit type 74283, is shown in Figure 3-58. Verify that the circuit implements a full adder.

3-51. *Obtain the 1s and 2s complements of the following unsigned binary numbers: 10011100, 10011101, 10101000, 00000000, and 10000000.

3-52. Perform the indicated subtraction with the following unsigned binary numbers by taking the 2s complement of the subtrahend:

(a) $11010 - 10001$

(b) $11110 - 1110$

(c) $1111110 - 1111110$

(d) $101001 - 101$

3-53. Repeat Problem 3-52, assuming the numbers are 2s complement signed numbers. Use extension to equalize the length of the operands. Indicate whether overflow occurs during the complement operations for any of the given subtrahends. Indicate whether overflow occurs overall for any of the given subtractions. When an overflow does occur, repeat the operation with the minimum number of bits required to perform the operation without overflow.

3-54. *Perform the arithmetic operations $(+36) + (-24)$ and $(-35) - (-24)$ in binary using signed 2s complement representation for negative numbers.

3-55. The following binary numbers have a sign in the leftmost position and, if negative, are in 2s complement form. Perform the indicated arithmetic operations and verify the answers.

(a) $110001 + 011101$

(b) $0110111 + 0101111$

(c) $0000\ 0111 - 1111\ 0100$

(d) $0110111 - 0101111$

Indicate whether overflow occurs for each computation.

3-56. +Design two versions of the combinational circuit whose input is a 4-bit number and whose output is the 2s complement of the input number, for each of the following cases using AND, OR, and NOT gates:

(a) The circuit is a simplified two-level circuit, plus inverters as needed for the input variables.

(b) The circuit is made up of four identical two-input, two-output cells, one for each bit. The cells are connected in cascade, with lines similar to a carry between them. The value applied to the rightmost carry bit is 1.

(c) Calculate the gate input costs for the designs in (a) and (b) and determine which is the better design in terms of gate-input cost.

3-57. Use contraction beginning with a 4-bit adder with carry out to design a 4-bit increment circuit with carry out that is incremented by 0011. The function to be implemented is $S = A + 0011$. Design the circuit with AND-OR-XOR gates.

3-58. Use contraction beginning with a 4-bit adder–subtractor with carry in, to design a 4-bit circuit with carry out that increments its input by 0010 for input $S = 0$ and decrements its input by 0010 for input $S = 1$. Perform the design by designing the distinct 1-bit full adder cells needed and indicating the type of cell use in each of the four bit positions.

3-59. Design a combinational circuit that compares two 4-bit unsigned numbers A and B to see whether B is greater than A. The circuit has one output X, so that $X = 1$ if $A < B$ and $X = 0$ if $A \geq B$.

3-60. +Repeat Problem 3-59 by using three-input, one-output circuits, one for each of the four bits. The four circuits are connected together in cascade by carry-like signals. One of the inputs to each cell is a carry input, and the single output is a carry output.

3-61. Repeat Problem 3-59 by applying contraction to a 4-bit subtractor and using the borrow out as X.

3-62. Design a combinational circuit that compares 4-bit unsigned numbers A and B to see whether $A = B$ or $A > B$. Use an iterative circuit as in Problem 3-60.

3-63. +Design a 5-bit signed-magnitude adder–subtractor. Divide the circuit for design into (1) sign generation and add–subtract control logic, (2) an unsigned number adder–subtractor using 2s complement of the minuend for subtraction, and (3) selective 2s complement result correction logic.

3-64. *The adder–subtractor circuit of Figure 3-45 has the following values for input select S and data inputs A and B:

	S	A	B
(a)	0	0111	0111
(b)	1	0100	0111
(c)	1	1101	1010
(d)	0	0111	1010
(e)	1	0001	1000

Determine, in each case, the values of the outputs S_3, S_2, S_1, S_0, and C_4.

3-65. Using Figure 3-28 as a guide, write a structural VHDL description for the full-adder circuit in Figure 3-58. Compile and simulate your description. Apply all eight input combinations to check the correction function of your description.

3-66. Compile and simulate the 4-bit adder in Figures 3-47 and 3-48. Apply combinations that check out the rightmost full adder for all eight input combinations; this also serves as a check for the other full adders. Also, apply combinations that check the carry chain connections between all full adders by demonstrating that a 0 and a 1 can be propagated from $C0$ to $C4$.

3-67. *Compile and simulate the behavioral description of the 4-bit adder in Figure 3-49. Assuming a ripple carry implementation, apply combinations that check out the rightmost full adder for all eight input combinations. Also apply combinations that check the carry chain connections between all full adders by demonstrating that a 0 and a 1 can be propagated from $C0$ to $C4$.

3-68. + Using Figure 3-49 as a guide and a "when-else" on S from Figure 3-29, write a high-level behavior VHDL description for the adder–subtractor in Figure 3-46 (see Figure 3-45 for details). Compile and simulate your description. Assuming a ripple carry implementation, apply combinations that check out one of the full adder–subtractor stages for all 16 possible input combinations. Also, apply combinations to check the carry chain connections in between the full adders by demonstrating that a 0 and a 1 can be propagated from $C0$ to $C4$. Check the overflow signals as well.

3-69. Using Figure 3-31 as a guide, write a structural Verilog description for the full-adder circuit in Figure 3-58. Compile and simulate your description. Apply all eight input combinations to check the correction function of your description.

3-70. Compile and simulate the 4-bit adder in Figure 3-50. Apply combinations that check out the rightmost full adder for all eight input combinations; this also serves as a check for the other full adders. Also, apply combinations that check the carry chain connections between all full adders by demonstrating that a 0 and a 1 can be propagated from C0 to C4.

3-71. *Compile and simulate the behavioral description of the 4-bit adder in Figure 3-51. Assuming a ripple carry implementation, apply all eight input combinations to check out the rightmost full adder. Also, apply combinations to check the carry chain connections between all full adders by demonstrating that a 0 and a 1 can be propagated from C0 to C4.

3-72. Using Figure 3-51 as a guide and a "binary decision" on S from Figure 3-34, write a high-level behavior Verilog description for the adder–subtractor in Figure 3-46 (see Figure 3-45 for details). Compile and simulate your description. Assuming a ripple carry implementation, apply input combinations to your design that will (1) cause all 16 possible input combinations to be applied to the full adder–subtractor stage for bit 2, and (2) simultaneously cause the carry output of bit 2 to appear at one of your design's outputs. Also, apply combinations that check the carry chain connections between all full adders by demonstrating that a 0 and a 1 can be propagated from C0 to C4.

CHAPTER

4

SEQUENTIAL CIRCUITS

To this point, we have studied only combinational logic. Although such logic is capable of interesting operations, such as addition and subtraction, the performance of useful sequences of operations using combinational logic alone requires cascading many structures together. The hardware to do this is very costly and inflexible. In order to perform useful or flexible sequences of operations, we need to be able to construct circuits that can store information between the operations. Such circuits are called sequential circuits. This chapter begins with an introduction to sequential circuits, describing the difference between synchronous sequential circuits, which have a clock signal to synchronize changes in the state of the circuit at discrete points in time, and asynchronous sequential circuits, which can change state at any time in response to changes in inputs. This introduction is followed by a study of the basic elements for storing binary information, called latches and flip-flops. We distinguish flip-flops from latches and study various types of each. We then analyze sequential circuits consisting of both flip-flops and combinational logic. State tables and state diagrams provide a means for describing the behavior of sequential circuits. Subsequent sections of the chapter develop the techniques for designing sequential circuits and verifying their correctness. The state diagram is modified into a more pragmatic model for use in Chapter 6 and beyond, which, for lack of a better term, we call a state-machine diagram. The chapter provides VHDL and Verilog hardware description language representations for storage elements and for the type of sequential circuits in this chapter. We then discuss the timing characteristics of flip-flops and how the timing characteristics are related to the frequency of the clock for sequential circuits. Next, we deal with problems associated with interaction with asynchronous circuits and circuits having multiple clock domains, focusing on the important topic of synchronization of signals entering a clocked circuit domain. The discussion of delay and timing concludes with the issue of synchronization failure due to a physical phenomenon called metastability.

Latches, flip-flops, and sequential circuits are fundamental components in the design of almost all digital logic. In the generic computer given at the beginning of Chapter 1, latches and flip-flops are widespread in the design. The exception is memory circuits, since large portions of memory are designed as electronic circuits rather than as logic circuits. Nevertheless, due to the wide use of logic-based storage, this chapter contains fundamental material for any in-depth understanding of computers and digital systems and how they are designed.

4-1 SEQUENTIAL CIRCUIT DEFINITIONS

The digital circuits considered thus far have been combinational. Although every digital system is likely to include a combinational circuit, most systems encountered in practice also include storage elements, requiring that the systems be described as sequential circuits.

Figure 4-1(a) is block diagram of a sequential circuit, formed by interconnecting a combinational circuit and storage elements. The storage elements are circuits that are capable of storing binary information. The binary information stored in these elements at any given time defines the *state* of the sequential circuit at that time. The sequential circuit receives binary information from its environment via the inputs. These inputs, together with the present state of the storage elements, determine the binary value of the outputs. They also determine the values used to specify the next state of the storage elements. The block diagram demonstrates that the outputs in a sequential circuit are a function not only of the inputs, but also of the present state of the storage elements. The next state of the storage elements is also a function of the inputs and the present state. Thus, a sequential circuit is specified by a time sequence of inputs, internal states, and outputs.

There are two main types of sequential circuits, and their classification depends on the times at which their inputs are observed and their internal state changes. The behavior of a *synchronous sequential circuit* can be defined from the knowledge of its signals at discrete instants of time. The behavior of an *asynchronous sequential circuit* depends upon the inputs at any instant of time and the order in continuous time in which the inputs change.

Information is stored in digital systems in many ways, including the use of logic circuits. Figure 4-2(a) shows a buffer. This buffer has a gate delay t_G. Since information present at the buffer input at time t appears at the buffer output at time $t + t_G$, the information has effectively been stored for time t_G. But, in general, we wish to store information for an indefinite time that is typically much longer than the time delay of one or even many gates. This stored value is to be changed at arbitrary times based on the inputs applied to the circuit and the duration of storage of a value should be longer than the specific time delay of a gate.

☐ **FIGURE 4-1**
Block Diagram of a Sequential Circuit

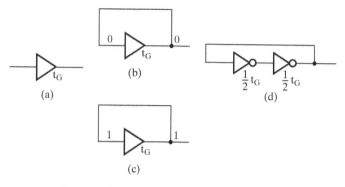

□ **FIGURE 4-2**
Logic Structures for Storing Information

Suppose that the output of the buffer in Figure 4-2(a) is connected to its input as shown in Figures 4-2(b) and (c). Suppose further that the value on the input to the buffer in part (b) has been 0 for at least time t_G, the delay of the buffer. Then the output produced by the buffer will be 0 at time $t + t_G$. This output is applied to the input so that the output will also be 0 at time $t + 2t_G$. This relationship between input and output holds for all t, so the 0 will be stored indefinitely. The same argument can be made for storing a 1 in the circuit in Figure 4-2(c).

The example of the buffer illustrates that storage can be constructed from logic with delay connected in a closed loop. Any loop that produces such storage must also have a property possessed by the buffer, namely, that there must be no inversion of the signal around the loop. A buffer is usually implemented by using two inverters, as shown in Figure 4-2(d). The signal is inverted twice, that is,

$$\overline{\overline{X}} = X$$

giving no net inversion of the signal around the loop. In fact, this example illustrates one of the most popular methods of implementing storage in computer memories. (See Chapter 7.) However, although the circuits in Figures 4-2(b) through (d) are able to store information, there is no way for the information to be changed without providing additional inputs to override with stored values. If the inverters are replaced with NOR or NAND gates, the information can be changed. Asynchronous storage circuits called latches are made in this manner and are discussed in the next section.

In general, more complex asynchronous circuits are difficult to design, since their behavior is highly dependent on the delays of the gates and on the timing of the input changes. Thus, circuits that fit the synchronous model are the choice of most designers. Nevertheless, some asynchronous design is necessary. A very important case is the use of asynchronous latches as blocks to build storage elements, called flip-flops, that store information in synchronous circuits.

A synchronous sequential circuit employs signals that affect the storage elements only at discrete instants of time. Synchronization is achieved by a timing device called a *clock generator* which produces a periodic train of *clock pulses*. The pulses are distributed throughout the system in such a way that synchronous storage elements are affected only in some specified relationship to every pulse. In practice,

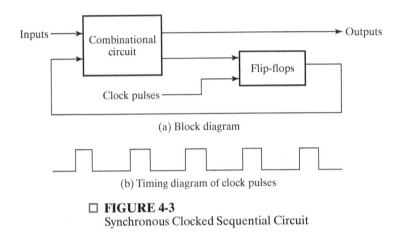

(a) Block diagram

(b) Timing diagram of clock pulses

☐ **FIGURE 4-3**
Synchronous Clocked Sequential Circuit

the clock pulses are applied with other signals that specify the required change in the storage elements. The outputs of storage elements can change their value only in the presence of clock pulses. Synchronous sequential circuits that use clock pulses as inputs for storage elements are called *clocked sequential circuits*. These are the types of circuits most frequently encountered in practice, since they operate correctly in spite of wide differences in circuit delays and are relatively easy to design.

The storage elements used in the simplest form of clocked sequential circuits are called flip-flops. For simplicity, assume circuits with a single clock signal. A *flip-flop* is a binary storage device capable of storing one bit of information and having timing characteristics to be defined in Section 4-9. The block diagram of a synchronous clocked sequential circuit is shown in Figure 4-3. The flip-flops receive their inputs from the combinational circuit and also from a clock signal with pulses that occur at fixed intervals of time, as shown in the timing diagram. The flip-flops can change state only in response to a clock pulse. For a synchronous operation, when a clock pulse is absent, the flip-flop outputs cannot change even if the outputs of the combinational circuit driving their inputs change in value. Thus, the feedback loops shown in the figure between the combinational logic and the flip-flops are broken. As a result, a transition from one state to the other occurs only at fixed time intervals dictated by the clock pulses, giving synchronous operation. The sequential circuit outputs are shown as outputs of the combinational circuit. This is valid even when some sequential circuit outputs are actually the flip-flop outputs. In this case, the combinational circuit part between the flip-flop outputs and the sequential circuit outputs consists of connections only.

A flip-flop has one or two outputs, one for the normal value of the bit stored and an optional one for the complemented value of the bit stored. Binary information can enter a flip-flop in a variety of ways, a fact that gives rise to different types of flip-flops. Our focus will be on the most prevalent type used today, the D flip-flop. Other flip-flop types, such as the JK and T flip-flops, are described in the online material available at the Companion Website. In preparation for studying flip-flops and their operation, necessary groundwork is presented in the next section on latches, from which the flip-flops are constructed.

4-2 LATCHES

A storage element can maintain a binary state indefinitely (as long as power is delivered to the circuit), until directed by an input signal to switch states. The major differences among the various types of latches and flip-flops are the number of inputs they possess and the manner in which the inputs affect the binary state. The most basic storage elements are latches, from which flip-flops are usually constructed. Although latches are most often used within flip-flops, they can also be used with more complex clocking methods to implement sequential circuits directly. The design of such circuits is, however, beyond the scope of the basic treatment given here. In this section, the focus is on latches as basic primitives for constructing storage elements.

SR and *S̄R̄* Latches

The *SR* latch is a circuit constructed from two cross-coupled NOR gates. It is derived from the single-loop storage element in Figure 4-2(d) by simply replacing the inverters with NOR gates, as shown in Figure 4-4(a). This replacement allows the stored value in the latch to be changed. The latch has two inputs, labeled *S* for set and *R* for reset, and two useful states. When output $Q = 1$ and $\overline{Q} = 0$, the latch is said to be in the *set state*. When $Q = 0$ and $\overline{Q} = 1$, it is in the *reset state*. Outputs Q and $\overline{Q}$ are normally the complements of each other. When both inputs are equal to 1 at the same time, an undefined state with both outputs equal to 0 occurs.

Under normal conditions, both inputs of the latch remain at 0 unless the state is to be changed. The application of a 1 to the *S* input causes the latch to go to the set (1) state. The *S* input must go back to 0 before *R* is changed to 1 to avoid occurrence of the undefined state. As shown in the function table in Figure 4-4(b), two input conditions cause the circuit to be in the set state. The initial condition is $S = 1$, $R = 0$, to bring the circuit to the set state. Applying a 0 to *S* with $R = 0$ leaves the circuit in the same state. After both inputs return to 0, it is possible to enter the reset state by applying a 1 to the *R* input. The 1 can then be removed from *R*, and the circuit remains in the reset state. Thus, when both inputs are equal to 0, the latch can be in either the set or the reset state, depending on which input was most recently a 1.

If a 1 is applied to both the inputs of the latch, both outputs go to 0. This produces an undefined state, because it violates the requirement that the outputs be the

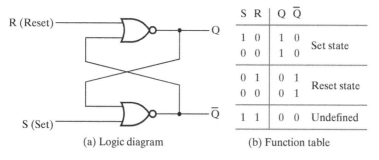

S R	Q Q̄	
1 0	1 0	Set state
0 0	1 0	
0 1	0 1	Reset state
0 0	0 1	
1 1	0 0	Undefined

(a) Logic diagram (b) Function table

☐ **FIGURE 4-4**
SR Latch with NOR Gates

complements of each other. It also results in an indeterminate or unpredictable next state when both inputs return to 0 simultaneously. In normal operation, these problems are avoided by making sure that 1s are not applied to both inputs simultaneously.

The behavior of the SR latch described in the preceding paragraph is illustrated by the ModelSim® logic simulator waveforms shown in Figure 4-5. Initially, the inputs and the state of the latch are unknown, as indicated by a logic level halfway between 0 and 1. When R becomes 1 with S at 0, the latch is reset, with Q first becoming 0 and, in response, Q_b (which represents $\overline{Q}$) becoming 1. Next, when R becomes 0, the latch remains reset, storing the 0 value present on Q. When S becomes 1 with R at 0, the latch is set, with Q_b going to 0 first and, in response, Q going to 1 next. The delays in the changes of Q and Q_b after an input changes are directly related to the delays of the two NOR gates used in the latch implementation. When S returns to 0, the latch remains set, storing the 1 value present on Q. When R becomes 1 with S equal to 0, the latch is reset, with Q changing to 0 and Q_b responding by changing to 1. The latch remains reset when R returns to 0. When S and R both become 1, both Q and Q_b become 0. When S and R simultaneously return to 0, both Q and Q_b take on unknown values. This form of indeterminate state behavior for the (S, R) sequence of inputs $(1, 1), (0, 0)$ results from assuming simultaneous input changes and equal gate delays. The actual indeterminate behavior that occurs depends on circuit delays and slight differences in the times at which S and R change in the actual circuit. Regardless of the simulation results, these indeterminate behaviors are viewed as undesirable, and the input combination $(1, 1)$ is avoided. In general, the latch state changes only in response to input changes and remains unchanged otherwise.

The $\overline{S}\,\overline{R}$ latch with two cross-coupled NAND gates is shown in Figure 4-6. It operates with both inputs normally at 1, unless the state of the latch has to be changed. The application of a 0 to the $\overline{S}$ input causes output Q to go to 1, putting the latch in the set state. When the $\overline{S}$ input goes back to 1, the circuit remains in the set state. With both inputs at 1, the state of the latch is changed by placing a 0 on the $\overline{R}$ input. This causes the circuit to go to the reset state and stay there, even after both inputs return to 1. The condition that is undefined for this NAND latch is when both inputs are equal to 0 at the same time, an input combination that should be avoided.

Comparing the NAND latch with the NOR latch, note that the input signals for the NAND require the complement of those values used for the NOR. Because

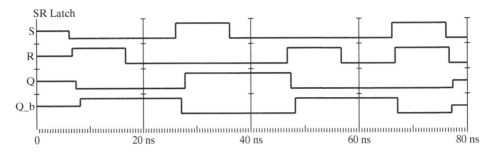

☐ **FIGURE 4-5**
Logic Simulation of SR Latch Behavior

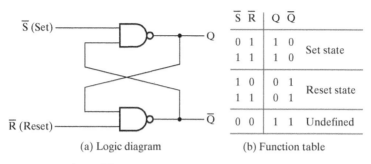

$\overline{S}$ $\overline{R}$	Q $\overline{Q}$	
0 1	1 0	Set state
1 1	1 0	
1 0	0 1	Reset state
1 1	0 1	
0 0	1 1	Undefined

(a) Logic diagram (b) Function table

□ **FIGURE 4-6**
$\overline{S}$ $\overline{R}$ Latch with NAND Gates

the NAND latch requires a 0 signal to change its state, it is referred to as an $\overline{S}$ $\overline{R}$ latch. The bar above the letters designates the fact that the inputs must be in their complement form in order to act upon the circuit state.

The operation of the basic NOR and NAND latches can be modified by providing an additional control input that determines when the state of the latch can be changed. An SR latch with a control input is shown in Figure 4-7. It consists of the basic NAND latch and two additional NAND gates. The control input C acts as an enable signal for the other two inputs. The output of the NAND gates stays at the logic-1 level as long as the control input remains at 0. This is the quiescent condition for the $\overline{S}$ $\overline{R}$ latch composed of two NAND gates. When the control input goes to 1, information from the S and R inputs is allowed to affect the $\overline{S}$ $\overline{R}$ latch. The set state is reached with $S = 1$, $R = 0$, and $C = 1$. To change to the reset state, the inputs must be $S = 0$, $R = 1$, and $C = 1$. In either case, when C returns to 0, the circuit remains in its current state. Control input $C = 0$ disables the circuit so that the state of the output does not change, regardless of the values of S and R. Moreover, when $C = 1$ and both the S and R inputs are equal to 0, the state of the circuit does not change. These conditions are listed in the function table accompanying the diagram.

An undefined state occurs when all three inputs are equal to 1. This condition places 0s on both inputs of the basic $\overline{S}$ $\overline{R}$ latch, giving an undefined state. When the

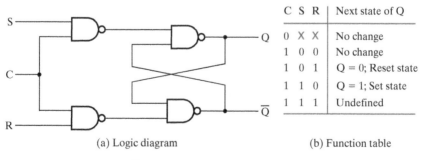

C S R	Next state of Q
0 X X	No change
1 0 0	No change
1 0 1	Q = 0; Reset state
1 1 0	Q = 1; Set state
1 1 1	Undefined

(a) Logic diagram (b) Function table

□ **FIGURE 4-7**
SR Latch with Control Input

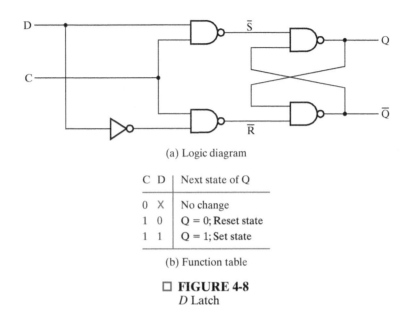

(a) Logic diagram

C	D	Next state of Q
0	X	No change
1	0	Q = 0; Reset state
1	1	Q = 1; Set state

(b) Function table

☐ **FIGURE 4-8**
D Latch

control input goes back to 0, one cannot conclusively determine the next state, since the $\overline{S}\,\overline{R}$ latch sees inputs $(0, 0)$ followed by $(1, 1)$. The *SR* latch with control input is an important circuit, because other latches and flip-flops are constructed from it. Sometimes the *SR* latch with control input is referred to as an *SR* (or *RS*) flip-flop— however, according to our terminology, it does not qualify as a flip-flop, since the circuit does not fulfill the flip-flop requirements presented in the next section.

D Latch

One way to eliminate the undesirable undefined state in the *SR* latch is to ensure that inputs *S* and *R* are never equal to 1 at the same time. This is done in the *D* latch, shown in Figure 4-8. This latch has only two inputs: *D* (data) and *C* (control). The complement of the *D* input goes directly to the $\overline{S}$ input, and *D* is applied to the $\overline{R}$ input. As long as the control input is 0, the $\overline{S}\,\overline{R}$ latch has both inputs at the 1 level, and the circuit cannot change state regardless of the value of *D*. The *D* input is sampled when *C* = 1. If *D* is 1, the *Q* output goes to 1, placing the circuit in the set state. If *D* is 0, output *Q* goes to 0, placing the circuit in the reset state.

The *D* latch receives its designation from its ability to hold *data* in its internal storage. The binary information present at the data input of the *D* latch is transferred to the *Q* output when the control input is enabled (1). The output follows changes in the data input, as long as the control input is enabled. When the control input is disabled (0), the binary information that was present at the data input at the time the transition in *C* occurred is retained at the *Q* output until the control input *C* is enabled again.

4-3 FLIP-FLOPS

A change in value on the control input allows the state of a latch in a flip-flop to switch. This change is called a *trigger*, and it enables, or triggers, the flip-flop. The *D* latch with clock pulses on its control input is triggered every time a pulse to the logic-1 level occurs. As long as the pulse remains at the active (1) level, any changes in the data input will change the state of the latch. In this sense, the latch is *transparent*, since its input value can be seen from the outputs while the control input is 1.

As the block diagram of Figure 4-3 shows, a sequential circuit has a feedback path from the outputs of the flip-flops to the combination circuit. As a consequence, the data inputs of the flip-flops are derived in part from the outputs of the same and other flip-flops. When latches are used for the storage elements, a serious difficulty arises. The state transitions of the latches start as soon as the clock pulse changes to the logic-1 level. The new state of a latch may appear at its output while the pulse is still active. This output is connected to the inputs of some of the latches through a combinational circuit. If the inputs applied to the latches change while the clock pulse is still in the logic-1 level, the latches will respond to *new state values* of other latches instead of the *original state values*, and a succession of changes of state instead of a single one may occur. The result is an unpredictable situation, since the state may keep changing and continue to change until the clock returns to 0. The final state depends on how long the clock pulse stays at the logic-1 level. Because of this unreliable operation, the output of a latch cannot be applied directly or through combinational logic to the input of the same or another latch when all the latches are triggered by a single clock signal.

Flip-flop circuits are constructed in such a way as to make them operate properly when they are part of a sequential circuit that employs a single clock. Note that the problem with the latch is that it is transparent: As soon as an input changes, shortly thereafter the corresponding output changes to match it. This transparency is what allows a change on a latch output to produce additional changes at other latch outputs while the clock pulse is at logic 1. The key to the proper operation of flip-flops is to prevent them from being transparent. In a flip-flop, before an output can change, the path from its inputs to its outputs is broken. So a flip-flop cannot "see" the change of its output or of the outputs of other, similar flip-flops at its input during the same clock pulse. Thus, the new state of a flip-flop depends only on the immediately preceding state, and the flip-flops do not go through multiple changes of state.

A common way to create a flip-flop is to connect two latches as shown in Figure 4-9, which is often referred to as a *master–slave* flip-flop. The left latch, the master, changes its value based upon the input while the clock is high. That value is

☐ **FIGURE 4-9**
Negative-Edge-Triggered D Flip-Flop

then transferred to the right latch, the slave, when the clock changes to low. Depending upon the type of latch that is used to construct the master–slave flip-flop, there are two possible ways that the flip-flop can respond to changes in the clock. One way is to combine two latches such that (1) the inputs presented to the flip-flop when a clock pulse is present control its state and (2) the state of the flip-flop changes only when a clock pulse is not present. Such a circuit is called a *pulse-triggered* flip-flop. A master–slave flip-flop constructed with SR latches is a pulse-triggered flip-flop, because changes on either the S or R inputs of the master during the clock pulse can change the master's output value. Thus a master–slave SR flip-flop depends on the input values throughout the entire high clock pulse.

In contrast, another way is to produce a flip-flop that triggers only during a signal *transition* from 0 to 1 (or from 1 to 0) on the clock and that is disabled at all other times, including for the duration of the clock pulse. Such a circuit is said to be an *edge-triggered* flip-flop. Edge-triggered flip-flops tend to be faster and have easier design constraints than pulse-triggered flip-flops, so they are much more commonly used. It is necessary to consider the SR flip-flop to illustrate the pulse-triggering approach, which is presented in the online Companion Website due to its lesser prevalence in contemporary design. The edge-triggered D flip-flop is currently the most common flip-flop, so its implementation is presented next.

Edge-Triggered Flip-Flop

An *edge-triggered* flip-flop ignores the clock pulse while it is at a constant level and triggers only during a *transition* of the clock signal. Some edge-triggered flip-flops trigger on the positive edge (0-to-1 transition), whereas others trigger on the negative edge (1-to-0 transition). The logic diagram of a negative-edge-triggered D flip-flop is shown in Figure 4-9. The logic diagram of a *D*-type positive-edge-triggered flip-flop to be analyzed in detail here appears in Figure 4-10. This flip-flop is a master-slave flip-flop, with the master a *D* latch and the slave an *SR* latch or a *D* latch. Also, an inverter is added to the clock input. Because the master latch is a *D* latch, the flip-flop exhibits edge-triggered rather than pulse-triggered behavior. For the clock input equal to 0, the master latch is enabled and transparent and follows the *D* input value. The slave latch is disabled and holds the state of the flip-flop fixed.

☐ **FIGURE 4-10**
Positive-Edge-Triggered D Flip-Flop

When the positive edge occurs, the clock input changes to 1. This disables the master latch so that its value is fixed and enables the slave latch so that it copies the state of the master latch. The state of the master latch to be copied is the state that is present at the positive edge of the clock. Thus, the behavior appears to be edge triggered. With the clock input equal to 1, the master latch is disabled and cannot change, so the state of both the master and the slave remain unchanged. Finally, when the clock input changes from 1 to 0, the master is enabled and begins following the D value. But during the 1-to-0 transition, the slave is disabled before any change in the master can reach it. Thus, the value stored in the slave remains unchanged during this transition. An alternative implementation that requires fewer gates is given in Problem 4-3 at the end of the chapter.

Standard Graphics Symbols

The standard graphics symbols for the different types of latches and flip-flops are shown in Figure 4-11. A flip-flop or latch is designated by a rectangular block with

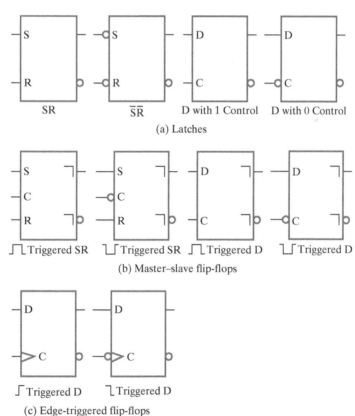

(a) Latches

(b) Master–slave flip-flops

(c) Edge-triggered flip-flops

□ **FIGURE 4-11**
Standard Graphics Symbols for Latches and Flip-Flop

inputs on the left and outputs on the right. One output designates the normal state of the flip-flop, and the other, with a bubble, designates the complement output. The graphics symbol for the SR latch or SR flip-flop has inputs S and R indicated inside the block. In the case of the $\overline{S}\,\overline{R}$ latch, bubbles are added to the inputs to indicate that setting and resetting occur for 0-level inputs. The graphics symbol for the D latch or D flip-flop has inputs D and C indicated inside the block.

Below each symbol, a descriptive title, which is not part of the symbol, is given. In the titles, ⊓ denotes a positive pulse, ⊔ a negative pulse, ⌐ a positive edge, and ⌐ a negative edge.

Triggering by the 0 level rather than the 1 level is denoted on the latch symbols by adding a bubble at the triggering input. The pulse-triggered flip-flop is indicated as such with a right-angle symbol called a *postponed output indicator* in front of the outputs. This symbol shows that the output signal changes at the end of the pulse. To denote that the master–slave flip-flop will respond to a negative pulse (i.e., a pulse to 0 with the inactive clock value at 1), a bubble is placed on the C input. To denote that the edge-triggered flip-flop responds to an edge, an arrowhead-like symbol in front of the letter C designates a *dynamic input*. This *dynamic indicator* symbol denotes the fact that the flip-flop responds to edge transitions of the input clock pulses. A bubble outside the block adjacent to the dynamic indicator designates a negative-edge transition for triggering the circuit. The absence of a bubble designates a positive-edge transition for triggering.

In contemporary practice, positive- or negative-edge-triggered D flip-flops are the most commonly used flip-flops; the symbols for pulse-triggered flip-flops are included for completeness but are not likely to be encountered outside of a textbook.

Often, all of the flip-flops used in a circuit are of the same triggering type, such as positive-edge triggered. All of the flip-flops will then change in relation to the same clocking event. When using flip-flops having different triggering in the same sequential circuit, one may still wish to have all of the flip-flop outputs change relative to the same clocking event. Those flip-flops that behave in a manner opposite from the adopted polarity transition can be changed by the addition of inverters to their clock inputs. The inverters unfortunately cause the clock signal to these flip-flops to be delayed with respect to the clocks to the other flip-flops. A preferred procedure is to provide both positive and negative pulses from the master clock generator that are carefully aligned. We apply positive pulses to positive-pulse-triggered and negative-edge-triggered flip-flops and negative pulses to negative-pulse-triggered and positive-edge-triggered flip-flops. In this way, all flip-flop outputs will change at the same time. Finally, to prevent specific timing problems, some designers use flip-flops having different triggering (i.e., both positive and negative edge-triggered flip-flops) with a single clock. In these cases, flip-flop outputs are purposely made to change at different times.

In the remainder of this text, it is assumed that all flip-flops are of the positive-edge-triggered type, unless otherwise indicated. This provides a uniform graphics symbol for the flip-flops and consistent timing diagrams.

Note that there is no input to the D flip-flop that produces a "no-change" condition. This condition can be accomplished either by disabling the clock pulses on the C input or by leaving the clock pulses undisturbed and connecting the output back into the D input using a multiplexer when the state of the flip-flop must remain the same. The technique that disables clock pulses is referred to as *clock gating*. This technique typically uses fewer gates and saves power, but is often avoided because the gated clock pulses into the flip-flops are delayed. The delay, called *clock skew*, causes gated clock and non-gated clock flip-flops to change at different times. This can make the circuit unreliable without careful design, since the outputs of some flip-flops may reach others while their inputs are still affecting their state. To avoid this problem, delays must be inserted in the clock circuitry to align inverted and non-inverted clocks. If possible, this situation should be avoided entirely by using flip-flops that trigger on the same edge.

Direct Inputs

Flip-flops often provide special inputs for setting and resetting them asynchronously (i.e., independently of the clock input C). The inputs that asynchronously set the flip-flop are called *direct set* or *preset*. The inputs that asynchronously reset the flip-flop are called *direct reset* or *clear*. Application of a logic 1 (or a logic 0 if a bubble is present) to these inputs affects the flip-flop output without the use of the clock. When power is turned on in a digital system, the states of its flip-flops can be anything. The direct inputs are useful for bringing flip-flops in a digital system to an initial state prior to the normal clocked operation.

The IEEE standard graphics symbol for a positive-edge-triggered D flip-flop with direct set and direct reset is shown in Figure 4-12(a). The notations $C1$ and $1D$ illustrate control dependency. An input labeled Cn, where n is any number, controls all the other inputs starting with the number n. In the figure, $C1$ controls input $1D$. S and R have no 1 in front of them, and therefore they are not controlled by the clock at $C1$. The S and R inputs have circles on the input lines to indicate that they are active at the logic-0 level (i.e., a 0 applied will result in the set or reset action).

The function table in Figure 4-12(b) specifies the operation of the circuit. The first three rows in the table specify the operation of the direct inputs S and R. These inputs behave like NAND $\overline{S}\,\overline{R}$ latch inputs (see Figure 4-6), operating independently

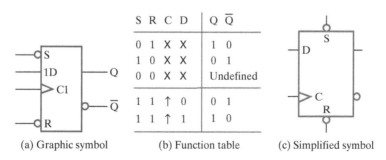

| (a) Graphic symbol | (b) Function table | (c) Simplified symbol |

□ **FIGURE 4-12**
D Flip-Flop with Direct Set and Reset

of the clock, and are therefore asynchronous inputs. The last two rows in the function table specify the clocked operation for values of D. The clock at C is shown with an upward arrow to indicate that the flip-flop is a positive-edge-triggered type. The D input effects are controlled by the clock in the usual manner.

Figure 4-12(c) shows a less formal symbol for the positive-edge-triggered flip-flop with direct set and reset. The positioning of S and R at the top and bottom of the symbol rather than on the left edge implies that resulting output changes are not controlled by the clock C.

FLIP-FLOP TIMING   Flip-flop timing is covered in Section 4-9.

4–4   SEQUENTIAL CIRCUIT ANALYSIS

The behavior of a sequential circuit is determined from the inputs, outputs, and present state of the circuit. The outputs and the next state are a function of the inputs and the present state. The analysis of a sequential circuit consists of obtaining a suitable description that demonstrates the time sequence of inputs, outputs, and states.

A logic diagram is recognized as a synchronous sequential circuit if it includes flip-flops with the clock inputs driven directly or indirectly by a clock signal and if the direct sets and resets are unused during the normal functioning of the circuit. The flip-flops may be of any type, and the logic diagram may or may not include combinational gates. In this section, an algebraic representation for specifying the logic diagram of a sequential circuit is given. A state table and a state diagram are presented that describe the behavior of the circuit. Specific examples will be used throughout the discussion to illustrate the various procedures.

Input Equations

The logic diagram of a sequential circuit consists of flip-flops and, usually, combinational gates. The knowledge of the type of flip-flops used and a list of Boolean functions for the combinational circuit provide all the information needed to draw the logic diagram of the sequential circuit. The part of the combinational circuit that generates the signals for the inputs of flip-flops can be described by a set of Boolean functions called *flip-flop input equations*. We adopt the convention of denoting the dependent variable in the flip-flop input equation by the flip-flop input symbol with the name of the flip-flop output as the subscript for the variable, e.g., D_A. A flip-flop input equation is a Boolean expression for a combinational circuit. The output of this combinational circuit is connected to the input of a flip-flop—thus the name "flip-flop input equation."

The flip-flop input equations constitute a convenient algebraic expression for specifying the logic diagram of a sequential circuit. They imply the type of flip-flop from the letter symbol, and they fully specify the combinational circuit that drives the flip-flops. Time is not included explicitly in these equations, but is implied from the clock at the C input of the flip-flops. An example of a sequential circuit is given in Figure 4-13. The circuit has two D-type flip-flops, an input X, and an output Y. It can be specified by the following equations:

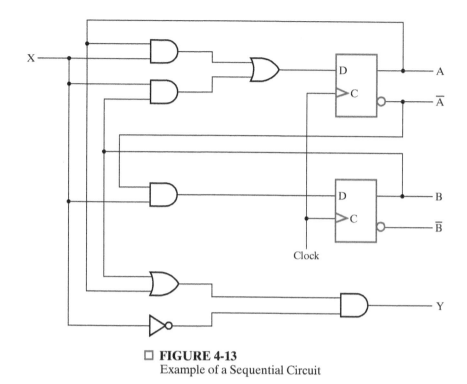

☐ **FIGURE 4-13**
Example of a Sequential Circuit

$$D_A = AX + BX$$

$$D_B = \overline{A}X$$

$$Y = (A + B)\overline{X}$$

The first two equations are for flip-flop inputs, and the third specifies the output Y. Note that the input equations use the symbol D, which is the same as the input symbol of the flip-flops. The subscripts A and B designate the outputs of the respective flip-flops.

State Table

The functional relationships among the inputs, outputs, and flip-flop states of a sequential circuit can be enumerated in a *state table*. The state table for the circuit of Figure 4-13 is shown in Table 4-1. It consists of four sections, labeled *present state, input, next state,* and *output*. The present-state section shows the states of flip-flops A and B at any given time t. The input section gives each value of X for each possible present state. Note that for each possible input combination, each of the present states is repeated. The next-state section shows the states of the flip-flops one clock period later, at time $t + 1$. The output section gives the value of output Y at time t for each combination of present state and input.

☐ **TABLE 4-1**
    State Table for Circuit of Figure 4-13

Present State		Input	Next State		Output
A	B	X	A	B	Y
0	0	0	0	0	0
0	0	1	0	1	0
0	1	0	0	0	1
0	1	1	1	1	0
1	0	0	0	0	1
1	0	1	1	0	0
1	1	0	0	0	1
1	1	1	1	0	0

The derivation of a state table consists of first listing all possible binary combinations of present state and inputs. In Table 4-1, there are eight binary combinations, from 000 to 111. The next-state values are then determined from the logic diagram or from the flip-flop input equations. For a D flip-flop, the relationship $A(t + 1) = D_A(t)$ holds. This means that the next state of flip-flop A is equal to the present value of its input D. The value of the D input is specified in the flip-flop input equation as a function of the present state of A and B and input X. Therefore, the next state of flip-flop A must satisfy the equation

$$A(t + 1) = D_A = AX + BX$$

The next-state section in the state table under column A has three 1s, where the present state and input value satisfy the conditions $(A, X) = 11$ or $(B, X) = 11$. Similarly, the next state of flip-flop B is derived from the input equation

$$B(t + 1) = D_B = \overline{A}X$$

and is equal to 1 when the present state of A is 0 and input X is equal to 1. The output column is derived from the output equation

$$Y = A\overline{X} + B\overline{X}$$

The state table of any sequential circuit with D-type flip-flops is obtained in this way. In general, a sequential circuit with m flip-flops and n inputs needs 2^{m+n} rows in the state table. The binary numbers from 0 through $2^{m+n} - 1$ are listed in the combined present-state and input columns. The next-state section has m columns, one for each flip-flop. The binary values for the next state are derived directly from the D flip-flop input equations. The output section has as many columns as there are output variables. Its binary values are derived from the circuit or from the Boolean functions in the same manner as in a truth table.

Table 4-1 is one-dimensional in the sense that the present state and input combinations are combined into a single column of combinations. A two-dimensional state table having the present state tabulated in the left column and the inputs tabulated across the top row is also frequently used. The next-state entries are made in each cell of the table for the present-state and input combination corresponding to the location of the cell. A similar two-dimensional table is used for the outputs if they depend upon the inputs. Such a state table is shown in Table 4-2. Sequential circuits in which the outputs depend on the inputs, as well as on the states, are referred to as *Mealy model* circuits. Otherwise, if the outputs depend only on the states, then a one-dimensional column suffices. In this case, the circuits are referred to as *Moore model* circuits. Each model is named after its originator.

As an example of a Moore model circuit, suppose we want to obtain the logic diagram and state table of a sequential circuit that is specified by the flip-flop input equation

$$D_A = A \oplus X \oplus Y$$

and output equation

$$Z = A$$

The D_A symbol implies a D-type flip-flop with output designated by the letter A. The X and Y variables are taken as inputs and Z as the output. The logic diagram and state table for this circuit are shown in Figure 4-14. The state table has one column for the present state and one column for the inputs. The next state and output are also in single columns. The next state is derived from the flip-flop input equation, which specifies an odd function. (See Section 2-6.) The output column is simply a copy of the column for the present-state variable A.

State Diagram

The information available in a state table may be represented graphically in the form of a state diagram. A state is represented by a circle, and transitions between states are indicated by directed lines connecting the circles. Examples of state diagrams are given in Figure 4-15. Figure 4-15(a) shows the state diagram for the sequential circuit in Figure 4-13 and its state table in Table 4-1. The state diagram provides the same

□ **TABLE 4-2**
Two-Dimensional State Table for the Circuit in Figure 4-13

Present State		Next State				Output	
		X = 0		X = 1		X = 0	X = 1
A	B	A	B	A	B	Y	Y
0	0	0	0	0	1	0	0
0	1	0	0	1	1	1	0
1	0	0	0	1	0	1	0
1	1	0	0	1	0	1	0

Clock
(a) Logic diagram

Present State	Inputs		Next State	Output
A	X	Y	A	Z
0	0	0	0	0
0	0	1	1	0
0	1	0	1	0
0	1	1	0	0
1	0	0	1	1
1	0	1	0	1
1	1	0	0	1
1	1	1	1	1

(b) State table

☐ **FIGURE 4-14**
Logic Diagram and State Table for $D_A = A \oplus X \oplus Y$

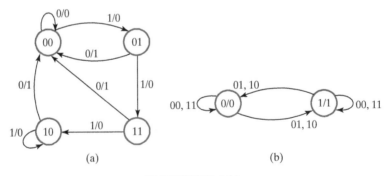

(a)

(b)

☐ **FIGURE 4-15**
State Diagrams

information as the state table and is obtained directly from it. The binary number inside each circle identifies the state of the flip-flops. For Mealy model circuits, the directed lines are labeled with two binary numbers separated by a slash. The input value during the present state precedes the slash, and the value following the slash gives the output value during the present state with the given input applied. For example, the directed line from state 00 to state 01 is labeled 1/0, meaning that when the sequential circuit is in the present state 00 and the input is 1, the output is 0. After the next clock transition, the circuit goes to the next state, 01. If the input changes to 0, then the output becomes 1, but if the input remains at 1, the output stays at 0. This information is obtained from the state diagram along the two directed lines emanating from the circle with state 01. A directed line connecting a circle with itself indicates that no change of state occurs.

The state diagram of Figure 4-15(b) is for the sequential circuit of Figure 4-14. Here, only one flip-flop with two states is needed. There are two binary inputs, and the output depends only on the state of the flip-flop. For such a Moore model circuit, the slash on the directed lines is not included, since the outputs depend only on the state and not on the input values. Instead, the output is included inside the state circle, indicated here with a slash. There are two input conditions for each state transition in the diagram, and they are separated by a comma. When there are two input variables, each state may have up to four directed lines coming out of the corresponding circle, depending upon the number of states and the next state for each binary combination of the input values.

There is no difference between a state table and a state diagram, except for their manner of representation. The state table is easier to derive from a given logic diagram and input equations. The state diagram follows directly from the state table. The state diagram gives a pictorial view of state transitions and is the form more suitable for human interpretation of the operation of the circuit. For example, the state diagram of Figure 4-15(a) clearly shows that, starting at state 00, the output is 0 as long as the input stays at 1. The first 0 input after a string of 1s gives an output of 1 and sends the circuit back to the initial state of 00. The state diagram of Figure 4-15(b) shows that the circuit stays at a given state as long as the two inputs have the same value (00 or 11). There is a state transition between the two states only when the two inputs are different (01 or 10).

The state diagram in Figure 4-15(a) is useful for illustrating two concepts: (1) the reduction of the number of states required by using the concept of equivalent states, and (2) the mixing of Mealy and Moore types of outputs in a single description. Two states are *equivalent* if the response for each possible input sequence is an identical output sequence. This definition can be recast in terms of states and outputs. Two states are *equivalent* if the output produced for each input symbol is identical and the next states for each input symbol are the same or equivalent.

EXAMPLE 4-1   Equivalent State Illustration

In the state diagram in Figure 4-15(a), consider states 10 and 11. Under input 0, both states produce output 1, and, under input 1, both states produce output 0. Under input 0, both states have the same state 00 as their next state. Under input 1, both states have state 10 as their next state. By the second definition above, states 11 and 10 are equivalent. These equivalent states can be merged into a single state entered from state 01 under input 1, with a transition under input 0 to state 00 with an output of 1, and a transition back to itself under input 1 with an output of 0. In the original diagram, consider states 01 and 11. These states satisfy the output conditions for being equivalent. Under 0, they both go to next state 00, and under 1, they go to next states 11 and 10, which have just been shown to be equivalent. So, states 01 and 11 are equivalent. Since state 11 is equivalent to state 10, all three of these states are equivalent. Merging these three states, states 11 and 10 can be deleted and state 01 can be modified to have the transition under 1 with output 0 back to state 01. If the circuit in Figure 4-13 was analyzed for redesign, the new design has two states and one flip-flop instead of four states and two flip-flops.   ■

State reduction through state equivalence may or may not result in reduced cost, since cost is dependent on combinational circuit cost as well as flip-flop cost. Nevertheless, combining equivalent states has inherent advantages in the design, verification, and testing processes.

Ordinarily, the Mealy and Moore output types are not mixed in a given sequential circuit representation. In doing real designs, however, such mixing may be convenient.

EXAMPLE 4-2   Mixed Mealy and Moore Outputs

The state diagram in Figure 4-15(a) can also be used to illustrate a mixed output model that uses both Mealy and Moore type outputs. For state 00, all input values produce the same output value 0 on Z. As a consequence, the output depends only on the state 00 and satisfies the definition of a Moore type output. If desired, the output value 0 can be moved from the outgoing transitions on state 00 to within the circle for state 00. For the remaining states, however, the outputs for the two input values on X differ, so the output values are the Mealy type and must remain on the state transitions.   ■

Unfortunately, this representation does not translate well to the two-dimensional state tables. It can be translated to a modified one-dimensional state table with rows that contain the state and the Moore output value without the output conditions, and rows that contain the state, an output condition, and the Mealy value output.

Sequential Circuit Clocks and Timing   The details of sequential circuit clocks and timing are discussed in Section 4-10.

Sequential Circuit Simulation

Simulation of sequential circuit involves issues not present in combinational circuits. First of all, rather than a set of input patterns for which the order of application is immaterial, the patterns must be applied in a sequence. This sequence includes timely application of input patterns as well as clock pulses. Second, there must be some means to place the circuit in a known state. Realistically, initialization to a known state is accomplished by application of an initialization subsequence at the beginning of the simulation. In the simplest case, this subsequence is a reset signal. For flip-flops lacking a circuit reset (or set), a longer sequence typically consisting of an initial reset followed by a sequence of normal input patterns is required. A simulator may also have a means of setting the initial state, which is useful to avoid long sequences that may be needed to get to an initial state. Aside from getting to an initial state, a third issue is observing the state to verify correctness. In some circuits, application of an additional sequence of inputs is required to determine the state of the circuit at a given point. The simplest alternative is to set up the simulation so that the state of the circuit can be observed directly; the approach to doing this varies depending on the simulator and whether or not the circuit contains hierarchy. A crude approach that works with all simulators is to add a circuit output with a path from each state variable signal.

A final issue to be dealt with in more detail is the timing of application of inputs and observation of outputs relative to the active clock edge. Initially, we discuss the timing for *functional simulation* having as its objective determination or verification of the function of the circuit. In functional simulation, components of the circuit have no delay or a very small delay. Much more complex is *timing simulation*, in which the circuit elements have realistic delays and verification of the proper operation of the circuit in terms of timing is the simulation objective.

Some simulators, by default, use a very small component delay for functional simulation so that the order of changes in signals can be observed, provided that the time range used for display is small enough. Suppose that the component delays for gates and the delays associated with flip-flops are all 0.1 ns for such a simulation and that the longest delay through a path from positive clock edge to positive clock edge is 1.2 ns in your circuit. If you happen to use a clock period of 1.0 ns for your simulation, when the result depends on the longest delay, the simulation results will be in error! So for functional simulation with such a simulator, either a longer clock period should be chosen for the simulation or the default delay needs to be changed by the user to a smaller value.

In addition to the clock period, the time of application of inputs relative to the positive clock edge is important. For functional simulation, to allow for any small, default component delays, the inputs for a given clock cycle should be changed well before the positive clock edge, preferably early in the clock cycle while the clock is still at a 1 value. This is also an appropriate time to change the reset signal values to insure that the reset signal is controlling the state rather than the clock edge or a meaningless combination of clock and reset.

A final issue is the time at which to examine a simulation result in functional simulation. At the very latest, the state-variable values and outputs should be at their final values just before the positive clock edge. Although it may be possible to observe the values at other locations, this location provides a foolproof observation time for functional simulation.

The ideas just presented are summarized in Figure 4-16. Input changes in Reset and Input, encircled in blue, occur at about the 25 percent point in the clock cycle. Signal values on State and Output, as well as on Input and Reset, all encircled in blue and listed, are observed just before the 100 percent point in the clock cycle.

☐ **FIGURE 4-16**
Simulation Timing

4-5 SEQUENTIAL CIRCUIT DESIGN

The design of clocked sequential circuits starts from a set of specifications and culminates in a logic diagram or a list of Boolean functions from which the logic diagram can be obtained. In contrast to a combinational circuit, which is fully specified by a truth table, a sequential circuit requires a state table for its specification. Thus, the first step in the design of a sequential circuit is to obtain a state table or an equivalent representation such as a state diagram.

A synchronous sequential circuit is made up of flip-flops and combinational gates. The design of the circuit consists of choosing the flip-flops and finding a combinational circuit structure which, together with the flip-flops, produces a circuit that fulfills the stated specifications. The minimum number of flip-flops is determined by the number of states in the circuit; n flip-flops can represent up to 2^n binary states. The combinational circuit is derived from the state table by finding the flip-flop input equations and output equations. In fact, once the type and the number of flip-flops are determined and binary combinations are assigned to the states, the design process transforms a sequential circuit problem into a combinational circuit problem. In this way, the techniques of combinational circuit design can be applied.

Design Procedure

The following procedure for the design of sequential circuits is similar to the procedure for combinational circuits that was introduced in Chapters 1 through 3, but the procedure for sequential circuits has some additional steps:

1. **Specification:** Write a specification for the circuit, if not already available.

2. **Formulation:** Obtain either a state diagram or a state table from the statement of the problem.

3. **State Assignment:** If only a state diagram is available from step 1, obtain the state table. Assign binary codes to the states in the table.

4. **Flip-Flop Input Equation Determination:** Select the flip-flop type or types. Derive the flip-flop input equations from the next-state entries in the encoded state table.

5. **Output Equation Determination:** Derive output equations from the output entries in the state table.

6. **Optimization:** Optimize the flip-flop input equations and output equations.

7. **Technology Mapping:** Draw a logic diagram of the circuit using flip-flops, ANDs, ORs, and inverters. Transform the logic diagram to a new diagram using the available flip-flop and gate technology.

8. **Verification:** Verify the correctness of the final design.

For convenience, we often omit the technology mapping in step 7, since it does not contribute to our understanding once it is understood. Also, for more complex circuits, we may skip the use of either the state table or state diagram.

Finding State Diagrams and State Tables

The specification for a circuit is often in the form of a verbal description of the behavior of the circuit. This description needs to be interpreted in order to find a state diagram or state table in the formulation step of the design procedure. This is often the most creative part of the design procedure, with many of the subsequent steps performed automatically by computer-based tools.

Fundamental to the formulation of state diagrams and tables is an intuitive understanding of the concept of a state. A state is used to "remember" something about the history of input combinations applied to the circuit either at triggering clock edges or during triggering pulses. In some cases, the states may literally store input values, retaining a complete history of the sequence appearing on the inputs. In most cases, however, a state is an *abstraction* of the sequence of input combinations at the triggering points. For example, a given state S_1 may represent the fact that among the sequence of values applied to a single bit input X, "the value 1 has appeared on X for the last three consecutive clock edges." Thus, the circuit would be in state S_1 after sequences ... 00111 or ... 0101111, but would not be in state S_1 after sequences ... 00011 or ... 011100. A state S_2 might represent the fact that the sequence of 2-bit input combinations applied are "in order 00, 01, 11, 10 with any number of consecutive repetitions of each combination permitted and 10 as the most recently applied combination." The circuit would be in state S_2 for the following example sequences: 00, 00, 01, 01, 01, 11, 10, 10 or 00, 01, 11, 11, 11, 10. The circuit would not be in state S_2 for sequences: 00, 11, 10, 10 or 00, 00, 01, 01, 11, 11. In formulating a state diagram or state table it is useful to write down the abstraction represented by each state. In some cases, it may be easier to describe the abstraction by referring to values that have occurred on the outputs as well as on the inputs. For example, state S_3 might represent the abstraction that "the output bit Z_2 is 1, and the input combination has bit X_2 at 0." In this case, Z_2 equal to 1 might uniquely represent a complex set of past sequences of input combinations that would be more difficult to describe in detail.

As one formulates a state table or state diagram, new states are added. There is potential for the set of states to become unnecessarily large or potentially even infinite in size! Instead of adding a new state for every current state and possible applied input combination, it is essential that states be reused as next states to prevent uncontrolled state growth as outlined above. The mechanism for doing this is a knowledge of the abstraction that each state represents. To illustrate, consider state S_1 defined previously as an abstraction: "the value 1 has appeared at the last three consecutive clock edges." If S_1 has been entered due to the sequence ...00111 and the next input is a 1, giving sequence ...001111, is a new state needed or can the next state be S_1? By examining the new sequence, we see that the last three input values are 1s, which matches the abstraction defined for state S_1. So, state S_1 can be used as the next state for current state S_1 and input value 1, avoiding the definition of a new state. This careful process of avoiding equivalent states is in lieu of applying a state-minimization procedure to combine equivalent states.

When the power in a digital system is first turned on, the state of the flip-flops is unknown. It is possible to apply an input sequence with the circuit in an unknown state, but that sequence must be able to bring a portion of the circuit to a known state before meaningful outputs can be expected. In fact, many of the larger sequential circuits we design in subsequent chapters will be of this type. In this chapter, however, the circuits that we design must have a known *initial state*, and further, a hardware mechanism must be provided to get the circuit from any unknown state into this state. This mechanism is a *reset* or *master reset* signal. Regardless of all other inputs applied to the circuit, the reset places the circuit in its initial state. In fact, the initial state is often called the *reset state*. The reset signal is usually activated automatically when the circuit is powered up. In addition, it may be activated electronically or by pushing a reset button.

The reset may be asynchronous, taking place without clock triggering. In this case, the reset is applied to the direct inputs on the circuit flip-flops. as shown in Figure 4-17(a). This design assigns 00...0 to the initial state of the flip-flops to be reset. If an initial state with a different code is desired, then the *Reset* signal can be selectively connected to direct set inputs instead of direct reset inputs. It is important to note that these inputs should not be used in the normal synchronous circuit design process. Instead, they are reserved only for an asynchronous reset that returns the system, of which the circuit is a component, to an initial state. Using these direct

(a) Asynchronous Reset   (b) Synchronous Reset

☐ **FIGURE 4-17**
Asynchronous and Synchronous Reset for D Flip-flops

inputs as a part of the synchronous circuit design violates the fundamental synchronous circuit definition, since it permits a flip-flop state to change asynchronously within direct clock triggering.

Alternatively, the reset may be synchronous and require a clock-triggering event to occur. The reset must be incorporated into the synchronous design of the circuit. A simple approach to synchronous reset for D flip-flops, without formally including the reset bit in the input combinations, is to add the AND gate shown in Figure 4-17(b) after doing the normal circuit design. This design also assigns 00 ... 0 to the initial state. If a different initial state code is desired, then OR gates with *Reset* as an input can selectively replace the AND gates with inverted *Reset*.

To illustrate the formulation process, two examples follow, each resulting in a different style of state diagram.

EXAMPLE 4-3   Finding a State Diagram for a Sequence Recognizer

The first example is a circuit that recognizes the occurrence of a particular sequence of bits, regardless of where it occurs in a longer sequence. This "sequence recognizer" has one input X and one output Z. It has Reset applied to the direct reset inputs on its flip-flops to initialize the state of the circuit to all zeros. The circuit is to recognize the occurrence of the sequence of bits 1101 on X by making Z equal to 1 when the previous three inputs to the circuit were 110 and current input is a 1. Otherwise, Z equals 0.

The first step in the formulation process is to determine whether the state diagram or table must be a Mealy model or Moore model circuit. The portion of the preceding specification that says "... making Z equal to 1 when the previous three inputs to the circuit are 110 and the current input is a 1" implies that the output is determined from not only the current state, but also the current input. As a consequence, a Mealy model circuit with the output dependent on both state and inputs is required.

Recall that a key factor in the formulation of any state diagram is to recognize that states are used to "remember" something about the history of the inputs. For example, for the sequence 1101 to be able to produce the output value 1 coincident with the final 1 in the sequence, the circuit must be in a state that "remembers" that the previous three inputs were 110. With this concept in mind, we begin to formulate the state diagram by defining an arbitrary initial state A as the reset state, and the state in which "none of the sequence to be recognized has occurred." If a 1 occurs on the input, since 1 is the first bit in the sequence, this event must be "remembered," and the state after the clock pulse cannot be A. So a second state, B, is established to represent the occurrence of the first 1 in the sequence. Further, to represent the occurrence of the first 1 in the sequence, a transition is placed from A to B and labeled with a 1. Since this is not the final 1 in the sequence 1101, its output is a 0. This initial portion of the state diagram is given in Figure 4-18(a).

The next bit of the sequence is a 1. When this 1 occurs in state B, a new state is needed to represent the occurrence of two 1s in a row on the input—that is, the occurrence of an additional 1 while in state B. So a state C and the associated transition are added, as shown in Figure 4-18(b). The next bit of the sequence is a 0. When

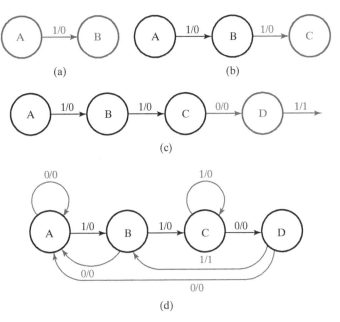

☐ **FIGURE 4-18**
Construction of a State Diagram for Example 4-3

this 0 occurs in state C, a state is needed to represent the occurrence of the two 1s in a row followed by a 0. So the additional state D with a transition having a 0 input and 0 output is added. Since state D represents the occurrence of 110 as the previous three input bit values on X, the occurrence of a 1 in state D completes the sequence to be recognized, so the transition for the input value 1 from state D has an output value of 1. The resulting partial state diagram, which completely represents the occurrence of the sequence to be recognized, is shown in Figure 4-18(c).

Note in Figure 4-18(c) that, for each state, a transition is specified for only one of the two possible input values. Also, the state that is the destination of the transition from D for input 1 is not yet defined. The remaining transitions must be based on the idea that the recognizer is to identify the sequence 1101, regardless of where it occurs in a longer sequence. Suppose that an initial part of the sequence 1101 is represented by a state in the diagram. Then, the transition from that state for an input value that represents the next input value in the sequence must enter a state such that the 1 output occurs if the remaining bits of the sequence are applied. For example, state C represents the first two bits, 11, of sequence 1101. If the next input value is 0, then the state that is entered, in this case, D, gives a 1 output if the remaining bit of the sequence, 1, is applied.

Next, evaluate where the transition for the 1 input from the D state is to go. Since the transition input is a 1, it could be the first or second bit in the sequence to be recognized. But because the circuit is in state D, it is evident that the prior input was a 0. So this 1 input is the first 1 in the sequence, since it cannot be preceded by a 1. The state that represents the occurrence of a first 1 in the sequence is B, so the transition with input 1 from state D is to state B. This transition is shown in the

☐ **TABLE 4-3**
State Table for State Diagram in Figure 4-18

Present State	Next State		Output Z	
	X = 0	X = 1	X = 0	X = 1
A	A	B	0	0
B	A	C	0	0
C	D	C	0	0
D	A	B	0	1

diagram in Figure 4-18(d). Examining state C, we can trace back through states B and A to see that the occurrence of a 1 input in C is at least the second 1 in the sequence. The state representing the occurrence of two 1s in sequence is C, so the new transition is to state C. Since the combination of two 1s is not the sequence to be recognized, the output for the transition is 0. Repeating this same analysis for missing transitions from states B and A, the final state diagram in Figure 4-18(d) is obtained. The resulting state table is given in two-dimensional form in Table 4-3. ■

One issue that arises in the formulation of any state diagram is whether, in spite of best designer efforts, excess states have been used. This is not the case in the preceding example, since each state represents input history that is essential for recognition of the stated sequence. If, however, excess states are present, then it may be desirable to combine states into the fewest needed. This can be done using ad hoc methods as in Example 4-1 or formal state-minimization procedures. Due to the complexity of the latter, particularly in the case in which don't-care entries appear in the state table, formal procedures are not covered here. For the interested student, state-minimization procedures are found in Reference 8 at the end of the chapter as well as in many other logic design texts.

The next example illustrates an additional method for avoiding extra states by recognizing potential state equivalence during the design process.

EXAMPLE 4-4   Finding a State Diagram for a BCD–to–Excess-3 Decoder

The *excess-3 code* for a decimal digit is the binary combination corresponding to the decimal digit plus 3. For example, the excess-3 code for decimal digit 5 is the binary combination for $5 + 3 = 8$, which is 1000. The excess-3 code has desirable properties with respect to implementing decimal subtraction. In this example, the function of the circuit is similar to that of the combinational decoders in Chapter 3 except that the inputs, rather than being presented to the circuit simultaneously, are presented serially in successive clock cycles, least significant bit first. In Table 4-4(a), the input sequences and corresponding output sequences are listed with the least significant bit first. For example, during four successive clock cycles, if 1010 is applied to the input, the output will be 0001. In order to produce each output bit in the same clock cycle as the corresponding input bit, the output depends on the present input

☐ **TABLE 4-4**
Sequence Tables for Code-Converter Example

(a) Sequences in Order of Digits Represented								(b) Sequences in Order of Common Prefixes							
BCD Input				Excess-3 Output				BCD Input				Excess-3 Output			
1	2	3	4	1	2	3	4	1	2	3	4	1	2	3	4
0	0	0	0	1	1	0	0	0	0	0	0	1	1	0	0
1	0	0	0	0	0	1	0	0	0	0	1	1	1	0	1
0	1	0	0	1	0	1	0	0	0	1	0	1	1	1	0
1	1	0	0	0	1	1	0	0	1	0	0	1	0	1	0
0	0	1	0	1	1	1	0	0	1	1	0	1	0	0	1
1	0	1	0	0	0	0	1	1	0	0	0	0	0	1	0
0	1	1	0	1	0	0	1	1	0	0	1	0	0	1	1
1	1	1	0	0	1	0	1	1	0	1	0	0	0	0	1
0	0	0	1	1	1	0	1	1	1	0	0	0	1	1	0
1	0	0	1	0	0	1	1	1	1	1	0	0	1	0	1

value as well as the state. The specifications also state that the circuit must be ready to receive a new 4-bit sequence as soon as the prior sequence has completed. The input to this circuit is labeled X and the output is labeled Z. In order to focus on the patterns for past inputs, the rows of Table 4-4(a) are sorted according to the first bit value, the second bit value, and the third bit value of the input sequences. Table 4-4(b) results.

The state diagram begins with an initial state, as shown in Figure 4-19(a). Examining the first column of bits in Table 4-4(b) reveals that a 0 produces a 1 output and a 1 produces a 0 output. Next, we ask, "Do we need to remember the value of the first bit?" In Table 4-4(b), when the first bit is a 0, a 0 in the second bit results in an output of 1 and a 1 in the second bit gives an output of 0. In contrast, if the first bit is a 1, a 0 in the second bit causes an output of 0, and a 1 in the second bit gives output 1. It is clear that we cannot determine the output for the second bit without "remembering" the value of the first bit. Thus, the first input equal to 0 and the first input equal to 1 must give different states, as shown in Figure 4-19(a), which also shows the input/output values for the arcs to the new states.

Next, it must be determined whether the inputs following the two new states need to have two states to remember the second bit value. In the first two columns of inputs in Table 4-4(b), sequence 00 produces outputs for the third bit that are 0 for input 0 and 1 for input 1. On the other hand, for sequence 01, the outputs for the third bit are 1 for input 0 and 0 for input 1. Since these are different for the same input values in the third bit, separate states are necessary, as shown in Figure 4-19(b). A similar analysis for input sequences 10 and 11, which examines the outputs for both the third and fourth bits, shows that the value of the second bit has no effect on the output values. Thus, in Figure 4-19(b), there is only a single next state for state $B1 = 1$.

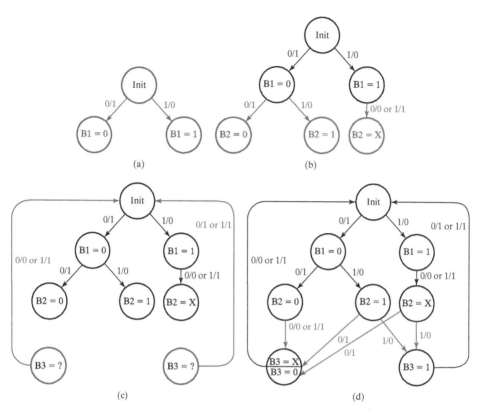

□ **FIGURE 4-19**
Construction of a State Diagram for Example 4-4

At this point, six potential new states might result from the three states just added. Note, however, that these states are needed only to define the outputs for the fourth input bit, since it is known that the next state thereafter will be *Init* in preparation for applying the next input sequence of four bits. How many states does one need to specify the different possibilities for the output value in the last bit? Looking at the final column, a 1 input always produces a 1 output and a 0 may produce either a 0 or a 1 output. Thus, at most two states are necessary, one that has a 0 output to a 0 and one that has a 1 output to a 0. The output for a 1 input is the same for both states. In Figure 4-19(c), we have added these two states. For the circuit to be ready to receive the next sequence, the next state for these new states is *Init*.

Remaining is the determination of the blue arcs shown in Figure 4-19(d). The arcs from each of the bit *B2* states can be defined based on the third bit in the input/output sequences. The next state can be chosen based on the response to input 0 in the fourth bit of the sequence. The *B2* state reaches the *B3* state on the left with $B3 = 0$ or $B3 = 1$ as indicated by $B3 = X$ on the upper half of the *B3* state. The other two *B2* states reach this same state with $B3 = 1$, as indicated on the lower half of the state. These same two *B2* states reach the *B3* state on the right with $B3 = 0$, as indicated by the label on the state. ∎

State Assignment

In contrast to the states in the analysis examples, the states in the diagrams con-structed have been assigned symbolic names rather than binary codes. It is necessary to replace these symbolic names with binary codes in order to proceed with the de-sign. In general, if there are m states, then the codes must contain at least n bits, where $2^n \geq m$, and each state must be assigned a unique code. So, for the circuit in Table 4-3 with four states, the codes assigned to the states require two bits. Note that minimizing the number of bits in the state code does not always minimize the cost of the overall sequential circuit. The combinational logic may have become more costly in spite of the gains achieved by having fewer flip-flops.

The first state assignment method we will consider is to assign codes with n bits $(2^n \geq m > 2^{n-1})$ such that the code words are assigned in *counting order*. For example, for states A, B, C, and D, the codes 00, 01, 10, and 11 are assigned to A, B, C, and D, respectively. An alternative that is attractive, particularly if K-maps are being used for optimization, is to assign the codes in *Gray code order*, with codes 00, 01, 11, and 10 assigned to A, B, C, and D, respectively.

More systematic assignment of codes attempts to reduce the cost of the sequential circuit combinational logic. A number of methods based on heuristics are available for targeting minimum two-level and minimum multilevel combina-tional logic. The problem is difficult and the solutions are too complex for treatment here.

There are a number of specialized state assignment methods, some of which are based on efficient structures for implementing at least a portion of the transi-tions. The most popular of these methods is the one flip-flop per state or *one-hot* assignment. This assignment uses a distinct flip-flop for each of the m states, so it generates codes that are m bits long. The sequential circuit is in a state when the flip-flop corresponding to that state contains a 1. By definition, all flip-flops corre-sponding to the other states must contain 0. Thus, each valid state code contains m bits, with one bit equal to 1 and all other $m - 1$ bits equal to 0. This code has the prop-erty that going from one state to another can be thought of as passing a *token*, the single 1, from the source state to the destination state. Since each state is represented by a single 1, before combinational optimization, the logic for entering a particular state is totally separate from the logic for entering other states. This is in contrast to the mixing of the logic that occurs when multiple 1s are present in the destination and source state codes. This separation can often result in simpler, faster logic, and in logic that is simpler to debug and analyze. On the other hand, the flip-flop cost may be overriding. Finally, while the state codes listed have values for m variables, when equations are written, only the variable which is 1 is listed. For example, for $ABCD = 0100$, instead of writing $\overline{A}B\overline{C}\overline{D}$, we can simply write B. This is because all of the remaining $2^m - m$ codes never occur and as a consequence produce don't cares.

The use of a sequentially assigned Gray code and of a one-hot code for the sequence recognizer design is illustrated in the following example. In the next sub-section, the designs will be completed and the costs of these two assignments compared.

EXAMPLE 4-5   State Assignments for the Sequence Recognizer

The Gray code is selected in this case simply because it makes it easier for the next-state and output functions to be placed on a Karnaugh map. The state table derived from Table 4-3 with codes assigned is shown in Table 4-5. States A, B, C, and D are replaced in the present state column by their respective codes, 00, 01, 11, and 10. Next, each of the next states is replaced by its respective code. This 2-bit code uses a minimum number of bits.

A one-hot code assignment is illustrated in Table 4-6. States A, B, C, and D are replaced in the Present State column by their respective codes, 1000, 0100, 0010, and 0001. Next, each of the next states is replaced by its respective code. Since there are four states, a 4-bit code is required, with one state variable for each state.   ■

☐ **TABLE 4-5**
   Table 4-3 with Names Replaced by a 2-Bit Binary Gray Code

Present State	Next State		Output Z	
AB	X = 0	X = 1	X = 0	X = 1
00	00	01	0	0
01	00	11	0	0
11	10	11	0	0
10	00	01	0	1

☐ **TABLE 4-6**
   Table 4-3 with Names Replaced by a 4-Bit One-Hot Code

Present State	Next State		Output Z	
ABCD	X = 0	X = 1	X = 0	X = 1
1000	1000	0100	0	0
0100	1000	0010	0	0
0010	0001	0010	0	0
0001	1000	0100	0	1

Designing with *D* Flip-Flops

The remainder of the sequential circuit design procedure will be illustrated by the next two examples. We wish to design two clocked sequential circuits for the sequence recognizer, one that operates according to the Gray-coded state table given in Table 4-5 and the other according to the one-hot coded table given in Table 4-6.

EXAMPLE 4-6   Gray Code Design for the Sequence Recognizer

For the Gray-coded design, two flip-flops are needed to represent the four states. Note that the two state variables are labeled with letters A and B.

Steps 1 through 3 of the design procedure have been completed for this circuit. Beginning step 4, D flip-flops are chosen. To complete step 4, the flip-flop input equations are obtained from the next-state values listed in the table. For step 5, the output equation is obtained from the values of Z in the table. The flip-flop input equations and output equation can be expressed as a sum of minterms of the present-state variables A and B and the input variable X:

$$A(t + 1) = D_A(A, B, X) = \Sigma m\,(3, 6, 7)$$

$$B(t + 1) = D_B(A, B, X) = \Sigma m\,(1, 3, 5, 7)$$

$$Z(A, B, X) = \Sigma m\,(5)$$

In the case of this table with the Gray code on the left margin and a trivial Gray code at the top of the table, the adjacencies of the cells of the state table match the adjacencies of a K-map. This permits the values for the two next state variables $A(t + 1)$ and $B(t = 1)$ and output Z to be transferred directly to the three K-maps in Figure 4-20, bypassing the sum-of-minterms equations. The three Boolean functions, simplified by using the K-maps, are:

$$D_A = AB + BX$$

$$D_B = X$$

$$Z = A\overline{B}X$$

The logic diagram of the sequential circuit is shown in Figure 4-21. The gate-input cost of the combinational logic is 9. A rough estimate for the gate-input cost for a flip-flop is 14. Thus the overall gate-input cost for this circuit is 37. ■

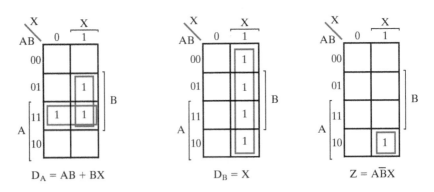

☐ **FIGURE 4-20**
   K-Maps for the Gray-Coded Sequential Circuit with D Flip-Flops

Logic Diagram for the Gray-Coded Sequence Recognizer with D Flip-Flops

EXAMPLE 4-7   One-Hot Code Design for the Sequence Recognizer

For the one-hot coded design in Table 4-6, four flip-flops are needed to represent the four states. Note that the four state variables are labeled $A, B, C,$ and D. As is often the case, the state variables have names that are the same as those of the corresponding states.

Just as for the Gray-coded case, steps 1 through 3 of the design procedure have been completed and D flip-flops have been chosen. To complete step 4, the flip-flop input equations are obtained from the next-state values. Although the state codes listed have values for four variables, recall that when equations from a one-hot code are written, only the variable with value 1 is included. Also, recall that each term of the excitation equation for state variable Y is based on a 1 value for variable Y in a next-state code entry and the sum of these terms is taken over all such 1s in the next-state code entries. For example, a 1 appears for next-state variable B for present state 1000 (A) and input value $X = 1$, and for present state 0001 (D) and input value $X = 1$. This gives $B(t + 1) = AX + DX$. For step 5, the output equation is obtained from the locations of the 1 values of Z in the output table. The resulting flip-flop input equations and output equation are:

$$A(t + 1) = D_A = A\overline{X} + B\overline{X} + D\overline{X} = (A + B + D)\overline{X}$$

$$B(t + 1) = D_B = AX + DX = (A + D)X$$

$$C(t + 1) = D_C = BX + CX = (B + C)X$$

$$D(t + 1) = D_D = C\overline{X}$$

$$Z = DX$$

The logic diagram of the sequential circuit is shown in Figure 4-22. The gate-input cost of the combinational logic is 19 and the cost of four flip-flops using the estimate

☐ **FIGURE 4-22**
Logic Diagram for the One-Hot Coded Sequence Recognizer with D Flip-Flops

from Example 4-5 is 56, giving a total gate input cost of 74, almost twice that of the Gray code design. This result supports the view that the one-hot design tends to be more costly, but, in general, there may be reasons for its use with respect to other factors such as performance, reliability, and ease of design and verification. ■

Designing with Unused States

A circuit with n flip-flops has 2^n binary states. The state table from which the circuit was originally derived, however, may have any number of states, $m \leq 2^n$. States that are not used in specifying the sequential circuit are not listed in the state table. In simplifying the input equations, the unused states can be treated as don't-care conditions. The state table in Table 4-7 defines three flip-flops, A, B, and C, and one input, X. There is no output column, which means that the flip-flops serve as outputs of the circuit. With three flip-flops, it is possible to specify eight states, but the state table lists only five. Thus, there are three unused states that are not included in the table: 000, 110, and 111. When an input of 0 or 1 is included with the unused present-state values, six unused combinations are obtained for the present-state and input columns: 0000, 0001, 1100, 1101, 1110, and 1111. These six combinations are not listed in the state table and hence may be treated as don't-care minterms.

□ **TABLE 4-7**
State Table for Designing with Unused States

Present State			Input	Next State		
A	B	C	X	A	B	C
0	0	1	0	0	0	1
0	0	1	1	0	1	0
0	1	0	0	0	1	1
0	1	0	1	1	0	0
0	1	1	0	0	0	1
0	1	1	1	1	0	0
1	0	0	0	1	0	1
1	0	0	1	1	0	0
1	0	1	0	0	0	1
1	0	1	1	1	0	0

The three input equations for the D flip-flops are derived from the next-state values and are simplified in the maps of Figure 4-23. Each map has six don't-care minterms in the squares corresponding to binary 0, 1, 12, 13, 14, and 15. The optimized equations are

$$D_A = AX + BX + \overline{B}\,\overline{C}$$

$$D_B = \overline{A}\,\overline{C}X + \overline{A}\,\overline{B}X$$

$$D_C = \overline{X}$$

The logic diagram can be obtained directly from the input equations and will not be drawn here.

It is possible that outside interference or a malfunction will cause the circuit to enter one of the unused states. Thus, it is sometimes desirable to specify, fully or at least

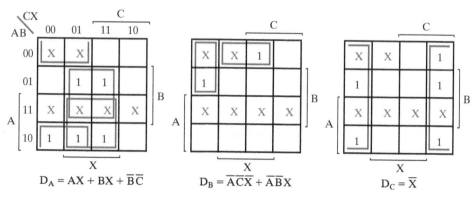

□ **FIGURE 4-23**
Maps for Optimizing Input Equations

partially, the next-state values or the output values for the unused states. Depending on the function and application of the circuit, a number of ideas may be applied. First, the outputs for the unused states may be specified so that any actions that result from entry into and transitions between the unused states are not harmful. Second, an additional output may be provided or an unused output code employed which indicates that the circuit has entered an incorrect state. Third, to ensure that a return to normal operation is possible without resetting the entire system, the next-state behavior for the unused states may be specified. Typically, next states are selected such that one of the normally occurring states is reached within a few clock cycles, regardless of the input values. The decision as to which of the three options to apply, either individually or in combination, is based on the application of the circuit or the policies of a particular design group.

Verification

Sequential circuits can be verified by showing that the circuit produces the original state diagram or state table. In the simplest cases, all possible input combinations are applied with the circuit in each of the states, and the state variables and outputs are observed. For small circuits, the actual verification can be performed manually. More generally, simulation is used. In manual simulation, it is straightforward to apply each of the state–input combinations and verify that the output and the next state are correct.

Verification with simulation is less tedious, but typically requires a sequence of input combinations and applied clocks. In order to check out a state–input combination, it is first necessary to apply a sequence of input combinations to place the circuit in the desired state. It is most efficient to find a single sequence to test all the state–input combinations. The state diagram is ideal for generating and optimizing such a sequence. A sequence must be generated to apply each input combination in each state while observing the output and next state that appear after the positive clock edge. The sequence length can be optimized by using the state diagram. The reset signal can be used as an input during this sequence. In particular, it is used at the beginning to reset the circuit to its initial state.

In Example 4-8, both manual and simulation-based verification are illustrated.

EXAMPLE 4-8   **Verifying the Sequence Recognizer**

The state diagram for the sequence recognizer appears in Figure 4-18(d) and the logic diagram in Figure 4-21. There are four states and two input combinations, giving a total of eight state–input combinations to verify. The next state can be observed as the state on the flip-flop outputs after the positive clock edge. For D flip-flops, the next state is the same as the D input just before the clock edge. For other types of flip-flops, the flip-flop inputs just before the clock edge are used to determine the next state of the flip-flop. Initially, beginning with the circuit in an unknown state, we apply a 1 to the Reset input. This input goes to the direct reset input on the two flip-flops in Figure 4-21. Since there is no bubble on these inputs, the 1 value resets both flip-flops to 0, giving state A $(0, 0)$. Next, we apply input 0, and manually simulate the circuit in Figure 4-21 to find that the output is 0 and the next state is A $(0, 0)$, which agrees with the transition for input 0 while in state A. Next, simulating state A

with input 1, next state B (0, 1) and output 0 result. For state B, input 0 gives output 0 and next state A (0, 0), and input 1 gives output 0 and next state C (1, 1). This same process can be continued for each of the two input combinations for states C and D.

For verification by simulation, an input sequence that applies all state–input combination pairs is to be generated accompanied by the output sequence and state sequence for checking output and next-state values. Optimization requires that the number of clock periods used exceed the number of state–input combination pairs by as few periods as possible (i.e., the repetition of state–input combination pairs should be minimized). This can be interpreted as drawing the shortest path through the state diagram that passes through each state–input combination pair at least once.

In Figure 4-24(a), for convenience, the codes for the states are shown and the path through the diagram is denoted by a sequence of blue integers beginning with 1. These integers correspond to the positive clock edge numbers in Figure 4-24(b), where the verification sequence is to be developed. The values shown for the clock edge numbers are those present just before the positive edge of the clock (i.e., during the setup time interval). Clock edge 0 is at $t = 0$ in the simulation and gives unknown values for all signals. We begin with value 1 applied to Reset (1) to place the circuit in state A. Input value 0 is applied first (2) so that the state remains A, followed by 1 (3) checking the second input combination for state A. Now in state B, we can either move forward to state C or go back to state A. It is not apparent which choice is best, so we arbitrarily apply 1 (4) and go to state C. In state C, 1 is applied (5) so the state remains C. Next, a 0 is applied to check the final input for state C. Now in state D, we have an arbitrary choice to return to state A or to state B. If we return to state B by

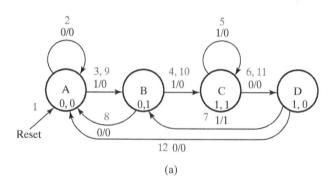

(a)

Clock Edge:	0	1	2	3	4	5	6	7	8	9	10	11	12	13
Input R:	X	1	0	0	0	0	0	0	0	0	0	0	0	
Input X:	X	0	0	1	1	1	0	1	0	1	1	0	0	
State (A, B):	X, X	0, 0*	0, 0	0, 0	0, 1	1, 1	1, 1	1, 0	0, 1	0, 0	0, 1	1, 1	1, 0	0, 0
Output Z:	X	0	0	0	0	0	0	1	0	0	0	0	0	

(b)

☐ **FIGURE 4-24**
Test Sequence Generation for Simulation in Example 4-3

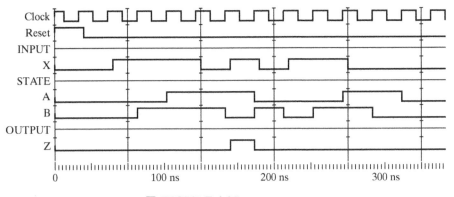

☐ **FIGURE 4-25**
Simulation for Example 4-8

applying 1 (7), then we can check the transition from B to A for input 0 (8). Then, the only remaining transition to check is state D for input 0. To reach state D from state A, we must apply the sequence 1, 1, 0 (9) (10) (11) and then apply 0 (12) to check the transition from D to A. We have checked eight transitions with a sequence consisting of reset plus 11 inputs. Although this test sequence is of optimum length, optimality is not guaranteed by the procedure used. However, it usually produces an efficient sequence.

In order to simulate the circuit, we enter the schematic in Figure 4-21 using the Xilinx ISE 4.2 Schematic Editor and enter the sequence from Figure 4-24(b) as a waveform using the Xilinx ISE 4.2 HDL Bencher. While entering the waveform, it is important that the input X changes well before the clock edge. This insures that there is time available to display the current output and to permit input changes to propagate to the flip-flop inputs before the setup time begins. This is illustrated by the INPUT waveforms in Figure 4-25, in which X changes shortly after the positive clock edge, providing a good portion of the clock period for the change to propagate to the flip-flops. The circuit is simulated with the MTI Model Sim simulator. We can then compare the values just before the positive clock edge on the STATE and OUTPUT waveforms in Figure 4-25 with the values shown on the state diagram for each clock period in Figure 4-24. In this case, the comparison verifies that the circuit operation is correct. ■

4-6 STATE-MACHINE DIAGRAMS AND APPLICATIONS

Thus far, we have used a traditional notation for state diagrams and tables, a notation illustrated by a Mealy model state diagram in Figure 4-26(a). Although this model serves well for very small designs, it often becomes cumbersome or unworkable for large designs. For example, all 2^n combinations of n input variables must be represented on the transitions from each of the states even though the next state or output may be affected by only one of the n input variables. Also, for a large number

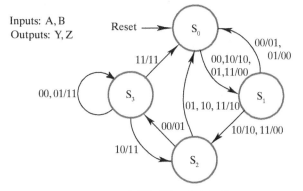

(a) Traditional state diagram

(b) Generic State Diagram Template

(c) State machine diagram

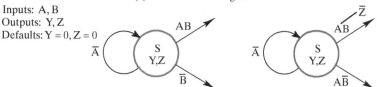

(d) Invalid Transition Conditions   (e) Invalid Ouput Action

☐ **FIGURE 4-26**
Traditional State and State-Machine Diagram Representations

of output variables, for each state or input combination label, up to 2^m output combinations must be specified even though only one among the m output variables is affected by the state and input values. Also, the Mealy model is very inefficient in specifying outputs because of the need to combine transition and output control functions together. To illustrate, the use of Moore outputs, in addition to Mealy, can greatly simplify output specification when applicable. Also, the use of Mealy outputs that are dependent upon input values, but not dependent on transition labels, can be useful.

These arguments suggest that for pragmatic design, a modified state diagram notation is critical. We call this modified state diagram a *state-machine diagram*. This term is also applied to the traditional state diagram representations, although here we use it primarily to identify departures in notation from that used for traditional diagrams. The main targets of the notation changes are to replace enumeration of input and output combinations with the use of Boolean expressions and equations to describe input combinations, and the expansion of the options for describing output functions beyond those permitted by the traditional model.

State-Machine Diagram Model

The development of this model is based on input conditions, transitions, and output actions. For a given state, an *input condition* can be described by a Boolean expression or equation in terms of input variables. An input condition as an expression is either equal to 1 or 0. As an equation, it is equal to 1 if it is satisfied, and equal to 0 if it is not. An input condition on a transition arc is called a *transition condition (TC)*, and causes a transition to occur if it is equal to 1. An input condition that, if equal to 1, causes an output action to occur is an *output condition (OC)*. In a Moore model state-machine diagram, only transition conditions appear. Output actions are a function of the state only and therefore are unconditional, i.e., with an implicit output condition equal to 1. In a traditional Mealy model, when a condition appears on an arc, by definition, it is both a transition condition and an output condition. Multiple transition and output conditions may appear on a given transition arc. In our model, we modify the Mealy model in two ways. First of all, we permit output conditions to appear on the state, not just on transitions. Second, we permit output conditions that depend on, but are not transition conditions on the arcs. This provides more modeling flexibility in the formulation of corresponding state tables and HDL descriptions. For this more flexible model, a generic state and one of its transitions and the various possible condition situations are shown in Figure 4-26(b).

For a given state, if a transition condition is equal to 1, then the corresponding transition represented by the arc occurs. For a given state and transition, if all transition conditions are 0, then the corresponding transition does not occur. An *unconditional transition* always occurs on the next clock regardless of input values and can be thought of as having an implicit transition condition equal to 1. In Figure 4-26(c), which has exactly the same function as the traditional state diagram given in Figure 4-26(a), transition concepts are illustrated. For example, for state S_0 the transition to state S_1 is unconditional. For state S_3 and input combination 11, transition condition AB equal to 1 causes a transition to state S_0. The effectiveness of this approach in simplifying input condition representation is illustrated well by transition conditions $\overline{A}$ in state S_1 and $A + B$ in state S_2. $\overline{A}$ is 1 for input combinations 00 and 01, and $A + B$ is 1 for input combinations 01, 10, and 11, causing the respective transitions from S_1 to S_0 and S_2 to S_0.

Outputs are handled by listing output conditions and output actions. The various forms of specifying the control of output actions by state and output conditions are shown in Figure 4-26(b). For convenience, output conditions (if any) followed by a slash and corresponding output actions are placed at the end of a straight or curved line from either the state or from a transition condition TC. Multiple output condition/output action pairs are separated by commas. We classify output actions based on the conditions that cause them into four types as shown in Figure 4-26(b). *Moore output actions* depend only on the state, i.e., they are unconditional. *Transition-condition independent (TCI) Mealy outputs* are preceded by their respective output condition and a slash. These two types of output actions are attached by a line to the state boundary as shown in Figure 4-26(b). *Transition-condition dependent (TCD) Mealy output actions* depend on both the state and a transition condition, thereby making the transition condition an output condition as well. *Transition and output-condition dependent (TOCD) output actions* depend on the state, a transition condition, and an output condition and are preceded by their respective output condition OC and a slash. These two types of output actions are attached by a line to the transition condition TC upon which they depend as shown in Figure 4-26(b).

In a given state, an output action occurs if: (a) it is unconditional (Moore), (b) TCI and its output condition $OC = 1$, (c) TCD and its transition condition $TD = 1$, and (d) TOCD and its transition condition TC and output condition OC are both equal to 1, i.e, $TC \cdot OC = 1$. Note that Moore and TCI output actions attached to a state, apply to *all transitions* from the state as well.

An output action may simply be an output variable. The output variable has value 1 for a given state present and its corresponding input conditions attached to the state or transition all equal to 1, and value 0 otherwise. For any state or state–input condition pair without an output action on a variable, that variable takes on a default value noting again the exception that Moore and TCI output actions attached to a state, apply to *all transitions* from the state. Ordinarily, we explicitly list default output actions for reference as shown in Figure 4-26(c).

It is also possible to have variables that are vectors with values assigned. For vectors, a specific default value may be assigned. Otherwise, for a vector, the implicit assignment to 0 used for scalar variables does not apply. Finally, in Chapter 6, register transfer statements are listed as output actions. All of the modifications described permit description of a complete system using complex input conditions and output actions. Note that many of these modifications relate somewhat to the algorithmic state machines previously used in this text.

Figure 4-26(c) can be used to illustrate the power of this notation. State S_3 has variables Y and Z as Moore output actions, so $Y = 1$ and $Z = 1$ when in state S_3. State S_0 has a TCI output condition and action $\overline{B}/Y$ which specifies that when in state S_0, $Y = 1$ whenever $B = 0$. State S_1 has a TCI output condition and action

$(\overline{A} + \overline{B})/Z$. In all these cases, repetitive occurrences of the output actions are avoided on the transitions. For state S_0 with the use of a TCI output action, the problem of specifying the transition as unconditional and the output condition $\overline{B}$ on the transition is avoided. Also, for state S_1 with the use of a TOCD output action, the transition condition A combined with output condition $\overline{B}$ is easily provided.

In this example, Figure 4-26(a) provided the information for deriving Figure 4-26(c). Transition and output conditions for each state were obtained by examining the binary input and output combinations in Figure 4-26(a) and determining the simplest way to describe an output action and then finding the simplest Boolean expression for the corresponding output condition. Likewise, the simplest transition condition can be found for each transition. This approach constitutes a transformation from the traditional state diagram to an equivalent state-machine diagram. It should be noted, however, that our principal goal is not this transformation, but instead, direct formulation of state-machine diagrams from specifications.

A final element that can appear on a state diagram is the binary code assigned to a state. This binary code appears in parentheses below the state name or at the end of a line drawn out from the state.

Constraints on Input Conditions

In formulating transition and output conditions, it is necessary to perform checks to make sure that invalid next state and output specifications do not arise. For all possible input conditions, each state must have exactly one next state and have every single-bit output variable with exactly one value, e.g., either 0 or 1, but not both. These conditions are described in terms of constraints.

For each state, there are two constraints on transition conditions:

1. The transition conditions from a given state S_i must be mutually exclusive, i.e., all possible pair of conditions (T_{ij}, T_{ik}) on distinct transition arcs from a given state have no identical input values, i.e.,

$$T_{ij} \cdot T_{ik} = 0,$$

2. The transition conditions from a given state must cover all possible combinations of input values, i.e.,

$$\Sigma T_{ij} = 1$$

in which Σ represents OR. If there are don't-care next states for state S_i, the transition conditions for these states must be included in the OR operation. Also, in applying these constraints, recall that an unconditional transition has an implicit transition condition of 1.

In the formulation of a state-machine diagram, transition conditions must be checked for each state and its set of transitions. If constraint 1 does not hold, then the next state for the current state is specified as two or more states. If constraint 2 does not hold, then there are cases with no specified next state for one or more transitions where one is expected to be specified. Both of these situations are invalid.

For each state, there are two similar constraints on output conditions:

1. For every output action in state S_i or on its transitions having coincident output variables with differing values, the corresponding pair of output conditions (O_{ij}, O_{ik}) must be mutually exclusive, i.e., satisfy

$$O_{ij} \cdot O_{ik} = 0$$

2. For every output variable, the output conditions for state S_i or its transitions must cover all possible combinations of input values that can occur, i.e.,

$$\Sigma O_{ij} = 1$$

If there are don't-care outputs for state S_i, the output conditions for the don't-care outputs must be included in the OR operation. In applying these constraints, recall that an unconditional output action on a state or an arc has an implicit output condition of 1. Note that default output actions must be considered in this analysis.

EXAMPLE 4-9   Checking Constraints

In this example, transition and output constraints are checked for the state-machine diagrams in Figure 4-26(c) and selected invalid cases in parts (d) and (e) of Figure 4-26. Beginning with Figure 4-26(c), the results for constraint 1 checks on transition conditions are:

S_0:   The constraint is satisfied by default since there are no pairs of transition conditions on distinct transition arcs.
S_1:   There is one pair of TCs to check: $\overline{A} \cdot A = 0$.
S_2:   There is one pair of TCs to check: $(A + B) \cdot \overline{A}\,\overline{B} = 0$.
S_3:   There are three pairs of TCs to check: $AB \cdot \overline{A} = 0$, $AB \cdot A\overline{B} = 0$, and $\overline{A} \cdot A\overline{B} = 0$.

Since all of the results are 0, constraint 1 is satisfied. Next, checking constraint 2:

S_0:   The transition is unconditional and has an implicit transition condition of 1.
S_1: $\overline{A} + A = 1$
S_2: $(A + B) + \overline{A}\,\overline{B} = 1$
S_3: $\overline{A} + AB + A\overline{B} = 1$

Since the results for all states are 1, constraint 2 is satisfied. Next, checking constraint 1 on output conditions:

S_0:   There is only one output condition, $\overline{B}$ on output action Y, so the constraint is satisfied by default.
S_1:   The first coincident output variable is Y and its values are 1 where Y appears for TOC $A \cdot \overline{B}$, and 0 by default where Y does not appear for input conditions $\overline{A}$ and AB. Note that if $\overline{B}$ is interpreted without ANDing with transition condition A, then check $\overline{A} . \overline{B} \neq 0$ incorrectly fails! The second coincident output variable is Z, with value 1 for $\overline{A} + \overline{B}$ and 0 by default for input condition AB. In general, it is impossible for an invalid case to occur due to a default output action. So the constraint is satisfied.

S_2: The first coincident output variable is Y and the second is Z. Y has value 1 for output condition $A + B$, and by default value 0 for $\overline{A}\,\overline{B}$. Z has value 1 for output condition $\overline{A}\,\overline{B}$ and 0 by default for $A + B$. Due to the use of a default value, the constraint is satisfied.

S_3: There is no coincident output variable with differing output values, so the output constraint is satisfied by default.

Since the output constraint is satisfied for all four states, it is satisfied for the state-machine diagram as are the other two constraints. Next, checking constraint 2 on output conditions:

S_0: There is a single output condition $\overline{B}$ for which $Y = 1$. By default, $Y = 0$ for the output condition for complement of $\overline{B} = B$. ORing the conditions, $\overline{B} + B = 1$. In general, with a default output specified, this will be the case since the default covers all input combinations not covered by specified output conditions, so the constraint is satisfied.

S_1 through S_3: Because of the default output action for variables Y and Z, as for S_0, the constraint is also satisfied.

Parts (d) and (e) of Figure 4-26 are examples that are used to demonstrate selected invalid cases for state-machine diagrams. For part (d), $\overline{A} \cdot \overline{B} = \overline{A\,B}$, so the transition constraint 1 is *not* satisfied. For part (e), variable Z appears as an output with distinct values 1 in state S and 0 on the transition for AB. Output condition constraint 1 gives $1 \cdot AB \neq 0$. So the constraint is *not* satisfied. Actually, this occurs only because the designer failed to realize that $Z = 1$ was already specified on the transition because of its specification on the state S. ∎

Design Applications Using State-Machine Diagrams

Two examples will be used to illustrate design using state-machine diagrams. In addition to design formulation, the effects of the use of a state-machine diagram formulation on the structure for state tables will be illustrated. These examples also illustrate that good solutions are possible for problems with larger numbers of inputs and states, in particular problems for which traditional state diagrams, traditional state tables, and K-maps are all impractical.

EXAMPLE 4-10 State-Machine Design for a Batch Mixing System Control

A mixing system for large batches of liquids is designed to add up to three ingredients to a large circular mixing tank, mix the ingredients, and then empty the mixed liquid from the tank. There are three inlets for ingredients, each with an on–off valve. There are three movable fluid sensors in the tank that can be set to turn off the respective valves at the level required for the first ingredient alone, for the first and second ingredients, and for all three ingredients. A switch is used to select either a two or three ingredient operation. There is a button for starting the operation and a second button for stopping the operation at any time. There is a timer for timing the mixing cycle. The length of the mixing cycle is specified by a manually operated dial that provides a starting value to a timer. The timer counts downward to zero to time the mixing. After mixing, the output valve is opened to remove the mixed liquid from the tank.

A sequential circuit is to be designed to control the batch mixing operation. The inputs and outputs for the circuit are given in Table 4-8. Before starting the operation of the mixing system, the operator places the fluid sensor $L1$, $L2$, and $L3$ in the proper locations. Next, the operator selects either two or three ingredients with switch NI and sets dial D to the mixing time. Then, the operator pushes the $START$ to begin the mixing operation which proceeds automatically unless the $STOP$ button is pushed. Valve $V1$ is opened and remains open until $L1$ indicates ingredient level 1 has been reached. Valve 1 closes and valve 2 opens and remains open until $L2$ indicates level 1 plus 2 has been reached. Valve 2 closes, and, if switch $NI = 1$, valve 3 opens and remains open until $L3$ indicates level 1, 2 plus 3 has been reached. If $NI = 0$, the value on dial D is then read into the timer, the mixing begins, and the timer starts counting down. In the case where $NI = 1$, these actions all occur when $L3$ indicates that the level for all three ingredients has been reached. When the timer reaches 0 as indicated by the signal TZ, the mixing stops. Next, the Output valve is opened and remains open until sensor $L0$ indicates the tank is empty. If $STOP$ is pushed at any time, addition of ingredients stops, mixing stops, and the output valve closes.

The first step in the design is to develop the state-machine diagram. During this development, the input and status signals from Table 4-8 are used, and the diagram

□ **TABLE 4-8**
Input and Output Variables for the Batch Mixing System

Input	Meaning for Value 1	Meaning for Value 0
NI	Three ingredients	Two ingredients
Start	Start a batch cycle	No action
Stop	Stop an on-going batch cycle	No action
L0	Tank empty	Tank not empty
L1	Tank filled to level 1	Tank not filled to level 1
L2	Tank filled to level 2	Tank not filled to level 2
L3	Tank filled to level 3	Tank not filled to level 3
TZ	Timer at value 0	Timer not at value 0

Output	Meaning for Value 1	Meaning for Value 0
MX	Mixer on	Mixer off
PST	Load timer with value from D	No action
TM	Timer on	Timer off
V1	Valve open for ingredient 1	Valve closed for ingredient 1
V2	Valve open for ingredient 2	Valve closed for ingredient 2
V3	Valve open for ingredient 3	Valve closed for ingredient 3
VE	Output valve open	Output valve closed

development can be traced in Figure 4-27. We begin with an initial state *Init*, which is the reset state. As long as *START* is 0 or *STOP* is 1, the state is to remain *Init*. When *START* is 1 with STOP at 0, a new state is required in which the addition of ingredient 1 is performed. State *Fill_1* with output *V1* is added to perform this operation. In state *Fill_1*, if the operator pushes *STOP*, then the state is to return to *Init* with the fill operation ceasing as indicated on the diagram. If *STOP* is not pushed and *L1* is still 0, then the filling must continue with the state remaining *Fill_1* as indicated by the transition back to *Fill_1* labeled $\overline{L1} \cdot \overline{STOP}$. The filling continues until $L1 = 1$ because the fill level for ingredient 1 has been reached. When $L1 = 1$ with $STOP = 0$, a new state, *Fill_2* is added. For the input condition, $L1 \cdot \overline{STOP}$, applied in state *Fill_1*, *V1* goes to 0, turning off valve 1, and the state becomes *Fill_2* with output *V2*, turning on valve 2. The loop on *Fill_2* specifies that the state remains *Fill_2* until *L2* becomes 1. When $L2 = 1$ with $STOP = 0$, for $NI = 1$ the state *Fill_3* is added for the three-ingredient case, and for $NI = 0$ state *Mix* is added for the two-ingredient case and output PST is added to present the timer to the mixing time on dial D. *Fill_3* has transitions the same as for state *Fill_1* except that *L1* is replaced by *L3*. For $L3 \cdot \overline{STOP}$, filling is complete, so state *Mix* is entered for mixing. Also, a Mealy output *PST* is added for $L3 \cdot \overline{STOP}$ to preset the timer to the mixing time. In state *Mix*, the output *MX* is used to activate the mixing. In addition, as long as $TZ = 0$ and $Stop = 0$, the state remains *Mix* and the timer is turned on by Mealy output *TM*, causing the timer to count downward. State *Empty* is added for the case where $TZ = 1$, since the timer has reached 0. With the mixing complete, the fluid can be emptied from the tank by opening the output valve with *VE*. The state remains *Empty* as long as $L0 = 0$ and $Stop = 0$ as indicated by the loop to *Empty* with input condition $\overline{L0} \cdot \overline{STOP}$. If at any time, *L0* or *STOP* becomes 1, the state returns to *Init*, turning off the output valve by changing to $VE = 0$. This completes the development of the state-machine diagram. The necessary analysis to verify the transition and output condition constraints is left to the reader in Problem 4-37(a).

Although the state-machine diagram is similar to a state diagram, it is difficult to form a standard state table since there are eight inputs, giving 256 columns. Instead, a table can be formed that enumerates rows for each the following: (1) each state with its unconditional next state and its TCI output actions and output conditions, (2) each transition condition for each state with the corresponding next state, and (3) corresponding TCD and TCOD output actions, the latter with output conditions. The results of this process for the state-machine diagram in Figure 4-27 are shown in Table 4-9. In this table, note that the entries in Non-Zero Outputs are either Moore outputs or TCD outputs. For the TCD outputs, Boolean expressions can be shared in the excitation and output equations. To this end, we define the following intermediate variables for use in excitation equations and output equations:

$$X = Fill\_2 \cdot L2 \cdot \overline{NI} \cdot \overline{STOP}$$

$$Y = Fill\_3 \cdot L3 \cdot \overline{STOP}$$

$$Z = Mix \cdot \overline{TZ} \cdot \overline{STOP}$$

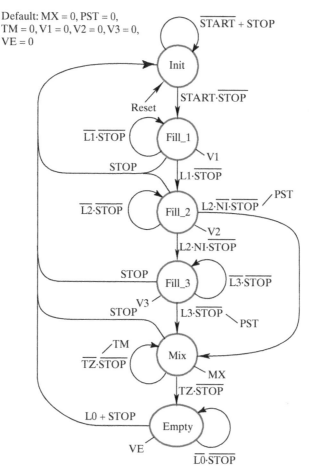

□ **FIGURE 4-27**
State-Machine Diagram for Batch Mixing System

Using the one-hot state assignment listed in the table assuming that each state variable is named with the state for which it is 1, the excitation and output equations are:

$$Init(t + 1) = Init \cdot \overline{START} + STOP + Empty \cdot L0$$

$$Fill\_1(t + 1) = Init \cdot START \cdot \overline{STOP} + Fill\_1 \cdot \overline{L1} \cdot \overline{STOP}$$

$$Fill\_2 = Fill\_1 \cdot L1 \cdot \overline{STOP} + Fill\_2 \cdot \overline{L2} \cdot \overline{STOP}$$

$$Fill\_3 = L2 \cdot NI \cdot \overline{STOP} + Fill\_3 \cdot \overline{L3} \cdot \overline{STOP}$$

$$Mix = X + Y + Z$$

☐ **TABLE 4-9**
State Table for the Batch Mixing System

State	State Code	Transition Condition	Next State	State Code	Non-Zero Outputs Including Mealy Outputs Using TCs*
Init	100000	$\overline{START}$ + STOP	Init	100000	
		START·$\overline{STOP}$	Fill_1	010000	
Fill_1	010000				V1
		STOP	Init	100000	
		$\overline{L1}$·$\overline{STOP}$	Fill_1	010000	
		L1·$\overline{STOP}$	Fill_2	001000	
Fill_2	001000				V2
		STOP	Init	100000	
		$\overline{L2}$·$\overline{STOP}$	Fill_2	001000	
		L2·$\overline{NI}$·$\overline{STOP}$	Mix	000010	PST*
		L2·NI·$\overline{STOP}$	Fill_3	000100	
Fill_3	000100				V3
		STOP	Init	100000	
		$\overline{L3}$·$\overline{STOP}$	Fill_3	000100	
		L3·$\overline{STOP}$	Mix	000010	PST*
Mix	000010				MX
		STOP	Init	100000	
		$\overline{TZ}$·$\overline{STOP}$	Mix	000010	TM*
		TZ·$\overline{STOP}$	Empty	000001	
Empty	000001				VE
		$\overline{LO}$·$\overline{STOP}$	Empty	000001	
		LO + STOP	Init	100000	

$$Empty(t + 1) = Mix \cdot TZ \cdot \overline{STOP} + Empty \cdot \overline{LO} \cdot \overline{STOP}$$

$$V1 = Fill\_1$$

$$V2 = Fill\_2$$

$$V3 = Fill\_3$$

$$PST = X + Y$$

$$MX = Mix$$

$$TM = Z$$

In the equation for *Init* $(t + 1)$, since all six states return to state *Init* for input *Stop*, there is no need to specify any states with *STOP*. It is interesting to note that indeed, *X*, *Y*, and *Z* are shared between next state and output equations. With the one-hot state assignment, the formulation of the equations is very straightforward using either the state table or state-machine diagram. ■

EXAMPLE 4-11   State-Machine Design of a Sliding Door Control

Automatic sliding entrance doors are widely used in retail stores. In this example, we consider the design of the sequential logic for controlling a sliding door. The one-way door opens in response to three sensors PA (Approach Sensor), PP (Presence Sensor), DR (Door Resistance Sensor), and to a pushbutton MO (Manual Open). PA senses a person or object approaching the door, and PP senses the presence of a person or object within the doorframe. DR senses a resistance to the door closing that is at least 15 pounds indicating that the door is pushing on a person or obstacle. MO is a manual pushbutton on the door control box that opens the door without dependence on the automatic control. The door control box also has a keyed lock LK for locking the door closed using an electrically-operated bolt BT to prevent entrance when the store is closed. In addition to these inputs to the door logic, there are two limit switches CL (close limit) and OL (open limit) that determine when the door mechanism has closed the door completely or opened the door completely, respectively. The control mechanism has just three outputs, BT (bolt), CD (close door), and OD (open door). All of the inputs or outputs are described along with the meaning of value 1 and value 0 for each of them in Table 4-10.

Using the description just given and additional constraints on the design, we will develop the state-machine diagram as the first step in the design of the sequential circuit. We begin by defining the initial state to which the circuit will be reset, *Closed*. After reset, the door will open for the first time from this state. What is the transition condition for opening the door? First of all, the door must be unlocked, denoted by $\overline{LK}$. Second, there must be a person approaching the door, a person within the door, or manual opening of the door requested by the pushbutton, denoted by $PA + PP + MO$. Ordinarily, one would not expect the opening operation to be initiated by PP since this

□ TABLE 4-10
Input and Output Variables for the Sliding Door Control

Input Symbol	Name	Meaning for Value 1	Meaning for Value 0
LK	Lock with Key	Locked	Unlocked
DR	Door Resistance Sensor	Door resistance $\geq$ 15 lb	Door resistance $<$ 15 lb
PA	Approach Sensor	Person/object approach	No person/object approach
PP	Presence Sensor	Person/object in door	No person/object in door
MO	Manual Open PB	Manual open	No manual open
CL	Close Limit Switch	Door fully closed	Door not fully closed
OL	Open Limit Switch	Door fully open	Door not fully open

Output Symbol	Name	Meaning for Value 1	Meaning for Value 0
BT	Bolt	Bolt closed	Bolt open
CD	Close Door	Close door	Null action
OD	Open Door	Close door	Null action

indicates that a person is within the doorframe. But this is included to cause the door to open in case of a *PA* failure. Both the lock and sensor conditions must be present for the door to open, so they are ANDed together to give the transition condition on the arrow from state *Closed* to state *Open*, the state in which the opening of the door occurs. If *LK* is 1 or all of *PA*, *PP*, and *MO* are 0, then the door is to remain closed. This gives the transition conditions $LK + \overline{PA \cdot PP \cdot MO}$ for remaining in state *Closed*. *LK* is also the output condition for *BT*. Because of this, two transition conditions are needed, *LK* and $\overline{PA \cdot PP \cdot MO} \cdot CD$ is to be activated for $\overline{PA \cdot PP \cdot MO}$, $\overline{CL}$ and for *BT* not activated, i.e., for $\overline{LK}$. This can be realized by the existing transition condition $\overline{PA \cdot PP \cdot MO}$ plus output condition $\overline{LK} \cdot CL$ as shown in Figure 4-28. The state remains *Open* and *OD* is 1 as long as the door is not fully open as indicated by limit switch value $\overline{OL}$. When this input condition changes to *OL*, the door is fully open and the new state is *Opened*. Note that there is no monitoring of the sensor inputs other than *OL* in *Open* since it is assumed that the door will fully open regardless of whether the person or object remains within sensor view. If at least one of the inputs that opened the door is 1, then the door will be held open by remaining in state *Opened*. The expression representing this condition is $PA + PP + MO$. To insure that the door is held open, the limit switch value $\overline{OL}$ which indicates the door is not fully open is ANDed with $PA + PP + MO$ to produce an output condition that activates door opening output *OD*. If all of the input values that opened the door are 0, then the door is to be closed. This transition condition is represented by $\overline{PA \cdot PP \cdot MO}$ which causes a transition from *Opened* to new

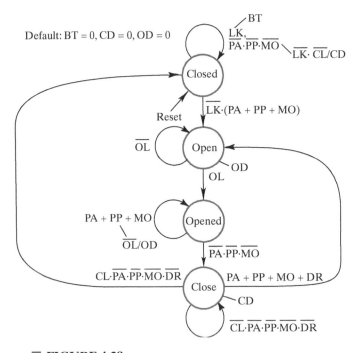

☐ **FIGURE 4-28**
State-Machine Diagram for the Automatic Sliding Door

state *Close* with output *CD*. In state *Close*, if any of the four sensors *PA*, *PP*, *MO*, or *DR* have value 1, represented by $PA + PP + MO + DR$, the door must reopen and the next state becomes *Open*. In state *Close*, because the door is closing, *DR* needs to be included here to indicate that the door may be blocked by a person or object. The form of the input conditions for the Close state differs from those for the Open state since door closure is to halt even if only partially completed when *PA*, *PP*, *MO*, and *DR* have value 1. In a similar manner to the use of the *OL* sensor for the *Open* state, we add the transition to the *Closed* state for transition condition $CL \cdot \overline{PA} \cdot \overline{PP} \cdot \overline{MO} \cdot \overline{DR}$. A value of 0 on *CL* and on all of the sensor signals causing opening is represented by the transition condition $\overline{CL} \cdot \overline{PA} \cdot \overline{PP} \cdot \overline{MO} \cdot \overline{DR}$ that causes the *Close* state to remain unchanged. This completes the development of the diagram. The necessary analysis to verify the transition and output condition constraints is left to the reader in Problem 4-37(b). Note that all of the output conditions for *OD* and *CD* to be 0 are implicit and not shown, a fact that must be taken into account when verifying the output constraints.

The state table derived from the state-machine diagram is shown in Table 4-11. The next step in the design is to make the state assignment. Since there are just four states, we choose a two-bit code, the Gray code. The state code information has been added to the state-machine table in Table 4-11. With the state assignment in place, we can now write the next state and output equations for the circuit. Because of the number of input variables, map optimization is not feasible, but some multilevel optimization can be applied to obtain efficient realizations. The equations to be written from Table 4-11 are based on the 1 values for the next state variables. For excitation equations, products are formed from the state and input condition combinations for each 1 present with the state combinations replaced by state variable products, e.g., 01 becomes $\overline{Y}_1 \cdot Y_2$. The product term for the third row of the table is $\overline{Y}_1 \cdot \overline{Y}_2 \cdot (\overline{LK} \, (PA + PP + MO))$. The product terms for each of the 1 values

$\Box$ **TABLE 4-11**
Modified State Table for the Automatic Sliding Door

State	State Code	Input Condition	Next State	State Code	Non-Zero Outputs (Including TCD and TOCD) Output Actions and Output Conditions*)
Closed	00	LK	Closed	00	BT*
	00	$\overline{PA} \cdot \overline{PP} \cdot \overline{MO}$	Closed	00	$LK \cdot \overline{CL}/CD$*
	00	$\overline{LK} \cdot (PA + PP + MO)$	Open	01	
Open	01				OD
	01	$\overline{OL}$	Open	01	
	01	OL	Opened	11	
Opened	11	$PA + PP + MO$	Opened	11	$\overline{OL}/OD$*
	11	$\overline{PA} \cdot \overline{PP} \cdot \overline{MO}$	Close	10	
Close	10				CD
	10	$\overline{CL} \cdot \overline{PA} \cdot \overline{PP} \cdot \overline{MO} \cdot \overline{DR}$	Close	10	
	10	$CL \cdot \overline{PA} \cdot \overline{PP} \cdot \overline{MO} \cdot \overline{DR}$	Closed	00	
	10	$PA + PP + MO + DR$	Open	01	

can then be ORed together to form an excitation equation. The expression $PA + PP + MO$ and its complement $\overline{PA \cdot PP \cdot MO}$ are transition conditions for TOCD output actions and appear frequently as factors in other transition conditions. As useful factors, these expressions will be denoted by X and $\overline{X}$, respectively. The excitation equations are:

$$X = PA + PP + MO$$

$$Y_1(t + 1) = \overline{Y}_1 \cdot Y_2 \cdot OL + Y_1 \cdot Y_2 + Y_1 \cdot \overline{Y}_2 \cdot \overline{CL} \cdot \overline{X} \cdot \overline{DR}$$

$$Y_2(t + 1) = \overline{Y}_1 \cdot \overline{Y}_2 \cdot \overline{LK} \cdot X + \overline{Y}_1 \cdot Y_2 + Y_1 \cdot Y_2 \cdot X + Y_1 \cdot \overline{Y}_2 \cdot (X + DR)$$

For the output equations, products are formed from the state combinations and state combination-Mealy output conditions for each output listed. As for the excitation equations, state combinations are replaced by state variable products. The products are ORed for each of the output variables. The resulting output equations with multilevel optimization applied are:

$$BT = \overline{Y}_1 \cdot \overline{Y}_2 \cdot LK$$

$$CD = Y_1 \cdot \overline{Y}_2 + \overline{Y}_1 \cdot \overline{Y}_2 \cdot \overline{LK} \cdot \overline{CL} \cdot \overline{X}$$

$$= (Y_1 + \overline{LK} \cdot \overline{CL} \cdot \overline{X}) \cdot \overline{Y}_2$$

$$OD = \overline{Y}_1 \cdot Y_2 + Y_1 \cdot Y_2 \cdot \overline{OL} \cdot X$$

$$= (\overline{Y}_1 + \overline{OL} \cdot X) \cdot Y_2$$

By using these six equations, the final circuit can be construction from the combinational logic represented along with the two flip-flops for Y_1 and Y_2 with their resets connected.   ■

Our introduction to design based on state-machine diagrams and state-machine tables is now complete. In Chapter 6, we will use these tools to describe systems including register transfers. This will lead to methods for designing datapaths made up of register transfer hardware and state-based controls.

Asynchronous Interfaces, Synchronization, and Synchronous Circuit Pitfalls   In this section, we have applied signals such as those coming from sensors, buttons, and switches that are not synchronized with the clock to synchronous sequential circuits. This is a practice that can cause catastrophic failure because of timing problems. These issues and problems are addressed in Sections 4-11, 4-12, and 4-13.

4-7 HDL Representation for Sequential Circuits—VHDL

In Chapters 2 and 3, VHDL was used to describe combinational circuits. Likewise, VHDL can describe storage elements and sequential circuits. In this section, descriptions of a positive-edge-triggered D flip-flop and a sequence recognizer circuit illustrate such uses of VHDL. These descriptions involve new VHDL concepts, the most important of which is the *process*. Thus far, concurrent statements have described combinations of conditions and actions in VHDL. A concurrent statement, however, is limited in the complexity that can be represented. Typically, the sequential circuits to be described are complex enough that description within a concurrent statement is very difficult. A process can be viewed as a replacement for a concurrent statement that permits considerably greater descriptive power. Multiple processes may execute concurrently, and a process may execute concurrently with concurrent statements.

The body of a process typically implements a sequential program. Signal values, however, which are assigned during the process, change only when the process is completed. If the portion of a process executed is

$$B \ \text{<=} \ A;$$
$$C \ \text{<=} \ B;$$

then, at the completion of the process, B will contain the original contents of A, and C will contain the original contents of B. In contrast, after execution of these two statements in a program, C would contain the original contents of A. To achieve program-like behavior, VHDL uses another construct called a *variable*. In contrast to a signal which evaluates after some delay, a variable evaluates immediately. Thus, if B is a variable in the execution of

$$B \ := \ A;$$
$$C \ := \ B;$$

B will instantaneously evaluate to the contents of A, and C will evaluate to the new contents of B, so that C finally contains the original contents of A. Variables appear only within processes. Note the use of := instead of <= for variable assignment.

EXAMPLE 4-12   VHDL for Positive-Edge-Triggered *D* Flip-Flop with Reset

The basic process structure is illustrated by an example process describing the architecture of a positive-edge-triggered *D* flip-flop in Figure 4-29. The process begins with the keyword **process**. Optionally, **process** can be preceded by a process name followed by a colon. Following in parentheses are two signals, CLK and RESET. This is the *sensitivity list* for the process. If either CLK or RESET changes, then the process is executed. In general, a process is executed whenever a signal or variable in its sensitivity list changes. It is important to note that the sensitivity list is not a parameter list containing all inputs and outputs. For example, D does not appear, since a change in its value cannot initiate a possible change in the value of Q. Following the sensitivity list at the beginning of the process is the keyword **begin**, and at the end of the process the keyword **end** appears. The word **process** following **end** is optional.

Within the body of the process, additional VHDL conditional structures can appear. Notable in the Figure 4-29 example is **if-then-else**. The general structure of an **if-then-else** in VHDL is

```
-- Positive-Edge-Triggered D Flip-Flop with Reset:
-- VHDL Process Description
library ieee;
use ieee.std_logic_1164.all;
entity dff is
    port(CLK, RESET, D : in std_logic;
         Q : out std_logic);
end dff;

architecture pet_pr of dff is
-- Implements positive-edge-triggered bit state storage
-- with asynchronous reset.

begin
process (CLK, RESET)
    begin
      if (RESET = '1') then
         Q <= '0';
      elsif (CLK'event and CLK = '1') then
            Q <= D;
        end if;
      end if;
    end process;
end;
```

☐ **FIGURE 4-29**
VHDL Process Description of Positive-Edge-Triggered Flip-Flop with Reset

```
if condition then
   sequence of statements
{elsif condition then
   sequence of statements}
else
   sequence of statements
end if;
```

The statements within braces { } can appear from zero to any number of times. The **if-then-else** within a process is similar in effect to the **when else** concurrent assignment statement. Illustrating, we have

```
if A = '1' then
   Q <= X;
elsif B = '0' then
   Q <= Y;
else
   Q <= Z;
end if;
```

If A is 1, then flip-flop Q is loaded with the contents of X. If A is 0 and B is 0, then flip-flop Q is loaded with the contents of Y. Otherwise, Q is loaded with the contents of Z. The end result for the four combination of values on A and B is

```
A = 0, B = 0     Q <= Y
A = 0, B = 1     Q <= Z
A = 1, B = 0     Q <= X
A = 1, B = 1     Q <= X
```

More complex conditional execution of statements can be achieved by nesting if-then-else structures, as in the following code:

```
if A = '1' then
  if C = '0' then
     Q <= W;
  else
     Q <= X;
  end if;
elsif B = '0' then
   Q <= Y;
else
   Q <= Z;
end if;
```

The end result for the eight combinations of values on A, B, and C is

```
A = 0, B = 0, C = 0      Q <= Y
A = 0, B = 0, C = 1      Q <= Y
A = 0, B = 1, C = 0      Q <= Z
A = 0, B = 1, C = 1      Q <= Z
A = 1, B = 0, C = 0      Q <= W
A = 1, B = 0, C = 1      Q <= X
A = 1, B = 1, C = 0      Q <= W
A = 1, B = 1, C = 1      Q <= X
```

With the information introduced thus far, the positive-edge-triggered D flip-flop in Figure 4-29 can now be studied. The sensitivity list for the process includes CLK and RESET, so the process is executed if either CLK or RESET or both change value. If D changes value, the value of Q is not to change for an edge-triggered flip-flop, so D does not appear on the sensitivity list. Based on the **if-then-else**, if RESET is 1, the flip-flop output Q is reset to 0. Otherwise, if the clock value changes, which is represented by appending 'event to CLK, and the new clock value is 1, which is represented by CLK = '1', a positive edge has occurred on CLK. The result of the positive-edge occurrence is the loading of the value on D into the flip-flop so that it appears on output Q. Note that, due to the structure of the **if-then-else**, RESET equal to 1 dominates the clocked behavior of the D flip-flop, causing the output Q to go to 0. Similar simple descriptions can be used to represent other flip-flop types and triggering approaches. ■

EXAMPLE 4-13   VHDL for the Sequence Recognizer

A more complex example in Figures 4-30 and 4-31 represents the sequence-recognizer state diagram in Figure 4-18(d). The architecture in this description consists of three

```
-- Sequence Recognizer: VHDL Process Description
-- (See Figure 4-18(d) for state diagram)
library ieee;
use ieee.std_logic_1164.all;
entity seq_rec is
    port(CLK, RESET, X: in std_logic;
         Z: out std_logic);
end seq_rec;

architecture process_3 of seq_rec is
    type state_type is (A, B, C, D);
    signal state, next_state : state_type;
begin

-- Process 1 - state_register: implements positive-edge-triggered
-- state storage with asynchronous reset.
    state_register: process (CLK, RESET)
    begin
       if (RESET = '1') then
          state <= A;
       elsif (CLK'event and CLK = '1') then
             state <= next_state;
       end if;
end process;

-- Process 2 - next_state_function: implements next state as
-- a function of input X and state.
    next_state_func: process (X, state)
    begin
       case state is
          when A =>
       if X = '1' then
          next_state <= B;
       else
          next_state <= A;
             end if;
          when B =>
       if X = '1' then
          next_state <= C;
       else
          next_state <= A;
             end if;
```

☐ **FIGURE 4-30**
VHDL Process Description of a Sequence Recognizer

```
-- Sequence Recognizer: VHDL Process Description (continued)
   when C =>
      if X = '1' then
         next_state <= C;
      else
         next_state <= D;
            end if;
         when D =>
      if X = '1' then
         next_state <= B;
      else
         next_state <= A;
            end if;
      end case;
   end process;


-- Process 3 - output_function: implements output as function
-- of input X and state.
   output_func: process (X, state)
   begin
      case state is
         when A =>
      Z <= '0';
   when B =>
      Z <= '0';
   when C =>
      Z <= '0';
         when D =>
      if X = '1' then
         Z <= '1';
      else
         Z <= '0';
            end if;
      end case;
   end process;
end;
```

□ **FIGURE 4-31**
VHDL Process Description of a Sequence Recognizer (continued)

distinct processes, which can execute simultaneously and interact via shared signal values. New concepts included are type declarations for defining new types and case statements for handling conditions.

The type declaration permits us to define new types analogous to existing types such as std_logic. A type declaration begins with the keyword **type** followed by the name of the new type, the keyword **is**, and, within parentheses, the list of values for signals of the new type. Using the example from Figure 4-30, we have

$$\textbf{type} \ \texttt{state\_type} \ \textbf{is} \ (\texttt{A, B, C, D});$$

The name of the new type is state_type and the values in this case are the names of the states in Figure 4-18(d). Once a **type** has been declared, it can be used for declaring signals or variables. From the example in Figure 4-30,

```
signal state, next_state : state_type;
```

indicates that `state` and `next_state` are signals that are of the type `state_type`. Thus, `state` and `next state` can have values A, B, C, and D.

The basic **if-then-else** (without using the **elsif**) makes a two-way decision based on whether a condition is TRUE or FALSE. In contrast, the **case** statement can make a multiway decision based on which of a number of statements is TRUE.

A simplified form for the generic **case** statement is

```
case expression is
  {when choices =>
    sequence of statements;}
end case;
```

The choices must be values that can be taken on by a signal of the type used in the expression. The **case** statement has an effect similar to the **with-select** concurrent assignment statement.

In the example in Figures 4-30 and 4-31, `Process 2` uses a **case** statement to define the next-state function for the sequence recognizer. The **case** statement makes a multiway decision based on the current state of the circuit, A, B, C, or D. **If-then-else** statements are used for each of the state alternatives to make a binary decision based on whether input X is 1 or 0. Concurrent assignment statements are then used to assign the next state based on the eight possible combinations of state value and input value. For example, consider the state alternative **when** B. If X equals 1, then the next state will be C; if X equals 0, then the next state will be A. This corresponds to the two transitions out of state B in Figure 4-18(d). For more complex circuits, case statements can also be used for handing the input conditions.

With this brief introduction to the **case** statement, the overall sequence recognizer can now be studied. Each of the three processes has a distinct function, but the processes interact to provide the overall sequence recognizer. `Process 1` describes the storage of the state. Note that the description is like that of the positive-edge-triggered flip-flop. There are two differences, however. First, the signals involved are of type `state_type` instead of type `std_logic`. Second, the state that results from applying RESET is state A rather than state 0. Also, since we are using state names such as A, B, and C, the number of state variables (i.e., the number of flip-flops) is unspecified and the state codes are unknown. `Process 1` is the only one of the three processes that contains storage.

`Process 2` describes the next-state function, as discussed earlier. The sensitivity list in this case contains signals X and `state`. In general, for describing combinational logic, all inputs must appear in the sensitivity list, since, whenever an input changes, the process must be executed.

`Process 3` describes the output function. The same **case** statement framework as in `Process 2` with state as the expression is used. Instead of assigning state names to next state, values 0 and 1 are assigned to Z. If the value assigned is the same for both values 0 and 1 on X, no **if-then-else** is needed, so an **if-then-else** appears only

```vhdl
-- Testbench for sequence recognizer example
library ieee;
use ieee.std_logic_1164.all, ieee.std_logic_unsigned.all;

entity seq_rec_testbench is
end seq_rec_testbench;

architecture testbench of seq_rec_testbench is
     signal clock, X, reset, Z: std_logic;
     signal test_sequence : std_logic_vector(0 to 10)
        := "01110101100";

     constant PERIOD : time := 100 ns;

     component seq_rec is
     port(CLK, RESET, X: in std_logic;
       Z: out std_logic);
     end component;

begin
     u1: seq_rec port map(clock, reset, X, Z);

     -- This process applies reset and
     -- then applies the test sequence to input X
     apply_inputs: process
     begin
       reset <= '1';
       X <='0';
       -- ensure that inputs are applied
       -- away from the active clock edge
       wait for 5*PERIOD/4;
       reset <= '0';
       for i in 0 to 10 loop
         X <= test_sequence(i);
         wait for PERIOD;
       end loop;
       wait;   --wait forever
     end process;

     -- This process provides the clock pulses
     generate_clock: process
     begin
       clock <= '1';
       wait for PERIOD/2;
       clock <= '0';
       wait for PERIOD/2;
     end process;
end  testbench;
```

□ **FIGURE 4-32**
Testbench for VHDL Sequence Recognizer Model

for state D. If there are multiple input variables, more complex **if-then-else** combinations or a **case** statement, as illustrated earlier, can be used to represent the conditioning of the outputs on the inputs. This example is a Mealy state machine in which the output is a function of the circuit inputs. If it were a Moore state machine, with the output dependent only on the state, input X would not appear on the sensitivity list, and there would be no **if-then-else** structures in the **case** statement.

Figure 4-32 shows a testbench for verifying the VHDL sequence recognizer. As with the testbenches in earlier chapters, the entity has no ports and the architecture declares the device under test, the signals to be connected to it, and then instantiates it. But in contrast to earlier testbenches, this testbench uses more than one process to provide stimulus to the inputs of the sequence recognizer. The apply_inputs process applies the RESET and X inputs, while the generate_clock process provides a periodic clock signal. The apply_inputs process uses the test sequence that was described in Example 4-8, which is stored in the std_logic_vector test_sequence. At the beginning of simulation, the process activates RESET to put the state machine in a known state. After deactivating RESET, the process applies the X input values stored in the test_sequence array using a **for** loop statement. The input values are applied shortly after the positive edge of the clock to ensure that there is sufficient time before the next positive edge that the timing conditions for storage elements are met, which will be described later in this chapter.

This testbench provides a template for verifying VHDL models of simple finite state machines: using multiple processes to generate a clock signal and to apply reset and other inputs. For more complex circuits, testbenches may read inputs from a file and compare the outputs of the device under test to known good outputs, automatically flagging erroneous outputs. The language constructs for supporting the file read/write and user input/output necessary for such behavior are beyond the scope of this introductory text, but interested readers will easily find them in one of the many fine books dedicated to the VHDL language. ▪

A common pitfall is present whenever an **if-then-else** or **case** statement is employed. During synthesis, unexpected storage elements in the form of latches or flip-flops appear. For the simple **if-then-else** used in Figure 4-29, using this pitfall gives a specification that synthesizes to a flip-flop. In addition to the two input signals, RESET and CLK, the signal CLK'event is produced by applying the predefined attribute 'event to the CLK signal. CLK'event is TRUE if the value of CLK changes. All possible combinations of values are represented in Table 4-12. Whenever RESET is 0 and the CLK is fixed at 0 or 1 or has a negative edge, no action is specified. In VHDL, it is assumed that, for any combinations of conditions that have unspecified actions in **if-then-else** or **case** statements, the left-hand side of an assignment statement remains unchanged. This is equivalent to Q <= Q, causing storage to occur. Thus, all combinations of conditions must have the resulting action specified when no storage is intended. If this is not a natural situation, an **others** can be used in the **if-then else** or **case**. If binary values are used in the **case** statement, just as in Section 2-9, an **others** must also be used to handle combinations including the seven values other than 0 and 1 permitted for std_logic.

□ **TABLE 4-12**
Illustration of Generation of Storage in VHDL

	Inputs		Action
RESET = 1	**CLK = 1**	**CLK' event**	
FALSE	FALSE	FALSE	Unspecified
FALSE	FALSE	TRUE	Unspecified
FALSE	TRUE	FALSE	Unspecified
FALSE	TRUE	TRUE	Q <= D
TRUE	—	—	Q <= '0'

Together, the three processes used for the sequence recognizer describe the state storage, the next-state function, and the output function for a sequential circuit. Since these are all of the components of a sequential circuit at the state-diagram level, the description is complete. The use of three distinct processes is only one methodology for sequential circuit description. Pairs of processes or all three processes can be combined for more elegant descriptions. Nevertheless, the three-process description is the easiest for new users of VHDL and also works well with synthesis tools.

To synthesize the circuit into actual logic, a state assignment is needed, in addition to a technology library. Many synthesis tools will make the state assignment independently or based on a directive from the user. It is also possible for the user to specify explicitly the state assignment. This can be done in VHDL by using an enumeration type. The encoding for the state machine in Figures 4-30 and 4-31 can be specified by adding the following after the **type** state_type declaration:

```
attribute  enum_encoding: string;
attribute  enum_encoding of  state_type:
type is   "00, 01, 10, 11";
```

This is not a standard VHDL construct, but it is recognized by many synthesis tools. Another option is not to use a type declaration for the states, but to declare the state variables as signals and use the actual codes for the states. In this case, if states appear in the simulation output, they will appear as the encoded state values.

4-8 HDL REPRESENTATION FOR SEQUENTIAL CIRCUITS—VERILOG

In Chapters 2 and 3, Verilog was used to describe combinational circuits. Likewise, Verilog can describe storage elements and sequential circuits. In this section, descriptions of a positive-edge-triggered D flip-flop and a sequence-recognizer circuit illustrate such uses of Verilog. These descriptions will involve new Verilog concepts, the most important of which are the process and the register type for nets.

Thus far, continuous assignment statements have been used to describe combinations of conditions and actions in Verilog. A continuous assignment statement is limited in what can be described, however. A *process* can be viewed as a replacement for a continuous assignment statement that permits considerably greater descriptive power. Multiple processes may execute concurrently and a process may execute concurrently with continuous assignment statements.

Within a process, procedural assignment statements, which are not continuous assignments, are used. Because of this, the assigned values need to be retained over time. This retention of information can be achieved by using the *register* type rather than the wire type for nets. The keyword for the register type is **reg**. Note that just because a net is of type **reg** does not mean that an actual register is associated with its implementation. Additional conditions need to be present to cause an actual register to exist. The type **reg** is intended for storing values in variables, which may represent either combinational or sequential logic when implemented in hardware.

There are two basic types of processes, the **initial** process and the **always** process. The **initial** process executes only once, beginning at $t = 0$. The **always** process also executes at $t = 0$, but executes repeatedly thereafter. To prevent rampant, uncontrolled execution, some timing control is needed in the form of delay or event-based waiting. The # operator followed by an integer can be used to specify delay. The @ operator can be viewed as "wait for event." @ is followed by an expression that describes the event or events, the occurrence of which will cause the process to execute.

The body of a process is like a sequential program. The process begins with the keyword **begin** and ends with the keyword **end**. Procedural assignment statements make up the body of the process. These assignment statements are classified as blocking or nonblocking. Blocking assignments use = as the assignment operator and nonblocking assignments use <= as the operator. *Blocking assignments* are executed sequentially, much like a program in a procedural language such as C. *Nonblocking assignments* evaluate the right-hand side, but do not make the assignment until all right-hand sides have been evaluated. Blocking assignments can be illustrated by the following process body, in which A, B, and C are of type **reg**:

```
begin
    B = A;
    C = B;
end
```

The first statement transfers the contents of A into B. The second statement then transfers the new contents of B into C. At process completion, C contains the original contents of A.

Suppose that the same process body uses nonblocking assignments:

```
begin
    B <= A;
    C <= B;
end
```

The first statement transfers the original contents of A into B and the second statement transfers the original contents of B into C. At process completion, C contains the original contents of B, not those of A. Effectively, the two statements have executed concurrently instead of in sequence. For reasons that are beyond the scope of this introductory text, when developing Verilog models that are meant to be synthesized, the following guidelines should be used to ensure that the synthesized hardware behaves in the same way as simulation:

- Blocking assignments should be used for statements that are meant to create combinational logic.

- Nonblocking assignments should be used for statements that are meant to create sequential logic.

- Blocking and nonblocking assignments should not be used in the same always block.

- Assignments to a particular variable (type **reg**) should be made in only one always block.

As a result of these guidelines, synthesizable Verilog models of finite state machines are generally arranged as two or three always blocks: One always block for the sequential logic (state registers) using nonblocking assignments, and one or two always blocks for the combinational logic (next state and output signals) using blocking assignments. Depending upon the complexity of the state machine, the next state and output combinational logic may be combined into one always block if they are simple, or described in separate blocks if they are more complex.

EXAMPLE 4-14   **Verilog for Positive-Edge-Triggered *D* Flip-Flop with Reset**

These new concepts can now be applied to the Verilog description of a positive-edge-triggered *D* flip-flop given in Figure 4-33. The module and its inputs and outputs are declared. Q is declared as of type **reg**, since it will store information. The process begins with the keyword **always**. Following is @ (**posedge** CLK **or posedge** RESET). This is the *event control* statement for the process that initiates process execution if an event (i.e., a specified change in a specified signal) occurs. For the *D* flip-flop, if either CLK or RESET changes to 1, then the process is executed. It is important to note that the event control statement is not a parameter list containing all inputs. For example, D does not appear, since a change in its value cannot initiate a possible change in the value of Q. Following the event control statement at the beginning of the process is the keyword **begin**, and at the end of the process the keyword **end** appears.

Within the body of the process, additional Verilog conditional structures can appear. Notable in the Figure 4-33 example is **if-else**. The general structure of an **if-else** in Verilog is

```
if  (condition)
    begin  procedural statements  end
{else if  (condition)
```

```
// Positive-Edge-Triggered D Flip-Flop with Reset:
// Verilog Process Description

module dff_v(CLK, RESET, D, Q);
    input CLK, RESET, D;
    output Q;
    reg Q;

always @(posedge CLK or posedge RESET)
begin
    if (RESET)
        Q <= 0;
    else
        Q <= D;
end
endmodule
```

☐ **FIGURE 4-33**
Verilog Process Description of Positive-Edge-Triggered Flip-Flop with Reset

```
    begin procedural statements end}
{else
    begin procedural statements end}
```

If there is a single procedural statement, then **begin** and **end** are unnecessary:

```
if(A == 1)
    Q <= X;
else if (B == 0)
    Q <= Y;
else
    Q <= Z;
```

Note that a double equals signs is used in conditions. If A is 1, then flip-flop Q is loaded with the contents of X. If A is 0 and B is 0, then flip-flop Q is loaded with the contents of Y. Otherwise, Q is loaded with the contents of Z. The end result for the four combination of values on A and B is

```
A = 0, B = 0    Q <= Y
A = 0, B = 1    Q <= Z
A = 1, B = 0    Q <= X
A = 1, B = 1    Q <= X
```

The **if-else** within a process is similar in effect to the conditional operator in a continuous assignment statement introduced earlier. The conditional operator can be used within a process, but the **if-else** cannot be used in a continuous assignment statement.

More complex conditional execution of statements can be achieved by nesting **if-else** structures. For example, we might have

```
if (A == 1)
   if (C == 0)
      Q <= W;
   else
      Q <= X;
else if (B == 0)
   Q <= Y;
else
   Q <= Z;
```

In this type of structure, an **else** is associated with the closest **if** preceding it that does not already have an **else**. The end result for the eight combinations of values on A, B, and C is

```
A = 0, B = 0, C = 0      Q <= Y
A = 0, B = 0, C = 1      Q <= Y
A = 0, B = 1, C = 0      Q <= Z
A = 0, B = 1, C = 1      Q <= Z
A = 1, B = 0, C = 0      Q <= W
A = 1, B = 0, C = 1      Q <= X
A = 1, B = 1, C = 0      Q <= W
A = 1, B = 1, C = 1      Q <= X
```

Returning to the **if-else** in the positive-edge-triggered D flip-flop shown in Figure 4-33, assuming that a positive edge has occurred on either CLK or RESET, if RESET is 1, the flip-flop output Q is reset to 0. Otherwise, the value on D is stored in the flip-flop so that Q equals D. Due to the structure of the **if-else**, RESET equal to 1 dominates the clocked behavior of the D flip-flop, causing the output Q to go to 0. Similar simple descriptions can be used to represent other flip-flop types and triggering approaches. ■

EXAMPLE 4-15   Verilog for the Sequence Recognizer

A more complex example in Figure 4-34 represents the sequence-recognizer state diagram in Figure 4-18(d). The architecture in this description consists of three distinct processes that can execute simultaneously and interact via shared signal values. New concepts included are state encoding and case statements for handling conditions.

In Figure 4-34, the module seq_rec_v and input and output variables CLK, RESET, X, and Z are declared. Next, registers are declared for state and next_state. Note that since next_state need not be stored, it could also be declared as a wire, but, since it is assigned within an **always** block, it must be declared as a **reg**. Both registers are two bits, with the most significant bit (MSB) numbered 1 and the least significant bit (LSB) numbered 0.

Next, a name is given to each of the states taken on by state and next_state, and binary codes are assigned to them. This can be done using a parameter statement or a compiler directive **define**. We will use the parameter statement, since the compiler directive requires a somewhat inconvenient ' before each state

```verilog
// Sequence Recognizer: Verilog Process Description
// (See Figure 4-18(d) for state diagram)
module seq_rec_v(CLK, RESET, X, Z);
    input CLK, RESET, X;
    output Z;
    reg [1:0] state, next_state;
    parameter A = 2'b00, B = 2'b01, C = 2'b10, D = 2'b11;
    reg Z;
// state register: implements positive edge-triggered
// state storage with asynchronous reset.
always @(posedge CLK or posedge RESET)
begin
    if (RESET)
        state <= A;
    else
        state <= next_state;
end
//.te function: implements next state as function
// of X and state
always @(X or state)
begin
    case (state)
        A: next_state = X ? B : A;
        B: next_state = X ? C : A;
        C: next_state = X ? C : D;
        D: next_state = X ? B : A;
    endcase
end

// output function: implements output as function
// of X and state
always @(X or state)
begin
    case (state)
        A: Z = 1'b0;
        B: Z = 1'b0;
        C: Z = 1'b0;
        D: Z = X ? 1'b1 : 1'b0;
    endcase
end
endmodule
```

☐ **FIGURE 4-34**
Verilog Process Description of a Sequence Recognizer

throughout the description. From the diagram in Figure 4-18(d), the states are A, B, C, and D. In addition, the parameter statements give the state codes assigned to each of these states. The notation used to define the state codes is 2'b followed by the binary code. The 2 denotes that there are two bits in the code and the 'b denotes that the base of the code given is binary.

The **if-else** (without using the **else if**) makes a two-way decision based on whether a condition is TRUE or FALSE. In contrast, the **case** statement can make a multiway decision based on which one of a number of statements is TRUE. A simplified form for the generic **case** statement is

```
case   expression
     {case expression : statements}
endcase
```

in which the braces { } represent one or more such entries.

The case expression must have values that can be taken on by a signal of the type used in expression. Typically, there are sequences of multiple statements. In the example in Figure 4-34, the **case** statement for the next-state function makes a multiway decision based on the current state of the circuit, A, B, C, or D. For each of the case expressions, conditional statements of various types are used to make a binary decision based on whether input X is 1 or 0. Blocking assignment statements are then used to assign the next state based on the eight possible combinations of state value and input value. For example, consider the expression B. If X equals 1, then the next state will be C; if X equals 0, then the next state will be A. This corresponds to the two transitions out of state B in Figure 4-18(d).

With this brief introduction to the **case** statement, the overall sequence recognizer can now be understood. Each of the three processes has a distinct function, but the processes interact to provide the overall sequence recognizer. The first process describes the state register for storing the sequence-recognizer state. Note that the description resembles that of the positive-edge-triggered flip-flop. There are two differences, however. First, there are two bits in the state register. Second, the state that results from applying RESET is state A rather than state 0. The first process is the only one of the three processes that has storage (sequential logic) associated with it. Following the coding guidelines provided earlier in this section, this always block uses nonblocking assignments.

The second process describes the next-state function as discussed earlier. The event control statement contains signals X and state. In general, for describing combinational logic, all inputs must appear in the event control statement, since, whenever an input changes, the process must be executed. Since the next state logic is combinational, this process uses blocking assignments.

The final process describes the output function and uses the same **case** statement framework as in the next-state function process, again using blocking assignments because the process describes combinational logic. Instead of assigning state names, values 0 and 1 are assigned to Z. If the value assigned is the same for both values 0 and 1 on X, no conditional statement is needed, so a conditional statement appears only for state D. If there are multiple input variables, more complex **if-else** combinations, as illustrated earlier, can be used to represent the conditioning of the outputs on the inputs.

This example is a Mealy state machine in which the output is a function of the circuit inputs. If it were a Moore state machine, with the output dependent only on the state, input X would not appear on the event control statement and there would be no conditional structures within the **case** statement.

Figure 4-35 shows a testbench for verifying the Verilog sequence recognizer. As with the testbenches in earlier chapters, the module has no ports, and the

```verilog
// Testbench for Verilog sequence recognizer
module seq_req_v_testbench();
    wire Z;
    reg clock, X, reset;

    reg [0:10] test_sequence = 11'b011_1010_1100;
    integer i;
    parameter PERIOD = 100;

    seq_rec_v DUT(clock, reset, X, Z);

// This initial block initializes the clock, applies reset,
// and then applies the test sequence to input X.
    initial
    begin
        reset = 1'b1;
        X = 1'b0;
        // Ensure that inputs are applied
        // away from the active clock edge
        #(5*PERIOD/4);
        reset = 1'b0;
        for (i = 0; i < 11; i = i+1)
        begin
            X = test_sequence[i];
            #PERIOD;
        end
        // Stop the simulation after all the inputs
        // in the sequence have been applied
        $stop;
    end

// This always block provides the clock pulses
    always
    begin
        clock = 1'b1;
        #(PERIOD/2);
        clock = 1'b0;
        #(PERIOD/2);
    end
endmodule
```

☐ **FIGURE 4-35**
Testbench for Verilog Sequence Recognizer Model

module declares the device under test, the wire and `regs` to be connected to it, and then instantiates it. But in contrast to earlier testbenches, this testbench uses more than one process to provide stimulus to the inputs of the sequence recognizer. The first process applies the `reset` and `X` inputs, while second process provides a periodic `clock` signal. The first process uses the test sequence that was described in Example 4-8, which is stored in the **reg** array `test_sequence`. At the beginning of simulation, the process activates `reset` to put the state machine in a known state. After deactivating `reset`, the process applies the `X` input values stored in the `test_sequence` array using a **for** loop statement. The input values are applied shortly after the positive edge of the clock to ensure that there is sufficient time before the next positive edge that the timing conditions for storage elements are met, which will be described later in this chapter.

This testbench provides a template for verifying Verilog models of simple finite state machines: using multiple processes to generate a clock signal and to apply reset and other inputs. For more complex circuits, testbenches may read inputs from a file and compare the outputs of the device under test to known good outputs, automatically flagging erroneous outputs. The language constructs for supporting the file read/write and user input/output necessary for such behavior are beyond the scope of this introductory text, but interested readers will easily find them in one of the many fine books dedicated to the Verilog language. ■

A common pitfall is present whenever an **if-else** or **case** statement is employed. During synthesis, unexpected storage elements in the form of latches or flip-flops appear. For the very simple **if-else** used in Figure 4-33, this pitfall is employed to give a specification that synthesizes to a flip-flop. In addition to the two input signals, RESET and CLK, events **posedge** CLK and **posedge** RESET are produced, which are TRUE if the value of the respective signal changes from 0 to 1. Selected combinations of values for RESET and the two events are shown in Table 4-13. Whenever RESET has no positive edge, or RESET is 0 and CLK is fixed at 0 or 1 or has a negative edge, no action is specified. In Verilog, the assumption is that, for any

□ **TABLE 4-13**
Illustration of Generation of Storage in Verilog

Inputs		Action
posedge RESET and RESET = 1	posedge CLK	
FALSE	FALSE	Unspecified
FALSE	TRUE	$Q <= D$
TRUE	FALSE	$Q <= 0$
TRUE	TRUE	$Q <= 0$

combination of conditions with unspecified actions in `if-else` or `case` statements, the left-hand side of an assignment statement will remain unchanged. This is equivalent to $Q \leq Q$, causing storage to occur. Thus, all combinations of conditions must have the resulting action specified when no storage is intended. To prevent undesirable latches and flip-flops from occurring, for `if-else` structures, care must be taken to include `else` in all cases if storage is not desired. In a `case` statement, a `default` statement which defines what happens for all choices not specified should be added. Within the `default` statement, a specific next state can be specified, which in the example could be state A.

Together, the three processes used for the sequence recognizer describe the state storage, the next-state function, and the output function for the sequential circuit. Since these are all of the components of a sequential circuit at the state-diagram level, the description is complete. The use of three distinct processes is only one methodology for sequential circuit description. For example, the next-state and output processes could be easily combined. Nevertheless, the three-process description is the easiest for new users of Verilog and also works well with synthesis tools.

4-9 FLIP-FLOP TIMING

Timing parameters are associated with the operation of both pulse-triggered (master–slave) and edge-triggered flip-flops. These parameters are illustrated for a master–slave *SR* flip-flop and for a negative-edge-triggered *D* flip-flop in Figure 4-36. The parameters for the positive-edge-triggered *D* flip-flop are the same, except that they are referenced to the positive rather than the negative clock edge.

The timing of the response of a flip-flop to its inputs and clock *C* must be taken into account when using the flip-flops. For both flip-flops, there is a minimum time called the *setup time*, t_s, for which the *S* and *R* or *D* inputs must be maintained at a constant value prior to the occurrence of the clock transition that causes the output to change. Otherwise, the master could be changed erroneously in the case of the master–slave flip-flop or be at an intermediate value at the time the slave copies it in the case of the edge-triggered flip-flop. Similarly, there is a minimum time called the *hold time*, t_h, for which the *S* and *R* or *D* inputs must not change after the application of the clock transition that causes the output to change. Otherwise, the master might respond to the input change and be changing at the time the slave latch copies it. In addition, there is a minimum *clock pulse width* t_w, to insure that the master has time enough to capture the input values correctly. Among these parameters, the one that differs most between the pulse-triggered and edge-triggered flip-flops is the setup time, as shown in Figure 4-36. The pulse-triggered flip-flop has its setup time equal to the clock pulse width, whereas the setup time for the edge-triggered flip-flop can be much smaller than the clock pulse width. As a consequence, edge triggering tends to provide faster designs, since the flip-flop inputs can change later with respect to the upcoming triggering clock edge.

The *propagation delay times*, t_{PHL}, t_{PLH}, or t_{pd}, of the flip-flops are defined as the interval between the triggering clock edge and the stabilization of the output to a new value. These times are defined in the same fashion as those for an inverter, except that the values are measured from the triggering clock edge rather than the inverter input. In Figure 4-36, all of these parameters are denoted by $t_{p\text{-}}$ and are given

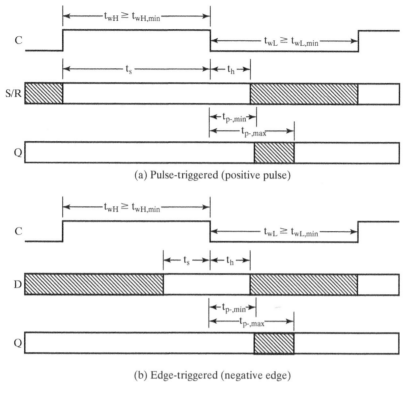

(a) Pulse-triggered (positive pulse)

(b) Edge-triggered (negative edge)

□ **FIGURE 4-36**
Flip-Flop Timing Parameters

minimum and maximum values. Since the changes of the flip-flop outputs are to be separated from the control by the flip-flop inputs, the minimum propagation delay time should be longer than the hold time for correct operation. These and other parameters are specified in manufacturers' data books for specific integrated circuit products.

Similar timing parameters can be defined for latches and direct inputs, with additional propagation delays needed to model the transparent behavior of latches.

4-10 Sequential Circuit Timing

In addition to analyzing the function of a circuit, it is also important to analyze its performance in terms of the *maximum input-to-output delay* and the *maximum clock frequency*, f_{max}, at which it can operate. First of all, the clock frequency is just the inverse of the clock period t_p shown in Figure 4-37. So, the maximum allowable clock frequency corresponds to the minimum allowable clock period t_p. To determine how small we can make the clock period, we need to determine the longest delay from the triggering edge of the clock to the next triggering edge of the clock. These delays are measured on all such paths in the circuit down which changing signals propagate.

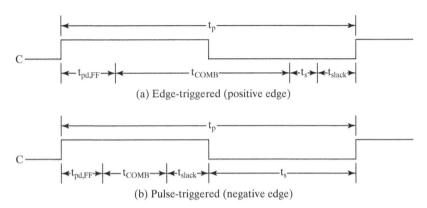

☐ **FIGURE 4-37**
Sequential Circuit Timing Parameters

Each of these path delays has three components: (1) a flip-flop propagation delay, $t_{pd, FF}$, (2) a combinational logic delay through the chain of gates along the path, $t_{pd,COMB}$, and (3) a flip-flop setup time, t_s. As a signal change propagates down the path, it is delayed successively by an amount equal to each of these delays. Note that we have used t_{pd}, instead of the more detailed values, t_{PLH} and t_{PHL}, for both the flip-flops and combinational logic gates to simplify the delay calculations. Figure 4-37 summarizes the delay picture for both the edge-triggered and pulse-triggered flip-flops.

After a positive edge on a clock, if a flip-flop is to change, its output changes at time $t_{pd,FF}$ after the clock edge. This change enters the combinational logic path and must propagate down the path to a flip-flop input. This requires an additional time, $t_{pd,COMB}$, for the signal change to reach the second flip-flop. Finally, before the next positive clock edge, this change must be held on the flip-flop input for setup time t_s. This path, $P_{FF,FF}$ and other possible paths are illustrated in Figure 4-38. For paths $P_{IN,FF}$ driven by primary inputs, $t_{pd,FF}$ is replaced by t_i, which is the latest time that the input changes after the positive clock edge. For a path $P_{FF,OUT}$ driving primary outputs, t_s is replaced by t_o, which is the latest time that the output is permitted to change prior to the next clock edge. Finally, in a Mealy model circuit, combinational paths from input to output, $P_{IN,OUT}$, that use both t_i and t_o can appear. Each path has a slack time, t_{slack}, the extra time allowed in the clock period beyond that required by the path. From Figure 4-38, the following equation for a path of type $P_{FF,FF}$ results:

$$t_p = t_{slack} + (t_{pd,FF} + t_{pd,COMB} + t_s)$$

In order to guarantee that a changing value is captured by the receiving flip-flop, t_{slack} must be greater than or equal to zero for all of the paths. This requires that

$$t_p \geq \max (t_{pd,FF} + t_{COMB} + t_s) = t_{p,min}$$

where the maximum is taken over all paths down which signals propagate from flip-flop to flip-flop. The next example presents representative calculations for paths $P_{FF,FF}$.

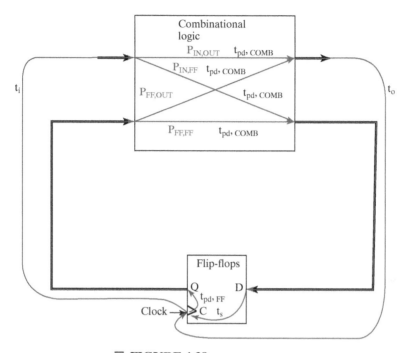

□ **FIGURE 4-38**
Sequential Circuit Timing Paths

EXAMPLE 4-16   Clock Period and Frequency Calculations

Suppose that all flip-flops used are the same and have $t_{pd} = 0.2$ ns (nanosecond $= 10^{-9}$ seconds) and $t_s = 0.1$ ns. Then the longest path beginning and ending with a flip-flop will be the path with the largest $t_{pd,COMB}$. Further, suppose that the largest $t_{pd,COMB}$ is 1.3 ns and that t_p has been set to 1.5 ns. From the previous equation for t_p, we can write

$$1.5 \text{ ns} = t_{slack} + 0.2 + 1.3 + 0.1 = t_{slack} + 1.6 \text{ ns}$$

Solving, we have $t_{slack} = -0.1$ ns, so this value of t_p is too small. In order for t_{slack} to be greater than or equal to zero for the longest path, $t_p \geq t_{p,min} = 1.6$ ns. The maximum frequency $f_{max} = 1/1.6$ ns $= 625$ MHz (megahertz $= 10^6$ cycles per second). We note that, if t_p is too large to meet the circuit specifications, we must either employ faster logic cells or change the circuit design to reduce the problematic path delays through the circuit while still performing the desired function.   ■

It is interesting to note that the hold time for a flip-flop, t_h, does not appear in the clock-period equation. It relates to another timing-constraint equation dealing with one or both of two specific situations. In one case, output changes arrive at the inputs of one or more flip-flops too soon. In the other case, the clock signals reaching one or more flip-flops are somehow delayed, a condition referred to as *clock skew*. Clock skew also can affect the maximum clock frequency.

4-11 ASYNCHRONOUS INTERACTIONS

The synchronous circuits studied thus far have their state-variable changes synchronized by a special input signal called a clock. An *asynchronous circuit* has one or more state-variable changes that occur without being directly synchronized by the special clock input. Instead, an asynchronous circuit may change state in response to any of its inputs. Here we briefly study some aspects of the interactions between asynchronous and synchronous circuits. In addition, we study interactions between two synchronous circuits having clocks that are unrelated to each other, i.e. have no specified timing relationships to each other. In this sense, these synchronous circuits are asynchronous with respect to each other due to the lack of a defined relationship between their respective clocks.

Philosophically, every flip-flop or latch we have considered can be modeled as an asynchronous circuit if the clock is regarded as just another input rather than a special clock input for synchronization. In fact, asynchronous circuit design can be used to design latches and flip-flops. The presentation here, however, does not dwell upon the details of asynchronous circuit design. Our reason for avoiding asynchronous design as it is presented in most textbooks is that it is very difficult to insure correct operation and, therefore, is to be avoided. The correct operation of such circuits is heavily dependent upon a myriad of timing relationships and timing constraints on changing of inputs, requiring delay control of the designed circuits. The use of clocks in synchronous circuits, however, is troublesome in terms of both speed of operation and power consumption. In response to this, more contemporary methods for asynchronous circuit design are being explored in a number of research and advanced development projects. These methods use significantly different design approaches that more easily insure correct operation compared to typical textbook approaches.

We focus here on solving problems that arise for the synchronous circuit designer in dealing with asynchronous circuits or asynchronous interfaces. The interfaces to be considered are shown in Figure 4-39.

The problems of driving an asynchronous circuit with the outputs of a synchronous circuit as in Figure 4-39(a) are due primarily to combinational circuit hazards. This is important because we deal with asynchronous circuits as components, particularly in the memory and input–output regions of systems. Because of space limitation, however, this problem is treated in a Companion Website supplement.

COMBINATIONAL HAZARDS   A supplement entitled *Combinational Hazards* is available on the text Companion Website.

We next consider the problem of an asynchronous circuit, driving a synchronous circuit as shown in Figure 4-39(b). The asynchronous circuit can be as simple as a latch that deals with a phenomenon called contact bounce generated by manually operated pushbuttons or switches. It is obvious that signals originating from a pushbutton are not synchronized with an internal electronic clock and can occur at any time. The same problem can also come from a synchronous circuit having a clock signal X unrelated to the clock Y of the circuit being driven as in Figure 4-39(c). In such a case, the signals entering the driven circuit are asynchronous with respect to

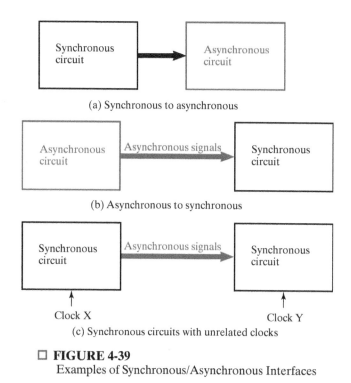

(a) Synchronous to asynchronous

(b) Asynchronous to synchronous

(c) Synchronous circuits with unrelated clocks

☐ **FIGURE 4-39**
Examples of Synchronous/Asynchronous Interfaces

clock Y. Both of these cases can cause circuit malfunction, so we offer the synchronizing of such signals as a solution. In line with the perverse nature of asynchronous behavior, this solution isn't perfect, but suffers from a troublesome phenomenon referred to as metastability, a topic treated briefly here.

Our final topic that affects the synchronous circuit designer, but not in an interface problem, is "I thought this was a synchronous circuit; after all, it does have a clock controlling state changes." Here we illustrate how a circuit designer can easily fall into the pitfall of unknowingly producing an asynchronous design, bringing into play timing-dependent factors controlling correct or incorrect operation.

4-12 SYNCHRONIZATION AND METASTABILITY

We now turn our attention to asynchronous signals driving synchronous circuits, the case shown in Figures 4-39(b) and (c). Initially, we look at the problem that occurs if an asynchronous signal is applied directly to the synchronous circuit without special treatment. Then we offer a solution but find that there is an additional problem with the solution, which we also attempt to remedy.

The circuit in Figure 4-40 can illustrate erroneous behavior due to an input signal not synchronized with the clock. The circuit is initialized by using the Reset signal which sets the state of the circuit to $S0$ ($y0, y1, y2 = 1, 0, 0$). As long as $RDY = 1$, the circuit cycles through the states $S0$ (1, 0, 0) and $S1$ (0, 1, 0) and $S2(0, 0, 1)$. If

(a) State diagram

(b) Logic diagram

◻ **FIGURE 4-40**
Example Circuit for Illustration of Synchronization

$RDY = 0$, then the circuit waits in state $S0$ until $RDY = 1$ causes it to go to state $S1$. Also, the state can change from $S1$ to $S2$ and from $S2$ to $S0$ with $RDY = 0$. All other combinations of state variables are invalid during the normal operation of the circuit.

Now suppose that RDY is asynchronous with respect to Clock. This means that it can change any time during the clock period. In Figure 4-41(a), the signal RDY changes well away from the positive clock edge, so that the setup and hold times for flip-flops y0 and y1 are easily met. The circuit operates normally. When RDY goes to 0 and the circuit reaches state $S0$, it waits in state $S0$ until RDY goes to 1. At the next positive clock edge, the stage changes to $S1$. The circuit then proceeds to state $S2$ and back to $S0$.

In Figures 4-41(b) and (c), the change in signal RDY from 0 to 1 reaches two flip-flops. The change arrives at the flip-flop inputs very near the positive clock edge within the setup-time, hold-time interval. This violates the specified operating conditions of the flip-flops. Instead of responding as if they correctly saw opposite values at their D inputs, the flip-flops may respond as if they saw the same inputs yielding circuit states $(0, 0, 0)$ or $(1, 1, 0)$.

In Figure 4-41(b), y0 resets to 0, but y1 fails to set to 1, giving state $(0, 0, 0)$. Since there is no 1 to circulate among the flip-flops, the state remains at $(0, 0, 0)$. The circuit is locked in this state and has failed.

In Figure 4-41(c), y1 sets and y0 fails to reset, giving state $(1, 1, 0)$. There are now two 1s circulating among the flip-flops, giving state sequence 110, 011, 101. These

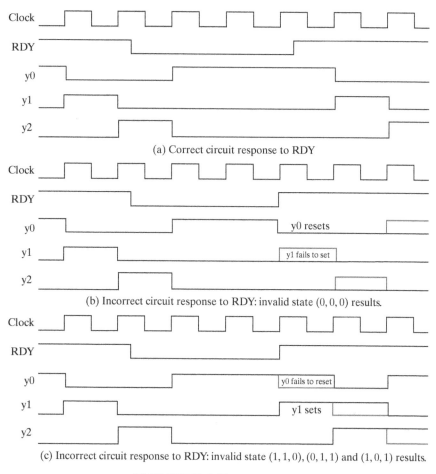

(a) Correct circuit response to RDY

(b) Incorrect circuit response to RDY: invalid state $(0, 0, 0)$ results.

(c) Incorrect circuit response to RDY: invalid state $(1, 1, 0)$, $(0, 1, 1)$ and $(1, 0, 1)$ results.

□ **FIGURE 4-41**
Behavior of Example Circuit

are all invalid states and give an incorrect output sequence. Thus, the circuit has again failed. Whether or not these failures occur depends upon circuit delays, the setup and hold times, and the detailed behavior of the flip-flops. Since none of these can be tightly controlled, we need a solution to prevent these failures that is independent of these parameters. Such a solution is the use of a synchronizing flip-flop.

SYNCHRONIZING FLIP-FLOP In Figure 4-42(a), a *D* flip-flop has been added to the example circuit. The asynchronous signal *RDY* enters the *D* flip-flop and *RDY_S*, its output, is synchronous with signal Clock in the sense that *RDY_S* changes one flip-flop delay after the positive edge. Since the asynchronous signal *RDY* enters the circuit through this single synchronizing flip-flop, the behavior exhibited when *RDY* reached two flip-flops is avoided. *RDY_S* cannot cause such behavior, since it does not change during the setup-time, hold-time interval for the normal circuit flip-flops.

☐ **FIGURE 4-42**
Example Circuit with Synchronizing D Flip-flop Added

A remaining question is, how does the synchronizing flip-flop behave when *RDY* changes during the setup-time, hold-time interval. Basically, either the flip-flop sees the change or it doesn't. If it doesn't see it, then the change is seen at the next positive clock edge, one clock period later. Note that this can happen only if the changes in the asynchronous signal are separated by a minimum-interval. It is the designer's responsibility to insure that this minimum interval specification is met by the asynchronous input. The behavior discussed in this paragraph is illustrated in Figure 4-43. The case in which the change in *RDY* is immediately sensed by the flip-flop and the case in which *RDY* is not sensed until the next positive clock edge are shown. In the latter case, the response to the change in *RDY* is delayed by an extra clock period. Since *RDY* is asynchronous, the fact that the times at which state changes occur due to changes in *RDY* may vary by a clock period should be of no consequence. If it is critical, then the circuit specifications may not be realizable.

METASTABILITY   At this point, it seems as if we have a solution that deals with the asynchronous-input-signal problem. Unfortunately, our solution is imperfect. Latches used to construct flip-flops actually have three potential states: stable 1, stable 0, and *metastable*. These states can best be described by the mechanical analogy in Figure 4-44. The state of the latch is represented by the position of a ball on a hilly surface. If the ball is in the left valley, then the state is a 0. If the ball is in the right valley, then the state is a 1. In order to move the ball between the valleys, say from state 0 to state 1, it is necessary to push the ball up the hill and over the top. This requires a certain amount of energy expenditure. If the energy runs out with the ball in position *M*, it just stays there, halfway between 0 and 1. In fact, however, it will eventually, at some nondeterministic time, go on to 1 or back to 0, due to some mechanical "noise" such as wind, a minor earthquake, or disturbance by some creature. The analogy of this situation in a latch is as follows. When an input to the cross-coupled pair of latch gates changes in just the right timing relationship with the clock edge, a narrow pulse can be generated. The pulse may have just enough energy to change the latch

(a) Circuit response to RDY with sensing at the Clock edge where RDY changes

(b) Circuit response to RDY with sensing at the next Clock edge where RDY changes

□ **FIGURE 4-43**
Behavior of Example Circuit with Synchronizing Flip-flop on RDY

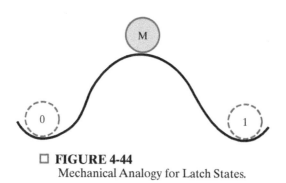

□ **FIGURE 4-44**
Mechanical Analogy for Latch States.

state to the metastable point where both gates have equal output values with voltages between 1 and 0. Like the mechanical system, the latch and hence the flip-flop containing it will eventually go to either 0 or 1 due to a tiny electronic "noise" disturbance. The length of time it remains in the metastable state is nondeterministic. The interval during which a change in the input will cause metastable behavior is very narrow, of the order of a few tens of picoseconds. Thus the behavior is unlikely, but it can happen. When it does, it is unknown how long the metastable state will persist.

If it does persist for a clock period, then the two flip-flops in our example will see a value on the synchronizing flip-flop output *RDY_S* that is between 0 and 1. Response by the two flip-flops to such a value is unpredictable, so there is a good chance that the circuit will fail.

This phenomenon was discovered by two electrical engineering faculty members at Washington University in St. Louis. In the late 1960s, the second author of this text attended a presentation they made at Wisconsin. They had pictures of oscilloscope traces showing the metastable behavior. At about the same time, a commercial computer manufacturer was experiencing infrequent, unexplained failures in their new, faster computers. You can probably guess the cause! The nature of metastable behavior for a particular CMOS *D* flip-flop used as a synchronizing flip-flop is shown in Figure 4-45; this data was gathered over 30 minutes. The normal delay from the Clock to *Q* is 13 ns as indicated by the dotted line. But by carefully controlling the timing of the changes in *D* and the Clock, the flip-flop is forced into its metastable region. In that region, the best flip-flop delay seen is 30 ns and the worst is 45 ns. Thus, if the clock period is less than 45 ns, a metastable event that can adversely affect the behavior of two or more flip-flops within the circuit being driven by the synchronizing flip-flop occurs many times in 30 minutes. Actually, although not shown in the figure, the changes in *Q* closer to 30 ns are much more frequent than those close to 45 ns. So the shorter the clock period, the worse the problem gets. If the sampling interval were 50 hours instead of 30 minutes, there would be only a few events appearing as late as 55 ns. The value between 1 and 0 that occurs for a time

☐ **FIGURE 4-45**
Metastable Behavior

inside the flip-flop in this experiment is converted to a longer delay by the output buffer of the flip-flop and so is not visible at the output.

So what can be done about this problem? Many solutions have been proposed, some of them ineffective. A simple one is to use a series of synchronizing flip-flops, i.e., a small shift register. The likelihood of the second flip-flop in the series going metastable because the first one applies a metastable or delayed input to it is less than that of the first flip-flop going metastable, and so on. Some commercial designs have used as many as six flip-flops in series to deal with this problem. More common is the use of three or so flip-flops in series. The more flip-flops, the more the circuit response to a change is delayed and the less likely the circuit is to fail due to metastability. But the probability never goes to zero. Some degree of uncertainty for incorrect operation always remains, however small. For a much more detailed discussion of metastability, see Wakerly's *Digital Design: Principles and Practices*, 4th ed., 2006.

4-13 SYNCHRONOUS CIRCUIT PITFALLS

Just because there is a clock does not mean that a circuit is synchronous. For example, in a ripple counter, such as in Figure 6-12, the clock drives at most one flip-flop clock input directly. All other clock inputs driving the flip-flops are actually state variables. So the changes in the state variables that are the outputs of these flip-flops are not synchronous with the clock. For a 16-bit ripple counter, in the worst case where all flip-flops change state, the most significant bit changes 16 flip-flop delays after the clock edge on the first flip-flop.

Also, consider the synchronous counter in Figure 4-46. The 4-bit synchronous binary counter counts up by 1 whenever a positive edge occurs on *Clock*. When the count reaches 1111, the count up results in 0000. The binary counter also has an *Asynchronous reset* with drives the four asynchronous reset inputs to the internal flip-flops. When the reset shown becomes 0, it clears all four flip-flops to 0 with only the inherent time delays, i.e., independent of the positive clock edge. Due to the attached NAND gate and its connections, when the count become 0110 (6) in response to a positive edge, the NAND produces a 0, causing the four flip-flops to be cleared, giving 0000 (0). So the counter is supposed to count 0, 1, 2, 3, 4, 5, 0, ... But suppose that A_2 goes to 0 a bit earlier than A_1. Then the output of the NAND can go

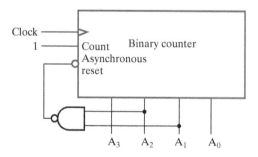

□ **FIGURE 4-46**
Example of an Asynchronous Circuit

to a 1 before all flip-flops in the counter have been reliably reset. If flip-flop A_1 is slow enough and A_2 fast enough, the state 0010 could result instead of 0000. We have actually seen this type of incorrect behavior in the laboratory. Because this counter "kills itself" back to value zero, it is called a *suicide counter*. Unfortunately, using it is more like committing "job suicide."

The suicide counter is just one example of a sneaky class of asynchronous circuits posing as synchronous ones. If you use the direct inputs, clear or preset, to a flip-flop for anything other than power-up reset and overall system reset, you have designed an asynchronous circuit, because flip-flop state changes are no longer occurring just in response to the clock signal present at the flip-flop clock input. Further, with the complexity of flip-flops plus whatever logic you may have added, you have no idea what sort of hazard problems or other timing problems you may have.

In summary, there are certainly situations where you must use asynchronous circuits to get the desired behavior. But these situations are far fewer than the cases where someone *thinks* they need an asynchronous circuit or a synchronous circuit that is really asynchronous. So try to avoid them whenever you can.

As for synchronizing flip-flops, their use is essential in making the transition from asynchronous signals to a synchronous circuit. Care must be taken to deal with metastability. There is a lot more to synchronization than we have presented here. For example, if the timing of a set of asynchronous signals is known relative to another particular asynchronous signal, only the latter signal may need to be synchronized.

4-14 CHAPTER SUMMARY

Sequential circuits are the foundation upon which most digital design is based. Flip-flops are the basic storage elements for synchronous sequential circuits. Flip-flops are constructed of more fundamental elements called latches. By themselves, latches are transparent and, as a consequence, are very difficult to use in synchronous sequential circuits using a single clock. When latches are combined to form flip-flops, nontransparent storage elements very convenient for use in such circuits are formed. Two triggering methods are used for flip-flops: pulse and edge triggering. In addition, there are a number of flip-flop types, including D, SR, JK, and T.

Sequential circuits are formed using these flip-flops and combinational logic. Sequential circuits can be analyzed to find state tables and state diagrams that represent the behavior of the circuits. Also, analysis can be performed by using logic simulation.

These same state diagrams and state tables can be formulated from verbal specifications of digital circuits. By assigning binary codes to the states and finding flip-flop input equations, sequential circuits can be designed. The design process also includes issues such as finding logic for the circuit outputs, resetting the state at power-up, and controlling the behavior of the circuit when it enters states unused in the original specification. Finally, logic simulation plays an important role in verifying that the circuit designed meets the original specification.

In order to deal with more complex, realistic designs, state-machine diagrams and state tables are introduced. The goal of this notation is to minimize the complexity of descriptions, maximize the flexibility of representation, permit the use of default conditions, and provide a model that facilitates modeling of pragmatic designs. In addition, this model builds toward the use of hardware description languages to model sequential circuits.

As an alternative to the use of logic diagrams, state diagrams, and state tables, sequential circuits can be defined in VHDL or Verilog descriptions. These descriptions provide a powerful, flexible approach to sequential circuit specification for both simulation and automatic circuit synthesis. These representations involve processes that provide added descriptive power beyond the concurrent assignment statements of VHDL and the continuous assignment statement of Verilog. The processes, which permit program-like coding and use if-then-else and case conditional statements, can also be used to efficiently describe combinational logic.

Finally, the timing parameters associated with flip-flops were presented, and the relationship between path delay in sequential circuits and clock frequency was established. Following this description, the important topics of synchronization of asynchronous signals, and metastability in synchronizing circuits were covered.

REFERENCES

1. BHASKER, J. *A Verilog HDL Primer*, 2nd ed. Allentown, PA: Star Galaxy Press, 1999.

2. CILETTI, M. *Advanced Digital Design with Verilog HDL*. Upper Saddle River, NJ: Pearson Prentice Hall, 2003.

3. CILETTI, M. *Starter's Guide to Verilog 2001*. Upper Saddle River, NJ: Pearson Prentice Hall, 2004.

4. CLARE, C. R. *Designing Logic Systems Using State Machines*. New York: McGraw-Hill Book Company, 1973.

5. *High-Speed CMOS Logic Data Book*. Dallas: Texas Instruments, 1989.

6. *IEEE Standard VHDL Language Reference Manual* (ANSI/IEEE Std 1076-1993; revision of IEEE Std 1076-1987). New York: The Institute of Electrical and Electronics Engineers, 1994.

7. *IEEE Standard Description Language Based on the Verilog Hardware Description Language* (IEEE Std 1364-1995). New York: The Institute of Electrical and Electronics Engineers, 1995.

8. KATZ, R. H. AND G. BORRIELLO. *Contemporary Logic Design*, 2nd ed. Upper Saddle River, NJ: Pearson Prentice Hall, 2005.

9. MANO, M. M. *Digital Design*, 3rd ed. Upper Saddle River, NJ: Pearson Prentice Hall, 2002.

10. PALNITKAR, S. *Verilog HDL: A Guide to Digital Design and Synthesis*, 2nd ed. Upper Saddle River, NJ: Pearson Prentice Hall, 2003.

11. PELLERIN, D. AND D. TAYLOR. *VHDL Made Easy!* Upper Saddle River, NJ: Prentice Hall PTR, 1997.

12. SMITH, D. J. *HDL Chip Design*. Madison, AL: Doone Publications, 1996.

13. STEFAN, S. AND L. LINDH. *VHDL for Designers*. London: Prentice Hall Europe, 1997.

14. THOMAS, D. AND P. MOORBY. *The Verilog Hardware Description Language*, 5th ed. New York: Springer, 2002.

15. WAKERLY, J. F. *Digital Design: Principles and Practices*, 4th ed. Upper Saddle River, NJ: Pearson Prentice Hall, 2006.

16. YALAMANCHILI, S. *VHDL Starter's Guide*, 2nd ed. Upper Saddle River, NJ: Pearson Prentice Hall, 2005.

 PROBLEMS

The plus (+) indicates a more advanced problem and the asterisk (*) indicates that a solution is available on the Companion Website for the text.

4-1. Perform a manual or computer-based logic simulation similar to that given in Figure 4-5 for the $\overline{S}\,\overline{R}$ latch shown in Figure 4-6. Construct the input sequence, keeping in mind that changes in state for this type of latch occur in response to 0 rather than 1.

4-2. Perform a manual or computer-based logic simulation similar to that given in Figure 4-5 for the *SR* latch with control input *C* in Figure 4-7. In particular, examine the behavior of the circuit when *S* and *R* are changed while *C* has the value 1.

4-3. A popular alternative design for a positive-edge-triggered *D* flip-flop is shown in Figure 4-47. Manually or automatically simulate the circuit to determine whether its functional behavior is identical to that of the circuit in Figure 4-10.

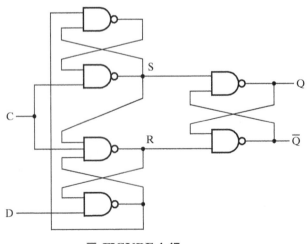

☐ **FIGURE 4-47**
Circuit for Problem 4-3

4-4. *Clock* and *D* waveforms, a *D* latch and an edge-triggered *D* flip-flop are shown in Figure 4-48. For both the latch and the flip-flop, carefully sketch the output waveform, Q_i, obtained in response to the input waveforms. Assume that the propagation delay of the storage elements is negligible. Initially, all storage elements store 0.

4-5. A sequential circuit with a *D* flip-flop *A*, two inputs *X* and *Y*, and one output *Z* is specified by the following input equations:

$$Z = A\overline{Y} + XY\overline{A}, + A\overline{X}$$

(a) Draw the logic diagram of the circuit.

(b) Derive the state table.

(c) Derive the state diagram.

(d) Is this a Mealy or a Moore machine?

4-6. A sequential circuit with two *D* flip-flops *A* and *B* and input *X* and output *Y* is specified by the following input equations:

$$Y = \overline{A} + B, \quad D_A = X + B, \quad D_B = X \cdot \overline{A}$$

(a) Draw the logic diagram of the circuit.

(b) Derive the state table.

(c) Derive the state diagram.

(d) Is this a Mealy or a Moore machine?

4-7. *A sequential circuit has three *D* flip-flops *A*, *B*, and *C*, and one input *X*. The circuit is described by the following input equations:

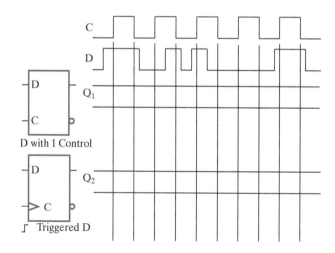

□ **FIGURE 4-48**
Waveforms and Storage Element for Problem 4-4

$$D_A = (B\overline{C} + \overline{B}C)X + (BC + \overline{B}\,\overline{C})\overline{X}$$

$$D_B = A$$

$$D_C = B$$

(a) Derive the state table for the circuit.

(b) Draw two state diagrams, one for $X = 0$ and the other for $X = 1$.

4-8. A sequential circuit has one flip-flop Q, two inputs X and Y, and one output S. The circuit consists of a D flip-flop with S as its output and logic implementing the function

$$D = S \oplus (X + Y)$$

with D as the input to the D flip-flop. Derive the state table and state diagram of the sequential circuit.

4-9. Starting from state 00 in the state diagram of Figure 4-15(a), determine the state transitions and output sequence that will be generated when an input sequence of 10011011110 is applied.

4-10. Draw the state diagram of the sequential circuit specified by the state table in Table 4-14.

☐ **TABLE 4-14**
State Table for Circuit of Problem 4-10

Present State		Inputs		Next State		Output
A	**B**	**X**	**Y**	**A**	**B**	**Z**
0	0	0	0	1	0	0
0	0	0	1	1	1	1
0	0	1	0	1	1	0
0	0	1	1	1	1	1
0	1	0	0	0	1	1
0	1	0	1	0	0	0
0	1	1	0	0	0	1
0	1	1	1	0	0	0
1	0	0	0	1	1	1
1	0	0	1	0	1	1
1	0	1	0	0	1	0
1	0	1	1	1	0	0
1	1	0	0	0	0	0
1	1	0	1	0	1	0
1	1	1	0	1	0	1
1	1	1	1	1	1	1

□ **FIGURE 4-49**
Circuit for Problem 4-11, Problem 4-40, Problem 4-41, Problem 4-49, Problem 4-50, and
Problem 4-59

4-11. A sequential circuit has two D flip-flops, one input X, and one output Y. The
logic diagram of the circuit is shown in Figure 4-49. Derive the state table and
state diagram of the circuit.

4-12. A sequential circuit is given in Figure 4-13.

(a) Add the necessary logic and/or connections to the circuit to provide an
asynchronous reset to state $A = 1, B = 0$ for signal $Reset = 0$.

(b) Add the necessary logic and/or connections to the circuit to provide a
synchronous reset to state $A = 0, B = 0$ for signal $Reset = 1$.

4-13. *Design a sequential circuit with two D flip-flops A and B and one
input X. When $X = 0$, the state of the circuit remains the same. When $X = 1$,
the circuit goes through the state transitions from 00 to 10 to 11 to 01, back to
00, and then repeats.

4-14. The state diagram for a sequential circuit appears in Figure 4-50.

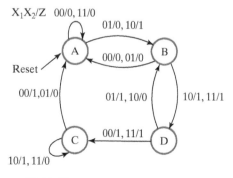

□ **FIGURE 4-50**
State Diagram for Problem 4-14

(a) Find the state table for the circuit.

(b) Make a state assignment for the circuit using 2-bit codes and find the encoded state table.

(c) Find an optimized circuit implementation using D flip-flops, NAND gates, and inverters.

(d) Repeat parts (b) and (c) using one-hot encoding for the state assignment.

4-15. The state diagram for a sequential circuit appears in Figure 4-51.

(a) Find the state table for the circuit.

(b) Make a state assignment for the circuit using 3-bit codes for the six states; make one of the code bits equal to the output to save logic, and find the encoded state table. The next states and outputs are don't cares for the two unused state codes.

(c) Find an optimized circuit implementation using D flip-flops, NAND gates, and inverters.

(d) Repeat parts (b) and (c) using one-hot encoding for the state assignment.

4-16. The circuit given in Figure 4-52 is to be redesigned to cut its cost.

(a) Find the state table for the circuit and replace the state codes with single-letter identifiers. States 100 and 111 were unused in the original design.

(b) Check for and combine equivalent states.

(c) Make a state assignment such that the output is one of the state variables.

(d) Find the gate-input costs of the original circuit and your circuit, assuming that the gate-input cost of a D flip-flop is 14. Is the cost of the new circuit reduced?

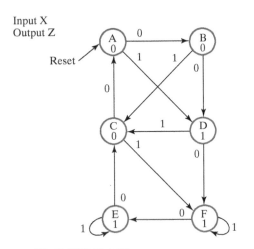

☐ **FIGURE 4-51**
State Diagram for Problem 4-15

□ **FIGURE 4-52**
Circuit for Problem 4-16

4-17. A sequential circuit for a luggage lock has ten pushbuttons labeled $0, 1, 2, 3, 4, 5,$
$6, 7, 8,$ and 9. Each pushbutton 0 through 9 produces a 1 on $X_i, i = 0$ through 9,
respectively, with all other values on variable $X_j, j \neq i$, equal to 0. Also, these
ten pushbuttons produce a positive pulse on the clock C for clocking the
flip-flops in the circuit. The circuitry that produces the X_i signals and the clock
C has already been designed. The lock opens in response to a sequence of
four X_i values, $i = 0, \ldots, 9$, set by the user. The logic for connecting the four
selected X_i values to variables $X_a, X_b, X_c,$ and X_d has also been designed. The
circuit is locked and reset to its initial state by pushing pushbutton *Lock*,
which provides L, the asynchronous reset signal for the circuit. The lock is to
unlock in response to the sequence X_a, X_b, X_c, X_d, regardless of all past inputs
applied to it since it was reset. The circuit has a single Moore type output U
which is 1 to unlock the lock, and 0 otherwise. Design the circuit with inputs
$X_a, X_b, X_c,$ and X_d, reset L, clock C, and output U. Use a one-hot code for the
state assignment. Implement the circuit with D flip-flops and AND gates, OR
gates, and inverters.

4-18. *A serial 2s complementer is to be designed. A binary integer of arbitrary
length is presented to the serial 2s complementer, least significant bit first, on
input X. When a given bit is presented on input X, the corresponding output
bit is to appear during the same clock cycle on output Z. To indicate that a
sequence is complete and that the circuit is to be initialized to receive another
sequence, input Y becomes 1 for one clock cycle. Otherwise, Y is 0.

(a) Find the state diagram for the serial 2s complementer.

(b) Find the state table for the serial 2s complementer.

(c) Write an HDL description for the state machine for the serial 2s complementer using Example 4-13 (VHDL) or Example 4-15 (Verilog) as a template.

4-19. A serial odd parity generator is to be designed. A binary sequence of arbitrary length is presented to the parity generator on input X. When a given bit is presented on input X, the corresponding odd parity bit for the binary sequence is to appear during the same clock cycle on output Z. To indicate that a sequence is complete and that the circuit is to be initialized to receive another sequence, input Y becomes 1 for one clock cycle. Otherwise, Y is 0.

(a) Find the state diagram for the serial odd parity generator.

(b) Find the state table for the serial odd parity generator.

(c) Write an HDL description for the state machine for the odd parity generator using Example 4-13 (VHDL) or Example 4-15 (Verilog) as a template.

4-20. A Universal Serial Bus (USB) communication link requires a circuit that produces the sequence 00000001. You are to design a synchronous sequential circuit that starts producing this sequence for input $E = 1$. Once the sequence starts, it completes. If $E = 1$, during the last output in the sequence, the sequence repeats. Otherwise, if $E = 0$, the output remains constant at 1.

(a) Draw the Moore state diagram for the circuit.

(b) Find the state table and make a state assignment.

(c) Design the circuit using D flip-flops and logic gates. A reset should be included to place the circuit in the appropriate initial state at which E is examined to determine if the sequence of constant 1s is to be produced.

4-21. Repeat Problem 4-20 for the sequence 01111110 that is used in a different communication network protocol.

4-22. +The sequence in Problem 4-21 is a flag used in a communication network that represents the beginning of a message. This flag must be unique. As a consequence, at most five 1s in sequence may appear anywhere else in the message. Since this is unrealistic for normal message content, a trick called zero insertion is used. The normal message, which can contain strings of 1s longer than 5, enters input X of a sequential zero-insertion circuit. The circuit has two outputs, Z and S. When a fifth 1 in sequence appears on X, a 0 is inserted in the stream of outputs appearing on Z and the output $S = 1$, indicating to the circuit supplying the zero-insertion circuit with inputs that it must stall and not apply a new input for one clock cycle. This is necessary because the insertion of 0s in the output sequence causes it to be longer than the input sequence without the stall. Zero insertion is illustrated by the following example sequences:

Sequence on X without any stalls:	011111001111110000101110101
Sequence on X with stalls:	0111111001111111100001011110101
Sequence on Z:	0111110001111101100001011110101
Sequence on S:	0000001000000010000000000000000

(a) Find the state diagram for the circuit.

(b) Find the state table for the circuit and make a state assignment.

(c) Find an implementation of the circuit using D flip-flops and logic gates.

4-23. In many communication and networking systems, the signal transmitted on the communication line uses a non-return-to-zero (NRZ) format. USB uses a specific version referred to as non-return-to-zero inverted (NRZI). A circuit that converts any message sequence of 0s and 1s to a sequence in the NRZI format is to be designed. The mapping for such a circuit is as follows:

(a) If the message bit is a 0, then the NRZI format message contains an immediate change from 1 to 0 or from 0 to 1, depending on the current NRZI value.

(b) If the message bit is a 1, then the NRZI format message remains fixed at 0 or 1, depending on the current NRZI value.

This transformation is illustrated by the following example, which assumes that the initial value of the NRZI message is 1:

Message:	10001110011010
NRZI Message:	10100001000110

(a) Find the Mealy model state diagram for the circuit.

(b) Find the state table for the circuit and make a state assignment.

(c) Find an implementation of the circuit using D flip-flops and logic gates.

4-24. +Repeat Problem 4-23, designing a sequential circuit that transforms an NRZI message into a normal message. The mapping for such a circuit is as follows:

(a) If a change from 0 to 1 or from 1 to 0 occurs between adjacent bits in the NRZI message, then the message bit is a 0.

(b) If no change occurs between adjacent bits in the NRZI message, then the message bit is a 1.

4-25. A pair of signals Request (R) and Acknowledge (A) is used to coordinate transactions between a CPU and its I/O system. The interaction of these signals is often referred to as a "handshake." These signals are synchronous with the clock and, for a transaction, are to have their transitions always appear in the order shown in Figure 4-53. A handshake checker is to be designed that will verify the transition order. The checker has inputs, R and A, asynchronous reset signal, RESET, and output, Error (E). If the transitions in a handshake are in order, $E = 0$. If the transitions are out of order, then E becomes 1 and remains at 1 until the asynchronous reset signal (RESET $= 1$) is applied to the CPU.

□ **FIGURE 4-53**
Signals for Problem 4–25

(a) Find the state diagram for the handshake checker.

(b) Find the state table for the handshake checker.

4-26. A serial sequence detector is to be designed for some serial communication line that is able to detect a bit pattern of three consecutive 1s. The circuit is connected with serial communication line and has output Z and input X. When the input has three consecutive 1s, then the output $Z = 0$; in all other case, it will be zero. Once the output $Z = 1$, it will remain in 1 state until some zero comes. Whenever $X = 0$, the circuit reset. The circuit always remains in 0 states in all other bit sequence condition. Say after a bit sequence of 0110, the circuit will go to initial state at the end of the last zero, i.e., whenever it detects some zero.

(a) Find the state diagram for the serial leading-1s detector.

(b) Is this a Mealy or a Moore machine.

4-27. *A sequential circuit has two flip-flops A and B, one input X, and one output Y. The state diagram is shown in Figure 4-54. Design the circuit with D flip-flops using a one-hot state assignment.

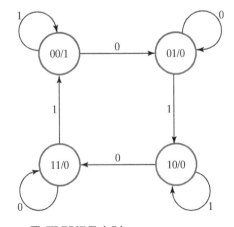

□ **FIGURE 4-54**
State Diagram for Problem 4–27

4-28. Repeat Problem 4-27 with D flip-flops using a Gray-code assignment.

4-29. +The state table for a 3-bit twisted ring counter is given in Table 4-15. This circuit has no inputs, and its outputs are the uncomplemented outputs of the flip-flops. Since it has no inputs, it simply goes from state to state whenever a clock pulse occurs. It has an asynchronous reset that initializes it to state 000.

   (a) Design the circuit using D flip-flops and assuming that the unspecified next states are don't-care conditions.

   (b) Add the necessary logic to the circuit to initialize it to state 000 on power-up master reset.

   (c) In the subsection "Designing with Unused States" of Section 4-5, three techniques for dealing with situations in which a circuit accidentally enters an unused state are discussed. If the circuit you designed in parts (a) and (b) is used in a child's toy, which of the three techniques given would you apply? Justify your decision.

   (d) Based on your decision in part (c), redesign the circuit if necessary.

   (e) Repeat part (c) for the case in which the circuit is used to control engines on a commercial airliner. Justify your decision.

   (f) Repeat part (d) based on your decision in part (e).

4-30. Do an automatic logic simulation-based verification of your design in Problem 4-14. The input sequence used in the simulation should include all transitions in Figure 4-50. The simulation output should include the input X and the state variables A, B, and output Z.

4-31. *Generate a verification sequence for the circuit described by the state table in Table 4-14. To reduce the length of the simulation sequence, assume that the simulator can handle X inputs and use X's whenever possible. Assume that a *Reset* input is available to initialize the state to $A = 0, B = 0$ and that all transitions in the state diagram must be exercised.

□ **TABLE 4-15**
State Table for Problem 4-29

Present State	Next State
ABC	ABC
000	100
100	110
110	111
111	011
011	001
001	000

☐ **TABLE 4-16**
State Table for Problem 4-33

Present State		Input	Next State		Output
A	B	Y	A	B	Z
0	0	0	0	0	1
0	0	1	0	1	1
0	1	0	1	0	0
0	1	1	1	1	0
1	0	0	1	0	0
1	0	1	0	0	0
1	1	0	0	0	1
1	1	1	1	0	1

4-32. Design the circuit specified by Table 4-14 and use the sequence from Problem 4-31 (either yours or the one posted on the text website) to perform an automatic logic simulation-based verification of your design.

4-33. The state table for a sequential circuit is given in Table 4-16.

(a) Draw the state diagram for the circuit.

(b) Implement the circuit using D flip-flops and minimal input functions for each flip-flop. Reset is asynchronous and active low (RESET $= 0$), and initializes the state to $A = 0, B = 0$.

4-34. Design a negative-edge-triggered flip-flop. The flip flop has three inputs; these are Data, Clock, and Enable. If, at the negative edge of the clock, the enable input equals to 0, then the state at Data input is stored in the flip-flop. If, at the negative edge of clock, Enable is in 1 state, then the current stored value in the flip-flop is held. Design the flip-flop using only SR latches, AND gates, and NOT gates.

4-35. Find a state-machine diagram that is equivalent to the state diagram in Figure 4-55. Reduce the complexity of the transition conditions as much as possible. Attempt to make outputs unconditional by changing Mealy outputs to Moore outputs. Make a state assignment to your state-machine diagram

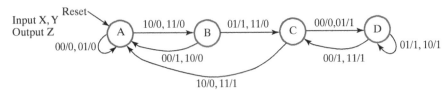

☐ **FIGURE 4-55**
State Diagram for Problem 4–35

and find an implementation for the corresponding sequential circuit using D flop-flops, AND gates, OR gates, and inverters.

4-36. Design the sequential circuit for the state-machine diagram from Problem 4-35. Use a one-hot state assignment, D flip-flops and AND gates, OR gates, and inverters.

4-37. (a) Verify that the transitions in the state-machine diagram in Figure 4-27 obey the two transition conditions for state diagrams. (b) Repeat part (a) for the state-machine diagram in Figure 4-28.

4-38. *You are to find the state-machine diagram for the following electronic vending-machine specification. The vending machine sells jawbreaker candy, one jawbreaker for 25¢. The machine accepts N (nickels = 5¢), D (dimes = 10¢), and Q (quarters = 25¢). When the sum of the coins inserted in sequence is 25¢ or more, the machine dispenses one jawbreaker by making DJ equal to 1 and returns to its initial state. No change is returned DJ equals 0 for all other states. If anything less than 25¢ is inserted and the CR (Coin Return) pushbutton is pushed, then the coins deposited are returned through the coin return slot by making RC equal to 1, after which the machine returns to its initial state. RC equals 0 in all other states. Use Moore outputs for your design.

4-39. You are to find the state-machine diagram for the following electronic vending-machine specification. The vending machine sells soda for $1.50 per bottle. The machine accepts only D ($1 bills) and Q (quarters = 25¢). When the sum of money is greater than $1.50, i.e., two $1 bills, the machine returns change in the coin return (two quarters). When $1.50 has been paid, the machine lights an LED to indicate that a soda flavor may be selected. The choices by pushbutton are C (Cola), L (Lemon soda), O (Orange soda), and R (Root Beer). When one pushbutton is pushed, the selected soda is dispensed and the machine returns to its initial state. One other feature is that an LED comes on to warn the user that two quarters are not available for change, so if a second $1 bill is inserted, no change will be given.

   (a) Find the state-machine diagram for the soda vending machine as specified.

   (b) The specification as given is not very user friendly. Rewrite it to provide a remedy for every possible situation that the user might encounter in using the machine.

All files referred to in the remaining problems are available in ASCII form for simulation and editing on the Companion Website for the text. A VHDL or Verilog compiler/simulator is necessary for the problems or portions of problems requesting simulation. Descriptions can still be written, however, for many of the problems without using compilation or simulation.

4-40. Write a gate-level structural VHDL description for the circuit from Problem 4-11. Use the VHDL model for a D flip-flop from Figure 4-29. Use the package `func_prims` in library `lcdf_vhdl` for the logic gate components.

4-41. Write a behavioral VHDL description for the circuit from Problem 4-11 using a process to describe the state diagram.

4-42. *Although this chapter has introduced VHDL processes to describe sequential circuits, combinational circuits can also be described using processes. Write a VHDL description for the multiplexer in Figure 3-25 by using a process containing a case statement rather than the continuous assignment statements as shown in Section 3-7.

4-43. Repeat Problem 4-42 by using a VHDL process containing if-then-else statements.

4-44. +Write a VHDL description for the sequential circuit with the state diagram given by Figure 4-19(d). Include an asynchronous RESET signal to initialize the circuit to state `Init`. Compile your description, apply an input sequence to pass through every transition of the state diagram at least once, and verify the correctness of the state and output sequence by comparing them to the state diagram.

4-45. Write a VHDL description for the circuit specified in Problem 4-14.

4-46. Write a VHDL description for the circuit specified in Problem 4-15.

4-47. Write a VHDL description for the state-machine diagram for the batch mixing system derived in Example 4-10.

4-48. Write a VHDL description for the state-machine diagram for the jawbreaker vending machine described in Problem 4-38. You may obtain the state-machine diagram by either solving Problem 4-38 or finding its solution on the textbook website.

4-49. Write a gate-level structural Verilog description for the circuit from Problem 4-11. Use the Verilog model for a D flip-flop from Figure 4-33.

4-50. Write a behavioral Verilog description for the circuit from Problem 4-11 using a process to describe the state diagram.

4-51. Although this chapter has introduced Verilog processes to describe sequential circuits, combinational circuits can also be described using processes. Write a Verilog description for the multiplexer in Figure 3-25 by using a process containing a case statement rather than the continuous assignment statements as shown in Section 3-7.

4-52. *Repeat Problem 4-51 by using a Verilog process containing if-else statements.

4-53. +Write a Verilog description for the sequential circuit given by the state diagram in Figure 4-19(d). Include an asynchronous *RESET* signal to initialize the circuit to state Init. Compile your description, apply an input sequence to pass through every arc of the state diagram at least once, and verify the correctness of the state and output sequence by comparing them to the state diagram.

4-54. Write a Verilog description for the circuit specified in Problem 4-14.

4-55. Write a Verilog description for the circuit specified in Problem 4-15.

4-56. Write a Verilog description for the state-machine diagram for the batch mixing system derived in Example 4-10.

4-57. Write a Verilog description for the state-machine diagram for the jawbreaker vending machine derived in Problem 4-38. You may obtain the state-machine diagram by either solving Problem 4-38 or finding its solution on the textbook website. In the parameter statement use a one-hot state assignment.

4-58. A set of waveforms applied to two D flip-flops is shown in Figure 4-56. These waveforms are applied to the flip-flops shown along with the values of their timing parameters.

(a) List the time(s) at which there are timing violations in signal D1 for flip-flop 2.

(b) List the time(s) at which there are timing violations in signal D2 for flip-flop 2.

4-59. *A sequential circuit is shown in Figure 4-49. The timing parameters for the gates and flip-flops are as follows:

$\qquad$ Inverter: $t_{pd} = 0.01$ ns
$\qquad$ XOR gate: $t_{pd} = 0.04$ ns
$\qquad$ Flip-flop: $t_{pd} = 0.08$ ns, $t_s = 0.02$ ns, and $t_h = 0.01$ ns

(a) Find the longest path delay from an external circuit input passing through gates only to an external circuit output.

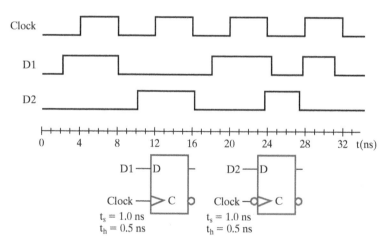

□ **FIGURE 4-56**
Circuit for Problem 4-58.

(b) Find the longest path delay in the circuit from an external input to positive clock edge.

(c) Find the longest path delay from positive clock edge to output.

(d) Find the longest path delay from positive clock edge to positive clock edge.

(e) Determine the maximum frequency of operation of the circuit in megahertz (MHz).

4-60. Repeat Problem 4-59, assuming that the circuit consists of two copies of the circuit in Figure 4-49 with input X of the second circuit copy driven by output Y of the first circuit copy.

4-61. Write a gate-level HDL description of the circuit from Problem 4-59 including delays for each component. Show that the circuit operates incorrectly when operated at a frequency greater than the maximum frequency you found as your answer for Problem 4-59.

CHAPTER

5

DIGITAL HARDWARE IMPLEMENTATION

To this point, we have studied the basics of design of combinational and sequential circuits. This chapter covers selected topics that are very important to our understanding of contemporary design. It begins by characterizing logic gates and circuits with a particular focus on complementary metal oxide semiconductor (CMOS) technology. Then basic programmable logic device (PLD) technologies are covered. This coverage includes read-only memories (ROMs), programmable logic arrays (PLAs), programmable array logic (PAL®), and Field Programmable Gate Array (FPGA) devices.

In the generic computer shown at the beginning of Chapter 1, CMOS technology forms the foundation for realization of most of the integrated circuits. Finally, programmable technologies are essential to efficient design in various parts of the computer and to the ability to upgrade systems in the field. A good example of this latter feature is updating of the operating system (OS) stored in programmable ROM in smart phones and other embedded devices, and the BIOS (Basic Input Output System) in a laptop computer.

5-1 THE DESIGN SPACE

For a given design, there is typically a target implementation technology that specifies the primitive elements available and their properties. The *design space* describes the target technologies and the parameters used to characterize them.

Integrated Circuits

Digital circuits are constructed with integrated circuits. An integrated circuit (abbreviated IC) is a silicon semiconductor crystal, informally called a *chip*, containing the electronic components for the digital gates and storage elements. The various components are interconnected on the chip. The chip is mounted in a ceramic or plastic container, and connections are welded from the chip to the external pins to form the integrated circuit. The number of pins may range from 14 on a small IC package to several hundred on a large package. Each IC has an alphanumeric designation printed on the surface of the package for identification. Each vendor publishes datasheets or a catalog containing the description and all the necessary information about the ICs that it manufactures. Typically, this information is available on vendor websites.

LEVELS OF INTEGRATION   As IC technology has improved, the number of gates present in a single silicon chip has increased considerably. Customary reference to a package as being either a small-, medium-, large-, or very-large-scale integrated device is used to differentiate between chips with just a few internal gates and those with thousands to hundreds of millions of gates.

Small-scale integrated (SSI) devices contain several independent primitive gates in a single package. The inputs and outputs of the gates are connected directly to the pins in the package. The number of gates is usually less than 10 and is limited by the number of pins available on the IC.

Medium-scale integrated (MSI) devices have approximately 10 to 100 gates in a single package. They usually perform specific elementary digital functions, such as the addition of four bits. MSI digital functions are similar to the functional blocks described in Chapter 3.

Large-scale integrated (LSI) devices contain between 100 and a few thousand gates in a single package. They include digital systems such as small processors, small memories, and programmable modules.

Very-large-scale integrated (VLSI) devices contain several thousand to hundreds of millions of gates in a single package. Examples are complex microprocessor and digital signal-processing chips. Because of their small transistor dimensions, high density, and comparatively low cost, VLSI devices have revolutionized digital system and computer design. VLSI technology enables designers to create complex structures that previously were not economical to manufacture.

CMOS Circuit Technology

Digital integrated circuits are classified not only by their function, but also by their specific implementation technology. Each technology has its own basic electronic device and circuit structures upon which more complex digital circuits and functions are developed. The specific electronic devices used in the construction of the basic circuits provide the name for the technology. Currently, silicon-based complementary metal oxide semiconductor (CMOS) technology dominates due to its high circuit density, high performance, and low power consumption. Some manufacturers are now using SOI (silicon on insulator) technology, which is a variant of CMOS in which an insulating material (silicon dioxide) isolates the transistors from the base silicon wafer. Alternative technologies based on gallium arsenide (GaAs) and silicon germanium (SiGe) are also used selectively for very high-speed circuits.

So far we have dealt largely with implementing logic circuits in terms of gates. Here we diverge briefly into electronic circuits made of electronic devices called transistors that implement the gates. For very high-performance logic or logic with specialized properties, CMOS electronic-circuit-level design is important, since to achieve the very highest performance, it is sometimes necessary to design directly from the Boolean equations to the circuit level, bypassing the logic-gate level. Also, it is important to realize that there is a circuit design process that is critical to production of the logic gates used in design.

CMOS TRANSISTOR The foundation for CMOS technology is the MOS (metal-oxide semiconductor) transistor. Transistors and the interconnections between them are fabricated as elements of an integrated circuit *die*, less formally referred to as a chip. Each rectangular die is cut from a very thin slice of crystalline silicon called a *wafer*. In the most modern fabrication facilities for making integrated circuits, wafers are typically 300 mm (about one foot) in diameter.

A sketch of a transistor is shown in Figure 5-1(a). In this sketch, the transistor has been sliced on a vertical plane through the integrated circuit chip on which it lies. In addition, the fabrication steps that form the interconnections between transistors and the protective covering over the chip have not yet occurred, leaving the transistor exposed. The substrate is the basic wafer material. The fabrication process has modified the substrate to be highly conductive in the source and the drain regions of the transistor. The conductive polysilicon *gate* has been deposited on top of a very thin insulating layer of silicon dioxide. The resulting structure consists of two identical conductive regions, the *source* and the *drain*, with a gap in between that lies under the gate. This gap is referred to as the *channel*. To give a sense of the size of the transistor, the channel length in Intel's most recent technology is 14 nanometers (14×10^{-9} meters), with 10 nanometer technology expected to be available in the near future. This ranges from approximately 1/1200 to 1/13000 of the diameter of a human hair, depending on the variability of the hair size.

In the normal operation of an n-channel MOS transistor, the drain is by definition at a higher voltage than the source. When the gate voltage is at least the threshold voltage of the transistor above the source voltage, and the drain voltage is sufficiently above the source voltage, a thin layer of the substrate just below the thin gate insulation becomes a conducting layer between the source and the drain. This permits a current to flow between the source and the drain. In this case, the transistor is said to be ON. If the gate-to-source voltage is less than the threshold voltage, the channel will be absent, blocking significant current flow. Under this condition, the transistor is said to be OFF. The use of ON and OFF refers to the present or absence of current flow between the source and the drain, respectively. Use of this terminology brings to mind the ON/OFF behavior of a switch. As a consequence, a switchlike behavior is a good first-order model for an MOS transistor.

CMOS TRANSISTOR MODELS The behavior of the MOS transistor model depends on the transistor type. CMOS technology employs two types of transistor: *n-channel* and *p-channel*. The behavior described in the preceding paragraph is that of an n-channel transistor. The two transistor types differ in the characteristics of the semiconductor

(a) Transistor geometry

(b)   (c)   (d)

Transistor symbols and models: n-channel

(e)   (f)   (g)

Transistor symbols and models: p-channel

☐ **FIGURE 5-1**
MOS Transistor, Symbols, and Switch Models

materials used in their implementation and in the mechanism governing the conduction of a current through them. Most important to us, however, is their difference in behavior. We will model this behavior using switches controlled by voltages corresponding to logic 0 and logic 1. Such a model ignores the complexity of electronic devices and captures only logical behavior.

The symbol for an n-channel transistor is shown in Figure 5-1(b). The transistor has three terminals: the gate (G), the source (S), and the drain (D), as shown. Here we make the usual assumption that a 1 represents the H voltage range and a 0 represents the L voltage range. The notion of whether a path for current to flow exists is easily modeled by a switch, as shown in Figure 5-1(c). The switch consists of two fixed terminals corresponding to the S and D terminals of the transistor. In addition, there is a movable contact that, depending on its position, determines whether the switch is open or closed. The position of the contact is controlled by the voltage applied to the gate terminal G. Since we are looking at logic behavior, this control voltage is represented on the symbol by the input variable X on the gate terminal. For an n-channel transistor, the contact is open (no path exists) for the input variable X equal to 0 and closed (a path exists) for the input variable X equal to 1. Such a contact is traditionally referred to as being *normally open*, that is, open without a positive voltage applied to activate or close it. Figure 5-1(d) shows a shorthand notation for the n-channel switch model with the variable X applied. This notation represents the fact that a path between S and D exists for X equal to 1 and does not exist for X equal to 0.

The symbol for a p-channel transistor is shown in Figure 5-1(e). The positions of the source S and drain D are seen to be interchanged relative to their positions in the n-channel transistor. The voltage applied between the gate G and the source S determines whether a path exists between the drain and source. Note that the negation indicator or bubble appears as a part of the symbol. This is because, in contrast to the behavior of an n-channel transistor, a path exists between S and D in the p-channel transistor for input variable X equal to 0 (at value L) and does not exist for input variable X equal to 1 (at value H). This behavior is represented by the model in Figure 5-1(f), which has a *normally closed* contact through which a path exists for X equal to 0. No path exists through the contact for X equal to 1. In addition, the shorthand notation of the p-channel switch model with variable X applied is given in Figure 5-1(g). Since a 0 on input X causes a path to exist through the switch and a 1 on X produces no path, the literal shown on the switch is $\overline{X}$ instead of X.

CIRCUITS OF SWITCHES   A circuit made up of switches that model transistors can be used to design CMOS logic. The circuit implements a function F if there is a path through the circuit for F equal to 1 and no path through the circuit for F equal to 0. A simple circuit of p-channel transistor switch models is shown in Figure 5-2(a). The function G_1 implemented by this circuit can be determined by finding the input combinations for which a path exists through the circuit. In order for the path to exist through G_1, both switches must be closed—that is, the path exists for $\overline{X}$ and $\overline{Y}$ both 1. This implies that $X = 0$ and $Y = 0$. Thus, the function G_1 of the circuit is $\overline{X} \cdot \overline{Y} = \overline{X + Y}$—in other words, the NOR function. In Figure 5-2(b), for function G_2, a path exists through the n-channel switch model circuit if either switch is closed—that is, for $X = 1$ or $Y = 1$. Thus, the function G_2 is $X + Y$.

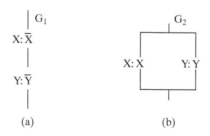

(a)   (b)

□ **FIGURE 5-2**
Example of Switch Model Circuits

In general, switches in series give an AND function and switches in parallel an OR function. (The function for the preceding circuit that models p-channel transistors is a NOR function because of the complementation of the variables and the application of DeMorgan's law.) By using these circuit functions to produce paths in a circuit that attach logic 1 (H) or logic 0 (L) to an output, we can implement a logic function on the output, as discussed next.

FULLY COMPLEMENTARY CMOS CIRCUITS   The subfamily of CMOS circuits that we will now consider has the general structure shown in Figure 5-3(a). Except during transitions, there is a path to the output of the circuit F either from the power supply +V (logic 1) or from ground (logic 0). Such a circuit is called *static* CMOS. In order to have a static circuit, the transistors must implement circuits of switches for both function F and function $\overline{F}$. In other words, both the 0s and the 1s of the function F must be implemented with paths through circuits. The switch circuit implementing F is constructed using p-channel transistors and connects the circuit output to logic 1. We use p-channel transistors because they conduct logic-1 values better than logic-0 values. The switch circuit implementing $\overline{F}$ is constructed using n-channel transistors and connects the circuit output to logic 0. Here n-channel transistors are used because they conduct logic-0 values better than logic-1 values. Note that the same input variables enter both the p-channel and n-channel switch circuits.

To illustrate a fully complementary circuit, we use transistors corresponding to the circuits G_1 and G_2 from Figure 5-2(a) and (b) as the p-channel implementation of G and the n-channel implementation of $\overline{G}$, respectively, in Figure 5-3(b). A path exists through G_1 for $\overline{X + Y} = 1$, which means that a path exists in Figure 5-3(b) from logic 1 to the circuit output, making $G = 1$ for $\overline{X + Y} = 1$. This provides the 1s on the output for the function G. A path exists through G_2 for $X + Y = 1$, which means that a path exists in Figure 5-3(b) from logic 0 to the output for $X + Y = \overline{\overline{X + Y}} = 1$. This path makes $G = 0$ for the complement of $\overline{X + Y}$. Thus, the n-channel circuit implements $\overline{G}$. This provides the 0s on the output for function G. Since both the 1s and 0s are provided for G, we can say that the circuit output $G = \overline{X + Y}$, which is a NOR gate. This is the standard static CMOS implementation for a NOR.

Since the NAND is just the dual of the NOR, we can implement the CMOS NAND by simply replacing the $+$ by $\cdot$ in the equations for G_1 and G_2. In terms of the switch circuit, the dual of switches in series is switches in parallel and vice versa. This duality applies to the transistors that are modeled as well, giving the NAND implementation in Figure 5-3(c). The final gate in Figure 5-3(d) is the implementation of the NOT.

Note that all of the circuits in Figure 5-3 implement inverting functions under DeMorgan's laws. This inversion property is characteristic of CMOS gates. In fact, as we look at a general design procedure, we assume that functions are implemented using $F = \overline{F}$. This avoids working directly with p-channel switches, which involve complementing variables. Thus, we will design the n-channel circuit for $\overline{F}$ and take the dual to get the p-channel circuit for F. For functions more complex than NAND, NOR, and NOT, the resulting circuits are called *complex gates*.

□ **FIGURE 5-3**
Fully Complementary CMOS Gate Structure and Examples

Design of complex gates, using a general design procedure, and transmission gates and their applications are covered in the supplement entitled *More CMOS Circuit-Level Design* appearing on the text Companion Website.

Technology Parameters

For each specific implementation technology, there are details that differ in their electronic circuit design and circuit parameters. The most important parameters used to characterize an implementation technology follow:

- *Fan-in* specifies the number of inputs available on a gate.
- *Fan-out* specifies the number of standard loads driven by a gate output. *Maximum fan-out* for an output specifies the fan-out that the output can drive without impairing gate performance. Standard loads may be defined in a variety of ways depending upon the technology.
- *Noise margin* is the maximum external noise voltage superimposed on a normal input value that will not cause an undesirable change in the circuit output.
- *Cost* for a gate specifies a measure of its contribution to the cost of the integrated circuit containing it.
- *Propagation delay* is the time required for a change in value of a signal to propagate from input to output. The operating speed of a circuit is inversely related to the longest propagation delays through the gates of the circuit.
- *Power consumption (dissipation)* is the power drawn from the power supply and consumed by the gate. The power consumed is dissipated as heat, so the power dissipation must be considered in relation to the operating temperature and cooling requirements of the chip. For battery-powered systems such as smart phones, the power consumption of the integrated circuits will determine the battery life of the system.

Although all of these parameters are important to the designer, further details on only selected parameters are provided here. Because of their major importance to the design process, propagation delay and circuit timing have already been discussed in Chapters 2 and 4.

FAN-IN   For high-speed technologies, *fan-in*, the number of inputs to a gate, is often restricted on gate primitives to no more than four or five. This is primarily due to electronic considerations related to gate speed. To build gates with large fan-in, interconnected gates with lower fan-in are used during technology mapping. A mapping for a 7-input NAND gate illustrated in Figure 5-4 is made up of two 4-input NANDs and an inverter.

☐ **FIGURE 5-4**
Implementation of a 7-Input NAND Gate Using
NAND Gates with Four or Fewer Inputs

FAN-OUT   One approach to measuring fan-out is the use of a *standard load*. Each input on a driven gate provides a load on the output of the driving gate which is measured in standard load units. For example, the input to a specific inverter can have a load equal to 1.0 standard load. If a gate drives six such inverters, then the fan-out is equal to 6.0 standard loads. In addition, the output of a gate has a maximum load that it can drive, called its maximum fan-out. The determination of the maximum fan-out is a function of the particular logic family. Our discussion will be restricted to CMOS, currently the most popular logic family. For CMOS gates, the loading of a gate output by the integrated circuit wiring and the inputs of other gates is modeled as a capacitance. This capacitive loading has no effect on the logic levels, as loading often does for other families. Instead, the load on the output of a gate determines the time required for the output of the gate to change from L to H and from H to L. If the load on the output is increased, then this time, called the *transition time*, increases. Thus, the maximum fan-out for a gate is the number of standard loads of capacitance that can be driven with the transition time no greater than its maximum allowable value. For example, a gate with a maximum fan-out of 8 standard loads could drive up to 8 inverters that present 1.0 standard load on each of their inputs.

Both fan-in and fan-out must be dealt with in the technology-mapping step of the design process. Gates with fan-ins larger than those available for technology mapping can be implemented with multiple gates. Gates with fan-outs that either exceed their maximum allowable fan-out or produce too high a delay need to be replaced with multiple gates in parallel or have buffers added at their outputs.

COST   For integrated circuits, the cost of a primitive gate is usually based on the area occupied by the layout cell for the circuit. The layout-cell area is proportional to the size of the transistors and the wiring in the gate layout. Ignoring the wiring area, the area of the gate is proportional to the number of transistors in the gate, which in turn is usually proportional to the gate-input cost. If the actual area of the layout is known, then a normalized value of this area provides a more accurate estimation of cost than gate-input cost.

From a system standpoint, as important as the manufacturing cost per primitive logic gate is the overall cost to design, verify, and test the integrated circuit. Designing an integrated circuit with millions of transistors and bringing it to market requires a large team of engineers and considerable non-recurring engineering (NRE) costs, one-time costs that will be incurred no matter how many units of the product are manufactured. In contrast to NRE costs, production costs are those costs that are incurred for each unit of the product that is built, based upon the labor, materials, and energy required to manufacture the unit. The NRE costs are amortized over the product volume, which is the total number of units that are manufactured. For a low volume product, the NRE costs of designing the integrated circuit can be much larger than the per-unit production costs. As an alternative to a custom integrated circuit, low volume products are often based on programmable logic devices, described in Section 5-2. The NRE costs for the programmable devices are much lower than for custom integrated circuits, as is the time required to bring the device to market. The disadvantages of programmable devices relative to custom integrated circuits include larger propagation delays (lower performance) and higher per-unit cost. Consequently, choosing between a fully custom integrated circuit and a programmable device requires understanding the required performance and the estimated product volume in order to design a product that will be profitable.

5-2 PROGRAMMABLE IMPLEMENTATION TECHNOLOGIES

Thus far, we have introduced implementation technologies that are fixed in the sense that they are fabricated as integrated circuits or by connecting together integrated circuits. In contrast, programmable logic devices (PLDs) are fabricated with structures that implement logic functions and structures that are used to control connections or to store information specifying the actual logic functions implemented. These latter structures require *programming*, a hardware procedure that determines which functions are implemented. The next four subsections deal with four types of basic programmable logic devices (PLDs): the read-only memory (ROM), the programmable logic array (PLA), the programmable array logic (PAL®) device, and the field programmable gate array (FPGA).

Before treating PLDs, we deal with the supporting programming technologies. The oldest of the programming technologies include fuses and anti-fuses. Fuses which are initially CLOSED are selectively "blown out" by a higher than normal voltage to established OPEN connections. The pattern of OPEN and CLOSED fuses establishes the connections defining the logic. Anti-fuses, the opposite of fuses, contain a material that is initially nonconducting (OPEN). Anti-fuses are selectively CLOSED by applying a higher-than-normal voltage to provide a pattern of OPEN and CLOSED anti-fuses to define the logic.

A third programming technology for controlling connections is *mask programming*, which is done by the semiconductor manufacturer during the last steps of the chip fabrication process. Connections are made or not made in the metal layers serving as conductors in the chip. Depending on the desired function for the chip, the structure of these layers is determined by the fabrication process.

All three of the preceding connection technologies are permanent. The devices cannot be reprogrammed, because irreversible physical changes have occurred as a result of device programming. Thus, if the programming is incorrect or needs to be changed, the device must be discarded.

The fourth programming technology which is very popular in large VLSI PLDs is a single-bit storage element driving the gate of an MOS n-channel transistor at the programming point. If the stored bit value is a 1, then the transistor is turned ON, and the connection between its source and drain forms a CLOSED path. For the stored bit value equal to 0, the transistor is OFF, and the connection between its source and drain is an OPEN path. Since storage element content can be changed electronically, the device can be easily reprogrammed. But in order to store values, the power supply must be available. Thus, the storage element technology is volatile — that is, the programmed logic is lost in the absence of the power-supply voltage.

The fifth and final programming technology we are considering is control of transistor switching. This popular technology is based on storing charge on a floating gate. The latter is located below the regular gate within an MOS transistor and is completely isolated by an insulating dielectric. Stored negative charge on the floating gate makes the transistor impossible to turn ON. The absence of stored negative charge makes it possible for the transistor to turn ON if a HIGH is applied to its regular gate. Since it is possible to add or remove the stored charge, these technologies can permit erasure and reprogramming.

Two approaches using control of transistor switching are called *erasable* and *electrically erasable*. Programming applies combinations of voltage higher-than-normal power-supply voltages to the transistor. Erasure uses exposure to a strong ultraviolet light source for a specified amount of time. Once this type of chip has been erased, it can be reprogrammed. An electrically erasable device can be erased by a process somewhat similar to the programming process, using voltages higher than the normal power-supply value. A third approach is *flash* technology, which is very widely used in *flash memories*. Flash technology is a form of electrically erasable technology that has a variety of erase options, including the erase of stored charge from individual floating gates, all of the floating gates, or specific subsets of floating gates.

Some, but not all, programmable-logic technologies have high fan-in gates. In order to show the internal logic diagram for such technologies in a concise form, we use a special gate symbology applicable to array logic. Figure 5-5 shows the conventional and array logic symbols for a multiple-input OR gate. Instead of having multiple input lines to the gate, we draw a single line to the gate. The input lines are drawn perpendicular to this line and are selectively connected to the gate. If an x is present at the intersection of two lines, there is a connection (CLOSED). If an x is not present, then there is no connection (OPEN). In a similar fashion, we can draw the array logic for an AND gate.

We next consider three distinct programmable device structures. We will describe each and indicate which of the technologies is typically used in its implementation. These types of PLDs differ in the placement of programmable connections in the AND-OR array. Figure 5-6 shows the locations of the connections for the three types. Programmable read-only memory (PROM) as well as flash memory has a fixed AND array constructed as a decoder and programmable connections for the output OR gates. This forms what appears to be a structure for implementing sum-of-minterm equations for the outputs. It also can be thought of as implementing a truth table (connections to OR gates for 1s and no connections to an OR gates for 0s). Also the ROM can be viewed as a memory in which the outputs provide words of binary data that are selected by the inputs applied to the decoder. The programmable array logic (PAL®) device has a programmable connection AND array and a fixed OR array. The AND gates are programmed to provide the product terms for the Boolean functions, which are logically summed in each OR gate. The most flexible of the three types of PLD is the programmable logic array (PLA), which has programmable connections for both AND and OR arrays. The product terms in the

(a) Conventional symbol   (b) Array logic symbol

□ **FIGURE 5-5**
Conventional and Array Logic Symbols for OR Gate

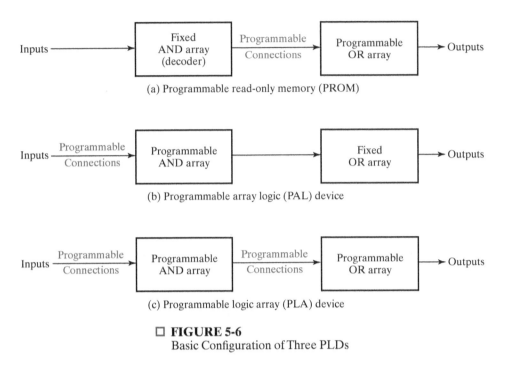

(a) Programmable read-only memory (PROM)

(b) Programmable array logic (PAL) device

(c) Programmable logic array (PLA) device

□ **FIGURE 5-6**
Basic Configuration of Three PLDs

AND array may be shared by any OR gates to provide the required sum-of-products implementations. The names PLA and PAL® emerged for devices from different vendors during the development of PLDs.

Read-Only Memory

A read-only memory (ROM) is essentially a device in which "permanent" binary information is stored. The information must be specified by the designer and is then embedded into the ROM to form the required interconnection or electronic device pattern. Once the pattern is established, it stays within the ROM even when power is turned off and on again — that is, ROM is nonvolatile.

A block diagram of a ROM device is shown in Figure 5-7(a). There are k inputs and n outputs. The inputs provide the *address* for the memory, and the outputs give the data bits of the stored word that is selected by the address. The number of words in a ROM device is determined from the fact that k address input lines can specify 2^k words. Note that ROM does not have data inputs, because it does not have a write operation. Integrated circuit ROM chips have one or more enable inputs and come with three-state outputs to facilitate the construction of large arrays of ROM. Permanent and reprogrammable ROMs are also included in VLSI circuits including processors.

Consider, for example, a 32 × 8 ROM. The unit consists of 32 words of 8 bits each. There are five input lines that form the binary numbers from 0 through 31 for the address. Figure 5-7(b) shows the internal logic construction of this ROM. The five inputs are decoded into 32 distinct outputs by means of a 5–to–32-line decoder.

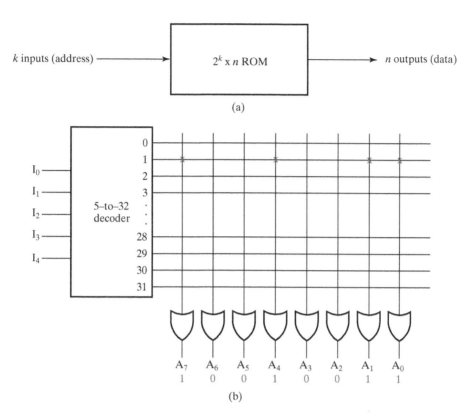

(a)

(b)

□ **FIGURE 5-7**
Block Diagram and Internal Logic of a ROM

Each output of the decoder represents a *memory address*. The 32 outputs are connected through programmable connections to each of the eight OR gates. The diagram uses the array logic convention used in complex circuits. (See Figure 5-5.) Each OR gate must be considered as having 32 inputs. Each output of the decoder is connected by a programming technology to one of the inputs of each OR gate. The ROM in Figure 5-7(b) is programmed with the word 10010011 in memory address 1. Since each OR gate has 32 internal programmable connections, and since there are eight OR gates, the ROM contains $32 \times 8 = 256$ programmable connections. In general, a $2^k \times n$ ROM will have an internal k–to–2^k–line decoder and n OR gates. Each OR gate has 2^k inputs, which are connected through programmable connections to each of the outputs of the decoder.

Depending on the programming technology and approaches, read-only memories have different names:

1. ROM—mask programmed,

2. PROM—fuse or anti-fuse programmed,

3. EPROM—erasable floating gate programmed,

4. EEPROM or E^2 PROM—electrically erasable floating gate programmed, and

5. FLASH Memory—electrically erasable floating gate with multiple erasure and programming modes.

The choice of programming technology depends on many factors, including the number of identical ROMs to be produced, the desired permanence of the programming, the desire for reprogrammability, and the desired performance in terms of delay.

ROM programming typically uses programming software that isolates the user from the details. A ROM stores computer programs, in which case the binary code produced by the usual programming tools such as compilers and assemblers is placed in the ROM. Otherwise, it can be programmed by tools that accept input, such as truth tables, Boolean equations, and hardware description languages. It can also, as in the case of FLASH memory, accept binary patterns representing, for example, photographs taken by a digital camera. In all of these cases, the input is transformed to a pattern of OPEN and CLOSED connections to the OR gates needed by the programming technology.

Programmable Logic Array

The programmable logic array (PLA) is similar in concept to the ROM, except that the PLA does not provide full decoding of the variables and does not generate all the minterms. The decoder is replaced by an array of AND gates that can be programmed to generate product terms of the input variables. The product terms are then selectively connected to OR gates to provide the sum of products for the required Boolean functions.

The internal logic of a PLA with three inputs and two outputs is shown in Figure 5-8. Such a circuit is too small to be cost effective but is presented here to demonstrate the typical logic configuration of a PLA. The diagram uses the array logic graphics symbols for complex circuits. Each input goes through a buffer and an inverter, represented in the diagram by a composite graphics symbol that has both the true and the complement outputs. Programmable connections run from each input and its complement to the inputs of each AND gate, as indicated by the intersections between the vertical and horizontal lines. The outputs of the AND gates have programmable connections to the inputs of each OR gate. The output of the OR gate goes to an XOR gate, where the other input can be programmed to receive a signal equal to either logic 1 or logic 0. The output is inverted when the XOR input is connected to 1 (since $X \oplus 1 = \overline{X}$). The output does not change when the XOR input is connected to 0 (since $X \oplus 0 = X$). The particular Boolean functions implemented in the PLA of the figure are

$$F_1 = A\overline{B} + AC + \overline{A}B\overline{C}$$

$$F_2 = \overline{AC + BC}$$

The product term is determined by the CLOSED connections from the input or their complements to the AND gates. The output of an OR gate gives the logic sum of the selected product terms as determined by the CLOSED connections

□ **FIGURE 5-8**
PLA with Three Inputs, Four Product Terms, and Two Outputs

from the AND gate outputs to the OR gate inputs. The output may be complemented or left in its true form, depending on the programming of the connection associated with the XOR gate. Due to this structure, the PLA implements sum-of-products or complemented sum-of-products functions. Product terms can be shared between the functions, since the same AND gate can be connected to multiple OR gates.

The size of a PLA is specified by the number of inputs, the number of product terms, and the number of outputs. For n inputs, k product terms, and m outputs, the internal logic of the PLA consists of n buffer-inverter gates, k AND gates, m OR gates, and m XOR gates. There are $2n \times k$ programmable connections between the inputs and the AND array, $k \times m$ programmable connections between the AND and OR arrays, and m programmable connections associated with the XOR gates.

The information needed to program a PLA are the CLOSED connections from true or complemented inputs, the CLOSED connections between AND gates and OR gates, and whether or not the sum of products form is inverted or not. As with the ROM, a variety of input forms may be acceptable to the tools that generate this information. Here we focus on implementing logic, so we consider only inverted or noninverted sum-of-products equations as the user input.

COMBINATIONAL CIRCUIT IMPLEMENTATION USING A PLA A careful investigation must be undertaken in order to reduce the number of distinct product terms, so that the size of the PLA can be minimized. Fewer product terms can be achieved by simplifying the Boolean function to a minimum number of terms. The number of literals in a term is less important, since all the input variables are available to each term anyway. It is wise, however, to avoid extra literals, as these may cause problems in testing the circuit and may reduce the speed of the circuit. An important factor in obtaining a minimum number of product terms is the sharing of terms between the outputs. Both the true and complement forms of each function should be simplified to see which one can be expressed with fewer product terms and which one provides product terms that are common to other functions. So, in terms of preparing equations to be implemented in a PLA, multiple-output, two-level function optimization is the approach needed and often incorporated in PLA design software. While we have not covered this process formally, we can informally illustrate it by using K-maps. This process is illustrated in Example 5-1.

EXAMPLE 5-1 Implementing a Combinational Circuit Using a PLA

Implement the following two Boolean functions with a PLA:

$$F_1(A,B,C) = \Sigma m(3,5,6,7)$$

$$F_2(A,B,C) = \Sigma m(1,2,3,7)$$

In Figure 5-9, using K-maps, two-level single-output optimization is applied to functions F_1 and F_2 with the resulting prime implicants used appearing in black. The resulting equations appear directly below the two maps. Product term BC can be shared between the two functions, so a total of five product terms are required. By considering the complement of F_1 and the true form of F_2, one discovers that there are two nonprime implicants, shown as blue squares, that can be used in both functions. The solutions that share these terms are given on the next line below the maps. Using the implicants in blue, the solution obtained is:

$$F_1 = \overline{\overline{A}\,\overline{B}C + \overline{A}B\overline{C} + \overline{B}\,\overline{C}}$$

$$F_2 = \overline{A}\,\overline{B}C + \overline{A}B\overline{C} + BC$$

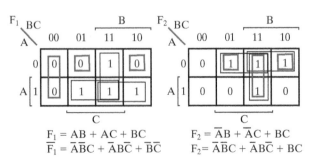

$$F_1 = AB + AC + BC$$
$$\overline{F_1} = \overline{A}\overline{B}C + \overline{A}B\overline{C} + \overline{B}\,\overline{C}$$

$$F_2 = \overline{A}B + \overline{A}C + BC$$
$$F_2 = \overline{A}\overline{B}C + \overline{A}B\overline{C} + BC$$

☐ **FIGURE 5-9**
K-Maps and Expressions for PLA Example 5-1

Because of the bar over all of F_1, a 1 must be applied to the control input of the output XOR gate. This solution requires only four AND gates. It requires both the use of an output inversion and multiple-output, two-level optimization to achieve this minimum-cost solution. The two implicants that are shared would normally result from the process of generating prime implicants for multiple-output optimization. ∎

Programmable Array Logic Devices

The programmable array logic (PAL®) device is a PLD with a fixed OR array and a programmable AND array. Because only the AND gates are programmable and cannot be shared by multiple functions, design for the PAL device is easier, but is not as flexible as that for the PLA. Figure 5-10 presents the logic configuration of a typical programmable array logic device. The particular device shown has four inputs and four outputs. Each input has a buffer-inverter gate, and each output is generated by a fixed OR gate. The device has four sections, each composed of a three-wide AND-OR array, meaning that there are three programmable AND gates in each section. Each AND gate has ten programmable input connections, indicated in the diagram by ten vertical lines intersecting each horizontal line. The horizontal line symbolizes the multiple-input configuration of an AND gate. One of the outputs shown is connected to a buffer-inverter gate and then fed back into the inputs of the AND gates through programmed connections. This is often done with all device outputs. Since the number of AND terms is not large, these paths permit the output of a PAL AND-OR circuit to be used as inputs to other PAL AND-OR circuits. This provides the capability to implement a limited variety of multiple-level circuits, which among other advantages increases the number of AND gates available for a given function.

Commercial PAL devices contain more gates than the one shown in Figure 5-10. A small PAL integrated circuit may have up to eight inputs, eight outputs, and eight sections, each consisting of an eight-wide AND-OR array. Each PAL device output is driven by a three-state buffer and also serves as an input. These input/outputs can be programmed to be an input only, an output only, or bidirectional with a variable signal driving the three-state buffer enable signal. Flip-flops are often included in a PAL device between the array and the three-state buffer at the outputs. Since each output is fed back as an input through a buffer-inverter gate into the AND programmed array, a sequential circuit can be easily implemented.

COMBINATIONAL CIRCUIT IMPLEMENTATION WITH A **PAL** DEVICE   In designing with a PAL device, because of the inability to share AND gates within a basic circuit, single-output, two-level optimization applies. But because of the connections from outputs to inputs, multilevel functions are easy to implement, so limited multilevel optimization and the sharing of sum-of-products forms and the complement of sum-of-products forms applies also. Unlike the arrangement in the PLA, a product term cannot be shared among two or more OR gates. Manual execution of optimization for a PAL device is illustrated in Example 5-2.

☐ **FIGURE 5-10**
PAL Device Structure with Connection Map for
PAL® Device for Example 5-2

EXAMPLE 5-2   Implementing a Combinational Circuit Using a PAL

As an example of a PAL device incorporated into the design of a combinational circuit, consider the following Boolean functions, given in sum-of-minterms form:

$$W(A,B,C,D) = \Sigma m(2,12,13)$$

$$X(A,B,C,D) = \Sigma m(7,8,9,10,11,12,13,14,15)$$

$$Y(A,B,C,D) = \Sigma m(0,2,3,4,5,6,7,8,10,11,15)$$

$$Z(A,B,C,D) = \Sigma m(1,2,8,12,13)$$

Simplifying the four functions to a minimum number of terms results in the following Boolean functions:

$$W = AB\overline{C} + \overline{A}\,BC\overline{D}$$

$$X = A + BCD$$

$$Y = \overline{A}B + CD + \overline{B}\,\overline{D}$$

$$Z = AB\overline{C} + \overline{A}\,\overline{B}C\overline{D} + A\,\overline{C}\,\overline{D} + \overline{A}\,\overline{B}CD$$

$$= W + A\,\overline{C}\,\overline{D} + \overline{A}\,\overline{B}\,\overline{C}\,D$$

Note that the all four equations are the result of two-level optimization. But the function for Z has four product terms. The logical sum of two of these terms is equal to W. Thus, by using W, it is possible to reduce the number of terms for Z from four to three, so that the equations above can fit into the PAL device in Figure 5-10. Even if W were not present as an output, the PAL device structure would permit the factor W to be designed and used to implement Z. In this case, however, the output at W would not be useful for implementing any other function but W. ■

Field Programmable Gate Array

The most common form of programmable logic device currently available is the field programmable gate array (FPGA). While FPGA devices from different manufacturers have a wide variety of features, most FPGA devices have three programmable elements in common: programmable logic blocks, programmable interconnect, and programmable input/output pins, as illustrated in Figure 5-11. In addition to these three common elements, many FPGAs have specialized blocks of dedicated logic such as memories, arithmetic components, and even microprocessors. This section focuses on the basic features of FPGAs, which should provide sufficient background

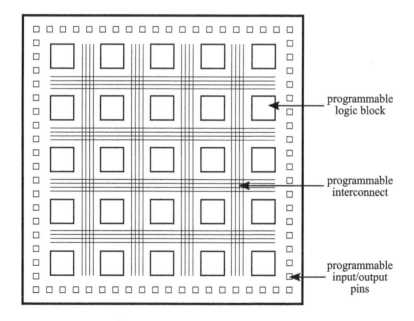

programmable logic block

programmable interconnect

programmable input/output pins

□ **FIGURE 5-11**
The Three Programmable Features of Most FPGA Devices:
Logic Blocks, Interconnect, and Input/Output

for readers who are interested in a particular FPGA to understand the data manuals from the manufacturer.

The advantage of the FPGA relative to other programmable logic families is the availability of configurable combinational logic and flip-flops, and ease of re-configuration. Most FPGA families are configured using static random access memory (SRAM), which will be more fully explained in Chapter 7. Other technologies for configuring FPGAs include Flash memory and anti-fuses (similar to the PROM described earlier in this section). FPGAs that use SRAM for their configuration are volatile, meaning that they lose their configuration when power is removed and the configuration must be loaded whenever power is re-applied. Regardless of the configuration technology, each configuration bit in the FPGA controls the behavior of a programmable element. Configuring the FPGA requires setting all of the configuration bits for the programmable logic blocks, routing, and I/O.

The first programmable feature common to many FPGAs that we will describe is the programmable logic block. A programmable logic block contains combinational and sequential logic that can be configured to implement many different functions. Many FPGA families have programmable logic blocks based upon a look-up table (LUT) to implement combinational functions. A look-up table is a $2^k \times 1$ memory that implements the truth table for a function of k variables, referred to as a k-LUT. Figure 5-12(a) illustrates a 2-input LUT. Any of the sixteen possible Boolean functions of two variables can be implemented by setting the SRAM configuration bits in the figure to the truth table for the desired function of a and b, as described in Section 3-7. To implement functions of more than k variables, several k-LUTs can be connected together with multiplexers, as shown in Figure 5-12(b). Combining the smaller LUTs with a multiplexer uses Shannon's expansion theorem, which states that any Boolean function $f(x_1, x_2, x_3, \ldots, x_k)$ can be expressed as

$$f(x_1, x_2, x_3, \ldots, x_k) = x_k \cdot f(x_1, x_2, x_3, \ldots, 1) + \overline{x_k} \cdot f(x_1, x_2, x_3, \ldots, 0)$$

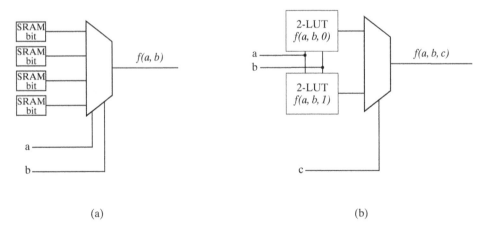

(a) (b)

☐ **FIGURE 5-12**
(a) A 2-Input Look-Up Table, (b) Implementing a 3-Input Function with Two 2-LUTs and a Multiplexer

In Figure 5-12(b), the Boolean function $f(a,b,c)$ has been implemented using the variable c on the select line of the multiplexer to choose between the two functions $f(a,b,0)$ and $f(a,b,1)$. Example 5-3 illustrates implementing a combinational function using a LUT and Shannon's expansion theorem.

EXAMPLE 5-3   Implementing a Combinational Circuit Using a Look-Up Table

Implement the following Boolean function with the look-up table circuit shown in Figure 5-12(b):

$$F(A,B,C) = \Sigma m(3,5,6,7)$$

The minterms of the function where $C = 1$ are m_3, m_5, and m_7, so $F(A,B,1) = \overline{A}B + A\overline{B} + AB = A + B$. The minterms of the function where $C = 0$ is m_6, so $F(A,B,0) = AB$. The truth tables for each of these two functions would then be stored into configuration bits of the appropriate 2-LUT of the circuit in the figure. ■

In addition to LUTs, programmable logic block typically have multiplexers, flip-flops and other logic to provide the ability to configure the block to implement a wide variety of functions. Figure 5-13 shows an example of a programmable logic block. The logic block has five major features: 1) A pair of 2-LUTs to implement combinational functions, 2) a D flip-flop for sequential functions, 3) addition logic that allows the block to implement a 1-bit full adder, 4) a set of multiplexers for selecting which functionality appears at the output, and 5) a set of SRAM configuration bits that control the behavior of the LUTs and multiplexers, denoted by squares numbered from 0 to 10.

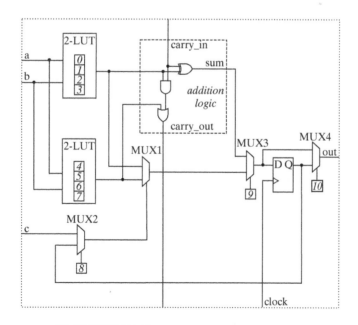

□ **FIGURE 5-13**
An Example of a Programmable Logic Block

In Figure 5-13, the multiplexer labeled MUX1, in combination with the pair of 2-LUTs, enables the logic block to implement any Boolean function of up to three variables, as was illustrated in Figure 5-12. Multiplexer MUX2 selects whether the third of the three variables is the logic block's c input or the flip-flop output. Multiplexer MUX3 selects between the output of the LUT logic or the addition logic for the input of the flip-flop and MUX4. Finally, MUX4 selects whether the logic block's output is the output of the flip-flop or combinational (the output of MUX3).

The three gates of the addition logic allow the efficient implementation of common digital functions based upon arithmetic. While it would be possible to implement an adder without having the addition logic included in the logic block, doing so would require two logic blocks to implement each bit of addition: one block for the sum and one block for the carry since the logic block would have only one output. But by including the three gates of the addition logic, one logic block can implement a one-bit full adder by configuring the upper 2-LUT to be the function $f(a,b) = a \oplus b$ and the lower 2-LUT to be the function $f(a,b) = ab$. Then the *sum* signal is equal to $a \oplus b \oplus carry\_in$ and the *carry_out* signal is equal to $ab + carry\_in(a \oplus b)$. Consequently, an n-bit ripple carry adder could be implemented with n logic blocks, whereas without the addition logic the adder would require $2n$ logic blocks. Similarly, in many of the commercially available FPGA families, the programmable logic block contains dedicated logic for implementing common arithmetic functions while requiring fewer logic resources and often with higher performance than would be possible without the dedicated logic. Rather than using a ripple carry adder as in this simple logic block, commercially available FPGAs use more complex, higher performance techniques for arithmetic such as carry lookahead addition that are beyond the scope of this introductory text.

Configuring the programmable logic block requires setting the eleven configuration bits to achieve the desired functionality. Configuration bits 0 through 7 set the truth tables to be implemented by the LUTs, bit 8 selects between the input c or the flip-flop output controlling the LUT output, bit 9 selects whether or not the addition logic is used, and bit 10 selects the output of the flip-flop or the combinational output of the LUTs or addition logic. The overall behavior of the logic block depends upon the settings of all of the configuration bits. For example, returning to the discussion of addition in the previous paragraph, implementing a full adder requires both selecting the sum output with MUX3 (configuration bit 9) and setting the 2-LUTs to the proper functions of inputs a and b (configuration bits 0–7). As another example, if MUX3 (configuration bit 9) is set to select the output of MUX1, depending upon the settings of MUX2 and MUX4 (configuration bits 8 and 10), the output signal can be either a combinational function of $a, b,$ and c; a Moore machine; or a Mealy machine. While the reset logic for the D flip-flop is omitted from this example for simplicity, in most commercial FPGAs, the flip-flop's set/reset behavior is also configurable.

The functionality included in the programmable logic block is a trade-off between the number of logic blocks required to implement a given function and the propagation delay through the logic block. As the functionality increases, the number of logic blocks required to implement a given function (and the number of logic blocks on the critical path) tends to decrease. But as the functionality increases, the propagation delay through an individual logic block also increases. The overall delay is a function of both the delay through the individual logic blocks as well as the delay through the connections between the logic blocks.

The connections between the logic blocks are the second programmable feature common to FPGAs. A programmable interconnection network provides the wiring between the logic blocks to create circuits that are too large to fit into a single logic block. The programmable interconnection network is made up of a set of wires and programmable switches. A programmable switch usually consists of a single n-channel MOS transistor as described in the programming technology discussion at the beginning of this section. As with the programmable logic blocks, the gate of this transistor is controlled using a configuration bit. The programmable interconnection must allow the FPGA to implement a wide range of circuit types, and thus must provide connections between logic blocks that are physically close as well as those that are physically distant. Furthermore, the interconnection network must allow the circuit's desired functionality to be implemented while meeting design goals for propagation delay, power, and cost.

To meet these constraints, most FPGAs provide a hierarchical set of interconnections. Although approaches to designing the interconnections vary across manufacturers, typically the programmable interconnection network provides a large number of short connections between physically close logic blocks, with a smaller number of longer connections to distant logic blocks. Because of the electrical properties of the programmable switch, two wires connected by a switch have a larger propagation delay than one longer wire of the same total length. FPGA manufacturers have designed the set of programmable interconnections to reduce the average number of switches through which signals must travel between logic blocks for most designs. The computer-aided design tools for programming the FPGAs are also designed to place the design on the available programmable logic blocks in such a way that interconnection delays are reduced.

In addition to the programmable interconnection network, there are usually dedicated wiring resources for clock and reset signals that are shared globally throughout the circuit. The dedicated wiring resources are designed to minimize the propagation delay and skew, which can create synchronization issues for sequential circuits, as described in Chapter 4. In addition to the global signals, dedicated wires are provided locally between adjacent logic blocks for connecting the dedicated arithmetic logic such as the carry chains in the example programmable logic block of Figure 5-13. This local wiring improves the speed of the dedicated logic circuitry while reducing the demands on the programmable interconnections.

The third programmable feature common to FPGAs is a set of programmable input/output (I/O) pins. The FPGA must be connected with the outside world. In particular, an FPGA must be capable of providing a broad range in the number of inputs and outputs depending upon the circuit that is to be implemented, and the FPGA must be compatible with the speed and voltage requirements of the other electrical components to which it will be connected. As a consequence of these two requirements, most FPGAs provide a large number of pins that can be configured to be either inputs or outputs, and that can be configured to support a number of different electrical interface standards. The electrical interface standards have requirements with respect to the voltages considered to be a logical 0 or 1, the electrical current sourced or sunk, the speed with which a signal can change, and many other electrical properties of the I/O signal. The FPGAs may also provide capabilities for synchronizing an input signal with the internal clock to deal with the metastability issues described in Chapter 4. The manufacturer's choice of which electrical standards to support depends largely upon the intended application market.

5-3 CHAPTER SUMMARY

This chapter presented a number of topics, all important to the designer. First, the CMOS transistor was introduced. Switch models for CMOS were provided and employed in modeling electronic circuits for gates. Various parameters for characterizing gate technology were introduced. Important technology parameters discussed including, fan-in, fan-out, noise margin, power dissipation, and propagation delays. Finally, a discussion of fundamentals of basic programmable implementation technologies was provided. This discussion included ROMs, PLAs, PAL and FPGA devices.

REFERENCES

1. ALTERA® CORPORATION, *Altera FLEX 10KE Embedded Programmable Logic Device Family Data Sheet*, ver. 2.4 (http://www.altera.com/literature/ds/dsf10ke.pdf). Altera Corporation, © 1995–2002.
2. KATZ, R. H., AND G. BORRIELLO. *Contemporary Logic Design*, 2nd ed. Upper Saddle River, NJ: Pearson Prentice Hall, 2005.
3. KUON, I., R. TESSIER, AND J. ROSE. "FPGA Architecture: Survey and Challenges," *Foundations and Trends in Electronic Design Automation*, Vol. 2, Issue 2, 2007, pp. 135–253. (http://www.nowpublishers.com/articles/foundations-and-trends-in-electronic-design-automation/EDA-005).
4. LATTICE SEMICONDUCTOR CORPORATION. *Lattice GALs®* (http://www.latticesemi.com/products/spld/GAL/index.cfm). Lattice Semiconductor Corporation, © 1995–2002.
5. SMITH, M. J. S. *Application-Specific Integrated Circuits.* Boston: Addison-Wesley, 1997.
6. TRIMBERGER, S. M., ED. *Field-Programmable Gate Array Technology.* Boston: Kluwer Academic Publishers, 1994.
7. WAKERLY, J. F. *Digital Design: Principles and Practices,* 4th ed. Upper Saddle River, NJ: Pearson Prentice Hall, 2004.
8. XILINX, INC., *Xilinx Spartan™-IIE Data Sheet* (http://direct.xilinx.com/bvdocs/publications/ds077_2.pdf). Xilinx, Inc. © 1994–2002.

 PROBLEMS

The plus (+) indicates a more advanced problem and the asterisk (*) indicates that a solution is available on the text website.

5-1. *Find the Boolean function that corresponds to the closed paths through each of the given switch model networks in Figure 5-14.

5-2. Find the CMOS switch model networks for the following functions:

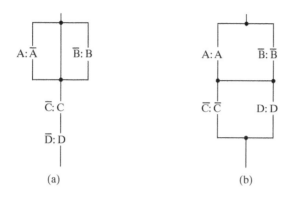

□ **FIGURE 5-14**
Switch Networks for Problem 5-1

(a) 2-input AND gate.

(b) 2-input OR gate.

5-3. An integrated circuit logic family has AND gates with a fan-out of 12 standard loads and buffers with a fan-out of 20 standard loads. Sketch a schematic showing how the output signal of a single AND gate can be applied to 88 other gate inputs, using as few buffers as possible. Assume that each input is one standard load.

5-4. **(a)** Given a 1024 × 8 ROM chip with an enable input, show the external connections necessary to construct a 4K × 32 ROM with eight chips and a decoder.

(b) How many 4K × 8 ROM chips would be required to construct a 32K × 64 ROM?

5-5. *A 64 × 8 ROM converts a 6-bit binary number to its corresponding two-digit BCD number. For example, binary 100001 converts to BCD 0011 0011 (decimal 33). Specify the truth table for the ROM.

5-6. Specify the size of a ROM (number of words and number of bits per word) that will accommodate the truth table for the following combinational circuit components:

(a) An 8-bit ripple carry adder with C_{in} and C_{out}.

(b) A 16-bit adder–subtractor with C_{in} and C_{out}.

(c) A code converter from a 5-digit BCD number to a binary number.

(d) An 8 × 8 multiplier.

5-7. Tabulate the truth table for an 8 × 3 ROM that implements the following four Boolean functions:

$$A(X, Y, Z) = \Sigma m(0, 6, 7)$$

$$B(X, Y, Z) = \Sigma m(1, 2, 3, 4, 5)$$

$$C(X, Y, Z) = \Sigma m(1, 5)$$

$$D(X, Y, Z) = \Sigma m(0, 1, 2, 3, 5, 6)$$

5-8. Obtain the PLA equations for programming the four Boolean functions listed in Problem 5–7. Minimize the number of product terms. Be sure to attempt to share product terms between functions that are not prime implicants of individual functions and to consider the use of complemented outputs.

5-9. Derive the PLA equations for the combinational circuit that convert one digit BCD number to 4-bit Gray code. Minimize the number terms. Find the optimize equations with minimum number of terms. If possible share product terms between functions that are not prime implicants of individual functions and consider the use of complemented outputs.

5-10. List the PLA equations for programming a BCD–to–excess-3 code converter. If necessary to reduce product terms, share product terms between functions that are not prime implicants of individual functions and consider the use of complemented outputs.

5-11. *Repeat Problem 5-10, using a PAL device.

5-12. The following is the truth table of a three-input, four-output combinational circuit. Obtain the equations for programming the PAL device shown in Figure 5-10.

Inputs			Outputs			
X	Y	Z	A	B	C	D
0	0	0	0	1	0	0
0	0	1	1	1	1	1
0	1	0	1	0	1	1
0	1	1	0	1	0	1
1	0	0	1	0	1	0
1	0	1	0	0	0	1
1	1	0	1	1	1	0
1	1	1	0	1	1	1

5-13. The following equations are to be implemented in the PAL device shown in Figure 5-10. Find the equations for programming the PAL.

$$F = \overline{A}B + CD + AB\overline{C}D + A\overline{B}C + ABC\overline{D}$$

$$G = \overline{A}B + B\overline{C}D + BC\overline{D} + A\overline{B}C$$

5-14. Use Shannon's expansion theorem to express the following functions in terms of C and $\overline{C}$.

(a) $F(A,B,C) = \overline{A}\,\overline{B} + BC + A\overline{C}$

(b) $F(A,B,C) = \Sigma m(0,2,3,5,6)$

5-15. (a) Design a 4-to-1 multiplexer using two 4-LUTs.

(b) Implement the following function in 4-input LUT form with 16-to-1 multiplexer.

$$F = \overline{A}\overline{B} + \overline{A}\overline{C} + \overline{C}D$$

5-16. For the programmable logic block shown in Figure 5-13, show the necessary configuration settings to implement each of the following types of circuits. You can assume that the upper data input of each multiplexer is chosen with a select input of 0.

(a) A combinational function of inputs a, b, and c.

(b) A Moore machine

(c) A Mealy machine

5-17. For the programmable logic block shown in Figure 5-13, what functions should be entered into the 2-LUTs to implement a 1-bit 2s complement subtractor performing the operation $a - b$?

5-18. Implement the Moore state machine described by the following state table using the programmable logic block shown in Figure 5-13. Your answer should include the configuration bits for the logic block.

| Present State | Inputs | | Next State | Output Z |
	in1	in2		
State0	0	0	State1	0
State0	0	1	State0	0
State0	1	0	State0	0
State0	1	1	State1	0
State1	0	0	State0	1
State1	0	1	State0	1
State1	1	0	State1	1
State1	1	1	State1	1

CHAPTER

6

REGISTERS AND REGISTER TRANSFERS

In Chapter 3, we studied combinational functional blocks, and in Chapter 4 we examined sequential circuits. Now, we bring the two ideas together and present sequential functional blocks, generally referred to as registers and counters. In Chapter 4, the circuits that were analyzed or designed did not have any particular structure, and the number of flip-flops was small. In contrast, the circuits we consider here have more structure, with multiple stages or cells that are identical or close to identical, making expansion very simple. Registers are particularly useful for storing information during the processing of data, and counters assist in sequencing the processing.

In a digital system, a datapath and a control unit are frequently present at the upper levels of the design hierarchy. A *datapath* consists of processing logic and a collection of registers that performs data processing. A *control unit* is made up of logic that determines the sequence of data-processing operations performed by the datapath. Register transfer notation describes elementary data-processing actions referred to as *microoperations*. *Register transfers* move information between registers, between registers and memory, and through processing logic. Dedicated transfer hardware using multiplexers and shared transfer hardware called *buses* implement these movements of data. The design of the control unit for controlling register transfers is also covered in this chapter. A design procedure for digital systems as combinations of register transfer logic and control logic brings together much of what we have studied thus far.

In the generic computer at the beginning of Chapter 1, registers are used extensively for temporary storage of data in areas aside from memory. Registers of this kind are often large, with at least 32 bits. Overall, sequential functional blocks are used widely in the generic computer. In particular, the CPU and FPU parts of the processor each contain large numbers of registers that are involved in register transfers and execution of microoperations. It is in the CPU and the FPU that data transfers, additions, subtractions, and other microoperations take place. Finally, the connections shown between various electronic parts of the computer are buses, which we discuss for the first time in this chapter.

6-1 REGISTERS AND LOAD ENABLE

A register includes a set of flip-flops. Since each flip-flop is capable of storing one bit of information, an n-bit register, composed of n flip-flops, is capable of storing n bits of binary information. By the broadest definition, a *register* consists of a set of flip-flops, together with gates that implement their state transitions. This broad definition includes the various sequential circuits considered in Chapter 4. More commonly, the term *register* is applied to a set of flip-flops, possibly with added combinational gates, that perform data-processing tasks. The flip-flops hold data, and the gates determine the new or transformed data to be transferred into the flip-flops.

A *counter* is a register that goes through a predetermined sequence of states upon the application of clock pulses. The gates in the counter are connected in a way that produces the prescribed sequence of binary states. Although counters are a special type of registers, it is common to differentiate them from registers.

Registers and counters are sequential functional blocks that are used extensively in the design of digital systems in general and in digital computers in particular. Registers are useful for storing and manipulating information; counters are employed in circuits that sequence and control operations in a digital system.

The simplest register is one that consists of only flip-flops without external gates. Figure 6-1(a) shows such a register constructed from four D-type flip-flops. The common *Clock* input triggers all flip-flops on the rising edge of each pulse, and the binary information available at the four D inputs is transferred into the 4-bit register. The four Q outputs can be sampled to obtain the binary information stored in the register. The $\overline{Clear}$ input goes to the $\overline{R}$ inputs of all four flip-flops and is used to clear the register to all 0s prior to its clocked operation. This input is labeled $\overline{Clear}$ rather than *Clear*, since a 0 must be applied to reset the flip-flops asynchronously. Activation of the asynchronous $\overline{R}$ inputs to flip-flops during normal clocked operation can lead to circuit designs that are highly delay dependent and that can, therefore, malfunction. Thus, we maintain $\overline{Clear}$ at logic 1 during normal clocked operation, allowing it to be logic 0 only when a system reset is desired. We note that the ability to clear a register to all 0s is optional; whether a clear operation is provided depends upon the use of the register in the system.

The transfer of new information into a register is referred to as *loading* the register. If all the bits of the register are loaded simultaneously with a common clock pulse, we say that the loading is done in parallel. A positive clock transition applied to the *Clock* input of the register of Figure 6-1(a) loads all four D inputs into the flip-flops in parallel.

Figure 6-1(b) shows a symbol for the register in Figure 6-1(a). This symbol permits the use of the register in a design hierarchy. It has all inputs to the logic circuit on its left and all outputs from the circuit on the right. The inputs include the clock input with the dynamic indicator to represent positive-edge triggering of the flip-flops. We note that the name *Clear* appears inside the symbol, with a bubble in the signal line on the outside of the symbol. This notation indicates that application of a logic 0 to the signal line activates the clear operation on the flip-flops in the register. If the signal line were labeled outside the symbol, the label would be $\overline{Clear}$.

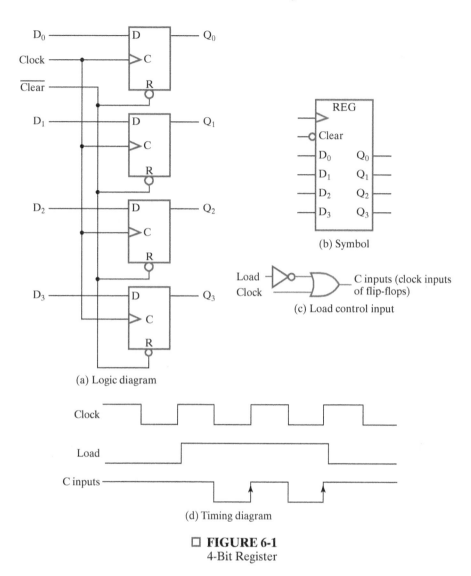

(a) Logic diagram

(b) Symbol

(c) Load control input

(d) Timing diagram

□ **FIGURE 6-1**
4-Bit Register

Register with Parallel Load

Most digital systems have a master clock generator that supplies a continuous train of clock pulses. The pulses are applied to all flip-flops and registers in the system. In effect, the master clock acts like a heart that supplies a constant beat to all parts of the system. For the design in Figure 6-1(a), the clock can be prevented from reaching the clock input to the circuit if the contents of the register are to be left unchanged. Thus, a separate control signal is used to control the clock cycles during which clock pulses are to have an effect on the register. The clock pulses are prevented from reaching the register when its content is not to be changed. This approach can be implemented with a load control input *Load* combined with the clock, as shown in

Figure 6-1(c). The output of the OR gate is applied to the C inputs of the register flip-flops. The equation for the logic shown is

$$C\ inputs = \overline{Load} + Clock$$

When the *Load* signal is 1, $C\ inputs = Clock$, so the register is clocked normally, and new information is transferred into the register on the positive transitions of the clock. When the *Load* signal is 0, $C\ inputs = 1$. With this constant input applied, there are no positive transitions on $C\ inputs$, so the contents of the register remain unchanged. The effect of the *Load* signal on the signal $C\ inputs$ is shown in Figure 6-1(d). Note that the clock pulses that appear on $C\ inputs$ are pulses to 0, which end with the positive edge that triggers the flip-flops. These pulses and edges appear when *Load* is 1 and are replaced by a constant 1 when *Load* is 0. In order for this circuit to work correctly, *Load* must be constant at the correct value, either 0 or 1, throughout the interval when *Clock* is 0. One situation in which this occurs is if *Load* comes from a flip-flop that is triggered on a positive edge of *Clock*, a normal circumstance if all flip-flops in the system are positive-edge triggered. Since the clock is turned on and off at the register C inputs by the use of a logic gate, the technique is referred to as *clock gating*.

Inserting gates in the clock pulse path produces different propagation delays between *Clock* and the inputs of flip-flops with and without clock gating. If the clock signals arrive at different flip-flops or registers at different times, *clock skew* is said to exist. But to have a truly synchronous system, we must ensure that all clock pulses arrive simultaneously throughout the system so that all flip-flops trigger at the same time. For this reason, in routine designs, control of the operation of the register without using clock gating is advisable. Otherwise, delays must be controlled to drive the clock skew as close to zero as possible. This is applicable in aggressive low-power or high-speed designs.

A 4-bit register with a control input *Load* that is directed through gates into the D inputs of the flip-flops, instead of through the C inputs, is shown in Figure 6-2(c). This register is based on a bit cell shown in Figure 6-2(a) consisting of a 2-to-1 multiplexer and a D flip-flop. The signal *EN* selects between the data bit D entering the cell and the value Q at the output of the cell. For $EN = 1$, D is selected and the cell is loaded. For $EN = 0$, Q is selected and the output is loaded back into the flip-flop, preserving its current state. The feedback connection from output to input of the flip-flop is necessary because the D flip-flop, unlike other flip-flop types, does not have a "no change" input condition: With each clock pulse, the D input determines the next state of the output. To leave the output unchanged, it is necessary to make the D input equal to the present value of the output. The logic in Figure 6-2(a) can be viewed as a new type of D flip-flop, a *D flip-flop with enable*, having the symbol shown in Figure 6-2(b).

The register is implemented by placing four D flip-flops with enables in parallel and connecting the *Load* input to the *EN* inputs. When *Load* is 1, the data on the four inputs is transferred into the register with the next positive clock edge. When *Load* is 0, the current value remains in the register at the next positive clock edge. Note that the clock pulses are applied continuously to the C inputs. *Load* determines whether the next pulse accepts new information or leaves the information in the register intact. The transfer of information from inputs to register is

□ **FIGURE 6-2**
4-Bit Register with Parallel Load

done simultaneously for all four bits during a single positive pulse transition. This method of transfer is traditionally preferred over clock gating, since it avoids clock skew and the potential for malfunctions of the circuit.

6-2 REGISTER TRANSFERS

A digital system is a sequential circuit made up of interconnected flip-flops and gates. In Chapter 4, we learned that sequential circuits can be specified by means of state tables. To specify a large digital system with state tables is very difficult, if not impossible, because the number of states is prohibitively large. To overcome this difficulty, digital systems are designed using a modular, hierarchical approach. The system is partitioned into subsystems or modules, each of which performs some functional task. The modules are constructed hierarchically from functional blocks such as registers, counters, decoders, multiplexers, buses, arithmetic elements, flip-flops, and primitive gates. The various subsystems communicate with data and control signals to form a digital system.

In most digital system designs, we partition the system into two types of modules: a *datapath*, which performs data-processing operations, and a *control unit*,

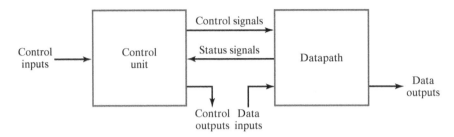

☐ **FIGURE 6-3**
Interaction Between Datapath and Control Unit

which determines the sequence of those operations. Figure 6-3 shows the general relationship between a datapath and a control unit. *Control signals* are binary signals that activate the various data-processing operations. To activate a sequence of such operations, the control unit sends the proper sequence of control signals to the datapath. The control unit, in turn, receives status bits from the datapath. These status bits describe aspects of the state of the datapath. The status bits are used by the control unit in defining the specific sequence of the operations to be performed. Note that the datapath and control unit may also interact with other parts of a digital system, such as memory and input–output logic, through the paths labeled data inputs, data outputs, control inputs, and control outputs.

Datapaths are defined by their registers and the operations performed on binary data stored in the registers. Examples of register operations are load, clear, shift, and count. The registers are assumed to be basic components of the digital system. The movement of the data stored in registers and the processing performed on the data are referred to as *register transfer operations*. The register transfer operations of digital systems are specified by the following three basic components:

1. the set of registers in the system,

2. the operations that are performed on the data stored in the registers, and

3. the control that supervises the sequence of operations in the system.

A register has the capability to perform one or more *elementary operations* such as load, count, add, subtract, and shift. For example, a right-shift register is a register that can shift data to the right. A counter is a register that increments a number by one. A single flip-flop is a 1-bit register that can be set or cleared. In fact, by this definition, the flip-flops and closely associated gates of any sequential circuit can be called registers.

An elementary operation performed on data stored in registers is called a *microoperation*. Examples of microoperations are loading the contents of one register into another, adding the contents of two registers, and incrementing the contents of a register. A microoperation is usually, but not always, performed in parallel on a vector of bits during one clock cycle. The result of the microoperation may replace the previous binary data in the register. Alternatively, the result may be transferred to another register, leaving the previous data unchanged. The sequential functional blocks introduced in this chapter are registers that implement one or more microoperations.

The control unit provides signals that sequence the microoperations in a prescribed manner. The results of a current microoperation may determine both the sequence of control signals and the sequence of future microoperations to be executed. Note that the term "microoperation," as used here, does not refer to any particular way of producing the control signals: specifically, it does not imply that the control signals are generated by a control unit based on a technique called microprogramming.

This chapter introduces registers, their implementations and register transfers using a simple register transfer language (RTL) to represent registers and specify the operations on their contents. The register transfer language uses a set of expressions and statements that resemble statements used in HDLs and programming languages. This notation can concisely specify part or all of a complex digital system such as a computer. The specification then serves as a basis for a more detailed design of the system.

6-3 REGISTER TRANSFER OPERATIONS

We denote the registers in a digital system by uppercase letters (sometimes followed by numerals) that indicate the function of the register. For example, a register that holds an address for the memory unit is usually called an address register and can be designated by the name AR. Other designations for registers are PC for program counter, IR for instruction register, and $R2$ for register 2. The individual flip-flops in an n-bit register are typically numbered in sequence from 0 to $n - 1$, starting with 0 in the least significant (often the rightmost) position and increasing toward the most significant position. Since the 0 bit is on the right, this order can be referred to as *little-endian*. The reverse order, with bit 0 on the left, is referred to as *big-endian*.

Figure 6-4 shows representations of registers in block-diagram form. The most common way to represent a register is by a rectangular box with the name of the register inside, as in part (a) of the figure. The individual bits can be identified as in part (b). The numbering of bits represented by just the leftmost and rightmost values at the top of a register box is illustrated by a 16-bit register $R2$ in part (c). A 16-bit program counter, PC, is partitioned into two sections in part (d) of the figure. In this case, bits 0 through 7 are assigned the symbol L (for low-order byte), and bits 8 through 15 are assigned the symbol H (for high-order byte). The label $PC(L)$, which

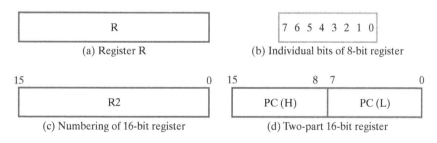

□ **FIGURE 6-4**
Block Diagrams of Registers

may also be written $PC(7:0)$, refers to the low-order byte of the register, and $PC(H)$ or $PC(15:8)$ refers to the high-order byte.

Data transfer from one register to another is designated in symbolic form by means of the replacement operator (←). Thus, the statement

$$R2 \leftarrow R1$$

denotes a transfer of the contents of register $R1$ into register $R2$. Specifically, the statement designates the copying of the contents of $R1$ into $R2$. The register $R1$ is referred to as the *source* of the transfer and the register $R2$ as the *destination*. By definition, the contents of the source register do not change as a result of the transfer — only the contents of the destination register, $R2$, change.

A statement that specifies a register transfer implies that datapath circuits are available from the outputs of the source register to the inputs of the destination register and that the destination register has a parallel load capability. Normally, we want a given transfer to occur not for every clock pulse, but only for specific values of the control signals. This can be specified by a *conditional statement*, symbolized by the *if-then* form

$$\text{if } (K_1 = 1) \text{ then } (R2 \leftarrow R1)$$

where K_1 is a control signal generated in the control unit. In fact, K_1 can be any Boolean function that evaluates to 0 or 1. A more concise way of writing the if-then form is

$$K_1: R2 \leftarrow R1$$

This control condition, terminated with a colon, symbolizes the requirement that the transfer operation be executed by the hardware only if $K_1 = 1$.

Every statement written in register-transfer notation presupposes a hardware construct for implementing the transfer. Figure 6-5 shows a block diagram that depicts the transfer from $R1$ to $R2$. The n outputs of register $R1$ are connected to the n inputs of register $R2$. The letter n is used to indicate the number of bits in the register-transfer path from $R1$ to $R2$. When the width of the path is known, n is replaced by an actual number. Register $R2$ has a load control input that is activated by the control signal K_1. It is assumed that the signal is synchronized with the same clock as the one applied to the register. The flip-flops are assumed to be positive-edge

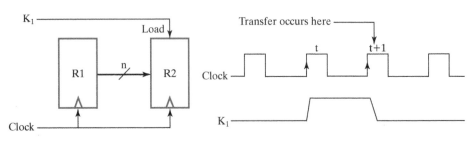

□ **FIGURE 6-5**
Transfer from $R1$ to $R2$ when $K_1 = 1$

□ **TABLE 6-1**
Basic Symbols for Register Transfers

Symbol	Description	Examples
Letters (and numerals)	Denotes a register	$AR, R2, DR, IR$
Parentheses	Denotes a part of a register	$R2(1), R2(7{:}0), AR(L)$
Arrow	Denotes transfer of data	$R1 \leftarrow R2$
Comma	Separates simultaneous transfers	$R1 \leftarrow R2, R2 \leftarrow R1$
Square brackets	Specifies an address for memory	$DR \leftarrow M[AR]$

triggered by this clock. As shown in the timing diagram, K_1 is set to 1 on the rising edge of a clock pulse at time t. The next positive transition of the clock at time $t + 1$ finds $K_1 = 1$, and the inputs of $R2$ are loaded into the register in parallel. In this case, K_1 returns to 0 on the positive clock transition at time $t + 1$, so that only a single transfer from $R1$ to $R2$ occurs.

Note that the clock is not included as a variable in the register-transfer statements. It is assumed that all transfers occur in response to a clock transition. Even though the control condition K_1 becomes active at time t, the actual transfer does not occur until the register is triggered by the next positive transition of the clock, at time $t + 1$.

The basic symbols we use in register-transfer notation are listed in Table 6-1. Registers are denoted by an uppercase letter, possibly followed by one or more uppercase letters and numerals. Parentheses are used to denote a part of a register by specifying the range of bits in the register or by giving a symbolic name to a portion of the register. The left-pointing arrow denotes a transfer of data and the direction of transfer. A comma is used to separate two or more register transfers that are executed at the same time. For example, the statement

$$K_3{:}\ R2 \leftarrow R1, R1 \leftarrow R2$$

denotes an operation that exchanges the contents of two registers simultaneously for a positive clock edge at which $K_3 = 1$. Such an exchange is possible with registers made of flip-flops but presents a difficult timing problem with registers made of latches. Square brackets are used in conjunction with a memory transfer. The letter M designates a memory word, and the register enclosed inside the square brackets provides the address of the word in memory. This is explained in more detail in Chapter 8.

6-4 REGISTER TRANSFERS IN VHDL AND VERILOG

Although there are some similarities, the register-transfer language used here differs from both VHDL and Verilog. In particular, different notation is used in each of the three languages. Table 6-2 compares the notation for many identical or similar register-transfer operations in the three languages. As you study this chapter and others to follow, this table will assist you in relating descriptions in the text RTL to the corresponding descriptions in VHDL or Verilog.

☐ **TABLE 6-2**
Textbook RTL, VHDL, and Verilog Symbols for Register Transfers

Operation	Text RTL	VHDL	Verilog
Combinational assignment	=	<= (concurrent)	assign = (nonblocking)
Register transfer	←	<= (concurrent)	<= (nonblocking)
Addition	+	+	+
Subtraction	−	−	−
Bitwise AND	∧	and	&
Bitwise OR	∨	or	|
Bitwise XOR	⊕	xor	^
Bitwise NOT	− (overline)	not	~
Shift left (logical)	Sl	sll	<<
Shift right (logical)	Sr	srl	>>
Vectors/registers	$A(3:0)$	$A(3 \text{ down to } 0)$	$A[3:0]$
Concatenation	||	&	{,}

6-5 MICROOPERATIONS

A microoperation is an elementary operation performed on data stored in registers or in memory. The microoperations most often encountered in digital systems are of four types:

1. *Transfer* microoperations, which transfer binary data from one register to another.

2. *Arithmetic* microoperations, which perform arithmetic operations on data in registers.

3. *Logic* microoperations, which perform bit manipulation on data in registers.

4. *Shift* microoperations, which shift data in registers.

A given microoperation may be of more than one type. For example, a 1s complement operation is both an arithmetic microoperation and a logic microoperation.

Transfer microoperations were introduced in the previous section. This type of microoperation does not change the binary data bits as they move from the source register to the destination register. The other three types of microoperations can produce new binary data and, hence, new information. In digital systems, basic sets of operations are used to form sequences that implement more complicated operations. In this section, we define a basic set of microoperations, symbolic notation for these microoperations, and descriptions of the digital hardware that implements them.

Arithmetic Microoperations

We define the basic arithmetic microoperations as add, subtract, increment, decrement, and complement. The statement

$$R0 \leftarrow R1 + R2$$

specifies an add operation. It states that the contents of register $R2$ are to be added to the contents of register $R1$ and the sum transferred to register $R0$. To implement this statement with hardware, we need three registers and a combinational component that performs the addition, such as a parallel adder. The other basic arithmetic operations are listed in Table 6-3. Subtraction is most often implemented through complementation and addition. Instead of using the minus operator, we can specify 2s complement subtraction by the statement

$$R0 \leftarrow R1 + \overline{R2} + 1$$

where $\overline{R2}$ specifies the 1s complement of $R2$. Adding 1 to $\overline{R2}$ gives the 2s complement of $R2$. Finally, adding the 2s complement of $R2$ to the contents of $R1$ is equivalent to $R1 - R2$.

The increment and decrement microoperations are symbolized by a plus-one and minus-one operation, respectively. These operations are implemented by using a special combinational circuit, an adder–subtractor, or a binary up–down counter with parallel load.

Multiplication and division are not listed in Table 6-3. Multiplication can be represented by the symbol * and division by /. These two operations are not included in the basic set of arithmetic microoperations because they are assumed to be implemented by sequences of basic microoperations. However, multiplication can be considered as a microoperation if implemented by a combinational circuit. In such a case, the result is transferred into a destination register at the clock edge after all signals have propagated through the entire combinational circuit.

□ **TABLE 6-3**
   Arithmetic Microoperations

Symbolic Designation	Description
$R0 \leftarrow R1 + R2$	Contents of $R1$ plus $R2$ transferred to $R0$
$R2 \leftarrow \overline{R2}$	Complement of the contents of $R2$ (1s complement)
$R2 \leftarrow \overline{R2} + 1$	2s complement of the contents of $R2$
$R0 \leftarrow R1 + \overline{R2} + 1$	$R1$ plus 2s complement of $R2$ transferred to $R0$ (subtraction)
$R1 \leftarrow R1 + 1$	Increment the contents of $R1$ (count up)
$R1 \leftarrow R1 - 1$	Decrement the contents of $R1$ (count down)

There is a direct relationship between the statements written in register-transfer notation and the registers and digital functions required for their implementation. To illustrate, consider the following two statements:

$$\overline{X}K_1: R1 \leftarrow R1 + R2$$
$$XK_1: R1 \leftarrow R1 + \overline{R2} + 1$$

Control variable K_1 activates an operation to add or subtract. If, at the same time, control variable X is equal to 0, then $\overline{X}K_1 = 1$, and the contents of $R2$ are added to the contents of $R1$. If X is equal to 1, then $XK_1 = 1$, and the contents of $R2$ are subtracted from the contents of $R1$. Note that the two control conditions are Boolean functions and reduce to 0 when $K_1 = 0$, a condition that inhibits the execution of both operations simultaneously.

A block diagram, showing the implementation of the preceding two statements, is given in Figure 6-6. An n-bit adder–subtractor, similar to the one shown in Figure 3-45, receives its input data from registers $R1$ and $R2$. The sum or difference is applied to the inputs of $R1$. The *Select* input S of the adder–subtractor selects the operation in the circuit. When $S = 0$, the two inputs are added, and when $S = 1$, $R2$ is subtracted from $R1$. Applying the control variable X to the S input activates the required operation. The output of the adder–subtractor is loaded into $R1$ on any positive clock edge at which $\overline{X}K_1 = 1$ or $XK_1 = 1$. We can simplify this to just K_1, since

$$\overline{X}K_1 + XK_1 = (\overline{X} + X)K_1 = K_1$$

Thus, the control variable X selects the operation, and the control variable K_1 loads the result into $R1$.

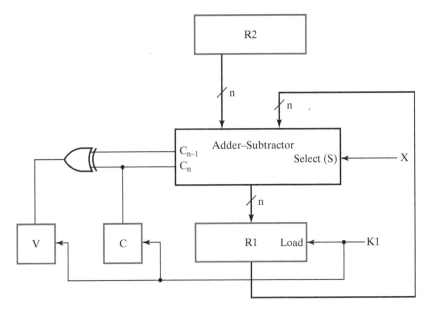

□ **FIGURE 6-6**
Implementation of Add and Subtract Microoperations

□ **TABLE 6-4**
   Logic Microoperations

Symbolic Designation	Description
$R0 \leftarrow \overline{R1}$	Logical bitwise NOT (1s complement)
$R0 \leftarrow R1 \wedge R2$	Logical bitwise AND (clears bits)
$R0 \leftarrow R1 \vee R2$	Logical bitwise OR (sets bits)
$R0 \leftarrow R1 \oplus R2$	Logical bitwise XOR (complements bits)

Based on the discussion of overflow in Section 3-11, the overflow output is transferred to flip-flop V, and the output carry from the most significant bit of the adder–subtractor is transferred to flip-flop C, as shown in Figure 6-6. These transfers occur when $K_1 = 1$ and are not represented in the register-transfer statements;—if desired, we could show them as additional simultaneous transfers.

Logic Microoperations

Logic microoperations are useful in manipulating the bits stored in a register. These operations consider each bit in the register separately and treat it as a binary variable. The symbols for the four basic logic operations are shown in Table 6-4. The NOT microoperation, represented by a bar over the source register name, complements all bits and thus is the same as the 1s complement. The symbol $\wedge$ is used to denote the AND microoperation and the symbol $\vee$ to denote the OR microoperation. By using these special symbols, we can distinguish between the add microoperation represented by a $+$ and the OR microoperation. Although the $+$ symbol has two meanings, we can distinguish between them by noting where the symbol occurs. If the $+$ occurs in a microoperation, it denotes addition. If the $+$ occurs in a control or Boolean function, it denotes OR. The OR microoperation will always use the $\vee$ symbol. For example, in the statement

$$(K_1 + K_2): R1 \leftarrow R2 + R3, \ R4 \leftarrow R5 \vee R6$$

the $+$ between K_1 and K_2 is an OR operation between two variables in a control condition. The $+$ between $R2$ and $R3$ specifies an add microoperation. The OR microoperation is designated by the symbol $\vee$ between registers $R5$ and $R6$. The logic microoperations can be easily implemented with a group of gates, one for each bit position. The NOT of a register of n bits is obtained with n NOT gates in parallel. The AND microoperation is obtained using a group of n AND gates, each receiving a pair of corresponding inputs from the two source registers. The outputs of the AND gates are applied to the corresponding inputs of the destination register. The OR and exclusive-OR microoperations require a similar arrangement of gates.

The logic microoperations can change bit values, clear a group of bits, or insert new bit values into a register. The following examples show how the bits stored in the 16-bit register $R1$ can be selectively changed by using a logic microoperation and a logic operand stored in the 16-bit register $R2$.

The AND microoperation can be used for clearing one or more bits in a register to 0. The Boolean equations $X \cdot 0 = 0$ and $X \cdot 1 = X$ dictate that, when ANDed with 0, a binary variable X produces a 0, but when ANDed with 1, the variable remains unchanged. A given bit or group of bits in a register can be cleared to 0 if ANDed with 0. Consider the following example:

10101101 10101011	$R1$	(data)
00000000 11111111	$R2$	(mask)
00000000 10101011	$R1 \leftarrow R1 \wedge R2$	

The 16-bit logic operand in $R2$ has 0s in the high-order byte and 1s in the low-order byte. By ANDing the contents of $R2$ with the contents of $R1$, it is possible to clear the high-order byte of $R1$ and leave the bits in the low-order byte unchanged. Thus, the AND operation can be used to selectively clear bits of a register. This operation is sometimes called *masking out* the bits, because it masks or deletes all 1s in the *data* in $R1$, based on bit positions that are 0 in the *mask* provided in $R2$.

The OR microoperation is used to set one or more bits in a register. The Boolean equations $X + 1 = 1$ and $X + 0 = X$ dictate that, when ORed with 1, the binary variable X produces a 1, but when ORed with 0, the variable remains unchanged. A given bit or group of bits in a register can be set to 1 if ORed with 1. Consider the following example:

10101101 10101011	$R1$	(data)
11111111 00000000	$R2$	(mask)
11111111 10101011	$R1 \leftarrow R1 \vee R2$	

The high-order byte of $R1$ is set to all 1s by ORing it with all 1s in the $R2$ operand. The low-order byte remains unchanged because it is ORed with 0s.

The XOR (exclusive-OR) microoperation can be used to complement one or more bits in a register. The Boolean equations $X \oplus 1 = \overline{X}$ and $X \oplus 0 = X$ dictate that, when a binary variable X is XORed with 1, it is complemented, but when XORed with 0, the variable remains unchanged. By XORing a bit or group of bits in register $R1$ with 1s in selected positions in $R2$, it is possible to complement the bits in the selected positions in $R1$. Consider the following example:

10101101 10101011	$R1$	(data)
11111111 00000000	$R2$	(mask)
01010010 10101011	$R1 \leftarrow R1 \oplus R2$	

The high-order byte in $R1$ is complemented after the XOR operation with $R2$, and the low-order byte is unchanged.

□ **TABLE 6-5**
   Examples of Shifts

Type	Symbolic Designation	Eight-Bit Examples	
		Source $R2$	After Shift: Destination $R1$
Shift left	$R1 \leftarrow$ sl $R2$	10011110	00111100
Shift right	$R1 \leftarrow$ sr $R2$	11100101	01110010

Shift Microoperations

Shift microoperations are used for lateral movement of data. The contents of a source register can be shifted either right or left. A *left shift* is toward the most significant bit, and a *right shift* is toward the least significant bit. Shift microoperations are used in the serial transfer of data. They are also used for manipulating the contents of registers in arithmetic, logical, and control operations. The destination register for a shift microoperation may be the same as or different from the source register. We use strings of letters to represent the shift microoperations defined in Table 6-5. For example,

$$R0 \leftarrow \text{sr } R0, \ \ R1 \leftarrow \text{sl } R2$$

are two microoperations that respectively specify a one-bit shift to the right of the contents of register $R0$ and a transfer of the contents of $R2$ shifted one bit to the left into register $R1$. The contents of $R2$ are not changed by this shift.

For a left-shift microoperation, we call the rightmost bit of the destination register the *incoming bit*. For a right-shift microoperation, we define the leftmost bit of the destination register as the incoming bit. The incoming bit may have different values, depending upon the type of shift microoperation. Here we assume that, for sr and sl, the incoming bit is 0, as shown in the examples in Table 6-5. The *outgoing bit* is the leftmost bit of the source register for the left-shift operation and the rightmost bit of the source register for the right-shift operation. For the left and right shifts shown, the outgoing bit value is simply discarded. In Chapter 9, we will explore other types of shifts that treat incoming and outgoing bits differently.

6-6   MICROOPERATIONS ON A SINGLE REGISTER

This section covers the implementation of one or more microoperations with a single register as the destination of all primary results. The single register may also serve as a source of an operand for binary and unary operations. Due to the close ties between a single set of storage elements and the microoperations, the combinational logic implementing the microoperations is assumed to be a part of the register and is called *dedicated logic* of the register. This is in contrast to logic which is shared by multiple destination registers. In this case, the combinational logic implementing the microoperations is called *shared logic* for the set of destination registers.

The combinational logic implementing the microoperations described in the previous section can use one or more functional blocks from Chapter 3 or can be designed specifically for the register. Initially, functional blocks will be used in combination with D flip-flops or D flip-flops with enable. A simple technique using multiplexers for selection is introduced to allow multiple microoperations on a single register. Next, single- and multiple-function registers that perform shifting and counting are designed.

Multiplexer-Based Transfers

There are occasions when a register receives data from two or more different sources at different times. Consider the following conditional statement having an *if-then-else* form:

$$\text{if } (K_1 = 1) \text{ then } (R0 \leftarrow R1) \text{ else if } (K_2 = 1) \text{ then } (R0 \leftarrow R2)$$

The value in register $R1$ is transferred to register $R0$ when control signal K_1 equals 1. When $K_1 = 0$, the value in register $R2$ is transferred to $R0$ when K_2 equals 1. Otherwise, the contents of $R0$ remains unchanged. The conditional statement may be broken into two parts using the following control conditions:

$$K_1: R0 \leftarrow R1, \quad \overline{K}_1 K_2: R0 \leftarrow R2$$

This specifies hardware connections from two registers, $R1$ and $R2$, to one common destination register $R0$. In addition, making a selection between two source registers must be based on values of the control variables K_1 and K_2.

The block diagram for a circuit with 4-bit registers that implements the conditional register-transfer statements using a multiplexer is shown in Figure 6-7(a). The quad 2-to-1 multiplexer selects between the two source registers. For $K_1 = 1$, $R1$ is loaded into $R0$, irrespective of the value of K_2. For $K_1 = 0$ and $K_2 = 1$, $R2$ is loaded into $R0$. When both K_1 and K_2 are equal to 0, the multiplexer selects $R2$ as the input to $R0$, but, because the control function, $K_2 + K_1$, connected to the LOAD input of $R0$ equals 0, the contents of $R0$ remain unchanged.

The detailed logic diagram for the hardware implementation is shown in Figure 6-7(b). The diagram uses functional block symbols based upon detailed logic for the registers in Figure 6-2 and for a quad 2-to-1 multiplexer from Chapter 3. Note that since this diagram represents just a part of a system, there are inputs and outputs that are not yet connected. Also, the clock is not shown in the block diagram, but is shown in the detailed diagram. It is important to relate the information given in a block diagram such as Figure 6-7(a) with the detailed

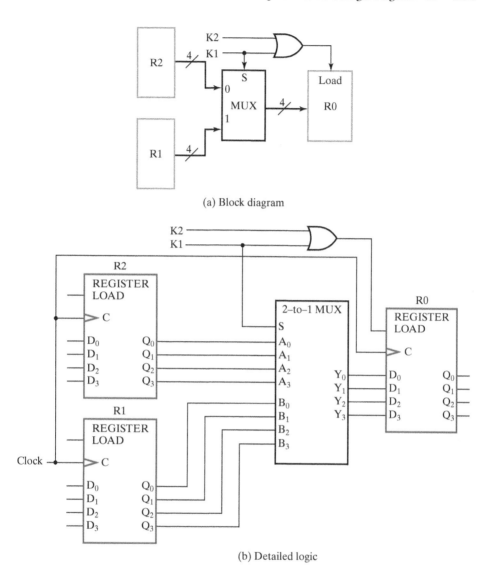

(a) Block diagram

(b) Detailed logic

☐ **FIGURE 6-7**
Use of Multiplexers to Select Between Two Registers

wiring connections in the corresponding logic diagram in Figure 6-7(b). In order to save space, we often omit the detailed logic diagrams in designs. However, it is possible to obtain a logic diagram with detailed wiring from the corresponding block diagram and a library of functional blocks. In fact, such a procedure is performed by computer programs used for automated logic synthesis.

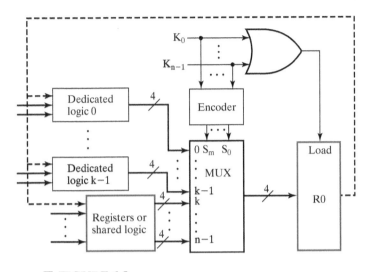

☐ **FIGURE 6-8**
Generalization of Multiplexer Selection for n Sources

The preceding example can be generalized by allowing the multiplexer to have n sources and these sources to be register outputs or combinational logic implementing microoperations. This generalization results in the block diagram shown in Figure 6-8. The diagram assumes that each source is either the outputs of a register or of combinational logic implementing one or more microinstructions. In those cases in which the microoperations are dedicated to the register, the corresponding dedicated logic is included as a part of the register. In Figure 6-8, the first k sources are dedicated logic and the last $n - k$ sources are either registers or shared logic. The control signals that select a given source are either a single control variable or the OR of all control signals corresponding to the microoperations associated with the source. To force $R0$ to load for a microoperation, these control signals are ORed together to form the *Load* signal. Since it is assumed that only one of the control signals is 1 at any time, these signals must be encoded to provide the selection codes for the multiplexer. Two modifications to the given structure are possible. The control signals could be applied directly to a $2 \times n$ AND-OR circuit (i.e., a multiplexer with the decoder deleted). Alternatively, the control signals could already be encoded, omitting the use of the all-zero code, so that the OR gate still forms the *Load* signal correctly.

Shift Registers

A register capable of shifting its stored bits laterally in one or both directions is called a *shift register*. The logical configuration of a shift register consists of a chain of flip-flops, with the output of one flip-flop connected to the input of

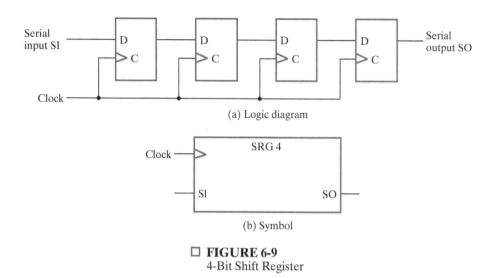

(a) Logic diagram

(b) Symbol

□ **FIGURE 6-9**
4-Bit Shift Register

the next flip-flop. All flip-flops have a common clock-pulse input that activates the shift.

The simplest possible shift register uses only flip-flops, as shown in Figure 6-9(a). The output of a given flip-flop is connected to the D input of the flip-flop at its right. The clock is common to all flip-flops. The *serial input SI* is the input to the leftmost flip-flop. The *serial output SO* is taken from the output of the rightmost flip-flop. A symbol for the shift register is given in Figure 6-9(b).

Sometimes it is necessary to control the register so that it shifts only on select positive clock edges. For the shift register in Figure 6-9, the shift can be controlled by connecting the clock through the logic shown in Figure 6-1(c), with *Shift* replacing *Load*. Again, due to clock skew, this is usually not the most desirable approach. Thus, we learn next that the shift operation can be controlled through the D inputs of the flip-flops rather than through the clock inputs C.

SHIFT REGISTER WITH PARALLEL LOAD   If all flip-flop outputs of a shift register are accessible, then information entered serially by shifting can be taken out in parallel from the flip-flop outputs. If a parallel load capability is also added to a shift register, then data entered in parallel can be shifted out serially. Thus, a shift register with accessible flip-flop outputs and parallel load can be used for converting incoming parallel data to outgoing serial data and vice versa.

The logic diagram for a 4-bit shift register with parallel load and the symbol for this register are shown in Figure 6-10. There are two control inputs, one for the shift and the other for the load. Each stage of the register consists of a D flip-flop, an OR gate, and three AND gates. The first AND gate enables the shift operation. The second AND gate enables the input data. The third AND gate restores the contents of the register when no operation is required.

☐ **FIGURE 6-10**
Shift Register with Parallel Load

The operation of this register is specified in Table 6-6 and is also given by the register transfers:

$$Shift: Q \leftarrow \text{sl } Q$$

$$\overline{Shift} \cdot Load: Q \leftarrow D$$

☐ **TABLE 6-6**
Function Table for the Register of Figure 6-10

Shift	Load	Operation
0	0	No change (Hold)
0	1	Load parallel data
1	$\times$	Shift left (down) from Q_0 to Q_3

The "No change" operation, also called "Hold", is implicit if neither of the conditions for transfers is satisfied. When both the shift and load control inputs are 0, the third AND gate in each stage is enabled, and the output of each flip-flop is applied to its own D input. A positive transition of the clock restores the contents to the register, and the output is unchanged. When the shift input is 0 and the load input is 1, the second AND gate in each stage is enabled, and the input D_i is applied to the D input of the corresponding flip-flop. The next positive clock transition transfers the parallel input data into the register. When the shift input is equal to 1, the first AND gate in each stage is enabled and the other two are disabled. Since the *Load* input is disabled by the $\overline{Shift}$ input on the second AND gate, we mark it with a don't-care condition in the *Shift* row of the table. When a positive edge occurs on the clock, the shift operation causes the data from the serial input *SI* to be transferred to flip-flop Q_0, the output of Q_0 to be transferred to flip-flop Q_1, and so on down the line. Note that because of the way the circuit is drawn, the shift occurs in the downward direction. If we rotate the page a quarter-turn clockwise, the register shifts from right to left.

Shift registers are often used to interface digital systems that are distant from each other. For example, suppose it is necessary to transmit an n-bit quantity between two points. If the distance is large, it is expensive to use n lines to transmit the n bits in parallel. It may be more economical to use a single line and transmit the information serially, one bit at a time. The transmitter loads the n-bit data in parallel into a shift register and then transmits the data serially along the common line. The receiver accepts the data serially into a shift register. When all n bits are accumulated, they can be taken in parallel from the outputs of the register. Thus, the transmitter performs a parallel-to-serial conversion of data, and the receiver does a serial-to-parallel conversion.

BIDIRECTIONAL SHIFT REGISTER   A register capable of shifting in only one direction is called a *unidirectional shift register*. A register that can shift in both directions is a *bidirectional shift register*. It is possible to modify the circuit of Figure 6-10, by adding a fourth AND gate in each stage, for shifting the data in the upward direction. An investigation of the resultant circuit will reveal that the four AND gates, together with the OR gate in each stage, constitute a multiplexer with the selection inputs controlling the operation of the register.

One stage of a bidirectional shift register with parallel load is shown in Figure 6-11(a). Each stage consists of a D flip-flop and a 4-to-1-line multiplexer. The two selection inputs S_1 and S_0 select one of the multiplexer inputs to apply to the D flip-flop. The selection lines control the mode of operation of the register according to Table 6-7 and the register transfers:

$$\overline{S}_1 \cdot S_0: Q \leftarrow \text{sl } Q$$

$$S_1 \cdot \overline{S}_0: Q \leftarrow \text{sr } Q$$

$$S_1 \cdot S_0: Q \leftarrow D$$

(a) Logic diagram of one typical stage

☐ **FIGURE 6-11**
Bidirectional Shift Register with Parallel Load

The "No Change" operation is implicit if none of the conditions for transfers is satisfied. When the mode control $S_1 S_0 = 00$, input 0 of the multiplexer is selected. This forms a path from the output of each flip-flop into its own input. The next clock transition transfers the current stored value back into each flip-flop, and no change of state occurs. When $S_1 S_0 = 01$, the terminal marked 1 on the multiplexer

☐ **TABLE 6-7**
Function Table for the Register of Figure 6-11

Mode Control		Register Operation
S_1	**S_0**	
0	0	No change (Hold)
0	1	Shift left
1	0	Shift right
1	1	Parallel load

has a path to the D input of each flip-flop. These paths cause a shift-left operation, with the bits being moved toward the most significant bit (down in the figure). The serial input is transferred into the first stage, and the content of each stage, Q_{i-1}, is transferred into stage Q_i. When $S_1 S_0 = 10$, a shift-right operation results in a second serial input that enters the last stage. In addition, the value in each stage Q_{i+1} is transferred into stage Q_i (up in the figure). Finally, when $S_1 S_0 = 11$, the binary information on each parallel input line is transferred into the corresponding flip-flop, resulting in a parallel load.

Figure 6-11(b) shows a symbol for the bidirectional shift register from Figure 6-11(a). Note that both a left serial input (*LSI*) and a right serial input (*RSI*) are provided. If serial outputs are desired, Q_3 is used for left shift and Q_0 for right shift.

Ripple Counter

A register that goes through a prescribed sequence of distinct states upon the application of a sequence of input pulses is called a *counter*. The input pulses may be clock pulses or may originate from some other source, and they may occur at regular or irregular intervals of time. In our discussion of counters, we assume clock pulses, but other signals can be substituted for the clock. The sequence of states may follow the binary number sequence or any other prescribed sequence of states. A counter that follows the binary number sequence is called a *binary counter*. An n-bit binary counter consists of n flip-flops and can count in binary from 0 through $2^n - 1$.

Counters are available in two categories: ripple counters and synchronous counters. In a ripple counter, the flip-flop output transitions serve as the sources for triggering the changes in other flip-flops. In other words, the C inputs of some of the flip-flops are triggered not by the common clock pulse, but rather by the transitions that occur on other flip-flop outputs. In a synchronous counter, the C inputs of all flip-flops receive the common clock pulse, and the change of state is determined from the present state of the counter. Synchronous counters are discussed in the next two subsections. Here we present the binary ripple counter and explain its operation.

The logic diagram of a 4-bit binary ripple counter is shown in Figure 6-12. The counter is constructed from D flip-flops connected such that the application of a positive edge to the C input of each flip-flop causes the flip-flop to complement its state. The complemented output of each flip-flop is connected to the C input of the next most significant flip-flop. The flip-flop holding the least significant bit receives the incoming clock pulses. Positive-edge triggering makes each flip-flop complement its value when the signal on its C input goes through a positive transition. The positive transition occurs when the complemented output of the previous flip-flop, to which C is connected, goes from 0 to 1. A 1-level signal on *Reset* driving the R inputs clears the register to all zeros asynchronously.

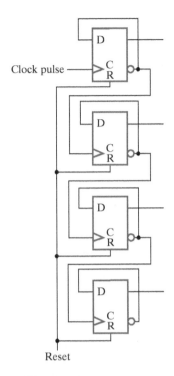

☐ **FIGURE 6-12**
4-Bit Ripple Counter

To understand the operation of a binary ripple counter, let us examine the upward counting sequence given in the left half of Table 6-8. The count starts at binary 0 and increments by one with each count pulse. After the count of 15, the counter goes back to 0 to repeat the count. The least significant bit (Q_0) is complemented by each count pulse. Every time that Q_0 goes from 1 to 0, $\overline{Q}_0$ goes from 0 to 1, complementing Q_1. Every time that Q_1 goes from 1 to 0, it complements Q_2. Every time that Q_2 goes from 1 to 0, it complements Q_3, and so on for any higher-order bits in the ripple counter. For example, consider the transition from count 0011 to 0100. Q_0 is complemented with the count pulse positive edge. Since Q_0 goes from 1 to 0, it triggers Q_1 and complements it. As a result, Q_1, goes from 1 to 0, which complements Q_2, changing it from 0 to 1. Q_2 does not trigger Q_3, because $\overline{Q}_2$ produces a negative transition, and the flip-flops respond only to positive transitions. Thus, the count from 0011 to 0100 is achieved by changing the bits one at a time. The counter goes from 0011 to 0010 (Q_0 from 1 to 0), then to 0000 (Q_1 from 1 to 0), and finally to 0100 (Q_2 from 0 to 1). The flip-flops change one at a time in quick succession as the signal propagates through the counter in a ripple fashion from one stage to the next.

A ripple counter that counts downward gives the sequence in the right half of Table 6-8. Downward counting can be accomplished by connecting the true output of each flip-flop to the C input of the next flip-flop.

The advantage of ripple counters is their simple hardware. Unfortunately, they are asynchronous circuits and, with added logic, can become circuits with delay

□ **TABLE 6-8**
Counting Sequence of Binary Counter

Upward Counting Sequence				Downward Counting Sequence			
Q_3	Q_2	Q_1	Q_0	Q_3	Q_2	Q_1	Q_0
0	0	0	0	1	1	1	1
0	0	0	1	1	1	1	0
0	0	1	0	1	1	0	1
0	0	1	1	1	1	0	0
0	1	0	0	1	0	1	1
0	1	0	1	1	0	1	0
0	1	1	0	1	0	0	1
0	1	1	1	1	0	0	0
1	0	0	0	0	1	1	1
1	0	0	1	0	1	1	0
1	0	1	0	0	1	0	1
1	0	1	1	0	1	0	0
1	1	0	0	0	0	1	1
1	1	0	1	0	0	1	0
1	1	1	0	0	0	0	1
1	1	1	1	0	0	0	0

dependence and unreliable operation. This is particularly true for logic that provides feedback paths from counter outputs back to counter inputs. Also, due to the length of time required for the ripple to finish, large ripple counters can be slow circuits. As a consequence, synchronous binary counters are favored in all but low-power designs, where ripple counters have an advantage. (See Problem 6-9.)

Synchronous Binary Counters

Synchronous counters, in contrast to ripple counters, have the clock applied to the C inputs of all flip-flops. Thus, the common clock pulse triggers all flip-flops simultaneously rather than one at a time, as in a ripple counter. A synchronous binary counter that counts up by 1 can be constructed from the incrementer in Figure 3-52 and D flip-flops, as shown in Figure 6-13(a). The carry output CO is added by not placing an x value on the C_4 output before the contraction of an adder to the incrementer in Figure 3-52. Output CO is used to extend the counter to more stages.

Note that the flip-flops trigger on the positive-edge transition of the clock. The polarity of the clock is not essential here, as it was for the ripple counter. The synchronous counter can be designed to trigger with either the positive or the negative clock transition.

SERIAL AND PARALLEL COUNTERS We will use the synchronous counter in Figure 6-13 to demonstrate two alternative designs for binary counters. In Figure 6-13(a), a chain of 2-input AND gates is used to provide information to each stage about the state of the prior stages in the counter. This is analogous to the carry logic in the ripple carry adder. A counter that uses such logic is said to have *serial gating* and is referred to

(a) Logic diagram—serial gating   (b) Logic diagram—parallel gating

(c) Symbol

☐ **FIGURE 6-13**
4-Bit Synchronous Binary Counter

as a *serial counter*. The analogy to the ripple carry adder suggests that there might be counter logic analogous to the carry lookahead adder. Such logic can be derived by contracting a carry lookahead adder, with the result shown in Figure 6-13(b). This logic can simply replace that in the blue box in Figure 6-13(a) to produce a counter with *parallel gating*, called a *parallel counter*. The advantage of parallel gating logic is that, in going from state 1111 to state 0000, only one AND-gate delay occurs instead of the four AND-gate delays that occur for the serial counter. This reduction in delay allows the counter to operate much faster.

If we connect two 4-bit parallel counters together by connecting the *CO* output of one to the *EN* input of the other, the result is an 8-bit serial-parallel counter. This counter has two 4-bit parallel parts connected in series with each other. The idea can be extended to counters of any length. Again, employing the analogy to carry lookahead adders, additional levels of gating logic can be introduced to replace the serial connections between the 4-bit segments. The added reduction in delay that results is useful for constructing large, fast counters.

The symbol for the 4-bit counter using positive-edge triggering is shown in Figure 6-13(c).

UP–DOWN BINARY COUNTER   A synchronous count-down binary counter goes through the binary states in reverse order from 1111 to 0000 and back to 1111 to repeat the count. The logic diagram of a synchronous count-down binary counter is similar to the circuit for the binary up-counter, except that a decrementer is used instead of an incrementer. The two operations can be combined to form a counter that can count both up and down, which is referred to as an up–down binary counter. Such a counter can be designed by contracting the adder–subtractor in Figure 3-45 into an incrementer–decrementer and adding the D flip-flops. The counter counts up for $S = 0$ and down for $S = 1$.

Alternatively, an up–down counter with ENABLE can be designed directly from counter behavior. It needs a mode input to select between the two operations. We designate this mode select input by S, with $S = 0$ for up-counting and $S = 1$ for down-counting. Let variable EN be a count enable input, with $EN = 1$ for normal up- or down-counting and $EN = 0$ for disabling both counts. A 4-bit up–down binary counter can be described by the following flip-flop input equations:

$$D_{A0} = Q_0 \oplus EN$$
$$D_{A1} = Q_1 \oplus ((Q_0 \cdot \overline{S} + \overline{Q}_0 \cdot S) \cdot EN)$$
$$D_{A2} = Q_2 \oplus ((Q_0 \cdot Q_1 \cdot \overline{S} + \overline{Q}_0 \cdot \overline{Q}_1 \cdot S) \cdot EN)$$
$$D_{A3} = Q_3 \oplus ((Q_0 \cdot Q_1 \cdot Q_2 \cdot \overline{S} + \overline{Q}_0 \cdot \overline{Q}_1 \cdot \overline{Q}_2 \cdot S) \cdot EN)$$

The logic diagram of the circuit can be easily obtained from the input equations but is not included here. It should be noted that the equations, as written, provide parallel gating using distinct carry logic for up-counting and down-counting. It is also possible to use two distinct serial gating chains. In contrast, the counter derived using the incrementer–decrementer uses only a single carry chain. Overall, the logic cost is similar.

BINARY COUNTER WITH PARALLEL LOAD   Counters employed in digital systems quite often require a parallel-load capability for transferring an initial binary number into the counter prior to the count operation. Two inputs control the operation, *Load* and *Count*. These inputs can take on four combinations, but only three operations are provided: *Load* (10), *Count* (01), and *Hold* (00). The effect of the remaining input combination (11) will be considered shortly. The implementation uses an incrementer plus $2n + 1$ ENABLEs, a NOT gate, and n 2-input OR gates as shown in Figure 6-14. The first n ENABLEs with enable input *Load* are used to enable and disable the parallel load of input data, D. The second n ENABLEs with enable input $\overline{Load}$ on the incrementer outputs are used to disable both the count and hold operations when *Load* = 1. When *Load* = 0, both count and hold are enabled. Without the additional ENABLE, *Count* = 1, causes counting, and *Count* = 0, the hold operation

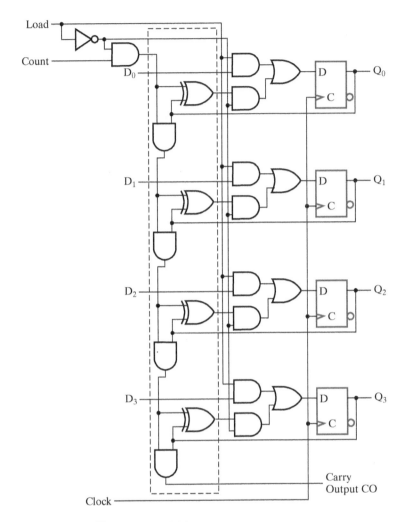

□ **FIGURE 6-14**
4-Bit Binary Counter with Parallel Load

occurs. What about the (11) combination? Counting is disabled by the $\overline{Load}$ signal and loading is enabled by *Load*. But what about the output *CO*? With *Count* = 1, the carry chain for the incrementer is active and can produce *CO* equal to 1. But *CO* should not be active outside of the counting operation. To deal with this problem, *Count* is enabled using $\overline{Load}$. With *Load* = 1, then $\overline{Load}$ = 0, which disables *Count* from going into the carry chain and forces *CO* to 0. Thus, for (11), a load occurs. This is sometimes described as *Load* overriding *Count*. When 4-bit counters are concatenated to form $4n$-bit counters, for the first state, a count control input is attached to *Count* in the least significant stage. For all other stages, *CO* from the prior state is attached to *Count*. Counters with parallel load are very useful in the design of digital computers. In subsequent chapters, we often refer to them as registers with load and increment operations.

□ **FIGURE 6-15**
BCD Counter

The binary counter with parallel load can be converted into a synchronous BCD counter (without load input) by connecting an external AND gate to it, as shown in Figure 6-15. The counter starts with an all-zero output, and the count input is always active. As long as the output of the AND gate is 0, each positive clock edge increments the counter by 1. When the output reaches the count of 1001, both Q_0 and Q_3 become 1, making the output of the AND gate equal to 1. This condition makes *Load* active—so on the next clock transition, the counter does not count, but is loaded from its four inputs. Since all four inputs are connected to logic 0, 0000 is loaded into the counter following the count of 1001. Thus, the circuit counts from 0000 through 1001, followed by 0000, as required for a BCD counter.

Other Counters

Counters can be designed to generate any desired number of states in sequence. A *divide-by-N counter* (also known as a *modulo-N counter*) is a counter that goes through a repeated sequence of N states. The sequence may follow the binary count or may be any other arbitrary sequence. In either case, the design of the counter follows the procedure presented in Chapter 4 for the design of synchronous sequential circuits. To demonstrate this procedure, we present the design of two counters: a BCD counter and a counter with an arbitrary sequence of states.

BCD COUNTER   As shown in the previous section, a BCD counter can be obtained from a binary counter with parallel load. It is also possible to design a BCD counter directly using individual flip-flops and gates. Assuming D-type flip-flops for the counter, we list the present states and corresponding next states in Table 6-9. An output Y is included in the table. This output is equal to 1 when the present state is 1001. In this way, CO can enable the count of the next decade while its own decade switches from 1001 to 0000.

The flip-flop input equations for D are obtained from the next-state values listed in the table and can be simplified by means of K-maps. The unused states for

□ **TABLE 6-9**
State Table and Flip-Flop Inputs for BCD Counter

Present State				Next State				Output
				$D_8 =$	$D_4 =$	$D_2 =$	$D_1 =$	
Q_8	Q_4	Q_2	Q_1	$Q_8(t+1)$	$Q_4(t+1)$	$Q_2(t+1)$	$Q_1(t+1)$	Y
0	0	0	0	0	0	0	1	0
0	0	0	1	0	0	1	0	0
0	0	1	0	0	0	1	1	0
0	0	1	1	0	1	0	0	0
0	1	0	0	0	1	0	1	0
0	1	0	1	0	1	1	0	0
0	1	1	0	0	1	1	1	0
0	1	1	1	1	0	0	0	0
1	0	0	0	1	0	0	1	0
1	0	0	1	0	0	0	0	1

minterms 1010 through 1111 are used as don't-care conditions. The simplified input equations for the BCD counter are

$$D_1 = \overline{Q}_1$$

$$D_2 = Q_2 \oplus Q_1\overline{Q}_8$$

$$D_4 = Q_4 \oplus Q_1Q_2$$

$$D_8 = Q_8 \oplus (Q_1Q_8 + Q_1Q_2Q_4)$$

$$CO = Q_1Q_8$$

Synchronous BCD counters can be cascaded to form counters for decimal numbers of any length. The cascading is done by replacing D_1 with $D_1 = Q_1 \oplus CI$, where CI is an input driven by CO from the next lower BCD counter. Also, CI needs to be ANDed with the product terms to the right of each of the XOR symbols in each of the equations for D_2 through D_8.

ARBITRARY COUNT SEQUENCE   Suppose we wish to design a counter that has a repeated sequence of six states, as listed in Table 6-10. In this sequence, flip-flops B and C repeat the binary count 00, 01, 10, while flip-flop A alternates between 0 and 1 every three counts. Thus, the count sequence for the counter is not straight binary, and two states, 011 and 111, are not included in the count. The D flip-flop input equations can be simplified using minterms 3 and 7 as don't-care conditions. The simplified functions are

$$D_A = A \oplus B$$

$$D_B = C$$

$$D_C = \overline{B}\,\overline{C}$$

□ **TABLE 6-10**
State Table and Flip-Flop Inputs for Counter

Present State			Next State		
			DA =	DB =	DC =
A	B	C	A(t + 1)	B(t + 1)	C(t + 1)
0	0	0	0	0	1
0	0	1	0	1	0
0	1	0	1	0	0
1	0	0	1	0	1
1	0	1	1	1	0
1	1	0	0	0	0

The logic diagram of the counter is shown in Figure 6-16(a). Since there are two unused states, we analyze the circuit to determine their effect. The state diagram obtained is drawn in Figure 6-16(b). This diagram indicates that if the circuit ever goes to one of the unused states, the next count pulse transfers it to one of the valid states, and the circuit then continues to count correctly.

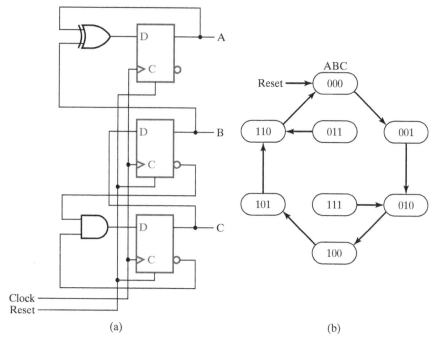

(a)   (b)

□ **FIGURE 6-16**
Counter with Arbitrary Count

6-7 REGISTER-CELL DESIGN

In Section 3-8, we discussed iterative combinational circuits. In this chapter, we connect such circuits to flip-flops to form sequential circuits. A single-bit cell of an iterative combinational circuit, connected to a flip-flop that provides the output, forms a two-state sequential circuit called a *register cell*. We can design an *n*-bit register with one or more associated microoperations by designing a register cell and making *n* copies of it. Depending on whether the output of the flip-flop is an input to the iterative circuit cell, the register cell may have its next state dependent on its present state and inputs or on its inputs only. If the dependency is only on inputs, then cell design for the iterative combinational circuit and attachment of the iterative circuit to flip-flops is appropriate. If, however, the state of the flip-flop is fed back to the inputs of the iterative circuit cell, sequential design methods can also be applied. The next example illustrates simple register-cell design in such a case.

> **EXAMPLE 6-1   Register-Cell Design**
>
> A register A is to implement the following register transfers:

$$\text{AND:} \quad A \leftarrow A \wedge B$$
$$\text{EXOR:} \quad A \leftarrow A \oplus B$$
$$\text{OR:} \quad A \leftarrow A \vee B$$

Unless specified otherwise, we assume that

1. Only one of AND, EXOR, and OR is equal to 1, and
2. For all of AND, EXOR, and OR equal to 0, the content of A remains unchanged.

A simple design approach for a register cell with conditions 1 and 2 uses a register with parallel load constructed from D flip-flops with Enable ($EN = LOAD$) from Figure 6-2. For this approach, the expression for $LOAD$ is the OR of all control signals that cause a transfer to occur. The expression for D_i consists of an OR of the AND of each control signal with the operation on the right-hand side of the corresponding transition.

For this example, the resulting equations for LOAD and D_i are

$$\text{LOAD} = \text{AND} + \text{EXOR} + \text{OR}$$
$$D_i = A(t+1)_i = \text{AND} \cdot A_i B_i + \text{EXOR} \cdot (A_i \overline{B_i} + \overline{A_i} B_i) + \text{OR} \cdot (A_i + B_i)$$

The equation for D_i has an implementation similar to that used for the selection part of a multiplexer in which a set of ENABLE blocks drive an OR gate. AND, EXOR, and OR are enabling signals, and the remaining part of the respective terms in D_i consists of the function enabled.

A more complex approach is to design directly for D flip-flops using a sequential circuit design approach rather than the ad hoc approach based on parallel load flip-flops.

We find a coded state table with A as the state variable and output, and AND, $EXOR$, OR, and B as inputs, as shown in Table 6-11. The assumption that at most one

☐ **TABLE 6-11**
State Table and Flip-Flop Inputs for Example 6-1

Present State A	Next State A(t + 1)						
	(AND = 0) (EXOR = 0) (OR = 0)	(OR = 1) (B = 0)	(OR = 1) (B = 1)	(EXOR = 1) (B = 0)	(EXOR = 1) (B = 1)	(AND = 1) (B = 0)	(AND = 1) (B = 1)
0	0	0	1	0	1	0	0
1	1	1	1	1	0	0	1

of the three control variables AND, $EXOR$, and OR is 1 is instrumental in defining the column headings. From the table, the equation for D_i can be written as:

$$D_i = A(t + 1)_i = AND \cdot A_i \cdot B_i + EXOR \cdot (A_i\overline{B}_i + \overline{A}_iB_i) + OR \cdot (A_i + B_i)$$
$$+ \overline{AND} \cdot \overline{EXOR} \cdot \overline{OR} \cdot A_i$$

In attempting to simplify this equation, it is important to note that factors involving only the control variables can be shared between register cells since they are the same for each cell. On the other hand, factors including variables A_i or B_i are implemented in each cell, so the gate-input cost is multiplied by n, the number of cells. In order to easily separate out the factors involving condition variables only, we rewrite D_i in terms of minterms of variables A_i and B_i:

$$D_i = (AND + OR + \overline{AND} \cdot \overline{EXOR} \cdot \overline{OR})(A_iB_i) + (EXOR + OR$$
$$+ \overline{AND} \cdot \overline{EXOR} \cdot \overline{OR})(A_i\overline{B}_i) + (EXOR + OR)(\overline{A}_iB_i)$$
$$= (AND + OR + \overline{EXOR})(A_iB_i) + (EXOR + OR$$
$$+ \overline{AND})(A_i\overline{B}_i) + (EXOR + OR)(\overline{A}_iB_i)$$

The terms $OR + AND + \overline{EXOR}$, $EXOR + OR$, and $(EXOR + OR) + \overline{AND}$ do not depend on the values A_i and B_i associated with any of the cells. The logic for these terms can be shared by all of the register cells. Using C_1, C_2, and C_3 as intermediate variables, the following set of equations results:

$$C_1 = OR + AND + \overline{EXOR}$$
$$C_2 = OR + EXOR$$
$$C_3 = C_2 + \overline{AND}$$
$$D_i = C_1A_iB_i + C_3A_i\overline{B}_i + C_2\overline{A}_iB_i$$

The logic shared by all of the cells and the logic for register cell i are given in Figure 6-17. Before comparing these results with those from the simple approach, we can apply similar simplification and logic sharing to the results of the simple approach:

$$C_1 = OR + AND$$
$$C_2 = OR + EXOR$$

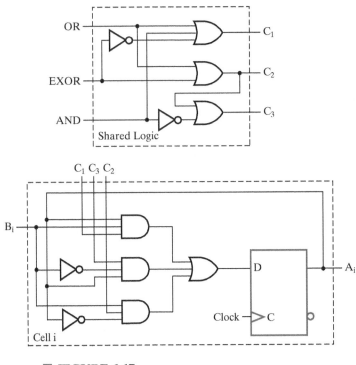

☐ **FIGURE 6-17**
Logic Diagram—Register-Cell Design Example 6-1

$$D_i = C_1 A_i B_i + C_2 A_i \overline{B_i} + C_2 \overline{A_i} B_i$$
$$LOAD = C_1 + C_2$$
$$D_{i,FF} = LOAD \cdot D_i + \overline{LOAD} \cdot A_i$$

If these equations are used directly the cost of the simple approach for a 16-cell design is about 40% higher. So by designing a custom register cell using a D flip-flop rather than finding input logic for a D flip-flop with enable, the cost can be reduced. Further, with the decrease in the number of levels of logic, the delay may also be reduced. ∎

   In the preceding example, there are no lateral connections between adjacent cells. Among the operations requiring lateral connections are shifts, arithmetic operations, and comparisons. One approach to the design of these structures is to combine combinational designs given in Chapter 3 with selection logic and flip-flops. A generic approach for multifunctional registers using flip-flops with parallel load is shown in Figure 6-8. This simple approach bypasses register-cell design but, if directly implemented, can result in excessive logic and too many lateral connections. The alternative is to do a custom register-cell design. In such designs, a critical factor is the definition of the lateral connection(s) needed. Also, different operations can be defined by controlling input to the least significant cell of the cell cascade. The custom design approach is illustrated in the next example by the design of a multifunctional register cell.

EXAMPLE 6-2   Register-Cell Design

A register A is to implement the following register transfers:

SHL: $A \leftarrow \text{sl } A$
EXOR: $A \leftarrow A \oplus B$
ADD: $A \leftarrow A + B$

Unless specified otherwise, we assume that

1. Only one of SHL, EXOR, and ADD is equal to 1, and
2. For all of SHL, EXOR, and ADD equal to 0, the content of A remains unchanged.

A simple approach to designing a register cell with conditions 1 and 2 is to use a parallel load with enable EN equal to LOAD. For this approach, the expression for LOAD is the OR of all control signals that cause a transfer to occur. The implementation for D_i consists of an AND-OR, with each AND having a control signal and the logic for the operation on the right-hand side as its inputs.

For this example, the resulting equations for LOAD and D_i are

$$\text{LOAD} = \text{SHL} + \text{EXOR} + \text{ADD}$$
$$D_i = A(t + 1)_i = \text{SHL} \cdot A_{i-1} + \text{EXOR} \cdot (A_i \oplus B_i) + \text{ADD} \cdot ((A_i \oplus B_i) \oplus C_i)$$
$$C_{i+1} = (A_i \oplus B_i)C_i + A_i B_i$$

These equations can be used without modification or can be optimized.

Now, suppose, that we do a custom design assuming that all of the register cells are identical. This means that the least and most significant cells will be the same as those internal to the cell chain. Because of this, the value of C_0 must be specified and the use, if any, of C_n must be determined for each of the three operations. For the left shift, a zero fill of the vacated rightmost bit is assumed, giving $C_0 = 0$. Since C_0 is not involved in the EXOR operation, it can be assumed to be a don't-care. Finally, for the addition, C_0 either can be assumed to be 0 or can be left as a variable to permit a carry from a previous addition to be injected. We assume that C_0 equals 0 for addition, since no additional carry-in is specified by the register transfer statement.

Our first formulation goal is to minimize lateral connections between cells. Two of the three operations, left shift and addition, require a lateral connection to the left (i.e., toward the most significant end of the cell chain). Our goal is to use one signal for both operations, say, C_i. It already exists for the addition but must be redefined to handle both the addition and the left shift. Also in our custom design, the parallel load flip-flop will be replaced by a D flip-flop. We can now formulate the state table for the register cell shown in Table 6-12:

$$D_i = A(t + 1)_i = \overline{\text{SHL}} \cdot \overline{\text{EXOR}} \cdot \overline{\text{ADD}} \cdot A_i + \text{SHL} \cdot C_i + \text{EXOR} \cdot (A_i \oplus B_i)$$
$$+ \text{ADD} \cdot (A_i \oplus B_i \oplus C_i)$$

$$C_{i+1} = \text{SHL} \cdot A_i + \text{ADD} \cdot ((A_i \oplus B_i)C_i + A_i B_i)$$

☐ **TABLE 6-12**
State Table and Flip-Flop Inputs for Register-Cell Design in Example 6-2

Present State A_i	Inputs	Next State $A_i(t + 1)$/Output C_{i+1}									
	SHL = 0	SHL = 1	1	1	1	EXOR = 1	1	ADD = 1	1	1	1
	EXOR = 0	B_i = 0	0	1	1	B_i = 0	1	B_i = 0	0	1	1
	ADD = 0	C_i = 0	1	0	1			C_i = 0	1	0	1
0	0/X	0/0	1/0	0/0	1/0	0/X	1/X	0/0	1/0	1/0	0/1
1	1/X	0/1	1/1	0/1	1/1	1/X	0/X	1/0	0/1	0/1	1/1

☐ **FIGURE 6-18**
Logic Diagram—Register-Cell Design Example 6-2

The term $A_i \oplus B_i$ appears in both the EXOR and ADD terms. In fact, if $C_i = 0$ during the EXOR operation, then the functions for the sum in ADD and for EXOR can be identical. In the C_{i+1} equation, since SHL and ADD are both 0 when EXOR is 1, C_i is 0 for all cells in the cascade except the least significant one. For the least significant cell, the specification states that $C_0 = 0$. Thus, input values C_i are 0 for all cells in register A. So we can combine the ADD and EXOR operations as follows:

$$D_i = A(t + 1)_i = \overline{SHL} \cdot \overline{EXOR} \cdot \overline{ADD} \cdot A_i + SHL \cdot C_i$$
$$+ (EXOR + ADD) \cdot ((A_i \oplus B_i) \oplus C_i)$$

The expressions $\overline{SHL} \cdot \overline{EXOR} \cdot \overline{ADD}$ and $EXOR + ADD$, which are independent of $A_i, B_i,$ and $C_i,$ can be shared by all cells. The resulting equations are

$$E_1 = EXOR + ADD$$

$$E_2 = \overline{E1 + SHL}$$

$$D_i = E_2 \cdot A_i + SHL \cdot C_i + E_1 \cdot ((A_i \oplus B_i) \oplus C_i)$$

$$C_{i+1} = SHL \cdot A_i + ADD \cdot ((A_i \oplus B_i)C_i + A_iB_i)$$

The resulting register cell appears in Figure 6-18. Comparing this result with the register cell for the simple design, we note the following two differences:

1. Only one lateral connection between cells exists instead of two.
2. Logic has been very efficiently shared by the addition and the EXOR operation.

The custom cell design has produced connection and logic savings not present in the block-level design with or without optimization.   ■

6-8   MULTIPLEXER AND BUS-BASED TRANSFERS FOR MULTIPLE REGISTERS

A typical digital system has many registers. Paths must be provided to transfer data from one register to another. The amount of logic and the number of interconnections may be excessive if each register has its own dedicated set of multiplexers. A more efficient scheme for transferring data between registers is a system that uses a shared transfer path called a *bus*. A bus is characterized by a set of common lines, with each line driven by selection logic. Control signals for the logic select a single source and one or more destinations on any clock cycle for which a transfer occurs.

In Section 6-4, we saw that multiplexers and parallel load registers can be used to implement dedicated transfers from multiple sources. A block diagram for such transfers between three registers is shown in Figure 6-19(a). There are three n-bit 2-to-1 multiplexers, each with its own select signal. Each register has its own load signal. The same system based on a bus can be implemented by using a single n-bit 3-to-1 multiplexer and parallel load registers. If a set of multiplexer outputs is shared as a common path, these output lines are a bus. Such a system with a single bus for transfers between three registers is shown in Figure 6-19(b). The control input pair, *Select*, determines the contents of the single source register that will appear on the multiplexer outputs (i.e., on the bus). The *Load* inputs determine the destination register or registers to be loaded with the bus data.

In Table 6-13, transfers using the single-bus implementation of Figure 6-19(b) are illustrated. The first transfer is from $R2$ to $R0$. *Select* equals 10, selecting input $R2$ to the multiplexer. *Load* signal $L0$ for register $R0$ is 1, with all other loads at 0, causing the contents of $R2$ on the bus to be loaded into $R0$ on the next positive clock transition. The second transfer in the table illustrates the loading of the contents of $R1$ into both $R0$ and $R2$. The source $R1$ is selected because *Select* is equal to 01. In

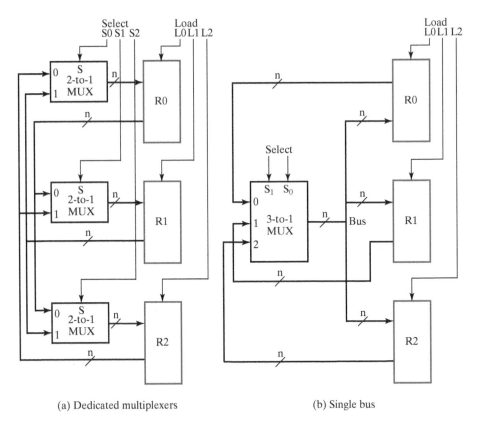

(a) Dedicated multiplexers   (b) Single bus

☐ **FIGURE 6-19**
Single Bus versus Dedicated Multiplexers

this case, $L2$ and $L0$ are both 1, causing the contents of $R1$ on the bus to be loaded into registers $R0$ and $R2$. The third transfer, an exchange between $R0$ and $R1$, is impossible in a single clock cycle, since it requires two simultaneous sources, $R0$ and $R1$, on the single bus. Thus, this transfer requires at least two buses or a bus combined with a dedicated path from one of the registers to the other. Note that such a transfer can be executed on the dedicated multiplexers in Figure 6-19(a). So, for a single-bus system, simultaneous transfers with different sources in a single clock cycle are

☐ **TABLE 6-13**
Examples of Register Transfers Using the Single Bus in Figure 6-19(b)

	Select		Load		
Register Transfer	**S1**	**S0**	**L2**	**L1**	**L0**
$R0 \leftarrow R2$	1	0	0	0	1
$R0 \leftarrow R1, R2 \leftarrow R1$	0	1	1	0	1
$R0 \leftarrow R1, R1 \leftarrow R0$			Impossible		

impossible, whereas for the dedicated multiplexers, any combination of transfers is possible. Hence, the reduction in hardware that occurs for a single bus in place of dedicated multiplexers results in limitations on simultaneous transfers.

If we assume that only single-source transfers are needed, then we can use Figure 6-19 to compare the complexity of the hardware in dedicated versus bus-based systems. First of all, assume a multiplexer design, as in Figure 3-27. In Figure 6-19(a), there are $2n$ AND gates and n OR gates per multiplexer (not counting inverters), for a total of $9n$ gates. In contrast, in Figure 6-19(b), the bus multiplexer requires only $3n$ AND gates and n OR gates, for a total of $4n$ gates. Also, the data input connections to the multiplexers are reduced from $6n$ to $3n$. Thus, the cost of the selection hardware is reduced by about half.

High-Impedance Outputs

Another method for constructing a bus involves a type of gate called a *three-state buffer*. Thus far, we have considered gates that have only output values logic 0 and logic 1. In this section, we introduce an important structure, the three-state buffer, that provides a third output value referred to as the *high-impedance state* and denoted by Hi-Z or just plain Z or z. The Hi-Z value behaves as an open circuit, which means that, looking back into the circuit, we find that the output appears to be disconnected internally. Thus, the output appears not to be there at all and, thus, is incapable of driving any attached inputs. Gates with Hi-Z output capability have two very useful properties. First of all, Hi-Z outputs can be connected together, provided that no two or more gates drive the line at the same time to opposite 0 and 1 values. In contrast, gates with only logic 0 and logic 1 outputs cannot have their outputs connected together. Second, an output in the Hi-Z states, since it appears as an open circuit, can have an input attached to it internally, so that the Hi-Z output can act as both an output and an input. This is referred to as a bidirectional input/output. Instead of carrying signals in just one direction, interconnections between Hi-Z outputs can carry information in both directions. This feature reduces significantly the number of interconnections required.

High-impedance outputs may appear on any gate, but here we restrict consideration to a primitive gate structure with a single data input, a three-state buffer. As the name implies, a three-state logic output exhibits three distinct states. Two of the "states" are the logic 1 and logic 0 of conventional logic. The third "state" is the Hi-Z value, which, for three-state logic, is referred to as the Hi-Z *state*.

The graphic symbol and truth table for a 3-state buffer are given in Figure 6-20(a). The symbol in Figure 6-20(a) is distinguished from the symbol for a normal buffer by the enable input, *EN*, entering the bottom of the buffer symbol. From the truth table in

EN	IN	OUT
0	X	Hi-Z
1	0	0
1	1	1

(a) Logic symbol (b) Truth table

☐ **FIGURE 6-20**
Three-State Buffer

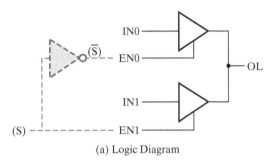

(a) Logic Diagram

EN1	EN0	IN1	IN0	OL
0	0	X	X	Hi-Z
(S) 0	$(\overline{S})$ 1	X	0	0
0	1	X	1	1
1	0	0	X	0
1	0	1	X	1
1	1	0	0	0
1	1	1	1	1
1	1	0	1	🌫🌫
1	1	1	0	

(b) Truth table

☐ **FIGURE 6-21**
Three-State Buffers Forming a Multiplexed Line OL

Figure 6-20(b), if $EN = 1$, OUT is equal to IN, behaving like a normal buffer. But for $EN = 0$, the output value is high impedance (Hi-Z), regardless of the value of IN.

Three-state buffer outputs can be connected together to form a multiplexed output line. Figure 6-21(a) shows two 3-state buffers with their outputs connected to form output line OL. We are interested in the output of this structure in terms of the four inputs $EN1$, $EN0$, $IN1$, and $IN0$. The output behavior is given by the truth table in Figure 6-21(b). For $EN1$ and $EN0$ equal to 0, both buffer outputs are Hi-Z. Since both appear as open circuits, OL is also an open circuit, represented by a Hi-Z value. For $EN1 = 0$ and $EN0 = 1$, the output of the top buffer is $IN0$ and the output of bottom buffer is Hi-Z. Since the value of $IN0$ combined with an open circuit is just $IN0$, OL has value $IN0$, giving the second and third rows of the truth table. A corresponding, but opposite, case occurs for $EN1 = 1$ and $EN0 = 0$, so OL has value $IN1$, giving the fourth and fifth rows of the truth table. For $EN1$ and $EN0$ both 1, the situation is more complicated. If $IN1 = IN0$, then their mutual value appears at OL. But if $IN1 \neq IN0$, then their values conflict at the output. The conflict results in an electrical current flowing from the buffer output that is at 1 into the buffer output that is at 0. This current is often large enough to cause heating and may even destroy the circuit, as symbolized by the "smoke" icons in the truth table. Clearly, such a situation must be avoided. The designer must ensure that $EN0$ and $EN1$ never equal 1 at the same time. In the general case, for n 3-state buffers attached to a bus line, EN can equal 1 for only one of the buffers and must be 0 for the rest. One way to ensure this is to use a decoder to generate the *EN* signals. For the two-buffer case, the decoder is just an inverter with select input *S*, as shown in dotted lines in Figure 6-21(a). It is interesting to examine the truth table with the inverter in place. It consists of the shaded area of the table in Figure 6-21(b). Clearly, the value on *S* selects between inputs *IN*0 and *IN*1. Further, the circuit output *OL* is never in the Hi-Z state.

Three-State Bus

A bus can be constructed with the three-state buffers introduced above instead of multiplexers. This has the potential for additional reductions in the number of connections. But why use three-state buffers instead of a multiplexer, particularly for implementing buses? The reason is that many three-state buffer outputs can be connected together to form a bit line of a bus, and this bus is implemented using only one level of logic gates. On the other hand, in a multiplexer, such a large number of sources means a high fan-in OR, which requires multiple levels of OR gates, introducing more logic and increasing delay. In contrast, three-state buffers provide a practical way to construct fast buses with many sources, so they are often preferred in such cases. More important, however, is the fact that signals can travel in two directions on a three-state bus. Thus, the three-state bus can use the same interconnection to carry signals into and out of a logic circuit. This feature, which is most important when crossing chip boundaries, is illustrated in Figure 6-22(a). The figure

(a) Register with bidirectional input–output lines and symbol

(b) Multiplexer bus

(c) Three-state bus using registers with bidirectional lines

□ **FIGURE 6-22**
Three-State Bus versus Multiplexer Bus

shows a register with n lines that serve as both inputs and outputs lying across the boundary of the shaded area. If the three-state buffers are enabled, then the lines are outputs; if the three-state buffers are disabled, then the lines can be inputs. The symbol for this structure is also given in the figure. Note that the bidirectional bus lines are represented by a two-headed arrow. Also, a small inverted triangle denotes the three-state outputs of the register.

Figures 6-22(b) and (c) show a multiplexer-implemented bus and a three-state bus, respectively, for comparison. The symbol from Figure 6-22(a) for a register with bidirectional input–output lines is used in Figure 6-22(c). In contrast to the situation in Figure 6-19, where dedicated multiplexers were replaced by a bus, these two implementations are identical in terms of their register–transfer capability. Note that, in the three-state bus, there are only three data connections to the set of register blocks for each bit of the bus. The multiplexer-implemented bus has six data connections per bit to the set of register blocks. This reduction in the number of data connections by half, along with the ability to easily construct a bus with many sources, makes the three-state bus an attractive alternative. The use of such bidirectional input–output lines is particularly effective between logic circuits in different physical packages.

6-9 SERIAL TRANSFER AND MICROOPERATIONS

A digital system is said to operate in a serial mode when information in the system is transferred or manipulated one bit at a time. Information is transferred one bit at a time by shifting the bits out of one register and into a second register. This transfer method is in contrast to parallel transfer, in which all the bits of the register are transferred at the same time.

The serial transfer of information from register A to register B is done with shift registers, as shown in the block diagram of Figure 6-23(a). The serial output of register A is connected to the serial input of register B. The serial input of register A receives 0s while its data is transferred to register B. It is also possible for register A to receive

(a) Block diagram

(b) Timing diagram

☐ **FIGURE 6-23**
Serial Transfer

other binary information, or if we want to maintain the data in register A, we can connect its serial output to its serial input so that the information is circulated back into the register. The initial content of register B is shifted out through its serial output and is lost unless it is transferred back into register A, to a third shift register, or to other storage. The shift control input *Shift* determines when and how many times the registers are shifted. The registers using *Shift* are controlled by means of the logic from Figure 6-23(a), which allows the clock pulses to pass to the shift register clock inputs only when *Shift* has the value logic 1.

In Figure 6-23, each shift register has four stages. The logic that supervises the transfer must be designed to enable the shift registers, through the *Shift* signal, for a fixed time of four clock pulses. Shift register enabling is shown in the timing diagram for the clock gating logic in Figure 6-23(b). Four pulses find *Shift* in the active state, so that the output of the logic connected to the clock inputs of the registers produces four pulses: $T_1, T_2, T_3,$ and T_4. Each positive transition of these pulses causes a shift in both registers. After the fourth pulse, *Shift* changes back to 0 and the shift registers are disabled. We note again that, for positive-edge triggering, the pulses on the clock inputs are 0, and the inactive level when no pulses are present is a 1 rather than a 0.

Now suppose that the binary content of register A before the shift is 1011, that of register B is 0010, and the *SI* of register A is logic 0. Then the serial transfer from A to B occurs in four steps, as shown in Table 6-14. With the first pulse T_1, the rightmost bit of A is shifted into the leftmost bit of B, the leftmost bit of A receives a 0 from the serial input, and at the same time, all other bits of A and B are shifted one position to the right. The next three pulses perform identical operations, shifting the bits of A into B one at a time while transferring 0s to A. After the fourth shift, the logic supervising the transfer changes the *Shift* signal to 0 and the shifts stop. Register B contains 1011, which is the previous value of A. Register A contains all 0s.

The difference between serial and parallel modes of operation should be apparent from this example. In the parallel mode, information is available from all bits of a register, and all bits can be transferred simultaneously during one clock pulse. In the serial mode, the registers have a single serial input and a single serial output, and information is transferred one bit at a time.

Serial Addition

Operations in digital computers are usually done in parallel because of the faster speed attainable. Serial operations are slower, but have the advantage of requiring

☐ **TABLE 6-14**
Example of Serial Transfer

Timing Pulse	Shift Register A				Shift Register B			
Initial value	1	0	1	1	0	0	1	0
After T_1	0	1	0	1	1	0	0	1
After T_2	0	0	1	0	1	1	0	0
After T_3	0	0	0	1	0	1	1	0
After T_4	0	0	0	0	1	0	1	1

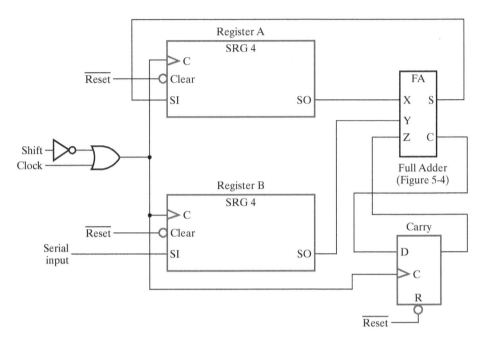

☐ **FIGURE 6-24**
Serial Addition

less hardware. To demonstrate the serial mode of operation, we will show the operation of a serial adder. Also, we compare the serial adder to the parallel counterpart presented in Section 3-9 to illustrate the time–space trade-off in design.

The two binary numbers to be added serially are stored in two shift registers. Bits are added, one pair at a time, through a single full-adder (FA) circuit, as shown in Figure 6-24. The carry out of the full adder is transferred into a D flip-flop. The output of this carry flip-flop is then used as the carry input for the next pair of significant bits. The sum bit on the S output of the full adder could be transferred into a third shift register, but we have chosen to transfer the sum bits into register A as the contents of the register are shifted out. The serial input of register B can receive a new binary number as its contents are shifted out during the addition.

The operation of the serial adder is as follows: Register A holds the augend, register B holds the addend, and the carry flip-flop has been reset to 0. The serial outputs of A and B provide a pair of significant bits for the full adder at X and Y. The output of the carry flip-flop provides the carry input at Z. When *Shift* is set to 1, the OR gate enables the clock for both registers and the flip-flop. Each clock pulse shifts both registers once to the right, transfers the sum bit from S into the leftmost flip-flop of A, and transfers the carry output into the carry flip-flop. Shift control logic enables the registers for as many clock pulses as there are bits in the registers (four pulses in this example). For each pulse, a new sum bit is transferred to A, a new carry is transferred to the flip-flop, and both registers are shifted once to the right. This process continues until the shift control logic changes *Shift* to 0. Thus, the addition is accomplished by passing each pair of bits and the previous carry through a single full-adder circuit and transferring the sum, one bit at a time, back into register A.

Initially, we can reset register A, register B, and the *Carry* flip-flop to 0. Then we shift the first number into B. Next, the first number from B is added to the 0 in A. While B is being shifted through the full adder, we can transfer a second number to it through its serial input. The second number can be added to the contents of register A at the same time that a third number is transferred serially into register B. Serial addition may be repeated to form the addition of two, three, or more numbers, with their sum accumulated in register A.

A comparison of the serial adder with the parallel adder described in Section 3-9 provides an example of space–time trade-off. The parallel adder has n full adders for n-bit operands, whereas the serial adder requires only one full adder. Excluding the registers from both, the parallel adder is a combinational circuit, whereas the serial adder is a sequential circuit because it includes the carry flip-flop. The serial circuit also takes n clock cycles to complete an addition. Identical circuits, such as the n full adders in the parallel adder, connected together in a chain constitute an example of an *iterative logic array*. If the values on the carries between the full adders are regarded as state variables, then the states from the least significant end to the most significant end are the same as the states appearing in sequence on the flip-flop output in the serial adder. Note that in the iterative logic array the states appear in space, but in the sequential circuit the states appear in time. By converting from one of these implementations to the other, one can make a space–time trade-off. The parallel adder in space is n times larger than the serial adder (ignoring the area of the carry flip-flop), but it is n times faster. The serial adder, although it is n times slower, is n times smaller in space. This gives the designer a significant choice in emphasizing speed or area, where more area translates into more cost.

6-10 CONTROL OF REGISTER TRANSFERS

In Section 6-2, we divided a digital system into two major components, a datapath and a control unit. Likewise, the binary information stored in a digital computer can be classified as either data or control information. As we saw earlier in this chapter, data is manipulated in a datapath by using microoperations implemented with register transfers. These operations are implemented with adder–subtractors, shifters, registers, multiplexers, and buses. The control unit provides signals that activate the various microoperations within the datapath to perform the specified processing tasks. The control unit also determines the sequence in which the various actions are performed. This separation of a system into two components and separation of the tasks performed carries over to the design process. The datapath and control unit are usually designed separately, but in close coordination with each other.

Generally, the timing of all registers in a synchronous digital system is controlled by a master clock generator. The clock pulses are applied to all flip-flops and registers in the system, including those in the control unit. To prevent clock pulses from changing the state of all registers on every clock cycle, some registers have a load control signal that enables and disables the loading of new data into the register. The binary variables that control the selection inputs of multiplexers, buses, and processing logic and the load control inputs of registers are generated by the control unit.

The control unit that generates the signals for sequencing the microoperations. is a sequential circuit with states that dictate the control signals for the system. At any given time, the state of the sequential circuit activates a prescribed set of micro-operations. Using status conditions and control inputs, the sequential control unit determines the next state. The digital circuit that acts as the control unit provides a sequence of signals for activating the microoperations and also determines its own next state.

Based on the overall system design, there are two distinct types of control units used in digital systems, one for a programmable system and the other for a nonprogrammable system.

In a *programmable system*, a portion of the input to the processor consists of a sequence of *instructions*. Each instruction specifies the operation that the system is to perform, which operands to use, where to place the results of the operation, and, in some cases, which instruction to execute next. For programmable systems, the instructions are usually stored in memory, either in RAM or in ROM. To execute the instructions in sequence, it is necessary to provide the memory address of the instruction to be executed. This address comes from a register called the *program counter* (*PC*). As the name implies, the *PC* has logic that permits it to count. In addition, in order to change the sequence of operations using decisions based on status information from the datapath, the *PC* needs parallel load capability. So, in the case of a programmable system, the control unit contains a *PC* and associated decision logic, as well as the necessary logic to interpret the instruction. *Executing* an instruction means activating the necessary sequence of microoperations in the datapath required to perform the operation specified by the instruction.

For a *nonprogrammable system*, the control unit is not responsible for obtaining instructions from memory, nor is it responsible for sequencing the execution of those instructions. There is no *PC* or similar register in such a system. Instead, the control unit determines the operations to be performed and the sequence of those operations, based on its inputs and the status bits from the datapath.

This section focuses on nonprogrammable system design. It illustrates the use of state machine diagrams for control unit design. Programmable systems are covered in Chapters 8 and 10.

Design Procedure

There are many possible design procedures for designing a datapath and control unit. Here, we will take an approach in which the actions of both the datapath and the control unit are described in a combined fashion using a state machine diagram or a combination of a state machine diagram with a register transfer table. Also, this procedure assumes that there may be some register transfer hardware in the control unit. Examples of such hardware are an iteration counter for implementation of an iterative algorithm, a program counter for a computer, or a set of register transfers to reduce the number of states in a state machine diagram. Here we use the term *system* to describe the target of the design; this term can be replaced with *circuit* if desired. This procedure assumes only one state machine diagram in the control unit. If desired, VHDL or Verilog can be used for any steps of the procedure.

REGISTER-TRANSFER SYSTEM DESIGN PROCEDURE

1. Write a detailed system specification.
2. Define all external data and control input signals, all external data, control, and status output signals, and the registers of the datapath and control unit.
3. Find a state machine diagram for the system including the register transfers in the datapath and in the control unit.
4. Define internal control and status signals. Use these signals to separate output conditions and actions, including register transfers, from the state diagram flow and represent them in tabular form.
5. Draw a block diagram of the datapath including all control and status inputs and outputs. Draw a block diagram of the control unit if it includes register transfer hardware.
6. Design any specialized register transfer logic in both the control and datapath.
7. Design the control unit logic.
8. Verify the correct operation of the combined datapath and control logic. If verification fails, debug the system and reverify it.

The next two examples provide the details of register-transfer system design. The concepts illustrated are very central to contemporary system design. These examples will cover the first seven of the eight steps, then step 8 will be briefly discussed.

EXAMPLE 6-3   DashWatch

The DashWatch is a very inexpensive stopwatch, intended only for runners in very short races referred to as dashes, e.g., the 100-yard dash.

1. The DashWatch times intervals less than or equal to 99.99 seconds. In addition to the stopwatch action, it also has a feature which permits the best performance (least time) to be stored in a register. The front of the stopwatch is shown in Figure 6-25(a). The primary stopwatch inputs are *START* and *STOP*. The *START* button causes a timer to reset to 0 and then starts the timer, and the *STOP* button stops the timer. After pressing *STOP*, the latest dash time is displayed on the 4-digit LCD (liquid crystal display). In addition, the *CSS* (compare and store shortest) pushbutton causes: (1) the last dash value to be compared with the stored minimum dash value so far in this session, (2) the least value to be stored as the minimum dash value, and (3) the minimum dash value to be displayed. The *RESET* button initializes the storage register to 10011001.10011001, the maximum possible value, and the BCD equivalent of 99.99. These reset actions also occur in response to turning the power on with a switch on the back of the DashWatch. The output is displayed in BCD on a seven-segment LCD which displays four digits, B_1, B_0, B_{-1}, B_{-2}, each of which has seven bits a, b, c, d, e, f, and g, for the seven segments. There is also an input to the display DP which is connected to the power supply. It provides the decimal point between B_0 and B_{-1}, and also acts as a power-on indicator.

☐ **FIGURE 6-25**

(a) External Appearance and (b) Register Requirements for DashWatch

2. The external control input signals, external data output signals, and registers are listed Table 6-15. The first four signals, provided through signal conditioning logic from pushbuttons on the face of the DashWatch, are 1 if the button is pushed and 0 if it is not pushed. The remaining signals are the 6-segment LCD display inputs for the four digits from left to right and the decimal point DP. DP is always 1 when the power is on. These five vectors are combined into the 29-bit vector B that drives the LCD. By looking at the specification in 1, we can conclude that two registers are needed. One is a timer, TM, that times the current dash, and the other SD, that stores the value of the shortest dash. The timer register needs to count up every 0.01 seconds, the period of the circuit clock. There are two choices for an up-counter: 1) a binary counter with a sufficient number of bits to be accurate to 0.01 seconds in decimal, or 2) a 4-digit BCD counter that counts in 0.01-second intervals. In this case, we have chosen the BCD counter to save on hardware required to convert from binary to BCD for the output display. The SD register has to be initialized to $(99.99)_{BCD}$ and to be loaded with the contents of TM. Thus a 4-digit (16-bit) parallel load register is required. The registers are shown in Figure 6-25(b).

3. The state machine diagram is given in Figure 6-26. In the formulation of this diagram, Moore model outputs were chosen, so all outputs are functions of state. Just after power-up or manual $RESET$, the DashWatch circuit is in state $S1$ in

□ **TABLE 6-15**
Inputs, Outputs, and Registers of the DashWatch

Symbol	Function	Type
START	Initialize timer to 0 and start timer	Control input
STOP	Stop timer and display timer	Control input
CSS	Compare, store, and display shortest dash time	Control input
RESET	Set shortest value to 10011001	Control input
B_1	Digit 1 data vector a, b, c, d, e, f, g to display	Data output vector
B_0	Digit 0 data vector a, b, c, d, e, f, g to display	Data output vector
DP	Decimal point to display (= 1)	Data output
B_{-1}	Digit −1 data vector a, b, c, d, e, f, g to display	Data output vector
B_{-2}	Digit −2 data vector a, b, c, d, e, f, g to display	Data output vector
B	The 29-bit display input vector (B_1, B_0, DP, B_{-1}, B_{-2})	Data output vector
TM	4-Digit BCD counter	16-Bit register
SD	Parallel load register	16-Bit register

which the register SD is synchronously reset to 0. The circuit proceeds to $S2$ to wait for $START = 1$. As long as $START = 0$, as indicated by $\overline{START}$ on a self-loop in state $S2$, the state remains $S2$. In state $S2$, TM is reset to 0 using a synchronous reset signal. If we use an asynchronous flip-flop input to change the state of one or more flip-flops buried in the midst of a synchronous design, we are violating the synchronous assumption that all state changes in normal operation must be synchronized with the clock at the flip-flop inputs. Under this assumption, asynchronous inputs are to be used only for power-up reset and master reset of the system to its required initial state.

By using an asynchronous input on the flip-flops to change flip-flop states, a designer might be caught by a timing problem that causes circuit failure, but is not easily detected during design and manufacturing.

$START = 1$ causes a transition to state $S3$ in which TM is enabled to count upward once every 0.01 seconds (the clock frequency is 100 Hz). The counting continues and is displayed ($DIS = TM$) while $STOP = 0$. When $STOP$ becomes 1, the state becomes $S4$, and the dash time stored in TM is displayed.

In state $S4$, the user can choose to time a new dash ($\overline{CSS} \cdot START = 1$), returning the state to $S2$, or to compare the dash time to the stored smallest dash time ($CSS = 1$), advancing the state to $S5$. Until one of these input events occurs, the state remains $S4$ due to $\overline{CSS} \cdot \overline{START}$. Note that instead of just $START$ as a transition condition, $\overline{CSS} \cdot START$ is used. This is to meet the mutually exclusive constraint, constraint 1 of the two transition constraint conditions for a state machine diagram.

In state $S5$, TM is compared to SD. If TM is less than SD, then the value in SD is replaced by TM. This operation occurs in state $S6$, after which the next

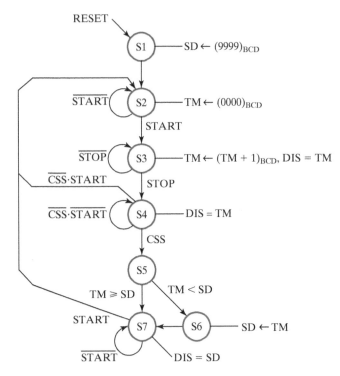

☐ **FIGURE 6-26**
State Machine Diagram for DashWatch

state becomes $S7$. If TM is greater than or equal to SD, then SD is unchanged, and the state becomes $S7$. In state $S7$, the smallest dash time stored in SD is displayed until $START$ is pushed to cause the state to change to $S2$, beginning the timing of another dash.

4. The next step is the separation of the datapath from the control, including the definition of the control and status signals that connect them together. The datapath actions can be read from the state machine diagram. The actions are grouped based on the destinations represented by the left-hand side of transfer statements ($\leftarrow$) or connection statements ($=$). Also, notation indicating status generation in the datapath needs to be interpreted and status signals named. The end results of these groupings are shown in Table 6-16 in the left column. For the two register transfers into SD, the variable $UPDATE$ is assigned to select the source of the transfers, and LSR is assigned to control the loading of SD. For TM, $RSTM$ is assigned as the synchronous reset signal for zeroing the register contents, and $ENTM$ (which will drive the carry $C0$ into the least significant digit of the BCD counter) is used to govern whether the count is up by 1 or 0. Signal DS has been assigned to select the register to be displayed. Finally, $ALTB$ is assigned as the status signal to indicate whether or not TM is less than SD. The variable names in true and complement form from Table 6-16

□ **TABLE 6-16**
Datapath Output Actions and Status Generation with Control and Status Signals

Action or Status	Control or Status Signals	Meaning for Values 1 and 0
$TM \leftarrow (0000)_{BCD}$	RSTM	1: Reset TM to 0 (synchronous reset) 0: No reset of TM
$TM \leftarrow (TM + 1)_{BCD}$	ENTM	1: BCD count up TM by 1, 0: hold TM value
$SD \leftarrow (9999)_{BCD}$	UPDATE LSR	0: Select 1001100110011001 for loading SD 1: Enable load SD, 0: disable load SD
$SD \leftarrow TM$	UPDATE LSR	1: Select TM for loading SD Same as above
$DIS = TM$ $DIS = SD$	DS	0: Select TM for DIS 1: Select SD for DIS
$TM < SD$ $TM \geq SD$	ALTB	1: TM less than SD 0: TM greater than or equal to SD

replace the output actions and status-based input conditions in Figure 6-26 to form the state diagram in Figure 6-27(b).

5. Next, we develop the block diagram of the datapath given in Figure 6-27(a). The two registers defined earlier appear in the diagram with their control terminals and signals from the control unit added. *RSTM* is the synchronous input for the zeroing of *TM*, and *ENTM* is applied to the carry input C_0. In order to supply the status signal *ALTB*, an $A < B$ comparator is required with the *TM* output as its *A* input and the *SD* output as its *B* input. The loading of *SD* needs selection hardware to select from either *TM* or 1001100110011001 as its input. A 16-bit 2-to-1 multiplexer with input *S* driven by *UPDATE* is used. In order to deliver the information to the LCD for display, it is necessary to select between *TM* and *SD* as the source. A 16-bit 2-to-1 multiplexer with select signal *DS* is used to produce the 16-bit signal *DIS*. Finally, this signal must be converted to the four vectors of variables a, b, c, d, e, f, g to control the LCD segments for the four digits. These vectors were previously labeled as B_1, B_0, B_{-1}, and B_{-2} data outputs. Placing the decimal point *DP* in between B_0 and B_{-1}, and combining all 29 bits, we obtain the output *B* that drives the LCD.

6. A number of components of the block diagram developed are already available to us. The BCD counter digit was already developed in Section 6-6. The 4-digit BCD counter can be constructed by connecting four of the digit counters together. A modification is required to provide the synchronous reset function for the counter. A 2-input AND gate is placed between the logic for each bit and the *D* input to the corresponding flip-flop. The second input on the AND gate is connected to $\overline{RSTM}$. When *RSTM* is 0, the circuit is normal. When

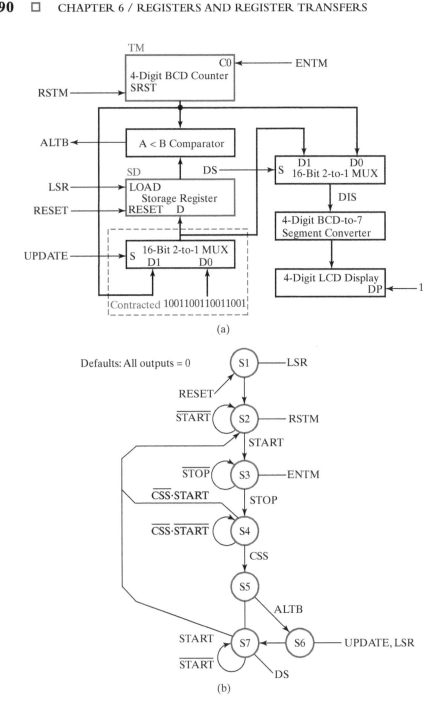

☐ FIGURE 6-27
(a) Datapath Block Diagram and (b) Control State-Machine Diagram for DashWatch

RSTM is 1, all inputs to the flip-flops are 0, and the flip-flops are reset to all 0s on the next clock.

The parallel load register is a 16-bit version of the register in Figure 6-2. The $A < B$ comparator can be designed easily as an iterative logic circuit. Assuming a carry that goes from right to left, the equation for each cell is $C_i = A_i \overline{B}_i + (A_i + \overline{B}_i)C_{i-1}$ and the incoming carry $C_0 = 1$. This represents the carries in an unsigned binary 2s complement subtractor using the circuit shown in Figure 3-45 with $S = 1$ to perform $A - B$. For this circuit, the result $A - B = A + (2^n - 1 - B) + 1 = 2^n + (A - B)$. If $A - B \geq 0$, then the results is greater than or equal to 2^n, and C_n (the carry out of the MSB) is 1. If $A - B < 0$, then the result is less than 2^n, and $C_n = 0$. Thus for $A < B, C_n = 0$ and $ALTB = \overline{C}_n$.

The multiplexer for loading *SD* is constructed based on the concept used for the quad 4-to-1 multiplexer in Figure 3-27. It uses one 1–to–2-line decoder driven by the *S* input and 16 pairs of enable circuits for handling the two 16-bit data vectors. The same multiplexer can be used for the formation of the 16-bit *DIS* data vector. The final circuit is the 4-digit BCD–to–7-segment code converter which can be constructed of four copies of the 1-digit BCD–to–7-segment code converter designed in Example 3-18.

Aside from one issue, this completes the design of the datapath. Because its input data vector on D_0 is a constant, the 16-bit 2-to-1 multiplexer for selecting the input to *SD* can be substantially reduced by applying contraction from Chapter 3. Doing this, for a bit with a data value of 0,

$$Y_i = (\overline{S} \cdot D_{0i} + S \cdot D_{1i})|_{D_{0i}=0} = S \cdot D_{1i}$$

For a bit with a data value of 1,

$$Y_i = (\overline{S} \cdot D_{0i} + S \cdot D_{1i})|_{D_{0i}=1} = \overline{S} + D_{1i}$$

The design of the datapath is now complete. There is no register transfer hardware to be designed for the control unit.

7. The next step is to design the control-unit hardware. For simplicity of design, we select a one-hot state assignment. For the state diagram in Figure 6-27, this assignment permits each of the states *Si* to be represented by a single state variable *Si* which is 1 when in the state *Si* and 0 otherwise. The next state functions (flip-flop input equations) are:

$$D_{S1} = S1(t + 1) = 0$$

$$D_{S2} = S2(t + 1) = S1 + S2 \cdot \overline{START} + S4 \cdot \overline{CSS} \cdot START + S7 \cdot START$$

$$D_{S3} = S3(t + 1) = S2 \cdot START + S3 \cdot \overline{STOP}$$

$$D_{S4} = S4(t + 1) = S3 \cdot STOP + S4 \cdot \overline{CSS} \cdot \overline{START}$$

$$D_{S5} = S5(t + 1) = S4 \cdot CSS$$

$$D_{S6} = S5 \cdot ALTB$$

$$D_{S7} = S7(t + 1) = S5 \cdot \overline{ALTB} + S6 + S7 \cdot \overline{START}$$

The output functions (output equations) are:

$$LSR = S1 + S6$$
$$RSTM = S2$$
$$ENTM = S3$$
$$UPDATE = S6$$
$$DS = S7$$

Note that $D_{S1} = 0$. The reason is that this state is entered only by power-up or master reset. It is never entered synchronously. As a consequence, there is no need for any value to be loaded into the flip-flop. It is, however, necessary to have this flip-flop reset to a state (output) having a 1 value due to the one-hot code used. If this is not possible with the inputs and outputs provided, this can be done with just an asynchronous reset R and an inverter added to the flip-flop output in this application.

With the one-hot state assignment, there are $128 - 7 = 121$ unused state codes that were treated as don't-cares. In the event of a failure that causes one of these states to occur, the circuit behavior is unknown. Is this a critical issue? This is an inexpensive consumer product bordering on a toy. For such a device, an infrequent failure is not particularly damaging. So this situation will be ignored. For more critical applications, the behavior in these states would need to be investigated. ■

EXAMPLE 6-4   Handheld Game: PIG

The goal of this example is to design a handheld game implementing a one-die version of the Game of PIG. The eight design steps are provided next for this simple game with a not-so-simple design.

1. PIG is a dice game that is used as a learning tool for instruction in probability. In contrast to the most prevalent versions that use two dice, this version of PIG is played with a single die that has 1 to 6 dots on its six faces (see Figure 3-57). During each turn, the player rolls the die one or more times until a) a 1 is rolled or b) the player chooses to hold. For each roll, the value rolled, except for a 1, is added to a subtotal for the current turn. If a 1 is rolled, the subtotal becomes 0, and the player's turn is ended. At the end of each turn, the subtotal is added to the player's overall total, and the play passes to the other player. The first player to reach or exceed 100 wins. On-line versions of PIG can be found by searching the web for: Game of PIG.

The exterior view of the game is shown in Figure 6-28(a). There are three 2-digit decimal LCDs. The displays from left to right are driven by signal vectors *TP1*, *ST*, and *TP2*, respectively. *TP1* controls the total score display for player 1 and *TP2* controls the total score display for player 2. During a turn, *ST* controls the subtotal display for the active player. There are four pushbuttons, *ROLL*, *HOLD*, *NEW_GAME*, and *RESET*, which produce conditioned signals with the same names. There is an LED array

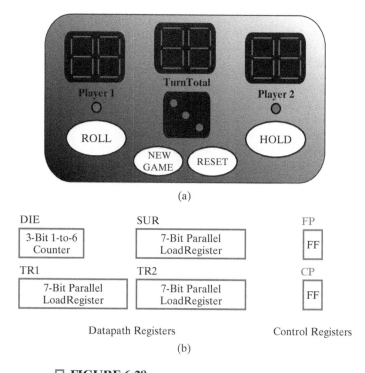

(a)

DIE	SUR	FP
3-Bit 1-to-6 Counter	7-Bit Parallel LoadRegister	FF

TR1	TR2	CP
7-Bit Parallel LoadRegister	7-Bit Parallel LoadRegister	FF

Datapath Registers Control Registers

(b)

□ **FIGURE 6-28**
PIG: (a) Exterior View of PIG, (b) PIG Registers

displaying the die value controlled by *DDIS* and two LEDs that indicate the active player. The left LED is controlled by signal *P1* and the right one by *P2*. When it is a player's turn, the LED for the player turns on and remains on for the remainder of the turn. When a player wins, the LED for the player flashes. When *ROLL* is pushed, the die begins rolling. When *ROLL* is released, the die stops rolling, and the rolled value is added to the current subtotal. If a 1 is rolled, *ST* becomes 0, 0 is added to the player's total, and the LED for the other player lights. When *HOLD* is pushed, the player's subtotal is added to the player's total, and the LED for the other player lights. When a player's total equals or exceeds 100, the player's LED flashes. A new game may be started at any time by pushing *NEW_GAME*. As long as the power remains on and *RESET* is not pushed, the new game will begin with the opposite player from the one starting the prior game. If the power has been off, Player 1 will be first. The external inputs and outputs for the game are shown in Table 6-17.

2. Next, we give consideration to the registers required in the PIG datapath. The die is represented by a 3-bit register *DIE* which counts from 1 to 6 repeatedly. This register must have an enable input, and is reset to 001 using RESET. It generates a "random number" depending on an arbitrary initial state and the time that ROLL is held down. The two totals and the subtotal

□ **TABLE 6-17**
Inputs, Outputs, and Registers of PIG

Symbol	Name/Function	Type
ROLL	1: Starts die rolling, 0: Stops die rolling	Control input
HOLD	1: Ends player turn, 0: Continues player turn.	Control input
NEW_GAME	1: Starts new game, 0: Continues current game	Control input
RESET	1: Resets game to INIT state, 0: No action	Control input
DDIS	7-Bit LED die display array	Data output vector
SUB	14-Bit 7-segment pair (a, b, c, d, e, f, g) to Turn Total display	Data output vector
TP1	14-Bit 7-segment pair (a, b, c, d, e, f, g) to Player 1 display	Data output vector
TP2	14-Bit 7-segment pair (a, b, c, d, e, f, g) to Player 2 display	Data output vector
P1	1: Player 1 LED on, 0: Player 1 LED off	Data output
P2	1: Player 2 LED on, 0: Player 2 LED off	Data output
DIE	Die value—specialized counter to count 1,...,6,1,...	3-Bit data register
SUR	Subtotal for active player—parallel load register	7-Bit data register
TR1	Total for Player 1—parallel load register	7-Bit data register
TR2	Total for Player 2—parallel load register	7-Bit data register
FP	First player—flip-flop 0: Player 1, 1: Player 2	1-Bit control register
CP	Current player—flip-flop 0: Player 1, 1: Player 2	1-Bit control register

each require a 7-bit register. These registers will be named *TR1*, *TR2*, and *SR*. Each of these three registers must have a synchronous reset and a load enable.

In addition to the datapath registers, a 2-bit control register stores 1) the first player in the current game, *FP*, and 2) the current player in the game, *CP*. The goal of separately storing this information is significant simplification of the control state machine. Otherwise, states would need to be duplicated for each player. The datapath and control registers for PIG are shown in Table 6-17.

3. The state machine diagram for PIG appears in Figure 6-29. In contrast with the prior example, Mealy outputs that depend on both state and input are permitted. It is helpful before developing the diagram to consider a number of situations that will exist in order to help define the states:

   a. A power-up or manual RESET has occurred.

   b. A new game is requested.

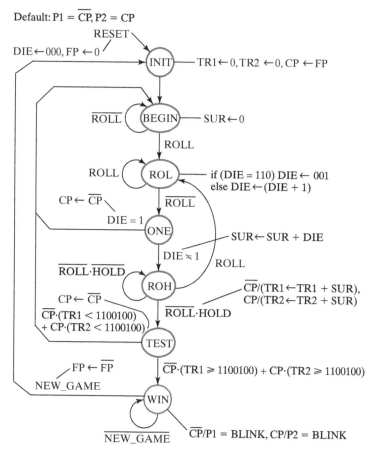

□ **FIGURE 6-29**
State Machine Diagram for PIG

c. One of the players is active and begins playing.

d. The active player may roll a 1.

e. The active player may select between *ROLL* and *HOLD*.

f. The active player needs to have the *HOLD* result tested for a win.

g. The active player has won.

Each of these situations may require a state and certain outputs. For situation a, we need to establish what must be reset by the *RESET* and establish the state that results from a *RESET*. In Figure 6-29, for starting out, we initialize DIE to 000, determine who plays first by initializing FP to 0, and choose a name of the reset state (*INIT*). Situation b, the start of a new game, whether the first game or a subsequent game, requires that registers *TP*1 and *TP*1 be reset. *SUR* needs to be set upon the change of players, so it can wait. Since these resets must occur for subsequent games, they should not be asynchronous, but be done synchronously in *INIT*. Also, we need to inform the player who is to become the active player, so *CP* is loaded with *FP*. At this point, a play turn can begin, so the state becomes *BEGIN*, representing the beginning of situation c. Since the active player is ready to begin accumulating points, SUR is synchronously reset to 0. The state remains *BEGIN* and the reset of *SUR* repeats, but this is not harmful. When a player pushes *ROLL*, the state becomes *ROL*, and addition of 1 to *DIE* is repeated as long as *ROLL* is 1. When ROLL becomes 0, *DIE* stops incrementing. Per situation d, a check on whether or not the player rolled a 1 is needed. So *ROLL* = 0 changes the state to *ONE* where this test occurs. If *DIE* = 1, then the player's turn is over, the other player becomes the active player ($CP \leftarrow \overline{CP}$), and the state returns to *BEGIN*. If *DIE* ≠ 1, *DIE* is added to *SUR*, and the state becomes *ROH* (Roll or Hold). Then the player may roll the die again by selecting *ROLL*, returning to *ROL*. Otherwise, the player may select *HOLD*, which causes *SUR* to be added to *TR1* or *TR2*, depending on the value of *CP*. (Note that in order to satisfy the mutual exclusion part of the transition condition constraints, $\overline{ROLL}$ has been ANDed with *HOLD*.) The next state becomes *TEST*, in which a test is performed on *TR1* or *TR2*, again depending on the value of *CP*, to determine whether or not the player has won. If the player has not won, then the other player becomes active and the state becomes *BEGIN*. If the player has won, the state becomes *WIN*. In state *WIN* the player's LED, as selected by *CP*, blinks due to the alternating *BLINK* signal. The state remains *WIN* until *NEW_GAME* is pushed, sending the play back to state *INIT*, with *FP* inverted to select the player not first in this game to be first in the new game.

4. In this step, we separate the datapath from the control and define the control and status signals that connect them together. The datapath actions can be read from the state machine diagram. The actions are grouped based on the destinations represented by the left-hand side of transfer statements ($\leftarrow$) or connection statements (=). Also, notation indicating status generation in the datapath needs to be interpreted and status signals generated. The end result of the groupings is shown in Table 6-18 in the left column. Synchronous resets are used for all registers except for *DIE* and *FP*, which have asynchronous resets. For the additions, the control signal is simply a load of the corresponding register, since aside from asynchronous reset, there are no other transfers on the involved registers. For *P1* and *P2*, note that the stated default values are used for the 0 inputs. Other default values are implicitly 0, hold stored values, or no action. Beginning with *DIE* = 1, the remainder of the table is for status conditions. Note how *CP* is used to select the total register *TRi* for the active player in determining a win. The variable names in true and complement form

□ **TABLE 6-18**
Datapath Output Actions and Control and Status Signals for PIG

Action or Status	Control or Status Signals	Meaning for Values 1 and 0
$TR1 \leftarrow 0$ $TR1 \leftarrow TR1 + SUR$	RST1 LDT1	1: Reset TR1 (synchronous reset), 0: No action 1: Add SUR to TR1, 0: No action
$TR2 \leftarrow 0$ $TR2 \leftarrow TR2 + SUR$	RST2 LDT2	1: Reset TR2 (synchronous reset), 0: No action 1: Add SUR to TR2, 0: No action
$SUR \leftarrow 0$ $SUR \leftarrow SUR + DIE$	RSSU LDSU	1: Reset SUR (synchronous reset), 0: No action 1: Add DIE to SUR, 0: No action
$DIE \leftarrow 000$ if $(DIE = 110)$ $DIE \leftarrow 001$ else $DIE \leftarrow DIE + 1$	RESET ENDI	1: Reset DIE to 000 (asynchronous reset) 1: Enable DIE to increment, 0: Hold DIE value
$P1 = BLINK$	BP1	1: Connect P1 to BLINK, 0: Connect P1 to 1
$P2 = BLINK$	BP2	1: Connect P2 to BLINK, 0: Connect P2 to 1
$CP \leftarrow FP$ $CP \leftarrow \overline{CP}$	CPFI LDCP CPFI LDCP	1: Select FP for CP 1: Load CP, 0: No action 0: Select $\overline{CP}$ for CP 1: Load CP, 0: No action
$FP \leftarrow 0$ $FP \leftarrow \overline{FP}$	RESET FPI	Asynchronous reset 1: Invert FP, 0: Hold FP
$DIE = 1$ $DIE \neq 1$	DIE1	1: DIE equal to 1 0: DIE not equal to 1
$TR1 \geq 1100100$	CP WN	0: Select TR1 for ≥ 1100100 1: The selected TRi ≥ 1100100 0: The selected TRi < 1100100
$TR2 \geq 1100100$	CP WN	1: Select TR2 for ≥ 1100100 1: The selected TRi ≥ 1100100 0: The selected TRi < 1100100

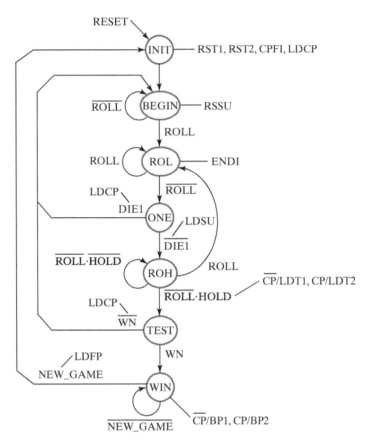

☐ **FIGURE 6-30**
Control State-Machine Diagram for PIG

from Table 6-18 replace the output actions and status-based input conditions in Figure 6-29 to form the state diagram in Figure 6-30.

5. The information in Table 6-18 also serves as a basis for developing the block diagram of the datapath given in Figure 6-31. The datapath registers shown in Table 6-17 anchor the datapath design. In addition to being added to SUR, *DIE* drives the Die Dot Display through a specialized decoder and must be tested for the value 001. The registers *SUR*, *TR*1, and *TR*2 are all identical with a signal for enabling loading and a synchronous reset. These three registers load from 7-bit ripple carry adders. The outputs from these registers each drive a 7-bit binary-to-BCD converter and a 2-digit BCD–to–7-segment converter in order to drive the corresponding 2-digit LCD display. In order to detect a win, a 7-bit 2-to-1 multiplexer selects the output of *TR*1 or *TR*2 as input to a circuit which detects whether the value is greater than or equal to 1100100 (decimal 100).

□ **FIGURE 6-31**
Datapath and Control Registers for PIG

The remainder of the diagram is the logic for controlling the contents of *FP* and *CP* in the control unit. *FP* is reset asynchronously with *RESET* and enabled for load of *FP* by LDFP. CP is initialized by loading from FP through the multiplexer with $CPF = 1$ and $LDCP = 1$. When $CPF = 0$ and $LDCP = 1$, CP is loaded with $\overline{CP}$.

6. The detailed logic for the control transfers on *FP* and *CP* has already been designed, and most of the datapath logic consists of components for which designs are already available. Logic in the form of AND gates with an inverted R on the second input needs to be added at the inputs to the *D* flip-flops in the parallel load register design in this chapter to implement the synchronous reset. The designs of DIE, the $D = 1$ comparator, the binary-to-BCD code converters, and the $D \geq 1100100$ comparator designs are given as problems in this chapter. The binary-to-LED die dots decoder is given as a problem in Chapter 3 and the BCD-to-7-segment converter is designed in Chapter 3.

7. The detailed design of the control unit is given as a problem at the end of the chapter. ■

Omitted in these examples, verification in step 8 has only been touched upon so far for simple circuits. The complexity of thoroughly verifying even the small systems given in the previous two examples is much more difficult and beyond the scope of what we can cover here. Rudimentary testing can be done by functional testing to see if the circuit performs its function correctly. This involves applying input sequences and using simulation to observe the outputs. The question now becomes, "What test sequence should be applied to make sure that the verification is thorough enough to place high confidence in the correctness of the circuit?" To illustrate the difficulty of answering this question, the average designer spends 40 percent or more of the design time doing verification.

6-11 HDL REPRESENTATION FOR SHIFT REGISTERS AND COUNTERS—VHDL

Examples of shift register and a binary counter illustrate the use of VHDL in representing registers and operations on register content.

EXAMPLE 6-5 VHDL for a 4-Bit Shift Register

The VHDL code in Figure 6-32 describes a 4-bit left shift register at the behavioral level. A RESET input is present that directly resets the register contents to zero. The shift register contains flip-flops and so has a process description resembling that of a *D* flip-flop. The four flip-flops are represented by the signal shift, of type std_logic_vector of size four. Q cannot be used to represent the flip-flops, since it is an output and the flip-flop outputs must be used internally. The left shift is achieved by applying the concatenation operator & to the right three bits of shift and to shift input SI. This quantity is transferred to shift, moving the contents one bit to the

```
// 4-Bit Left Shift Register with Reset

library ieee;
use ieee.std_logic_1164.all;

entity srg_4_r is
    port(CLK, RESET, SI : in std_logic;
        Q : out std_logic_vector(3 downto 0);
        SO :` out std_logic);
end srg_4_r;

architecture behavioral of srg_4_r is
signal shift : std_logic_vector(3 downto 0);
begin
process (RESET, CLK)
begin
    if (RESET = '1') then
        shift <= "0000";
    elsif (CLK'event and (CLK = '1')) then
        shift <= shift(2 downto 0) & SI;
    end if;
end process;
    Q <= shift;
    SO <= shift(3);
end behavioral;
```

□ **FIGURE 6-32**
Behavioral VHDL Description of 4-Bit Left Shift Register with Direct Reset

left and loading the value of SI into the rightmost bit. Following the process that performs the shift are two statements, one which assigns the value in shift to output Q and the other which defines the shift out signal SO as the contents of the leftmost bit of shift. ∎

EXAMPLE 6-6   VHDL for a 4-Bit Counter

The VHDL code in Figure 6-33 describes a 4-bit counter at the behavioral level. A RESET input is present that directly resets the counter contents to zero. The counter contains flip-flops and, therefore, has a process description resembling that of a D flip-flop. The four flip-flops are represented by the signal count, of type std_logic_vector and of size four. Q cannot be used to represent the flip-flops, since it is an output and the flip-flop outputs must be used internally. Counting up is achieved by adding 1 in the form of "0001" to count. Since addition is not a normal operation on type std_logic_vector, it is necessary to use an additional package from the ieee library, std_logic_unsigned.all, which defines unsigned number operations on type std_logic. Following the process that performs reset and counting are two statements, one which assigns the value in count to output Q and the other which

```
// 4-bit Binary Counter with Reset

library ieee;
use ieee.std_logic_1164.all;
use ieee.std_logic_unsigned.all;

entity count_4_r is
   port(CLK, RESET, EN : in std_logic;
        Q : out std_logic_vector(3 downto 0);
        CO : out std_logic);
end count_4_r;

architecture behavioral of count_4_r is
signal count : std_logic_vector(3 downto 0);
begin
process (RESET, CLK)
begin
   if (RESET = '1') then
      count <= "0000";
   elsif (CLK'event and (CLK = '1') and (EN = '1')) then
        count <= count + "0001";
   end if;
end process;
Q <= count;
CO <= '1' when count = "1111" and EN = '1' else '0';
end behavioral;
```

☐ **FIGURE 6-33**
Behavioral VHDL Description of 4-Bit Binary Counter with Direct Reset

defines the count out signal CO. A **when-else** statement is used in which CO is set to 1 only for the maximum count with EN equal to 1. ■

6-12 HDL REPRESENTATION FOR SHIFT REGISTERS AND COUNTERS—VERILOG

Examples of a shift register and a binary counter illustrate the use of Verilog in representing registers and operations on register content.

EXAMPLE 6-7   Verilog Code for a Shift Register

The Verilog description in Figure 6-34 describes a left shift register at the behavioral level. A RESET input is present that directly resets the register contents to zero. The shift register contains flip-flops, so has a process description beginning with **always** resembling that of a *D* flip-flop. The four flip-flops are represented by the vector Q, of type **reg** with bits numbered 3 down to 0. The left shift is achieved by applying { } to concatenate the right three bits of Q and shift input SI. This quantity is transferred to Q, moving the contents one bit to the left and loading the value of SI into the rightmost bit. Just

```
// 4-bit Left Shift Register with Reset

module srg_4_r_v (CLK, RESET, SI, Q,SO);
   input CLK, RESET, SI;
   output [3:0] Q;
   output SO;

reg [3:0] Q;

 assign SO = Q[3];

always @(posedge CLK or posedge RESET)
begin
   if (RESET)
     Q <= 4'b0000;
   else
     Q <= {Q[2:0], SI};
end
endmodule
```

□ **FIGURE 6-34**
Behavioral Verilog Description of 4-Bit Left Shift Register with Direct Reset

prior to the process that performs the shift is a continuous assignment statement that assigns the contents of the leftmost bit of Q to the shift output signal SO. ∎

EXAMPLE 6-8   Verilog Code for a Counter

The Verilog description in Figure 6-35 describes a 4-bit binary counter at the behavioral level. A RESET input is present that directly resets the register contents to zero.

```
// 4-bit Binary Counter with Reset

module count_4_r_v (CLK, RESET, EN, Q, CO);
   input CLK, RESET, EN;
   output [3:0] Q;
   output CO;

reg [3:0] Q;

assign CO = (count == 4'b1111 && EN == 1'b1) ? 1 : 0;
always @(posedge CLK or posedge RESET)
   begin
   if RESET)
     Q <= 4'b0000;
   else if (EN)
     Q <= Q + 4'b0001;
   end
endmodule
```

□ **FIGURE 6-35**
Behavioral Verilog Description of 4-Bit Binary Counter with Direct Reset

The counter contains flip-flops and, therefore, the description contains a process resembling that for a D flip-flop. The four flip-flops are represented by the signal Q of type `reg` and size four. Counting up is achieved by adding 1 to Q. Prior to the process that performs reset and counting is a conditional continuous assignment statement that defines the count out signal CO. CO is set to 1 only for the maximum count and EN equal to 1. Note that logical AND is denoted by `&&`. ■

6-13 MICROPROGRAMMED CONTROL

A control unit with its binary control values stored as a group of bits, which are referred to as *words*, in memory is called a *microprogrammed control*. Each word in the control memory contains a *microinstruction* that specifies one or more microoperations for the system. A sequence of microinstructions constitutes a *microprogram*. The microprogram is usually fixed at the system design time and so is stored in ROM. Microprogramming involves placing representations for combinations of values of control variables in words of ROM. These representations are accessed via successive read operations for use by the rest of the control logic. The contents of a word in ROM at a given address specify the microoperations to be performed for both the datapath and the control unit. A microprogram can also be stored in RAM. In this case, it is loaded at system startup from some form of nonvolatile storage, such as a magnetic disk. With either ROM or RAM, the memory in the control unit is called *control memory*. If RAM is used, the memory is referred to as *writable control memory*.

Figure 6-36 shows the general configuration of a microprogrammed control. The control memory is assumed to be a ROM within which all control microprograms are permanently stored. The *control address register* (*CAR*) specifies the address of the microinstruction. The *control data register* (*CDR*), which is optional, may hold the microinstruction currently being executed by the datapath and the control unit. One function of the control word is to determine the address of the next microinstruction to be executed. This microinstruction may be the next one in sequence, or it may be located somewhere else in the control memory. Therefore, one or more bits that specify the method for determining the address of the next microinstruction are present in the current microinstruction. The next address may also be a function of status and external control inputs. When a microinstruction is executed, the *next-address generator* produces the next address. This address is transferred to the *CAR* on the next clock pulse and is used to read the next microinstruction to be executed from ROM. Thus, the microinstructions contain bits for activating microoperations in the datapath and bits that specify the sequence of microinstructions executed.

The next-address generator, in combination with the *CAR*, is sometimes called a microprogram *sequencer*, since it determines the sequence of instructions read from control memory. The address of the next microinstruction can be specified in several ways, depending on the sequencer inputs. Typical functions of a microprogram sequencer are incrementing the *CAR* by one and loading the *CAR*. Possible sources for the load operation include an address from control memory, an externally provided address, and an initial address to start control-unit operation.

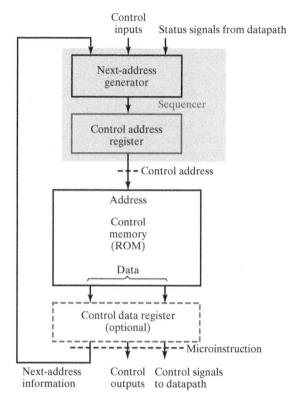

□ **FIGURE 6-36**
Microprogrammed Control Unit Organization

The *CDR* holds the present microinstruction while the next address is computed and the next microinstruction is read from memory. The *CDR* breaks up the long combinational delay paths through the control memory followed by the datapath. Its presence allows the system to use a higher clock frequency and process information faster. The inclusion of a *CDR* in a system, however, complicates the sequencing of microinstructions, particularly when decisions are made based on status bits. For simplicity in our brief discussion, we omit the *CDR* and take the microinstructions directly from the ROM outputs. The ROM operates as a combinational circuit, with the address as the input and the corresponding microinstruction as the output. The contents of the specified word in ROM remain on the output lines as long as the address value is applied to the inputs. No read/write signal is needed, as it is with RAM. Each clock pulse executes the microoperations specified by the microinstruction and also transfers a new address to the *CAR*. In this case, the *CAR* is the only component in the control that receives clock pulses and stores state information. The next-address generator and the control memory are combinational circuits. Thus, the state of the control unit is given by the contents of the *CAR*.

Microprogrammed control has been a very popular alternative implementation technique for control units for both programmable and nonprogrammable systems. However, as systems have become more complex and performance specifications have increased the need for concurrent parallel sequences of activities, the lockstep nature of microprogramming has become less attractive for control-unit implementation. Further, a large ROM or RAM tends to be much slower than the corresponding combinational logic. Finally, HDLs and synthesis tools facilitate the design of complex control units without the need for a lockstep programmable design approach. Overall, microprogrammed control for the design of control units, particularly direct datapath control in CPUs, has declined significantly. However, a new flavor of microprogrammed control has emerged, for implementing legacy computer architectures. These architectures have instruction sets that do not follow contemporary architecture principles. Nevertheless, such architectures must be implemented due to massive investments in software that uses them. Further, contemporary architecture principles must be used in the implementations to meet performance goals. The control for these systems is hierarchical, with microprogrammed control selectively used at the top level for complex instruction implementation and hardwired control at the lower level for implementing simple instructions and steps of complex instructions at a very rapid rate. This flavor of microprogramming is covered for a complex instruction set computer (CISC) in Chapter 10.

Information on the more traditional flavor of microprogrammed control, derived from past editions of this text, is available in a supplement, *Microprogrammed Control*, on the Companion Website for the text.

6-14 CHAPTER SUMMARY

Registers are sets of flip-flops, or interconnected sets of flip-flops, and combinational logic. The simplest registers are flip-flops that are loaded with new contents from their inputs on every clock cycle. More complex are registers in which the flip-flops can be loaded with new contents under the control of a signal on only selected clock cycles. Register transfers are a means of representing and specifying elementary processing operations. Register transfers can be related to corresponding digital system hardware, both at the block-diagram level and at the detailed logic level. Microoperations are elementary operations performed on data stored in registers. Arithmetic microoperations include addition and subtraction, which are described as register transfers and are implemented with corresponding hardware. Logic microoperations—that is, the bitwise application of logic primitives such as AND, OR, and XOR, combined with a binary word—provide masking and selective complementing on other binary words. Left- and right-shift microoperations move data laterally one or more bit positions at a time. Shift registers, counters, and buses implement particular register transfers that are widely used in digital systems.

In this chapter, the control of register transfers provided the final major component of digital systems design. Finally, all of the background material was present to define a procedure for designing register-transfer systems, one of the most general classes of digital systems. The details for the design procedure were illustrated by two extensive examples that are key to understanding the foundation of digital design.

REFERENCES

1. CLARE, C. R. *Designing Logic Systems Using State Machines*. New York: McGraw-Hill, 1973.
2. *IEEE Standard VHDL Language Reference Manual* (ANSI/IEEE Std 1076-1993; revision of IEEE Std 1076-1987). New York: The Institute of Electrical and Electronics Engineers, 1994.
3. *IEEE Standard Description Language Based on the Verilog™ Hardware Description Language* (IEEE Std 1364-1995). New York: The Institute of Electrical and Electronics Engineers, 1995.
4. MANO, M. M. *Digital Design*, 3rd ed. Englewood Cliffs, NJ: Prentice Hall, 2002.
5. THOMAS, D. E. AND P. R. MOORBY. *The Verilog Hardware Description Language*, 5th ed. New York: Springer, 2002.
6. WAKERLY, J. F. *Digital Design: Principles and Practices*, 4th ed. Upper Saddle River, NJ: Prentice Hall, 2006.

PROBLEMS

The plus (+) indicates a more advanced problem and the asterisk (*) indicates that a solution is available on the Companion Website for the text.

6-1. Assume that registers $R1$ and $R2$ in Figure 6-6 hold two unsigned numbers. When select input X is equal to 1, the adder–subtractor circuit performs the arithmetic operation "$R1$ + 2s complement of $R2$." This sum and the output carry C_n are transferred into $R1$ and C when $K_1 = 1$ and a positive edge occurs on the clock.

   (a) Show that if $C = 1$, then the value transferred to $R1$ is equal to $R1 - R2$, but if $C = 0$, the value transferred to $R1$ is the 2s complement of $R2 - R1$.

   (b) Indicate how the value in the C bit can be used to detect a borrow after the subtraction of two unsigned numbers.

   (c) How does the behavior of the C bit change if $R1$ and $R2$ hold signed 2s complement numbers?

6-2. *Perform the bitwise logic AND, OR, and XOR of the two 8-bit operands 10011001 and 11000011.

6-3. Find suitable operand and logical micro-operations for the 8-bit operand 1101 0100 (assume bit positions are 7 through 0 from left to right.)

   (a) to complement left most 4 bits.

   (b) to clear the left most bit.

   (c) to set left most 4 bits to 1.

6-4. *Starting from the 8-bit operand 11001010, show the values obtained after applying each shift microoperation given in Table 6-5.

6-5. *Modify the register of Figure 6-11 so that it will operate according to the following function table, using mode selection inputs S_1 and S_0:

S_1	S_0	Register Operation
0	0	No change
0	1	Load parallel data
1	0	Shift left (down)
1	1	Clear register to 0

6-6. *A ring counter is a shift register, as in Figure 6-9, with the serial output connected to the serial input.

(a) Starting from an initial state of 1000, list the sequence of states of the four flip-flops after each shift.

(b) Beginning in state 10...0, how many states are there in the count sequence of an n-bit ring counter?

6-7. A switch-tail counter (also called twisted ring counter, Johnson counter) uses the complement of the serial output of a right shift register as its serial input.

(a) Starting from an initial state of 000, list the sequence of states after each shift until the register returns to 000.

(b) Beginning in state 00...0, how many states are there in the count sequence of an n-bit switch-tail counter?

(c) Design a decoder to be driven by the counter that produces a one-hot code output for each of the states. Make use of the don't-care states in your design.

6-8. How many flip-flop values are complemented in a 4-bit binary ripple down counter to reach the next count value after:

(a) 0011?   **(b)** 1000?   **(c)** 0000?

6-9. + For the CMOS logic family, the power consumption is proportional to the sum of the changes from 1-to-0 and 0-to-1 on all gate inputs and outputs in the circuit. When designing counters in very low-power circuits, ripple counters are preferred over regular synchronous binary counters. Carefully count the numbers of changing inputs and outputs, including those related to the clock for a complete cycle of values in a 4-bit ripple counter versus a regular synchronous counter of the same length. Based on this examination, explain why the ripple counter is superior in terms of power consumption.

6-10. **(a)** Construct a 4-bit ripple down counter that uses a binary code counting sequence.

(b) Count the number of state (1-to-0 and 0-to-1) changes on all gate input and output, for the binary ripple down counter and for a 4-bit regular synchronous binary counter.

6-11. Construct a 16-bit serial-parallel counter, using two 8-bit parallel counters. Suppose that all added logic is AND gates and that serial connections are employed between the two counters. What is the maximum number of AND gates in a chain that a signal must propagate through in the 16-bit counter?

6-12. **(a)** Using the synchronous binary counter of Figure 6-14 and an AND gate, construct a counter that counts from 0000 through 1010.

(b) Repeat for a count from 0000 to 1110. Minimize the number of inputs to the AND gate.

6-13. Using two binary counters of the type shown in Figure 6-14 and logic gates, construct a binary counter that counts from decimal 11 through decimal 233. Also, add an additional input and logic to the counter to initialize it synchronously to 11 when the signal INIT is 1.

6-14. *Verify the flip-flop input equations of the synchronous BCD counter specified in Table 6-9. Draw the logic diagram of the BCD counter with a count enable input.

6-15. *Use D flip-flops and gates to design a binary counter with each of the following repeated binary sequences:

(a) $0, 1, 2$　　　　**(b)** $0, 1, 2, 3, 4, 5$

6-16. Use D-type flip-flops and gates to design a counter with the following repeated binary sequence: $0, 2, 4, 6, 8, 10, 12,$ and 14.

6-17. Draw the logic diagram of a 4-bit register with mode selection inputs S_1 and S_0. The register is to be operated according to the function table below.

S_1	S_0	Register Operation
0	0	No change
0	1	Parallel load
1	0	Shift left
1	1	Clear register to 0

6-18. Represent the following conditional control statement by two register transfer statements with control functions:

If $(A = 1)$ then $(R0 \leftarrow R1)$ else if $(B = 1)$ then $(R0 \leftarrow R2)$ else if $(C = 1)$ then $(R0 \leftarrow R1 \wedge R2)$

6-19. *Show the diagram of the hardware that implements the register transfer statement

$$C_3: R2 \leftarrow R1, R1 \leftarrow R2$$

6-20. The outputs of registers $R0$ and $R1$ are connected through a 4-to-1 multiplexer to the inputs of a third register, $R2$. Each register is 8 bits long. The required transfers, as dictated by four control variables, are:

$$C_0: R2 \leftarrow \overline{R2}$$

$$C_1: R2 \leftarrow R0$$

$$C_2: R2 \leftarrow R1$$

$$C_3: R2 \leftarrow \overline{R1}$$

The control variables are mutually exclusive (i.e., only one variable can be equal to 1 at any time) while the other three are equal to 0. Also, no transfer into $R4$ is to occur for all control variables equal to 0. Using registers and a multiplexer, draw a detailed logic diagram of the hardware that implements a single bit of these register transfers. Also draw a logic diagram of the simple logic that maps the control variables as inputs to three outputs: the two select variables for the multiplexer and the load signal for the register $R2$.

6-21. Construct a digital circuit that can implement the following operations under the control of only two multiplexer select inputs, using two 4-bit registers $R0$ and $R1$, three 2-to-1 multiplexers, and logic gates. Show diagram for one bit of operation.

$$\overline{S_1} \cdot \overline{S_0}: R0 \leftarrow R0 \wedge R1$$

$$S_1 \cdot \overline{S_0}: R0 \leftarrow R0 \vee \overline{R1}$$

$$\overline{S_1} \cdot S_0: R0 \leftarrow \overline{R0} \vee R1$$

$$S_1 \cdot S_0: R0 \leftarrow \overline{R0} \wedge \overline{R1}$$

6-22. *Using two 4-bit registers $R1$ and $R2$, and AND gates, OR gates, and inverters, draw one bit slice of the logic diagram that implements all of the following statements:

$$C_0: R2 \leftarrow 0 \qquad \text{Clear } R2 \text{ synchronously with the clock}$$

$$C_1: R2 \leftarrow \overline{R2} \qquad \text{Complement } R2$$

$$C_2: R2 \leftarrow R1 \qquad \text{Transfer } R1 \text{ to } R2$$

The control variables are mutually exclusive (i.e., only one variable can be equal to 1 at any time) while the other two are equal to 0. Also, no transfer into $R2$ is to occur for all control variables equal to 0.

6-23. A register cell is to be designed for an 8-bit register A that has the following register transfer functions:

$$C_0: A \leftarrow A \wedge B$$

$$C_1: A \leftarrow A \vee \overline{B}$$

Find optimum logic using AND, OR, and NOT gates for the D input to the D flip-flop in the cell.

6-24. A register cell is to be designed for 8-bit registers $R0$ and $R1$ that has the following register transfer functions. Use add-sub block and show diagram for one bit of operation.

$$\overline{S_1} \cdot \overline{S_0}: R1 \leftarrow R0 + R1$$

$$S_1 \cdot \overline{S_0}: R0 \leftarrow R0 + R1$$

$$\overline{S_1} \cdot S_0: R1 \leftarrow R0 - R1$$

$$S_1 \cdot S_0: R0 \leftarrow R0 - R1$$

6-25. A register cell is to be designed with registers $R0$ and $R1$ that has the following register transfers:

$$\overline{S_1} \cdot \overline{S_0}: R1 \leftarrow R0 + R1, \quad S_1 \cdot \overline{S_0}: R0 \leftarrow R0 + 1$$

$$\overline{S_1} \cdot S_0: R1 \leftarrow R0 - R1, \quad S_1 \cdot S_0: R0 \leftarrow R0 - 1$$

Use AND, OR, NOT gates and adder-subtract for the operation.

6-26. Logic to implement transfers among three registers, $R0$, $R1$, and $R2$, is to be implemented. Use the control variable assumptions given in Problem 6–20. The register transfers are as follows:

$$CA: R1 \leftarrow R0$$

$$CB: R0 \leftarrow R1, R2 \leftarrow R0$$

$$CC: R1 \leftarrow R2, R0 \leftarrow R2$$

Using registers and dedicated multiplexers, draw a detailed logic diagram of the hardware that implements a single bit of these register transfers.

Draw a logic diagram of simple logic that converts the control variables CA, CB, and CC as inputs to outputs that are the SELECT inputs for the multiplexers and LOAD signals for the registers.

6-27. *Two register transfer statements are given (otherwise, $R1$ is unchanged):

$$C1: R1 \leftarrow R1 + R2 \quad \text{Add } R2 \text{ to } R1$$

$$\overline{C1}\,C2: R1 \leftarrow R1 + 1 \quad \text{Increment } R1$$

(a) Using a 4-bit counter with parallel load as in Figure 6-14 and a 4-bit adder as in Figure 4-5, draw the logic diagram that implements these register transfers.

(b) Repeat part (a) using a 4-bit adder as in Figure 3-43 plus external gates as needed. Compare with the implementation in part (a).

6-28. Repeat Problem 6-26 using one multiplexer-based bus and one direct connection from one register to another instead of dedicated multiplexers.

6-29. (a) Construct an AND gate by interconnecting two three-state buffers and one inverters.

(b) Implement function $H = WZX + WY\overline{Z} + \overline{W}V$ using four three-state buffers and two inverters.

6-30. Draw a logic diagram of a circuit similar to the one shown in Figure 6-7, but use three-state buffers and a decoder instead of the multiplexers.

6-31. *A system is to have the following set of register transfers, implemented using buses:

$$C_a\colon R0 \leftarrow R1$$

$$C_b\colon R3 \leftarrow R1,\ R1 \leftarrow R4,\ R4 \leftarrow R0$$

$$C_c\colon R2 \leftarrow R3,\ R0 \leftarrow R2$$

$$C_d\colon R2 \leftarrow R4,\ R4 \leftarrow R2$$

(a) For each destination register, list all of the source registers.

(b) For each source register, list all of the destination registers.

(c) With consideration for which of the transfers must occur simultaneously, what is the minimum number of buses that can be used to implement the set of transfers? Assume that each register will have a single bus as its input.

(d) Draw a block diagram of the system, showing the registers and buses and the connections between them.

6-32. The following register transfers are to be executed in, with minimum clock cycles:

$$\overline{S_1} \cdot \overline{S_0}\colon R3 \leftarrow R0,\ R1 \leftarrow R2$$

$$S_1 \cdot \overline{S_0}\colon R2 \leftarrow R0,\ R1 \leftarrow R3$$

$$\overline{S_1} \cdot S_0\colon R3 \leftarrow R1,\ R0 \leftarrow R2$$

$$S_1 \cdot S_0\colon R2 \leftarrow R1,\ R0 \leftarrow R3$$

(a) What is the minimum number of buses required? Construct the register transfer operations so that the transfers can occur in one clock indicate the individual load line for each of the registers.

(b) Draw a block diagram connecting registers and multiplexers to implement the transfers.

6-33. Construct a registar transfer system, with one 4-to-1 multiplexer, and one bus and minimum number of clock cycles to perform the following set of register transfers:

$$R3 \leftarrow R0, \qquad R5 \leftarrow R0$$
$$R1 \leftarrow R2, \qquad R6 \leftarrow R4$$
$$R3 \leftarrow R7, \qquad R5 \leftarrow R4$$

Assume that only one bus can be attached to a register input and that any net connected to a register input is counted as a bus.

6-34. *The content of a 4-bit register is initially 0101. The register is shifted eight times to the right, with the sequence 10110001 as the serial input. The leftmost bit of the sequence is applied first. What is the content of the register after each shift?

6-35. *The serial adder of Figure 6-24 uses two 4-bit registers. Register A holds the binary number 0111 and register B holds 0101. The carry flip-flop is initially reset to 0. List the binary values in register A and the carry flip-flop after each of four shifts.

6-36. *A state diagram of a sequential circuit is given in Figure 6-37. Find the corresponding state machine diagram using a minimum amount of notation. The inputs to the circuit are $X1$ and $X2$, and the outputs are $Z1$ and $Z2$.

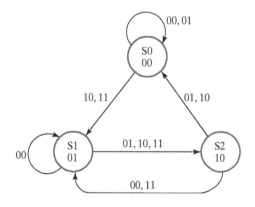

□ **FIGURE 6-37**
State Diagram for Problem 6-36

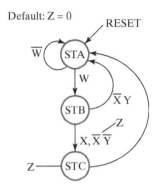

☐ **FIGURE 6-38**
State Machine Diagram for Problems 6-37, 6-38, 6-43, 6-57, and 6-58

6-37. *Find the response for the state machine diagram in Figure 6-38 to the following sequence of inputs (assume that the initial state is STA):

W:	0	1	1	0	1	1	0	1
X:	1	1	0	1	0	1	0	1
Y:	0	1	0	1	0	1	0	1

State: STA
Z:

6-38. A state machine diagram is given in Figure 6-38. Find the state table for the corresponding sequential circuit.

6-39. Find the state machine diagram corresponding to the following description: There are three states A, B, and C, two inputs X and Y, and an output Z. If in state A and $X = 1$, then the next state is A. If in state A and $X = 0$, then the next state is B. If in state B, $Y = 0$, then the next state is B. If in state B, $Y = 1$, then the next is C. If in state C and input $X = 0$, then the next state is C. If in state C and input $Y = 0$, then next the state is A. At state C, $Z = 1$.

6-40. *Find the state machine diagram for a circuit that detects a difference in value in an input signal X at two successive positive clock edges. If X has different values at two successive positive clock edges, then output Z is equal to 1 for the next clock cycle. Otherwise, output Z is 0.

6-41. +The state machine diagram for a synchronous circuit with clock CK for a washing machine is to be developed. The circuit has three external inputs, $START$, $FULL$, and $EMPTY$ (which are 1 for at most a single clock cycle and are mutually exclusive), and external outputs, HOT, $COLD$, $DRAIN$, and $TURN$. The datapath for the control consists of a down-counter, which has three inputs, $RESET$, DEC, and $LOAD$. This counter synchronously decrements once each minute for $DEC = 1$, but can be loaded or synchronously reset on any cycle of clock CK. It has a single output, $ZERO$, which is 1 whenever the counter contains value zero and is 0 otherwise.

In its operation, the circuit goes through four distinct cycles, *WASH*, *SPIN*, *RINSE*, and *SPIN*, which are detailed as follows:

WASH: Assume that the circuit is in its power-up state *IDLE*. If *START* is 1 for a clock cycle, *HOT* becomes 1 and remains 1 until *FULL* = 1, filling the washer with hot water. Next, using *LOAD*, the down-counter is loaded with a value from a panel dial which indicates how many minutes the wash cycle is to last. *DEC* and *TURN* then become 1 and the washer washes its contents. When *ZERO* becomes 1, the wash is complete, and *TURN* and *DEC* become 0.

SPIN: Next, *DRAIN* becomes 1, draining the wash water. When *EMPTY* becomes 1, the down-counter is loaded with 7. *DEC* and *TURN* then become 1 and the remaining wash water is wrung from the contents. When *ZERO* becomes 1, *DRAIN*, *DEC*, and *TURN* return to 0.

RINSE: Next, *COLD* becomes 1 and remains 1 until *FULL* = 1, filling the washer with cold rinse water. Next, using *LOAD*, the down-counter is loaded with value 10. *DEC* and *TURN* then become 1 and the washer rinses its contents. When *ZERO* becomes 1, the rinse is complete, and *TURN* and *DEC* become 0.

SPIN: Next, *DRAIN* becomes 1, draining the rinse water. When *EMPTY* becomes 1, the down-counter is loaded with 8. *DEC* and *TURN* then become 1 and the remaining rinse water is wrung from the contents. When *ZERO* becomes 1, *DRAIN*, *DEC*, and *TURN* return to 0 and the circuit returns to state *IDLE*.

(a) Find the state machine diagram for the washer circuit.

(b) Modify your design in part (a) assuming that there are two more inputs, *PAUSE* and *STOP*. *PAUSE* causes the circuit, including the counter, to halt and all outputs to go to 0. When *START* is pushed, the washer resumes operation at the point it paused. When *STOP* is pushed, all outputs are reset to 0 except for *DRAIN*, which is set to 1. When *EMPTY* becomes 1, the state returns to *IDLE*.

6-42. Find a state machine diagram for a traffic light controller that works as follows: A timing signal *T* is the input to the controller. *T* defines the yellow light interval, as well as the changes of the red and green lights. The outputs to the signals are defined by the following table:

Output	Light Controlled
GN	Green Light, North/South Signal
YN	Yellow Light, North/South Signal
RN	Red Light, North/South Signal
GE	Green Light, East/West Signal
YE	Yellow Light, East/West Signal
RE	Red Light, East/West Signal

While $T = 0$, the green light is on for one signal and the red light for the other. With $T = 1$, the yellow light is on for the signal that was previously green, and the signal that was previously red remains red. When T becomes 0, the signal that was previously yellow becomes red, and the signal that was previously red becomes green. This pattern of alternating changes in color continues. Assume that the controller is synchronous with a clock that changes much more frequently than input T.

6-43. *Implement the state machine diagram in Figure 6-38 by using one flip-flop per state assignment.

6-44. Implement the state machine diagram derived in Problem 6-40 by using a Gray-code state assignment.

6-45. Do two designs for the DIE circuit for the Game of PIG and compare the gate-input costs of your two designs using information from Figure 6-14. Note that the register transfer description of DIE is:

$$\text{if (Reset) DIE} \leftarrow 000 \text{ else}$$

$$\text{if (END1) (if (DIE} = 110) \text{ DIE} \leftarrow 001 \text{ else DIE} \leftarrow \text{DIE} + 1)$$

(a) Perform the design by using the technique given for the BCD counter design in Figure 6-15.

(b) Perform the design by using a state diagram and doing a custom circuit design with the next state for state 111 a don't-care state.

6-46. Design the following combinational circuits for the Game of PIG datapath given in Figure 6-31:

(a) $D = 1$ comparator.

(b) $D \geq 1100100$ comparator.

Use AND gates, OR gates, and inverters. Assume the maximum gate fan-in is four.

6-47. Design the 2-digit binary-to-BCD code converter in the datapath for the Game of PIG. Design the least significant digit as a function of (B_3, B_2, B_1, B_0) without an incoming carry C_0. The outputs are to be C_4, D_3, D_2, D_1, D_0. Design the same circuit with an incoming carry C_0 fixed to 1. For the most significant digit combine the results of these two designs to handle the actual case in which the incoming carry C_0 can be both 0 and 1. Minimize the combined result for the most significant digit.

6-48. **(a)** Show the details of a check of the constraints given on transition conditions as applied to Figure 6-30.

(b) Implement the state machine diagram for the Game of PIG in Figure 6-30 using a one-hot state assignment D flip-flops, and gates.

6-49. +Find the state machine diagram in the form of Figure 6-29 for a Game of PIG using two dice. Also, add the following rule: If a pair of 1s is rolled, then the player's total score becomes 0. The two dice create an interesting problem: How do you make sure that the values rolled on the two dice are not correlated with each other? The current scheme of having the die roll for the interval of time between the pushing and release will cause the values on the two dice to advance the same amount so that the values will be correlated from turn to turn. This will give only six of the 36 possible pairs of rolls of the two dice! You will need to devise a scheme to insure that all of the pairs are equally likely. Include a well-justified scheme in your solution.

6-50. *Design a digital system with three 16-bit registers AR, BR, and CR and 16-bit data input IN to perform the following operations, assuming a 2s complement representation and ignoring overflow:

   (a) Transfer two 16-bit signed numbers to AR and BR on successive clock cycles after a go signal G becomes 1.

   (b) If the number in AR is positive but nonzero, multiply the contents of BR by two and transfer the result to register CR.

   (c) If the number in AR is negative, multiply the contents of AR by two and transfer the result to register CR.

   (d) If the number in AR is zero, reset register CR to 0.

 All files referred to in the remaining problems are available in ASCII form for simulation and editing on the Companion Website for the text. A VHDL or Verilog compiler/simulator is necessary for the problems or portions of problems requesting simulation. Descriptions can still be written, however, for many problems without using compilation or simulation.

6-51. Write a Verilog description for the 4-bit binary counter in Figure 6-13(a) using a register for the D flip-flops and Boolean equations for the logic. Compile and simulate your description to demonstrate correctness.

6-52. *Write a behavioral VHDL description for the 4-bit register in Figure 6-1(a). Compile and simulate your description to demonstrate correctness.

6-53. Repeat Problem 6-52 for the 4-bit register with parallel load in Figure 6-2.

6-54. Write a VHDL description for the 4-bit binary counter in Figure 6-13(a), using a register for the D flip-flops and Boolean equations for the logic. Compile and simulate your description to demonstrate correctness.

6-55. *Write a behavioral Verilog description for the 4-bit register in Figure 6-1(a). Compile and simulate your description to demonstrate correctness.

6-56. Repeat Problem 6-55 for the 4-bit register with parallel load in Figure 6-2.

6-57. *Write, compile, and simulate a VHDL description for the state machine diagram shown in Figure 6-38. Use a simulation input that passes through all paths in the state machine diagram, and include both the state and output Z as simulation outputs. Correct and resimulate your design if necessary.

6-58. *Write, compile, and simulate a Verilog description for the state machine diagram in Figure 6-38. Use code 00 for state STA, 01 for state STB, and 10 for state STC. Use a simulation input that passes through all paths in the state-machine diagram and include both the state and Z as simulation outputs. Correct and resimulate your design if necessary.

7

MEMORY BASICS

Memory is a major component of a digital computer and is present in a large proportion of all digital systems. Random-access memory (RAM) stores data temporarily, and read-only memory (ROM) stores data permanently. ROM is one form of a variety of components called programmable logic devices (PLDs) that use stored information to define logic circuits.

Our study of RAM begins by looking at it in terms of a model with inputs, outputs, and signal timing. We then use equivalent logical models to understand the internal workings of RAM chips. Both static RAM and dynamic RAM are considered. The various types of dynamic RAM used for movement of data at high speeds between the CPU and memory are surveyed. Finally, we put RAM chips together to build simple RAM systems.

In many of the previous chapters, the concepts presented were broad, pertaining to much of the generic computer at the beginning of Chapter 1. In this chapter, for the first time, we can be more precise and point to specific uses of memory and related components. Beginning with the processor, the internal cache is very fast static RAM. Outside the CPU, the external cache is fast static RAM. The RAM subsystem, by its very name, is a type of memory. In the I/O area, we find substantial memory for storing information about the screen image in the video adapter. RAM appears in disk cache in the disk controller, to speed up disk access. Aside from the highly central role of the RAM subsystem in storing data and programs, we find memory in various forms applied in most subsystems of the generic computer.

7-1 MEMORY DEFINITIONS

In digital systems, memory is a collection of cells capable of storing binary information. In addition to these cells, memory contains electronic circuits for storing and retrieving the information. As indicated in the discussion of the generic computer, memory is used in many different parts of a modern computer, providing temporary or permanent storage for substantial amounts of binary information. In order for this information to be processed, it is sent from the memory to processing hardware consisting of registers and combinational logic. The processed information is then returned to the same or to a different memory. Input and output devices also interact with memory. Information from an input device is placed in memory so that it can be used in processing. Output information from processing is placed in memory, and from there it is sent to an output device.

Two types of memories are used in various parts of a computer: *random-access memory* (RAM) and *read-only memory* (ROM). RAM accepts new information for storage to be available later for use. The process of storing new information in memory is referred to as a *memory write* operation. The process of transferring the stored information out of memory is referred to as a *memory read* operation. RAM can perform both the write and the read operations, whereas ROM, as introduced in Section 6-8, performs only read operations. RAM sizes may range from hundreds to billions of bits.

7-2 RANDOM-ACCESS MEMORY

Memory is a collection of binary storage cells together with associated circuits needed to transfer information into and out of the cells. Memory cells can be accessed to transfer information to or from any desired location, with the access taking the same time regardless of the location, hence the name *random-access memory*. In contrast, *serial memory*, such as is exhibited by a hard drive, takes different lengths of time to access information, depending on where the desired location is relative to the current physical position of the disk.

Binary information is stored in memory in groups of bits, each group of which is called a *word*. A word is an entity of bits that moves in and out of memory as a unit—a group of 1s and 0s that represents a number, an instruction, one or more alphanumeric characters, or other binary-coded information. A group of eight bits is called a *byte*. Most computer memories use words that are multiples of eight bits in length. Thus, a 16-bit word contains two bytes, and a 32-bit word is made up of four bytes. The capacity of a memory unit is usually stated as the total number of bytes that it can store. Communication between a memory and its environment is achieved through data input and output lines, address selection lines, and control lines that specify the direction of transfer of information. A block diagram of a memory is shown in Figure 7-1. The n data input lines provide the information to be stored in memory, and the n data output lines supply the information coming out of memory. The k address lines specify the particular word chosen among the many available. The two control inputs specify the direction of transfer desired: the Write input causes binary data to be transferred into memory, and the Read input causes binary data to be transferred out of memory.

The memory unit is specified by the number of words it contains and the number of bits in each word. The address lines select one particular word. Each word in memory is assigned an identification number called an *address*. Addresses range from 0 to $2^k - 1$, where k is the number of address lines. The selection of a specific word inside memory is done by applying the k-bit binary address to the address lines. A decoder accepts this address and opens the paths needed to select the word

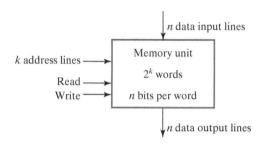

□ **FIGURE 7-1**
Block Diagram of Memory

specified. Computer memory varies greatly in size. It is customary to refer to the number of words (or bytes) in memory with one of the letters K (kilo), M (mega), or G (giga). K is equal to 2^{10}, M to 2^{20}, and G to 2^{30}. Thus, 64K $= 2^{16}$, 2M $= 2^{21}$, and 4G $= 2^{32}$.

Consider, for example, a memory with a capacity of 1K words of 16 bits each. Since 1K $= 1024 = 2^{10}$, and 16 bits constitute two bytes, we can say that the memory can accommodate 2048, or 2K, bytes. Figure 7-2 shows the possible contents of the first three and the last three words of this size of memory. Each word contains 16 bits that can be divided into two bytes. The words are recognized by their decimal addresses from 0 to 1023. An equivalent binary address consists of 10 bits. The first address is specified using ten 0s, and the last address is specified with ten 1s. This is because 1023 in binary is equal to 1111111111. A word in memory is selected by its binary address. When a word is read or written, the memory operates on all 16 bits as a single unit.

The 1K $\times$ 16 memory of the figure has 10 bits in the address and 16 bits in each word. The number of address bits needed in memory is dependent on the total

Memory Address

Binary	Decimal	Memory Contents
0000000000	0	10110101 01011100
0000000001	1	10101011 10001001
0000000010	2	00001101 01000110
.	.	.
.	.	.
.	.	.
.	.	.
1111111101	1021	10011101 00010101
1111111110	1022	00001101 00011110
1111111111	1023	11011110 00100100

□ **FIGURE 7-2**
Contents of a 1024 $\times$ 16 Memory

number of words that can be stored and is independent of the number of bits in each word. The number of bits in the address for a word is determined from the relationship $2^k \geq m$, where m is the total number of words and k is the minimum number of address bits satisfying the relationship.

Write and Read Operations

The two operations that a random-access memory can perform are write and read. A *write* is a transfer into memory of a new word to be stored. A *read* is a transfer of a copy of a stored word out of memory. A Write signal specifies the transfer-in operation, and a Read signal specifies the transfer-out operation. On accepting one of these control signals, the internal circuits inside memory provide the desired function.

The steps that must be taken for a write are as follows:

1. Apply the binary address of the desired word to the address lines.

2. Apply the data bits that must be stored in memory to the data input lines.

3. Activate the Write input.

The memory unit will then take the bits from the data input lines and store them in the word specified by the address lines.

The steps that must be taken for a read are as follows:

1. Apply the binary address of the desired word to the address lines.

2. Activate the Read input.

The memory will then take the bits from the word that has been selected by the address and apply them to the data output lines. The contents of the selected word are not changed by reading them.

Memory is made up of RAM integrated circuits (chips), plus additional logic circuits. RAM chips usually provide the two control inputs for the read and write operations in a somewhat different configuration from that just described. Instead of having separate Read and Write inputs to control the two operations, most integrated circuits provide at least a Chip Select that selects the chip to be read from or written to, and a Read/Write that determines the particular operation. The memory operations that result from these control inputs are shown in Table 7-1.

☐ **TABLE 7-1**
Control Inputs to a Memory Chip

Chip Select CS	Read/Write R/W̅	Memory Operation
0	×	None
1	0	Write to selected word
1	1	Read from selected word

The Chip Select is used to enable the particular RAM chip or chips containing the word to be accessed. When Chip Select is inactive, the memory chip or chips are not selected, and no operation is performed. When Chip Select is active, the Read/Write input determines the operation to be performed. While Chip Select accesses chips, a signal is also provided that accesses the entire memory. We will call this signal the Memory Enable.

Timing Waveforms

The operation of the memory unit is controlled by an external device, such as a CPU. The CPU is synchronized by its own clock pulses. The memory, however, does not employ the CPU clock. Instead, its read and write operations are timed by changes in values on the control inputs. The *access time* of a memory read operation is the maximum time from the application of the address to the appearance of the data at the Data Output. Similarly, the *write cycle time* is the maximum time from the application of the address to the completion of all internal memory operations required to store a word. Memory writes may be performed one after the other at the intervals of the cycle time. The CPU must provide the memory control signals in such a way as to synchronize its own internal clocked operations with the read and write operations of memory. This means that the access time and the write cycle time of the memory must be related within the CPU to a period equal to a fixed number of CPU clock periods.

Assume, as an example, that a CPU operates with a clock frequency of 50 MHz, giving a period of 20 ns ($1 \text{ ns} = 10^{-9}\text{ s}$) for one clock pulse. Suppose now that the CPU communicates with a memory with an access time of 65 ns and a write cycle time of 75 ns. The number of clock pulses required for a memory request is the integer value greater than or equal to the larger of the access time and the write cycle time, divided by the clock period. Since the period of the CPU clock is 20 ns, and the larger of the access time and write cycle time is 75 ns, it will be necessary to devote at least four clock pulses to each memory request.

The memory cycle timing shown in Figure 7-3 is for a CPU with a 50 MHz clock and memory with a 75 ns write cycle time and a 65 ns access time. The write cycle in part (a) shows four pulses $T1$, $T2$, $T3$, and $T4$ with a cycle of 20 ns. For a write operation, the CPU must provide the address and input data to the memory. The address is applied, and Memory Enable is set to the high level at the positive edge of the $T1$ pulse. The data, needed somewhat later in the write cycle, is applied at the positive edge of $T2$. The two lines that cross each other in the address and data waveforms designate a possible change in value of the multiple lines. The shaded areas represent unspecified values. A change of the Read/Write signal to 0 to designate the write operation is also at the positive edge of $T2$. To avoid destroying data in other memory words, it is important that this change occur after the signals on the address lines have become fixed at the desired values. Otherwise, one or more other words might be momentarily addressed and accidentally written over with different data. The Read/Write signal must stay at 0 long enough after application of the address and Memory Enable to allow the write operation to complete. Finally, the address and data signals must remain

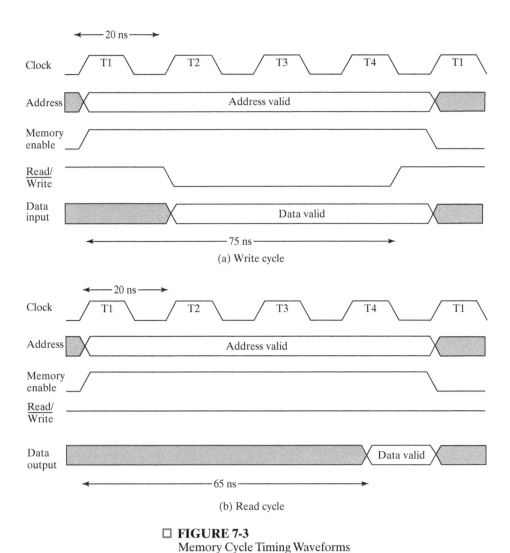

☐ **FIGURE 7-3**
Memory Cycle Timing Waveforms

stable for a short time after the Read/Write goes to 1, again to avoid destroying data in other memory words. At the completion of the fourth clock pulse, the memory write operation has ended with 5 ns to spare, and the CPU can apply the address and control signals for another memory request with the next $T1$ pulse.

The read cycle shown in Figure 7-3(b) has an address for the memory that is provided by the CPU. The CPU applies the address, sets the Memory Enable to 1, and sets Read/Write to 1 to designate a read operation, all at the positive edge of $T1$. The memory places the data of the word selected by the address onto the data output lines within 65 ns from the time that the address is applied and the memory enable is activated. Then, the CPU transfers the data into one of its internal registers during the positive transition of the next $T1$ pulse, which can also change the address and controls for the next memory request.

Properties of Memory

Integrated-circuit RAM may be either static or dynamic. *Static* RAM (SRAM) consists of internal latches that store the binary information. The stored information remains valid as long as power is applied to the RAM. *Dynamic* RAM (DRAM) stores the binary information in the form of electric charges on capacitors. The capacitors are accessed inside the chip by *n*-channel MOS transistors. The stored charge on the capacitors tends to discharge with time, and the capacitors must be periodically recharged by *refreshing* the DRAM. This is done by cycling through the words every few milliseconds, reading and rewriting them to restore the decaying charge. DRAM offers reduced power consumption and larger storage capacity in a single memory chip, but SRAM is easier to use and has shorter read and write cycles. Also, no refresh is required for SRAM.

Memory units that lose stored information when power is turned off are said to be *volatile*. Integrated-circuit RAMs, both static and dynamic, are of this category, since the binary cells need external power to maintain the stored information. In contrast, a *nonvolatile memory*, such as magnetic disk, retains its stored information after the removal of power. This is because the data stored on magnetic components is represented by the direction of magnetization, which is retained after power is turned off. Another nonvolatile memory is ROM, discussed in Section 5-2.

7-3 SRAM INTEGRATED CIRCUITS

As indicated earlier, memory consists of RAM chips plus additional logic. We will consider the internal structure of the RAM chip first. Then we will study combinations of RAM chips and additional logic used to construct memory. The internal structure of a RAM chip of *m* words with *n* bits per word consists of an array of *mn* binary storage cells and associated circuitry. The circuity is made up of decoders to select the word to be read or written, read circuits, write circuits, and output logic. The *RAM cell* is the basic binary storage cell used in the RAM chip, which is typically designed as an electronic circuit rather than a logic circuit. Nevertheless, it is possible and convenient to model the RAM chip using a logic model.

A static RAM chip serves as the basis for our discussion. We first present RAM cell logic for storing a single bit and then use the cell in a hierarchy to describe the RAM chip. Figure 7-4 shows the logic model of the RAM cell. The storage part of the

□ **FIGURE 7-4**
Static RAM Cell

cell is modeled by an *SR* latch. The inputs to the latch are enabled by a Select signal. For Select equal to 0, the stored content is held. For Select equal to 1, the stored content is determined by the values on B and $\overline{B}$. The outputs from the latch are gated by Select to produce cell outputs C and $\overline{C}$. For Select equal to 0, both C and $\overline{C}$ are 0, and for Select equal to 1, C is the stored value and $\overline{C}$ is its complement.

To obtain simplified static RAM diagrams, we interconnect a set of RAM cells and read and write circuits to form a *RAM bit slice* that contains all of the circuitry associated with a single bit position of a set of RAM words. The logic diagram for a RAM bit slice is shown in Figure 7-5(a). The portion of the model representing each RAM cell

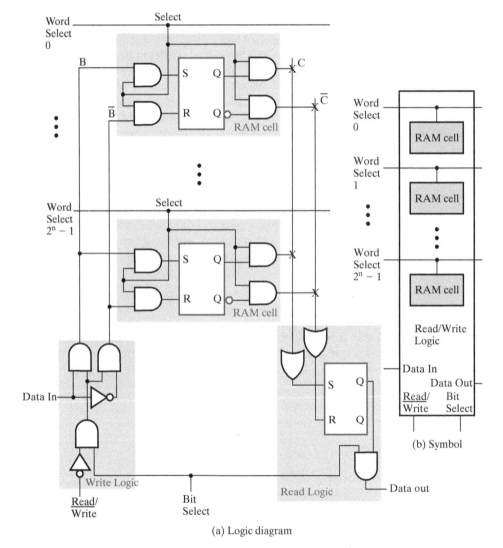

(a) Logic diagram

☐ **FIGURE 7-5**
RAM Bit Slice Model

is highlighted in blue. The loading of a cell latch is now controlled by a Word Select input. If this is 0, then both S and R are 0, and the cell latch contents remain unchanged. If the Word Select input is 1, then the value to be loaded into the latch is controlled by two signals B and $\overline{B}$ from the Write Logic. In order for either of these signals to be 1 and potentially change the stored value, Read/$\overline{\text{Write}}$ must be 0 and Bit Select must be 1. Then the Data In value and its complement are applied to B and $\overline{B}$, respectively, to set or reset the latch in the RAM cell selected. If Data In is 1, the latch is set to 1, and if Data In is 0, the latch is reset to 0, completing the write operation.

Only one word is written at a time. That is, only one Word Select line is 1, and all other Word Select lines are 0. Thus, only one RAM cell attached to B and $\overline{B}$ is written. The Word Select also controls the reading of the RAM cells, using shared Read Logic. If Word Select is 0, then the stored value in the SR latch is prevented by the AND gates from reaching the pair of OR gates in the Read Logic. But if Word Select is 1, the stored value passes through to the OR gates and is captured in the Read Logic SR latch. If Bit Select is also 1, the captured value appears on the Data Out line of the RAM bit slice. Note that for this particular Read Logic design, the read occurs regardless of the value of Read/$\overline{\text{Write}}$.

The symbol for the RAM bit slice given in Figure 7-5(b) is used to represent the internal structure of RAM chips. Each Word Select line extends beyond the bit slice, so that when multiple RAM bit slices are placed side by side, corresponding Word Select lines connect. The other signals in the lower portion of the symbol may be connected in various ways, depending on the structure of the RAM chip.

The symbol and block diagram for a 16×1 RAM chip are shown in Figure 7-6. Both have four address inputs for the 16 one-bit words stored in RAM. There are also Data Input, Data Output, and Read/$\overline{\text{Write}}$ signals. The Chip Select at the chip level corresponds to the Memory Enable at the level of a RAM consisting of multiple chips. The internal structure of the RAM chip consists of a RAM bit slice having 16 RAM cells. Since there are 16 Word Select lines to be controlled such that one and only one has the value logic 1 at a given time, a 4–to–16-line decoder is used to decode the four address bits into 16 Word Select bits.

The only additional logic in the figure is a triangular symbol with one normal input, one normal output, and a second input on the bottom of the symbol. This symbol is a three-state buffer that allows construction of a multiplexer with an arbitrary number of inputs. Three-state outputs are connected together and properly controlled using the Chip Select inputs. By using three-state buffers on the outputs of RAM chips, these outputs can be connected together to provide the word from the chip being read on the bit lines attached to the RAM outputs. The enable signals in the preceding discussion correspond to the Chip Select inputs on the RAM chips. To read a word from a particular RAM chip, the Chip Select value for that chip must be 1, and for all other chips attached to the same output bit lines, the Chip Select must be 0. These combinations containing a single 1 can be obtained from a decoder.

Coincident Selection

Inside a RAM chip, the decoder with k inputs and 2^k outputs requires 2^k AND gates with k inputs per gate if a straightforward design approach is used. In addition, if the

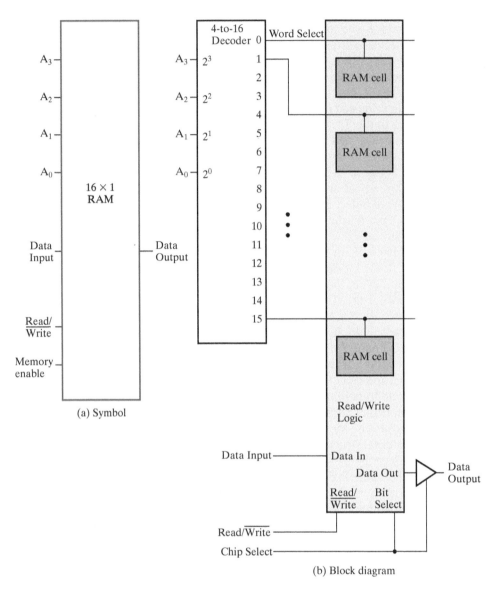

☐ **FIGURE 7-6**
16-Word by 1-Bit RAM Chip

number of words is large, and all bits for one bit position in the word are contained in a single RAM bit slice, the number of RAM cells sharing the read and write circuits is also large. The electrical properties resulting from both of these situations cause the access and write cycle times of the RAM to become long, which is undesirable.

The total number of decoder gates, the number of inputs per gate, and the number of RAM cells per bit slice can all be reduced by employing two decoders with a *coincident selection* scheme. In one possible configuration, two *k*/2-input decoders are used instead of one k-input decoder. One decoder controls the word select lines and the other controls the bit select lines. The result is a two-dimensional matrix selection scheme. If the RAM chip has m words with 1 bit per word, then the scheme selects the RAM cell at the intersection of the Word Select row and the Bit Select column. Since the Word Select is no longer strictly selecting words, its name is changed to *Row Select*. An output from the added decoder that selects one or more bit slices is referred to as a *Column Select*.

Coincident selection is illustrated for the 16×1 RAM chip with the structure shown in Figure 7-7. The chip consists of four RAM bit slices of four bits each and has a total of 16 RAM cells in a two-dimensional array. The two most significant address inputs go through the 2–to–4-line row decoder to select one of the four rows of the array. The two least significant address inputs go through the

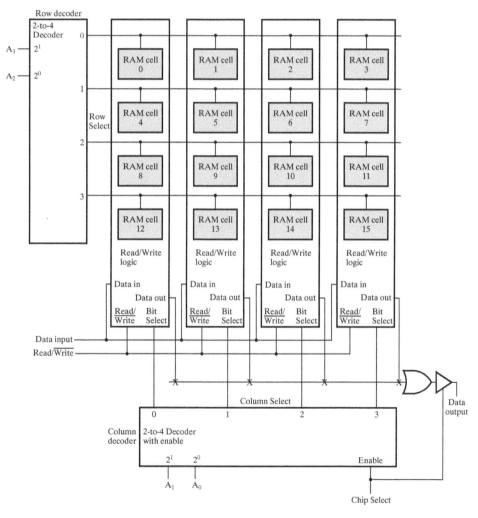

□ **FIGURE 7-7**
Diagram of a 16×1 RAM Using a 4×4 RAM Cell Array

2–to–4–line column decoder to select one of the four columns (RAM bit slices) of the array. The column decoder is enabled with the Chip Select input. When the Chip Select is 0, all outputs of the decoder are 0 and none of the cells is selected. This prevents writing into any RAM cell in the array. With Chip Select at 1, a single bit in the RAM is accessed. For example, for the address 1001, the first two address bits are decoded to select row 10 of the RAM cell array. The second two address bits are decoded to select column 01 of the array. The RAM cell accessed, in row 2 and column 1 of the array, is cell 9 ($10_2 01_2$). With a row and column selected, the Read/$\overline{\text{Write}}$ input determines the operation. During the read operation (Read/$\overline{\text{Write}}$ = 1), the selected bit of the selected row goes through the OR gate to the three-state buffer. Note that the gate is drawn according to the array logic established in Figure 5-5. Since the buffer is enabled by Chip Select, the value read appears at the Data Output. During the write operation (Read/$\overline{\text{Write}}$ = 0), the bit available on the Data Input line is transferred into the selected RAM cell. Those RAM cells not selected are disabled, and their previous binary values remain unchanged.

The same RAM cell array is used in Figure 7-8 to produce an 8 × 2 RAM chip (eight words of two bits each). The row decoding is unchanged from that in Figure 7-7; the only changes are in the column and output logic. Since there are just three address bits, and two are handled by the row decoder, the column decoder has only one address bit and Chip Select as inputs and produces just two Column Select lines. Since two bits at a time are to be written or read, the Column Select lines go to adjacent pairs of RAM bit slices. Two input lines, Data Input 0 and Data Input 1, each go to a different bit in all of the pairs. Finally, corresponding bits of the pairs share output OR gates and three-state buffers, giving output lines Data Output 0 and Data Output 1. The operation of this structure can be illustrated by the application of the address 3 (011_2). The first two bits of the address, 01, access row 1 of the array. The final bit, 1, accesses column 1, which consists of bit slices 2 (10_2) and 3 (11_2). So the word to be written or read lies in RAM cells 6 and 7 ($011\ 0_2$ and $011\ 1_2$), which contain bits 0 and 1, respectively, of word 3.

We can demonstrate the savings of the coincident selection scheme by considering a more realistic static RAM size, 32K × 8. This RAM chip contains a total of 256K bits. To make the number of rows and columns in the array equal, we take the square root of 256K, giving $512 = 2^9$. So the first nine bits of the address are fed to the row decoder and the remaining six bits to the column decoder. Without coincident selection, the single decoder would have 15 inputs and 32,768 outputs. With coincident selection, there is one 9–to–512-line decoder and one 6–to–64-line decoder. The number of gates for a straightforward design of the single decoder would be 32,800. For the two coincident decoders, the number of gates is 608, reducing the gate count by a factor of more than 50. In addition, although it appears that there are 64 times as many Read/Write circuits, the column selection can be done between the RAM cells and the Read/Write circuits, so that only the original eight circuits are required. Because of the reduced number of RAM cells attached to each Read/Write circuit at any time, the access time of the chip is also improved.

☐ **FIGURE 7-8**
Block Diagram of an 8 × 2 RAM Using a 4 × 4 RAM Cell Array

7-4 ARRAY OF SRAM ICS

Integrated-circuit RAM chips are available in a variety of sizes. If the memory unit needed for an application is larger than the capacity of one chip, it is necessary to combine a number of chips in an array to form the required size of memory. The capacity of the memory depends on two parameters: the number of words and the number of bits per word. An increase in the number of words requires that we increase the address length. Every bit added to the length of the address doubles the number of words in memory. An increase in the number of bits per word requires that we increase the number of data input and output lines, but the address length remains the same.

☐ **FIGURE 7-9**
Symbol for a 64K × 8 RAM Chip

To illustrate an array of RAM ICs, let us first introduce a RAM chip using the condensed representation for inputs and outputs shown in Figure 7-9. The capacity of this chip is 64K words of 8 bits each. The chip requires a 16-bit address and 8 input and output lines. Instead of 16 lines for the address and 8 lines each for data input and data output, each is shown in the block diagram by a single line. Each line has a slash across it with a number indicating the number of lines represented. The CS (Chip Select) input selects the particular RAM chip, and the $R/\overline{W}$ (Read/$\overline{Write}$) input specifies the read or write operation when the chip is selected. The small triangle shown at the outputs is the standard graphics symbol for three-state outputs. The CS input of the RAM controls the behavior of the data output lines. When $CS = 0$, the chip is not selected, and all its data outputs are in the high-impedance state. With $CS = 1$, the data output lines carry the eight bits of the selected word.

Suppose that we want to increase the number of words in the memory by using two or more RAM chips. Since every bit added to the address doubles the binary number that can be formed, it is natural to increase the number of words in factors of two. For example, two RAM chips will double the number of words and add one bit to the composite address. Four RAM chips multiply the number of words by four and add two bits to the composite address.

Consider the possibility of constructing a 256K × 8 RAM with four 64K × 8 RAM chips, as shown in Figure 7-10. The eight data input lines go to all the chips. The three-state outputs can be connected together to form the eight common data output lines. This type of output connection is possible only with three-state outputs. Just one Chip Select input will be active at any time, while the other three chips will be disabled. The eight outputs of the selected chip will contain 1s and 0s, and the other three will be in a high-impedance state, presenting only open circuits to the binary output signals of the selected chip.

The 256K-word memory requires an 18-bit address. The 16 least significant bits of the address are applied to the address inputs of all four chips. The two most significant bits are applied to a 2 × 4 decoder. The four outputs of the decoder are applied to the CS inputs of the four chips. The memory is disabled when the EN input of the decoder, Memory Enable, is equal to 0. All four outputs of the decoder are then 0, and none of the chips is selected. When the decoder is enabled, address bits 17 and 16 determine the particular chip that is selected. If these bits are equal to 00, the first

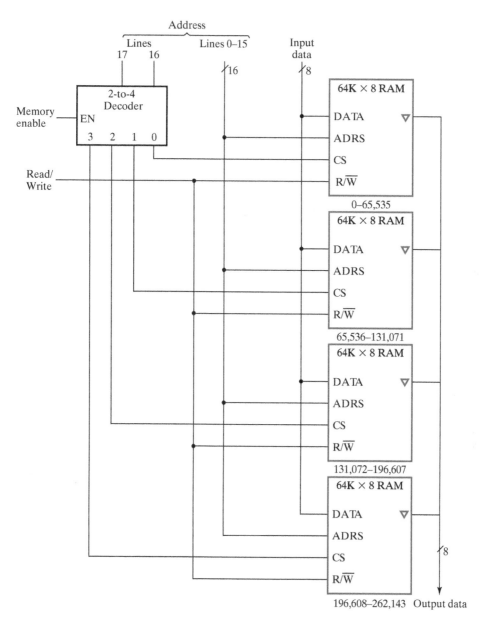

□ **FIGURE 7-10**
Block Diagram of a 256K × 8 RAM

RAM chip is selected. The remaining 16 address bits then select a word within the chip in the range from 0 to 65,535. The next 65,536 words are selected from the second RAM chip with an 18-bit address that starts with 01 followed by the 16 bits from the common address lines. The address range for each chip is listed in decimal under its symbol in the figure.

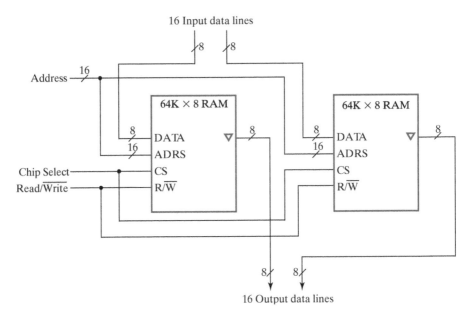

☐ **FIGURE 7-11**
Block Diagram of a 64K × 16 RAM

It is also possible to combine two chips to form a composite memory containing the same number of words, but with twice as many bits in each word. Figure 7-11 shows the interconnection of two 64K × 8 chips to form a 64K × 16 memory. The 16 data input and data output lines are split between the two chips. Both receive the same 16-bit address and the common CS and $R/\overline{W}$ control inputs.

The two techniques just described may be combined to assemble an array of identical chips into a large-capacity memory. The composite memory will have a number of bits per word that is a multiple of that for one chip. The total number of words will increase in factors of two times the word capacity of one chip. An external decoder is needed to select the individual chips based on the additional address bits of the composite memory.

To reduce the number of pins on the chip package, many RAM ICs provide common terminals for the data input and data output. The common terminals are said to be *bidirectional*, which means that for the read operation they act as outputs, and for the write operation they act as inputs. Bidirectional lines are constructed with three-state buffers and are discussed further in Section 6-8. The use of bidirectional signals requires control of the three-state buffers by both Chip Select and Read/Write.

7-5 DRAM ICs

Because of its ability to provide high storage capacity at low cost, dynamic RAM (DRAM) dominates the high-capacity memory applications, including the primary RAM in computers. Logically, DRAM in many ways is similar to SRAM. However, because of the electronic circuit used to implement the storage cell, its electronic design is considerably more challenging. Further, as the name "dynamic" implies, the storage of information is inherently only temporary. As a consequence, the information must be periodically "refreshed" to mimic the behavior of static storage. This need for refresh is the primary logical difference in the behavior of DRAM compared to SRAM. We explore this logical difference by examining the dynamic RAM cell, the logic required to perform the refresh operation, and the impact of the need for refresh on memory system operation.

DRAM Cell

The dynamic RAM cell circuit is shown in Figure 7-12(a). It consists of a capacitor C and a transistor T. The capacitor is used to store electrical charge. If sufficient charge is stored on the capacitor, it can be viewed as storing a logical 1. If insufficient charge is stored on the capacitor, it can be viewed as storing a logical 0. The transistor acts much like a switch, as described in Section 5-1. When the switch is "open," the charge on the capacitor roughly remains fixed—in other words, is stored. But when the switch is "closed," charge can flow into and out of the capacitor from the external Bit (B) line. This charge flow allows the cell to be written with a 1 or 0 and to be read.

In order to understand the read and write operations for the cell, we will use a hydraulic analogy with charge replaced by water, the capacitor by a small storage tank, and the transistor by a valve. Since the bit line has a large capacitance, it is represented by a large tank, and pumps which can fill and empty this tank rapidly. This analogy is given in Figures 7-12(b) and (c) with the valve closed. Note that in one case the small storage tank is full, representing a stored 1, and in the other case it is empty, representing a stored 0. Suppose that a 1 is to be written into the cell. The valve is opened and the pumps fill up the large tank. Water flows through the valve, filling the

□ **FIGURE 7-12**
Dynamic RAM cell, hydraulic analogy of cell operation, and cell model

small storage tank, as shown in Figure 7-12(d). Then the valve is closed, leaving the small tank full, which represents a 1. A 0 can be written using the same sort of operations, except that the pumps empty the large tank as shown in Figure 7-12(e).

Now, suppose we want to read a stored value and that the value is a 1 corresponding to a full storage tank. With the large tank at a known intermediate level, the valve is opened. Since the small storage tank is full, water flows from the small tank to the large tank, increasing the level of the water surface in the large tank slightly as shown in Figure 7-12(f). This increase in level is observed as the reading of 1 from the storage tank. Correspondingly, if the storage tank is initially empty, there will be a slight decrease in the level in the large tank in Figure 7-12(g), which is observed as the reading of a 0 from the storage tank.

In the read operation just described, Figures 7-12(f) and (g) show that, regardless of the initial stored value in the storage tank, it now contains an intermediate value which will not cause enough change in the level of the external tank to permit a 0 or 1 to be observed. So the read operation has destroyed the stored value; this is referred to as a *destructive read*. To be able to read the original stored value in the future, we must *restore* it (i.e., return the storage tank to its original level). To perform the restore for a stored 1 observed, the large tank is filled by the pumps and the small tank fills through the open valve. To perform the restore for a stored 0 observed, the large tank is emptied by the pumps, and the small tank drains through the open valve.

In the actual storage cell, there are other paths present for charge flow. These paths are analogous to small leaks in the storage tank. Due to these leaks, a full small storage tank will eventually drain to a point at which the increase in the level of the large tank on a read cannot be observed as an increase. In fact, if the small tank is less than half full when read, it is possible that a decrease in the level of the large tank may be observed. To compensate for these leaks, the small storage tank storing a 1 must be periodically refilled. This is referred to as a refresh of the cell contents. Every storage cell must be refreshed before its level has declined to a point at which the stored value can no longer be properly observed.

Through the hydraulic analogy, the DRAM operation has been explained. Just as for the SRAM, we employ a logic model for the cell. The model shown in Figure 7-12(h) is a D latch. The C input to the D latch is Select and the D input to the D latch is B. In order to model the output of the DRAM cell, we use a three-state buffer with Select as its control input and C as its output. In the original electronic circuit for the DRAM cell in Figure 7-12(a), B and C are the same signal, but in the logical model they are separate. This is necessary in the modeling process to avoid connecting gate outputs together.

DRAM Bit Slice

Using the logic model for the DRAM cell, we can construct the DRAM bit-slice model shown in Figure 7-13. This model is similar to that for the SRAM bit slice in Figure 7-5. It is apparent that, aside from the cell structure, the two RAM bit slices are logically similar. However, from the standpoint of cost per bit, they are quite different. The DRAM cell consists of a capacitor plus one transistor. The SRAM cell typically contains six transistors, giving a cell complexity roughly three times that of the DRAM. Therefore, the number of SRAM cells in a chip of a given size is less

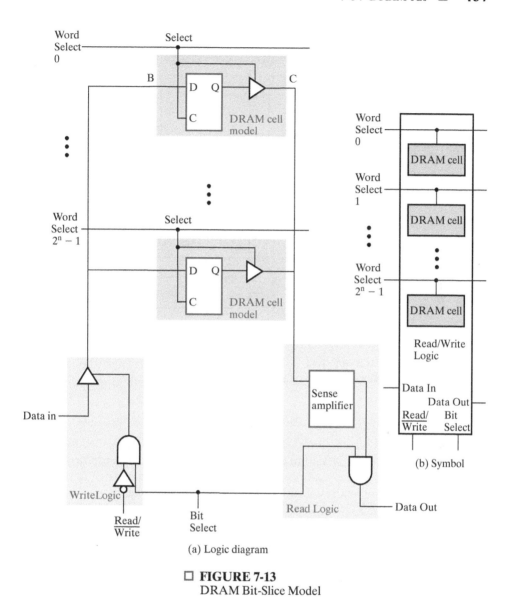

□ **FIGURE 7-13**
DRAM Bit-Slice Model

than one-third of those in the DRAM. The DRAM cost per bit is less than one-third the SRAM cost per bit, which justifies the use of DRAM in large memories.

Refresh of the DRAM contents remains to be discussed. But first, we need to develop the typical structure used to handle addressing in DRAMs. Since many DRAM chips are used in a DRAM, we want to reduce the physical size of the DRAM chips. Large DRAMs require 20 or more address bits, which would require 20 address pins on each DRAM chip. To reduce the number of pins, the DRAM address is applied serially in two parts with the row address first and the column address second. This can be done

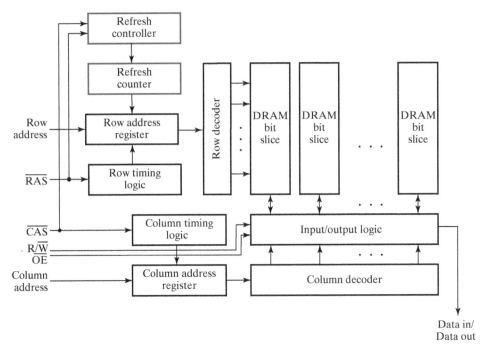

☐ **FIGURE 7-14**
Block Diagram of a DRAM Including Refresh Logic

since the row address, which performs the row selection, is actually needed before the column address, which reads out the data from the row selected. In order to hold the row address throughout the read or write cycle, it is stored in a register, as shown in Figure 7-14. The column address is also stored in a register. The load signal for the row address register is $\overline{\text{RAS}}$ (Row Adress Strobe) and for the column addresses is $\overline{\text{CAS}}$ (Column Address Strobe). Note that in addition to $\overline{\text{RAS}}$ and $\overline{\text{CAS}}$, control signals for the DRAM chip include R/$\overline{\text{W}}$ (Read/Write) and $\overline{\text{OE}}$ (Output enable). Note that this design uses signals active at the LOW (0) level.

The timing for DRAM write and read operation appears in Figure 7-15(a). The row address is applied to the address inputs, and then RAS changes from 1 to 0, loading the row address into the row address register. This address is applied to the row address decoder and selects a row of DRAM cells. Meanwhile, the column address is applied, and then CAS changes from 1 to 0, loading the column address into the column address register. This address is applied to the column address decoder, which selects a set of columns of the RAM array of size equal to the number of RAM data bits. The input data with Read/$\overline{\text{Write}}$ = 0 is applied over a time interval similar to that for the column address. The data bits are applied to the set of bit lines selected by the column address decoder, which in turn apply the values to the DRAM cells in the selected row, writing the new data into the cells. When CAS and RAS return to 1, the write cycle is complete and the DRAM cells store the newly written data. Note that the stored data in all of the other cells in the addressed row has been restored.

The read operation timing shown in Figure 7-15(b) is similar. Timing of the address operations is the same. However, no data is applied and Read/$\overline{\text{Write}}$ is 1 instead of 0. Data values in the DRAM cells in the selected row are applied to the bit

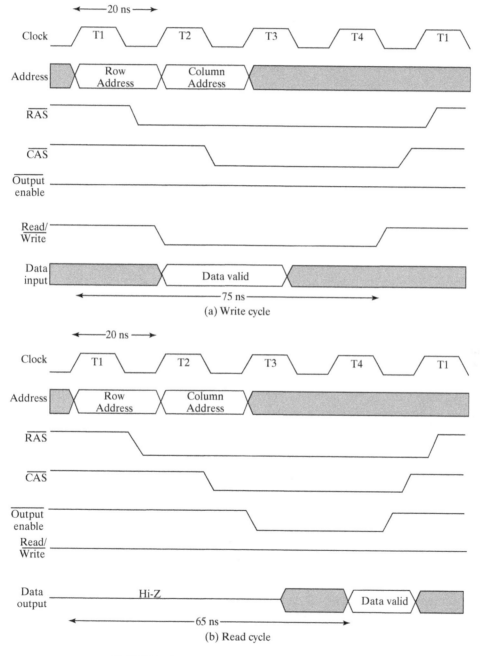

□ **FIGURE 7-15**
Timing for DRAM Write and Read Operations

lines and sensed by the sense amplifiers. The column address decoder selects the values to be sent to the Data output, which is enabled by $\overline{\text{Output enable}}$. During the read operation, all values in the addressed row are restored.

To support refresh, additional logic shown in color is present in the block diagram in Figure 7-14. There is a Refresh counter and a Refresh controller. The Refresh counter is used to provide the address of the row of DRAM cells to be refreshed. It is essential for the refresh modes that require the address to be provided from within the DRAM chip. The refresh counter advances on each refresh cycle. Due to the number of bits in the counter, when it reaches $2^n - 1$, where n is the number of rows in the DRAM array, it advances to 0 on the next refresh. The standard ways in which a refresh cycle can be triggered and the corresponding refresh types are as follows:

1. **RAS-only refresh.** A row address is placed on the address lines and RAS is changed to 0. In this case, the refresh addresses must be applied from outside the DRAM chip, typically by an IC called a DRAM controller.

2. **CAS-before-RAS refresh.** The CAS is changed from 1 to 0 followed by a change from 1 to 0 on RAS. Additional refresh cycles can be performed by changing RAS without changing CAS. The refresh addresses for this case come from the refresh counter, which is incremented after the refresh for each cycle.

3. **Hidden refresh.** Following a normal read or write, CAS is left at 0 and RAS is cycled, effectively performing a CAS-before-RAS refresh. During a hidden refresh, the output data from the prior read remains valid. Thus, the refresh is hidden. Unfortunately, the time taken by the hidden refresh is significant, so a subsequent read or write operation is delayed.

In all cases, note that the initiation of a refresh is controlled externally by using the $\overline{\text{RAS}}$ and $\overline{\text{CAS}}$ signals. Each row of a DRAM chip requires refreshing within a specified maximum refresh time, typically ranging from 16 to 64 milliseconds (ms). Refreshes may be performed at evenly spaced points in the refresh time, an approach called distributed refresh. Alternatively, all refreshes may be performed one after the other, an approach called burst refresh. For example, a 4M × 4 DRAM has a refresh time of 64 ms and has 4096 rows to be refreshed. The length of time to perform a single refresh is 60 ns, and the refresh interval for distributed refresh is 64 ms/4096 = 15.6 microseconds (μs). A total time out for refresh of 0.25 ms is used out of the 64 ms refresh interval. For the same DRAM, a burst refresh also takes 0.25 ms. The DRAM controller must initiate a refresh every 15.6 µs for distributed refresh and must initiate 4096 refreshes sequentially every 64 ms for burst refresh. During any refresh cycle, no DRAM reads or writes can occur. Since use of burst refresh would halt computer operation for a fairly long period, distributed refresh is more commonly used.

7-6 DRAM TYPES

Over the last two decades, both capacity and speed of DRAM have increased significantly. The quest for speed has resulted in the evolution of many types of DRAM. Several are listed with brief descriptions in Table 7-2. Of the memory types listed, the first two have largely been replaced in the marketplace by the more advanced SDRAM and RDRAM approaches. Since we have chosen to provide a discussion of

□ **TABLE 7-2**
  DRAM Types

Type	Abbreviation	Description
Fast page mode DRAM	FPM DRAM	Takes advantage of the fact that, when a row is accessed, all of the row values are available to be read out. By changing the column address, data from different addresses can be read out without reapplying the row address and waiting for the delay associated with reading out the row cells to pass if the row portions of the addresses match.
Extended data output DRAM	EDO DRAM	Extends the length of time that the DRAM holds the data values on its output, permitting the CPU to perform other tasks during the access, since it knows the data will still be available.
Synchronous DRAM	SDRAM	Operates with a clock rather than being asynchronous. This permits a tighter interaction between memory and CPU, since the CPU knows exactly when the data will be available. SDRAM also takes advantage of the row value availability and divides memory into distinct banks, permitting overlapped accesses.
Double-data-rate synchronous DRAM	DDR SDRAM	The same as SDRAM except that data output is provided on both the negative and the positive clock edges.
Rambus® DRAM	RDRAM	A proprietary technology that provides very high memory access rates using a relatively narrow bus.
Error-correcting code	ECC	May be applied to most of the DRAM types above to correct single-bit data errors and often detect double errors.

error-correcting codes (ECC) for memories on the text website, our discussion of memory types here will omit the ECC feature and focus on synchronous DRAM, double-data-rate synchronous DRAM, and Rambus® DRAM. Before considering these, we briefly cover some underlying concepts.

First, all three of these DRAM types work well because of the particular environment in which they operate. In modern high-speed computer systems, the processor interacts with the DRAM within a memory hierarchy. Most of the instructions and data for the processor are fetched from two lower levels of the hierarchy, the L1 and L2 caches. These are comparatively smaller SRAM-based memory structures that are covered in detail in Chapter 12. For our purposes, the key issue is that most of the reads from the DRAM are not directly from the CPU, but instead are initiated to bring data and instructions into these caches. The reads are in the form of a *line* (i.e., some number of bytes in contiguous addresses in memory) that is brought into the cache. For example, in a given read, the 16 bytes in hexadecimal addresses 000000 through 00000F would be read. This is referred to as a *burst read*. For burst reads, the effective *rate* of reading bytes, which is dependent upon reading bursts from contiguous addresses, rather than the access time is the important measure. With this measure, the three DRAM types we are discussing provide very fast performance.

Second, the effectiveness of these three DRAM types depends upon a very fundamental principle involved in DRAM operation, the reading out of all of the bits in a row for each read operation. The implication of this principle is that all of the bits in a row are available after a read using that row if only they can be accessed. With these two concepts in mind, the synchronous DRAM can be introduced.

Synchronous DRAM (SDRAM)

The use of clocked transfers differentiates SDRAM from conventional DRAM. A block diagram of a 16-megabyte SDRAM IC appears in Figure 7-16. The inputs and outputs differ little from those for the DRAM block diagram in Figure 7-14 with the exception of the presence of the clock for synchronous operation. Internally, there are a number of differences. Since the SDRAM appears synchronous from the outside,

☐ **FIGURE 7-16**
Block Diagram of a 16 MB SDRAM

there are synchronous registers on the address inputs and the data inputs and outputs. In addition, a column address counter has been added, which is key to the operation of the SDRAM. While the control logic may appear to be similar, the control in this case is much more complex, since the SDRAM has a mode control word that can be loaded from the address bus. Considering a 16 MB memory, the memory array contains 134,217,728 bits and is almost square, with 8192 rows and 16,384 columns. There are 13 row address bits. Since there are 8 bits per byte, the number of column addresses is 16,384 divided by 8, which equals 2048. This requires 11 column address bits. Note that 13 plus 11 equals 24, giving the correct number of bits to address 16 MB.

As with the regular DRAM, the SDRAM applies the row address first, followed by the column address. The timing, however, is somewhat different, and some new terminology is used. Before performing an actual read operation from a specified column address, the entire row of 2048 bytes specified by the applied row address is read out internally and stored in the I/O logic. Internally, this step takes a few clock cycles. Next, the actual read step is performed with the column address applied. After an additional delay of a few clock cycles, the data bytes begin appearing on the output, one per clock period. The number of bytes that appear, the burst length, has been set by loading a mode control word into the control logic from the address input.

The timing of a burst read cycle with burst length equal to four is shown in Figure 7-17. The read begins with the application of the row address and the row address strobe (RAS), which causes the row address to be captured in the address register and the reading of the row to be initiated. During the next two clock periods,

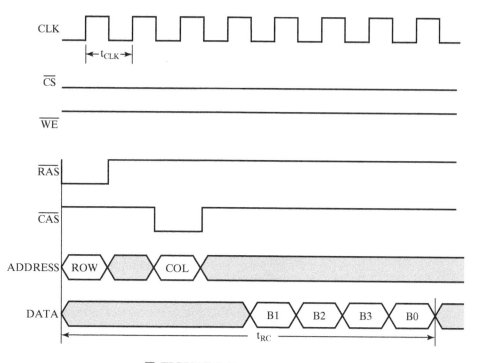

☐ **FIGURE 7-17**
Timing Diagram for an SDRAM

the reading of the row is taking place. During the third clock period, the column address and the column address strobe are applied, with the column address captured in the address register and the reading of the first data byte initiated. The data byte is then available to be read from the SDRAM at the positive clock edge occurring two cycles later. The second, third, and fourth bytes are available for reading on subsequent clock edges. In Figure 7-17, note that the bytes are presented in the order 1, 2, 3, 0. This is because, in the column address identifying the byte immediately needed by the CPU, the last two bits are 01. The subsequent bytes appear in the order of these two bits counted up modulo (burst length) by the column address counter, giving addresses ending in 01, 10, 11, and 00, with all other address bits fixed.

It is interesting to compare the byte rate for reading bytes from SDRAM to that of the basic DRAM. We assume that the read cycle time t_{RC} for the basic DRAM is 60 ns and that the clock period t_{CLK} for the SDRAM is 7.5 ns. The byte rate for the basic DRAM is one byte per 60 ns, or 16.67 MB/s. For the SDRAM, from Figure 7-17, it requires 8.0 clock cycles, or 60 ns, to read four bytes, giving a byte rate of 66.67 MB/s. If the burst is eight instead of four bytes, a read cycle time of 90 ns is required, giving a byte rate of 88.89 MB/s. Finally, if the burst is the entire 2048-byte row of the SDRAM, the read cycle time becomes $60 + (2048 - 4) \times 7.5 = 15,390$ ns, giving a byte rate of 133.07 MB, which approaches the limit of one byte per 7.5 ns clock period.

Double-Data-Rate SDRAM (DDR SDRAM)

The second DRAM type, double-data-rate SDRAM (DDR SDRAM) overcomes the preceding limit without decreasing the clock period. Instead, it provides two bytes of data per clock period by using both the positive and negative clock edges. In Figure 7-17, four bytes are read, one per positive clock edge. By using both clock edges, eight bytes can be transferred in the same read cycle time t_{RC}. For a 7.5 ns clock period, the byte rate limit doubles in the example to 266.14 MB/s.

Additional basic techniques can be applied to further increase the byte rate. For example, instead of having single byte data, an SDRAM IC can have the data I/O length of four bytes (32 bits). This gives a byte rate limit of 1.065 GB/s with a 7.5 ns clock period. Eight bytes give a byte rate limit of 2.130 GB/s.

The byte rates achieved in the examples are upper limits. If the actual accesses needed are to different rows of the RAM, the delay from the application of the RAS pulse to read out the first byte of data is significant and leads to performance well below the limit. This can be partially offset by breaking up the memory into multiple banks, where each bank performs the row read independently. Provided that the row and bank addresses are available early enough, row reads can be performed on one or more banks while data is still being transferred from the currently active row. When the column reads from the currently active row are complete, data can potentially be available immediately from other banks, permitting an uninterrupted flow of data from the memory. This permits the actual read rate to more closely approach the limit. Nevertheless, due to the fact that multiple row accesses to the same bank may occur in sequence, the maximum rate is not reached.

More recent versions of DDR memory include DDR2 and DDR3, with DDR4 expected to become available in 2014. While none of the versions of DDR are compatible with each other due to differences in electrical properties and timing, all of the versions depend on the same principle of transferring data on both the rising and the falling edges of the memory bus clock. Each succeeding version has increased the number of data transfers per memory bus clock cycle.

RAMBUS® DRAM (RDRAM)

The final DRAM type to be discussed is RAMBUS DRAM (RDRAM). Although no longer widely available, we include a description of RDRAM to illustrate its alternative design for the memory interface. RDRAM ICs are designed to be integrated into a memory system that uses a packet-based bus for the interaction between the RDRAM ICs and the memory bus to the processor. The primary components of the bus are a 3-bit path for the row address, a 5-bit path for the column address, and a 16-bit or 18-bit path for data. The bus is synchronous and performs transfers on both clock edges, the same property possessed by the DDR SDRAM. Information on the three paths mentioned above is transferred in packets that are four clock cycles long, which means that there are eight transfers/packet. The number of bits per packet for each of the paths is 24 bits for the row address packet, 40 bits for the column address packet, and 128 bits or 144 bits for the data packet. The larger data packet includes 16 parity bits for implementing an error-correcting code. The RDRAM IC employs the concept of multiple memory banks mentioned earlier to provide capability for concurrent memory accesses with different row addresses. RDRAM uses the usual row-activate technique in which the addressed row data of the memory is read. From this row data, the column address is used to select byte pairs in the order in which they are to be transmitted in the packet. A typical timing picture for an RDRAM read access is shown in Figure 7-18. Due to the sophisticated electronic design of the RAMBUS

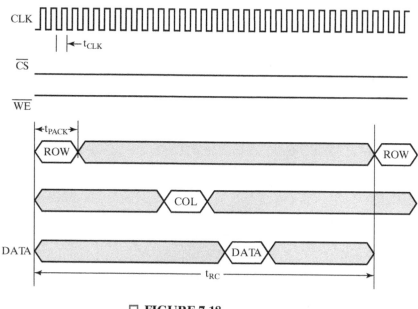

□ **FIGURE 7-18**
Timing of a 16 MB RDRAM

system, we can consider a clock period of 1.875 ns. Thus, the time for transmission of a packet is $t_{PACK} = 4 \times 1.875 = 7.5$ ns. The cycle time for accessing a single data packet of 8 byte pairs or 16 bytes is 32 clock cycles or 60 ns, as shown in Figure 7-18. The corresponding byte rate is 266.67 MB/s. If four of the byte packets are accessed from the same row, the rate increases to 1.067 GB/s. By reading an entire RDRAM row of 2048 bytes, the cycle time increases to $60 + (2048 - 64) \times 1.875/4 = 990$ ns or a byte rate limit of $2048/(990 \times 10^{-9}) = 2.069$ MB/s, approaching the ideal limit of 4/1.875 ns or 2.133 GB/s.

7-7 ARRAYS OF DYNAMIC RAM ICs

Many of the same design principles used for SRAM arrays in Section 7-4 apply to DRAM arrays. There are, however, a number of different requirements for the control and addressing of DRAM arrays. These requirements are typically handled by a *DRAM controller*, which performs the following functions:

1. controlling separation of the address into a row address and a column address, and providing these addresses at the required times,

2. providing the $\overline{RAS}$ and $\overline{CAS}$ signals at the required times for read, write, and refresh operations,

3. performing refresh operations at the necessary intervals, and

4. providing status signals to the rest of the system (e.g., indicating whether the memory is busy performing refresh).

The DRAM controller is a complex synchronous sequential circuit with the external CPU clock providing synchronization of its operation.

7-8 CHAPTER SUMMARY

Memory is of two types: random-access memory (RAM) and read-only memory (ROM). For both types, we apply an address to read from or write into a data word. Read and write operations have specific steps and associated timing parameters, including access time and write cycle time. Memory can be static or dynamic and volatile or nonvolatile. Internally, a RAM chip consists of an array of RAM cells, decoders, write circuits, read circuits, and output circuits. A combination of a write circuit, read circuit, and the associated RAM cells can be logically modeled as a RAM bit slice. RAM bit slices, in turn, can be combined to form two-dimensional RAM cell arrays, which, with decoders and output circuits added, form the basis for a RAM chip. Output circuits use three-state buffers in order to facilitate connecting together an array of RAM chips without significant additional logic. Due to the need for refresh, additional circuitry is required within DRAMs, as well as in arrays of DRAM chips. In a quest for faster memory access, a number of new DRAM types have been developed. The most recent forms of these high-speed DRAMs employ a synchronous interface that uses a clock to control memory accesses.

Error-detection and correction codes, often based on Hamming codes, are used to detect or correct errors in stored RAM data. Material from Edition 1 covering these codes is available on the Companion Website for the text.

REFERENCES

1. Micron Technology, Inc. *Micron 64Mb:×32 DDR SDRAM.* www.micron.com, 2001.

2. Micron Technology, Inc. *Micron 256Mb:×4, ×8, ×16 SDRAM.* www.micron.com, 2002.

3. Rambus, Inc. *Rambus Direct RDRAM 128/144-Mbit (256×16/18×32s) — Preliminary Information,* Document DL0059 Version 1.11.

4. SOBELMAN, M. "Rambus Technology Basics," *Rambus Developer Forum.* Rambus, Inc., October 2001.

5. WESTE, N. H. E. AND K. ESHRAGHIAN. *Principles of CMOS VLSI Design: A Systems Perspective,* 2nd ed. Reading, MA: Addison-Wesley, 1993.

PROBLEMS

The plus (+) indicates a more advanced problem and the asterisk (*) indicates that a solution is available on the Companion Website for the text.

7-1. *The following memories are specified by the number of words times the number of bits per word. How many address lines and input–output data lines are needed in each case? (a) 48K × 8, (b) 512K × 32, (c) 64M × 64, and (d) 2G × 1.

7-2. **(a)** Word number $(835)_{10}$ in the memory shown in Figure 7-2 contains the binary equivalent of $(15,103)_{10}$. List the 10-bit address and the 16-bit memory contents of the word.

   (b) Repeat part (a) for word number $(513)_{10}$ containing the binary equivalent of $(44,252)_{10}$.

7-3. *A 64K × 16 RAM chip uses coincident decoding by splitting the internal decoder into row select and column select. (a) Assuming that the RAM cell array is square, what is the size of each decoder, and how many AND gates are required for decoding an address? (b) Determine the row and column selection lines that are enabled when the input address is the binary equivalent of $(32000)_{10}$.

7-4. **(a)** How many address and data lines are needed for memory chips with the following organization?

   (1) 256 × 4
   (2) 512 × 8
   (3) 1K × 16
   (4) 32K × 8

(b) Design an address decoder for two RAM chips and two ROM chips each organized as 1K × 8 chip. Assume that a 20-bit address is available. Use gates for the decoding circuitry and specify the address range of each chip.

7-5. A DRAM has 8 address lines on which row and column addresses are placed one after the other. What is the memory capacity of the DRAM?

7-6. Two DRAM chips of 8K capacity are used to obtain a total memory of 16K × 16. How many address and data lines will each chip have assuming that the row X column matrix is a square, for addresses?

7-7. A DRAM has a refresh interval of 64 ms and has 8192 rows. What is the interval between refreshes for distributed refresh? What is the total time required out of the 64 ms for a refresh of the entire DRAM? What is the minimum number of address pins on the DRAM?

7-8. *(a) How many 128K × 16 RAM chips are needed to provide a memory capacity of 2 MB?

(b) How many address lines are required to access 2 MB? How many of these lines are connected to the address inputs of all chips?

(c) How many lines must be decoded to produce the chip select inputs? Specify the size of the decoder.

7-9. Draw a decoding circuitry for 32K × 8 RAM using an OR gate for address decoding. The number of address lines to be decoded is 20. What is the address map obtained with this decoding scheme? The address range of this memory chip is 00000 to 07FFFH.

7-10. Why is a refresh cycle needed for DRAMs? Name one standard method used for doing "refreshing".

7-11. What are the features that an SDRAM possesses that makes it superior to asynchronous DRAM?

COMPUTER DESIGN BASICS

In Chapter 6, the separation of a design into a datapath that implements microoperations and a control unit that determines the sequence of microoperations was introduced. In this chapter, we continue by defining a generic computer datapath that implements register transfer microoperations and serves as a framework for the design of detailed processing logic. The concept of a control word provides a tie between the datapath and the control unit associated with it.

The generic datapath combined with a control unit and memory forms a programmable system—in this case, a simple computer. The concept of an instruction set architecture (ISA) is introduced as a means of specifying the computer. In order to implement the ISA, a control unit and the generic datapath are combined to form a CPU (central processing unit). In addition, since this is a programmable system, memories are also present for storage of programs and data. Two different computers with two different control units are considered. The first computer has two memories, one for instructions and one for data, and performs all of its operations in a single clock cycle. The second computer has a single memory for both instructions and data, and a more complex architecture requiring multiple clock cycles to perform its operations.

In the generic computer at the beginning of Chapter 1, register transfers, microoperations, buses, datapaths, datapath components, and control words are used quite broadly. Likewise, control units appear in most of the digital parts of the generic computer. The design of processing units consisting of control units interacting with datapaths has its greatest impact within the generic computer in the CPU and FPU in the processor chip. These two components contain major datapaths that perform processing. The CPU and the FPU perform additions, subtractions, and most of the other operations specified by the instruction set.

8-1 INTRODUCTION

Computers and their design are introduced in this chapter. The specification for a computer consists of a description of its appearance to a programmer at the lowest level, its *instruction set architecture* (*ISA*). From the ISA, a high-level description of the hardware to implement the computer, called the *computer architecture*, is formulated. This architecture, for a simple computer, is typically divided into a datapath and a control. The datapath is defined by three basic components:

1. a set of registers,
2. the microoperations performed on data stored in the registers, and
3. the control interface.

The control unit provides signals that control the microoperations performed in the datapath and in other components of the system, such as memories. In addition, the control unit controls its own operation, determining the sequence of events that occur. This sequence may depend upon the results of current and past microoperations executed. In a more complex computer, typically multiple control units and datapaths are present.

To build a foundation for considering computer designs, initially, we extend the ideas in Chapter 6 to the implementation of computer datapaths. Specifically, we consider a generic datapath, one that can be used, in some cases in modified form, in all of the computer designs considered in the remainder of the text. These future designs show how a given datapath can be used to implement different instruction set architectures by simply combining the datapath with different control units.

8-2 DATAPATHS

Instead of having each individual register perform its microoperations directly, computer systems often employ a number of storage registers in conjunction with a shared operation unit called an *arithmetic/logic unit*, abbreviated ALU. To perform a microoperation, the contents of specified source registers are applied to the inputs of the shared ALU. The ALU performs an operation, and the result of this operation is transferred to a destination register. With the ALU as a combinational circuit, the entire register transfer operation from the source registers, through the ALU, and into the destination register is performed during one clock cycle. The shift operations are often performed in a separate unit, but sometimes these operations are also implemented within the ALU.

Recall that the combination of a set of registers with a shared ALU and interconnecting paths is the datapath for the system. The rest of this chapter is concerned with the organization and design of computer datapaths and associated control units used to implement simple computers. The design of a particular ALU is undertaken to show the process involved in implementing a complex combinational circuit. We also design a shifter, combine control signals into control words, and then add control units to implement two different computers.

The datapath and the control unit are the two parts of the processor, or CPU, of a computer. In addition to the registers, the datapath contains the digital logic that implements the various microoperations. This digital logic consists of buses, multiplexers, decoders, and processing circuits. When a large number of registers is included in a datapath, the registers are most conveniently connected through one or more buses. Registers in a datapath interact by the direct transfer of data, as well as in the performance of the various types of microoperations. A simple bus-based datapath with four registers, an ALU, and a shifter is shown in Figure 8-1. The

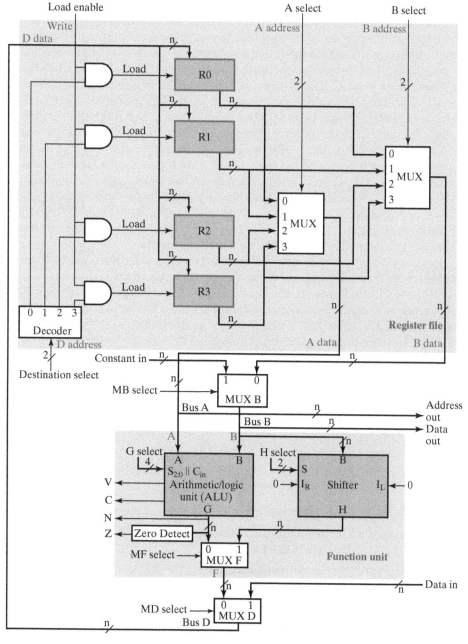

□ **FIGURE 8-1**
Block Diagram of a Generic Datapath

shading and blue signal names relate to Figure 8-10 and will be discussed in Section 8-5. The black signal names are used here to describe the details in Figure 8-1. Each register is connected to two multiplexers to form ALU and shifter input buses A and B. The select inputs on each multiplexer select one register for the corresponding bus. For Bus B, there is an additional multiplexer, MUX B, so that constants can be brought into the datapath from outside using *Constant in*. Bus B also connects to Data out, to send data outside the datapath to other components of the system, such as memory or input–output. Likewise, Bus A connects to Address out, to send address information outside of the datapath for memory or input–output.

Arithmetic and logic microoperations are performed on the operands on the A and B buses by the ALU. The G select inputs select the microoperation to be performed by the ALU. The shift microoperations are performed on data on Bus B by the shifter. The H select input either passes the operand on Bus B directly through to the shifter output or selects a shift microoperation. MUX F selects the output of the ALU or the output of the shifter. MUX D selects the output of MUX F or external data on input *Data in* to be applied to Bus D. The latter is connected to the inputs of all the registers. The destination select inputs determine which register is loaded with the data on Bus D. Since the select inputs are decoded, only one register Load signal is active for any transfer of data into a register from Bus D. A Load enable signal that can force all register Load signals to 0 using AND gates is present for transfers that are not to change the contents of any of the four registers.

It is useful to have certain information, based on the results of an ALU operation, available for use by the control unit of the CPU to make decisions. Four status bits are shown with the ALU in Figure 8-1. The status bits, carry C and overflow V, were explained in conjunction with Figure 3-46. The zero status bit Z is 1 if the output of the ALU contains all zeros and is 0 otherwise. Thus, $Z = 1$ if the result of an operation is zero, and $Z = 0$ if the result is nonzero. The sign status bit N (for negative) is the leftmost bit of the ALU output, which is the sign bit for the result in signed-number representations. Status values from the shifter can also be incorporated into the status bits if desired.

The control unit for the datapath directs the information flow through the buses, the ALU, the shifter, and the registers by applying signals to the select inputs. For example, to perform the microoperation

$$R1 \leftarrow R2 + R3$$

the control unit must provide binary selection values to the following sets of control inputs:

1. *A select*, to place the contents of $R2$ onto A *data* and, hence, Bus A.

2. *B select*, to place the contents of $R3$ onto the 0 input of MUX B; and *MB select*, to put the 0 input of MUX B onto Bus B.

3. *G select*, to provide the arithmetic operation $A + B$.

4. *MF select*, to place the ALU output on the MUX F output.

5. *MD select*, to place the MUX F output onto Bus D.

6. *Destination select*, to select $R1$ as the destination of the data on Bus D.

7. *Load enable*, to enable a register—in this case, $R1$—to be loaded.

The sets of values must be generated and must become available on the corresponding control lines early in the clock cycle. The binary data from the two source registers must propagate through the multiplexers and the ALU and on into the inputs of the destination register, all during the remainder of the same clock cycle. Then, when the next positive clock edge arrives, the binary data on Bus D is loaded into the destination register. To achieve fast operation, the ALU and shifter are constructed with combinational logic having a limited number of levels.

8-3 THE ARITHMETIC/LOGIC UNIT

The ALU is a combinational circuit that performs a set of basic arithmetic and logic microoperations. It has a number of selection lines used to determine the operation to be performed. The selection lines are decoded within the ALU, so that k selection lines can specify up to 2^k distinct operations.

Figure 8-2 shows the symbol for a typical n-bit ALU. The n data inputs from A are combined with the n data inputs from B to generate the result of an operation at the G outputs. The mode-select input S_2 distinguishes between arithmetic and logic operations. The two Operation select inputs S_1 and S_0 and the Carry input C_{in} specify the eight arithmetic operations with S_2 at 0. Operand select input S_0 and C_{in} specify the four logic operations with S_2 at 1.

We perform the design of this ALU in three stages. First, we design the arithmetic section. Then we design the logic section, and finally, we combine the two sections to form the ALU.

Arithmetic Circuit

The basic component of an arithmetic circuit is a parallel adder, which is constructed with a number of full-adder circuits connected in cascade, as shown in Figure 3-43. By

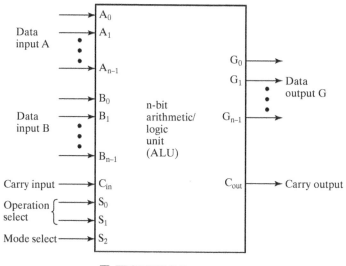

□ **FIGURE 8-2**
Symbol for an n-Bit ALU

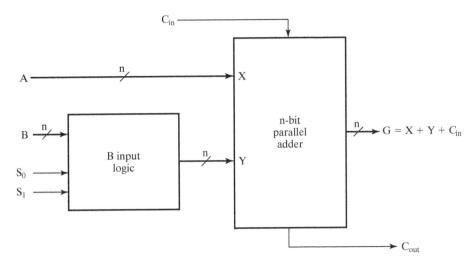

☐ **FIGURE 8-3**
Block Diagram of an Arithmetic Circuit

controlling the data inputs to the parallel adder, it is possible to obtain different types of arithmetic operations. The block diagram in Figure 8-3 demonstrates a configuration in which one set of inputs to the parallel adder is controlled by the select lines S_1 and S_0. There are n bits in the arithmetic circuit, with two inputs A and B and output G. The n inputs from B go through the B input logic to the Y inputs of the parallel adder. The input carry C_{in} goes in the carry input of the full adder in the least-significant-bit position. The output carry C_{out} is from the full adder in the most-significant-bit position. The output of the parallel adder is calculated from the arithmetic sum as

$$G = X + Y + C_{in}$$

where X is the n-bit binary number from the inputs and Y is the n-bit binary number from the B input logic. C_{in} is the input carry, which equals 0 or 1. Note that the symbol $+$ in the equation denotes arithmetic addition.

Table 8-1 shows the arithmetic operations that are obtainable by controlling the value of Y with the two selection inputs S_1 and S_0. If the inputs from B are ignored

☐ **TABLE 8-1**
Function Table for Arithmetic Circuit

Select		Input	$G = (A + Y + C_{in})$	
S_1	S_0	Y	$C_{in} = 0$	$C_{in} = 1$
0	0	all 0s	$G = A$ (transfer)	$G = A + 1$ (increment)
0	1	B	$G = A + B$ (add)	$G = A + B + 1$
1	0	$\overline{B}$	$G = A + \overline{B}$	$G = A + \overline{B} + 1$ (subtract)
1	1	all 1s	$G = A - 1$ (decrement)	$G = A$ (transfer)

and we insert all 0s at the Y inputs, the output sum becomes $G = A + 0 + C_{in}$. This gives $G = A$ when $C_{in} = 0$ and $G = A + 1$ when $C_{in} = 1$. In the first case, we have a direct transfer from input A to output G. In the second case, the value of A is incremented by 1. For a straight arithmetic addition, it is necessary to apply the B inputs to the Y inputs of the parallel adder. This gives $G = A + B$ when $C_{in} = 0$. Arithmetic subtraction is achieved by applying the complement of inputs B to the Y inputs of the parallel adder, to obtain $G = A + \overline{B} + 1$ when $C_{in} = 1$. This gives A plus the 2s complement of B, which is equivalent to 2s complement subtraction. All 1s is the 2s complement representation for -1. Thus, applying all 1s to the Y inputs with $C_{in} = 0$ produces the decrement operation $G = A - 1$.

The B input logic in Figure 8-3 can be implemented with n multiplexers. The data inputs to each multiplexer in stage i for $i = 0, 1, \ldots, n - 1$ are $0, B_i, \overline{B}_i$, and 1, corresponding to selection values $S_1 S_0$: 00, 01, 10, and 11, respectively. Thus, the arithmetic circuit can be constructed with n full adders and n 4-to-1 multiplexers.

The number of gates in the B input logic can be reduced if, instead of using 4-to-1 multiplexers, we go through the logic design of one stage (one bit) of the B input logic. This can be done as shown in Figure 8-4. The truth table for one typical stage i of the logic is given in Figure 8-4(a). The inputs are S_1, S_0, and B_i, and the output is Y_i. Following the requirements specified in Table 8-1, we let $Y_i = 0$ when $S_1 S_0 = 00$, and similarly assign the other three values of Y_i for each of the combinations of the selection variables. Output Y_i is simplified in the map in Figure 8-4(b) to give

$$Y_i = B_i S_0 + \overline{B}_i S_1$$

where S_1 and S_0 are common to all n stages. Each stage i is associated with input B_i and output Y_i for $i = 0, 1, 2, \ldots, n - 1$. This logic corresponds to a 2-to-1 multiplexer with B_i on the select input and S_1 and S_0 on the data inputs.

Figure 8-5 shows the logic diagram of an arithmetic circuit for $n = 4$. The four full-adder (FA) circuits constitute the parallel adder. The carry into the first stage is the input carry C_{in}. All other carries are connected internally from one stage to the next.

Inputs	Output
S_1 S_0 B_i	Y_i
0 0 0	0 $Y_i = 0$
0 0 1	0
0 1 0	0 $Y_i = B_i$
0 1 1	1
1 0 0	1 $Y_i = \overline{B}_i$
1 0 1	0
1 1 0	1 $Y_i = 1$
1 1 1	1

(a) Truth table

(b) Map simplification:
$Y_i = B_i S_0 + \overline{B}_i S_1$

□ **FIGURE 8-4**
B Input Logic for One Stage of Arithmetic Circuit

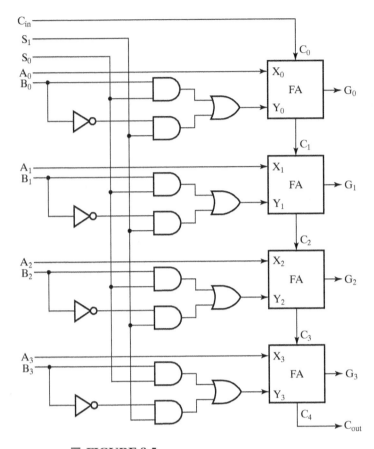

☐ **FIGURE 8-5**
Logic Diagram of a 4-Bit Arithmetic Circuit

The selection variables are S_1, S_0, and C_{in}. Variables S_1 and S_0 control all Y inputs of the full adders according to the Boolean function derived in Figure 8-4(b). Whenever C_{in} is 1, $A + Y$ has 1 added. The eight arithmetic operations for the circuit as a function of S_1, S_0, and C_{in} are listed in Table 8-2. It is interesting to note that the operation $G = A$ appears twice in the table. This is a harmless by-product of using C_{in} as one of the control variables while implementing both increment and decrement instructions.

Logic Circuit

The logic microoperations manipulate the bits of the operands by treating each bit in a register as a binary variable, giving bitwise operations. There are four commonly used logic operations—AND, OR, XOR (exclusive-OR), and NOT—from which others can be conveniently derived.

Figure 8-6(a) shows one stage of the logic circuit. It consists of four gates and a 4-to-1 multiplexer, although simplification could yield less complex logic. Each of the four logic operations is generated through a gate that performs the required

☐ **TABLE 8-2**
Function Table for ALU

Operation Select				Operation	Function
S_2	S_1	S_0	C_{in}		
0	0	0	0	$G = A$	Transfer A
0	0	0	1	$G = A + 1$	Increment A
0	0	1	0	$G = A + B$	Addition
0	0	1	1	$G = A + B + 1$	Add with carry input of 1
0	1	0	0	$G = A + \overline{B}$	A plus 1s complement of B
0	1	0	1	$G = A + \overline{B} + 1$	Subtraction
0	1	1	0	$G = A - 1$	Decrement A
0	1	1	1	$G = A$	Transfer A
1	X	0	0	$G = A \wedge B$	AND
1	X	0	1	$G = A \vee B$	OR
1	X	1	0	$G = A \oplus B$	XOR
1	X	1	1	$G = \overline{A}$	NOT (1s complement)

logic. The outputs of the gates are applied to the inputs of the multiplexer with two selection variables S_1 and S_0. These choose one of the data inputs of the multiplexer and direct its value to the output. The diagram shows a typical stage with subscript i. For the logic circuit with n bits, the diagram must be repeated n times, for $i = 0, 1, 2, \ldots, n-1$. The selection variables are applied to all stages. The function table in Figure 8-6(b) lists the logic operations obtained for each combination of the selection values.

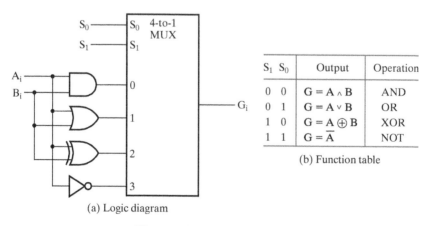

(a) Logic diagram

S_1	S_0	Output	Operation
0	0	$G = A \wedge B$	AND
0	1	$G = A \vee B$	OR
1	0	$G = A \oplus B$	XOR
1	1	$G = \overline{A}$	NOT

(b) Function table

☐ **FIGURE 8-6**
One Stage of Logic Circuit

Arithmetic/Logic Unit

The logic circuit can be combined with the arithmetic circuit to produce an ALU. The configuration for one stage of the ALU is illustrated in Figure 8-7. The outputs of the arithmetic and logic circuits in each stage are applied to a 2-to-1 multiplexer with selection variable S_2. When $S_2 = 0$, the arithmetic output is selected, and when $S_2 = 1$, the logic output is selected. Note that the diagram shows just one typical stage of the ALU; the circuit must be repeated n times for an n-bit ALU. The output carry C_{i+1} of a given arithmetic stage must be connected to the input carry C_i of the next stage in sequence. C_0, the input carry to the first stage, is the input carry C_{in} for the ALU, as well as a selection variable for logic operations instead of using S_1. This somewhat strange use of C_{in} provides a more systematic encoding of the control variables when the shifter is added later.

The ALU specified in Figure 8-7 provides eight arithmetic and four logic operations. Each operation is selected through the variables S_2, S_1, S_0, and C_{in}. Table 8-2 lists the 12 ALU operations. The first eight are arithmetic operations and are selected with $S_2 = 0$. The next four are logic operations and are selected with $S_2 = 1$. Selection input S_1 has no effect during the logic operations and is marked with X to indicate that its value may be either 0 or 1. Later in the design, it is assigned value 0 for logic operations.

The ALU logic we have designed is not as simple as it could be and has a fairly high number of logic levels, contributing to propagation delay in the circuit. With the use of logic simplification software, we can simplify this logic and reduce the delay. For example, it is quite easy to simplify the logic for a single stage of the ALU. For realistic n, a means of further reducing the carry propagation delay in the ALU, such as the carry lookahead adder, described in a Website Supplement, is usually necessary.

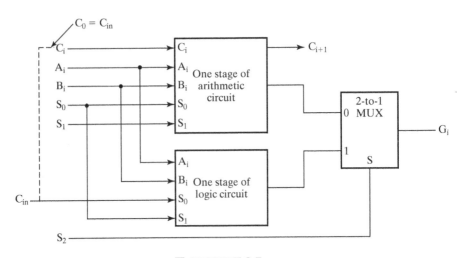

☐ **FIGURE 8-7**
One Stage of ALU

8-4 THE SHIFTER

The shifter shifts the value on Bus B, placing the result on an input of MUX F. The basic shifter performs one of two main types of transformations on the data: right shift and left shift.

A seemingly obvious choice for a shifter would be a bidirectional shift register with parallel load. Data from Bus B can be transferred to the register in parallel and then shifted to the right, the left, or not at all. A clock pulse loads the output of Bus B into the shift register, and a second clock pulse performs the shift. Finally, a third clock pulse transfers the data from the shift register to the selected destination register.

Alternatively, the transfer from a source register to a destination register can be done using only one clock pulse if the shifter is implemented as a combinational circuit as done in Chapter 3. Because of the faster operation that results from the use of one clock pulse instead of three, this is the preferred method. In a combinational shifter, the signals propagate through the gates without the need for a clock pulse. Hence, the only clock needed for a shift in the datapath is for loading the data from Bus H into the selected destination register.

A combinational shifter can be constructed with multiplexers as shown in Figure 8-8. The selection variable S is applied to all four multiplexers to select the type of operation within the shifter. $S = 00$ causes B to be passed through the shifter unchanged. $S = 01$ causes a right-shift operation and $S = 10$ causes a left-shift operation. The right shift fills the position on the left with the value on serial input I_R. The left shift fills the position on the right with the value on serial input I_L. Serial outputs are available from serial output R and serial output L for right and left shifts, respectively.

The diagram of Figure 8-8 shows only four stages of the shifter, which has n stages in a system with n-bit operands. Additional selection variables may be

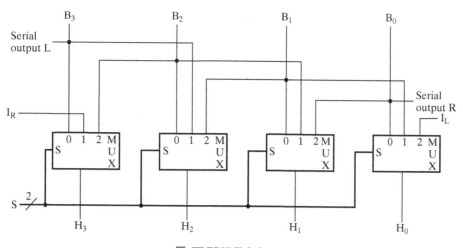

□ **FIGURE 8-8**
4-Bit Basic Shifter

employed to specify what goes into I_R and I_L during a single bit-position shift. Note that to shift an operand by $m > 1$ bit positions, this shifter must perform a series of m 1-bit position shifts, taking m clock cycles.

Barrel Shifter

In datapath applications, often the data must be shifted more than one bit position in a single clock cycle. A *barrel shifter* is one form of combinational circuit that shifts or rotates the input data bits by the number of bit positions specified by a binary value on a set of selection lines. The shift we consider here is a rotation to the left, which means that the binary data is shifted to the left, with the bits coming from the most significant part of the register rotated back into the least significant part of the register.

A 4-bit version of this kind of barrel shifter is shown in Figure 8-9. It consists of four multiplexers with common select lines S_1 and S_0. The selection variables determine the number of positions that the input data will be shifted to the left by rotation. When $S_1S_0 = 00$, no shift occurs, and the input data has a direct path to the outputs. When $S_1S_0 = 01$, the input data is rotated one position, with D_0 going to Y_1, D_1 going to Y_2, D_2 going to Y_3, and D_3 going to Y_0. When $S_1S_0 = 10$, the input is rotated two positions, and when $S_1S_0 = 11$, the rotation is by three bit positions. Table 8-3 gives the function table for the 4-bit barrel shifter. For each binary value of the selection variables, the table lists the inputs that go to the corresponding output. Thus, to rotate three positions, S_1S_0 must be equal to 11, causing D_0 to go to Y_3, D_1 to go to Y_0, D_2 to go to Y_1, and D_3 to go to Y_2. Note that, by using this left-rotation barrel shifter, one can generate all desired right rotations as well. For example, a left rotation by three positions is the same as a right rotation by one position in this 4-bit barrel shifter. In general, in a 2^n-bit barrel shifter, i positions of left rotation are the same as $2^n - i$ bits of right rotation.

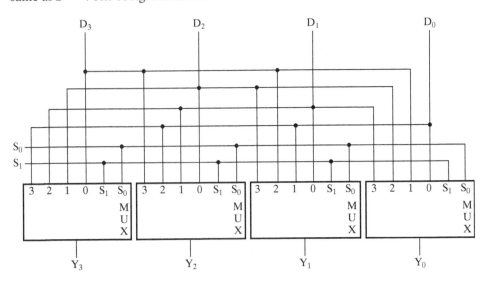

☐ **FIGURE 8-9**
4-Bit Barrel Shifter

□ **TABLE 8-3**
Function Table for 4-Bit Barrel Shifter

Select		Output				
S_1	S_0	Y_3	Y_2	Y_1	Y_0	Operation
0	0	D_3	D_2	D_1	D_0	No rotation
0	1	D_2	D_1	D_0	D_3	Rotate one position
1	0	D_1	D_0	D_3	D_2	Rotate two positions
1	1	D_0	D_3	D_2	D_1	Rotate three positions

A barrel shifter with 2^n input and output lines requires 2^n multiplexers, each having 2^n data inputs and n selection inputs. The number of positions for the data to be rotated is specified by the selection variables and can be from 0 to $2^n - 1$ positions. For a large n, the fan-in to gates is too large, so larger barrel shifters consist of layers of multiplexers, as shown in Section 10-3, or of special structures designed at the transistor level.

8-5 DATAPATH REPRESENTATION

The datapath in Figure 8-1 includes the registers, selection logic for the registers, the ALU, the shifter, and three additional multiplexers. With a hierarchical structure, we can reduce the apparent complexity of the datapath. This reduction is important, since we frequently use this datapath. Also, as illustrated by the register file to be discussed next, the use of a hierarchy allows one implementation of a module to be replaced with another, so that we are not tied to specific logic implementations.

A typical datapath has more than four registers. Indeed, computers with 32 or more registers are common. The construction of a bus system with a large number of registers requires different techniques. A set of registers having common microoperations performed on them may be organized into a *register file*. The typical register file is a special type of fast memory that permits one or more words to be read and one or more words to be written, all simultaneously. Functionally, a simple register file contains the equivalent of the logic shaded in blue in Figure 8-1. Due to the memory-like nature of register files, the *A select*, *B select*, and *Destination select* inputs in the figure become three addresses. As shown in Figure 8-1 in blue and on the register file symbol in Figure 8-10, the *A address* accesses a word to be read onto *A data*, the *B address* accesses a second word to be read onto *B data*, and the *D address* accesses a word to be written into from *D data*. All of these accesses occur in the same clock cycle. A *Write* input corresponding to the Load Enable signal is also provided. When at 1, the *Write* signal permits registers to be loaded during the current clock cycle, and when at 0, prevents register loading. The size of the register file is $2^m \times n$, where m is the number of register address bits and n is the number of bits per register. For the datapath in Figure 8-1, $m = 2$, giving four registers, and n is unspecified.

Since the ALU and the shifter are shared processing units with outputs that are selected by MUX F, it is convenient to group the two units and the MUX together to

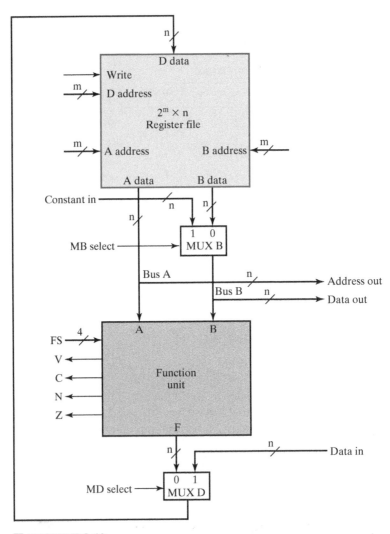

Block Diagram of Datapath Using the Register File and Function Unit

form a shared function unit. Gray shading in Figure 8-1 highlights the function unit, which can be represented by the symbol given in Figure 8-10. The inputs to the function unit are from Bus A and Bus B, and the output of the function unit goes to MUX D. The function unit also has the four status bits V, C, N, and Z as added outputs.

In Figure 8-1, there are three sets of select inputs: the *G select*, *H select*, and *MF select*. In Figure 8-10, there is a single set of select inputs labeled FS, for "function select." To fully specify the function unit symbol in the figure, all of the codes for *MF select*, *G select*, and *H select* must be defined in terms of the codes for *FS*. Table 8-4 defines these code transformations. The codes for *FS* are given in the left column. From Table 8-4, it is apparent that *MF* is 1 for the leftmost two bits of *FS* both equal to 1. If *MF select* = 0, then the *G select* codes determine the function on the output

☐ **TABLE 8-4**
G Select, *H* Select, and *MF* Select Codes Defined
in Terms of *FS* Codes

FS(3:0)	MF Select	G Select(3:0)	H Select(3:0)	Microoperation
0000	0	0000	XX	$F = A$
0001	0	0001	XX	$F = A + 1$
0010	0	0010	XX	$F = A + B$
0011	0	0011	XX	$F = A + B + 1$
0100	0	0100	XX	$F = A + \overline{B}$
0101	0	0101	XX	$F = A + \overline{B} + 1$
0110	0	0110	XX	$F = A - 1$
0111	0	0111	XX	$F = A$
1000	0	1 X00	XX	$F = A \wedge B$
1001	0	1 X01	XX	$F = A \vee B$
1010	0	1 X10	XX	$F = A \oplus B$
1011	0	1 X11	XX	$F = \overline{A}$
1100	1	XXXX	00	$F = B$
1101	1	XXXX	01	$F = \text{sr } B$
1110	1	XXXX	10	$F = \text{sl } B$

of the function unit. If *MF select* = 1, then the *H select* codes determine the function on the output of the function unit. To show this dependency, the codes that determine the function-unit outputs are highlighted in blue in the table. From Table 8-4, the code transformations can be implemented using the Boolean equations: $MF = F_3 \cdot F_2, G_3 = F_3, G_2 = F_2, G_1 = F_1, G_0 = F_0, H_1 = F_1,$ and $H_0 = F_0$.

The status bits are assumed to be meaningless when the shifter is selected, although in a more complex system, shifter status bits can be designed to replace those for the ALU whenever a shifter microoperation is specified. Note that the status bit implementation depends on the specific implementation that has been used for the arithmetic circuit. Alternative implementations may not produce the same results.

8-6 THE CONTROL WORD

The selection variables for the datapath control the microoperations executed within the datapath for any given clock pulse. For the datapath in Section 8-5, the selection variables control the addresses for the data read from the register file, the function performed by the function unit, and the data loaded into the register file, as well as the selection of external data. We will now demonstrate how these control variables select the microoperations for the datapath. The choice of control variable values for typical microoperations will be discussed, and a simulation of the datapath will be illustrated.

A block diagram of a datapath that is a specific version of the datapath in Figure 8-10 is shown in Figure 8-11(a). It has a register file with eight registers, $R0$ through $R7$. The register file provides the inputs to the function unit through Bus A and Bus B. MUX B selects between constant values on *Constant in* and register values on *B data*. The ALU and zero-detection logic within the function unit generate the binary data for the four status bits: V (overflow), C (carry),

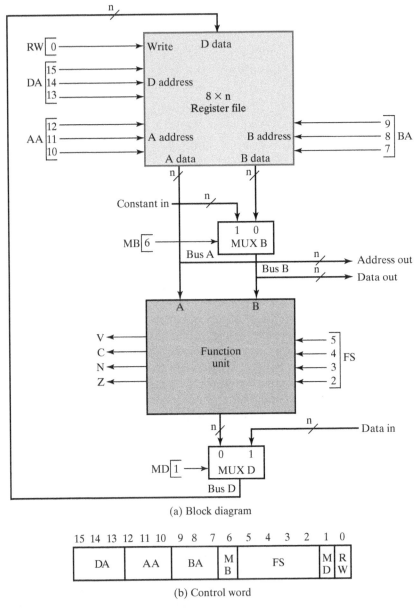

(a) Block diagram

15 14 13	12 11 10	9 8 7	6	5 4 3 2	1	0
DA	AA	BA	M B	FS	M D	R W

(b) Control word

☐ **FIGURE 8-11**
Datapath with Control Variables

N (sign), and Z (zero). MUX D selects the function unit output or the data on *Data in* as input for the register file.

There are 16 binary control inputs. Their combined values specify a *control word*. The 16-bit control word is defined in Figure 8-11(b). It consists of seven parts called *fields*, each designated by a pair of letters. The three register fields are three bits each. The remaining fields have one or four bits. The three bits of DA select one of eight destination registers for the result of the microoperation. The three bits of AA select one of eight source registers for the Bus A input to the ALU. The three bits of BA select a source register for the 0 input of the MUX B. The single MB bit determines whether Bus B carries the contents of the selected source register or a constant value. The 4-bit FS field controls the operation of the function unit. The FS field contains one of the 15 codes from Table 8-4. The single bit of MD selects the function unit output or the data on *Data in* as the input to Bus D. The final field, RW, determines whether a register is written or not. When applied to the control inputs, the 16-bit control word specifies a particular microoperation.

The functions of all meaningful control codes are specified in Table 8-5. For each field a binary code for each function is given. The register selected by each of the address fields DA, AA, and BA is the one with the decimal equivalent equal to the binary number for the code. MB selects either the register selected by the BA field or a constant from outside the datapath on Constant in. The ALU operations, the shifter operations, and the selection of the ALU or shifter outputs are all specified by the FS field. The field MD controls the information to be loaded into the

□ **TABLE 8-5**
Encoding of Control Word for the Datapath

DA, AA, BA		MB		FS		MD		RW	
Function	Code	Function	Code	Function	Code	Function	Code	Function	Code
$R0$	000	Register	0	$F = A$	0000	Function	0	No Write	0
$R1$	001	Constant	1	$F = A + 1$	0001	Data in	1	Write	1
$R2$	010			$F = A + B$	0010				
$R3$	011			$F = A + B + 1$	0011				
$R4$	100			$F = A + \overline{B}$	0100				
$R5$	101			$F = A + \overline{B} + 1$	0101				
$R6$	110			$F = A - 1$	0110				
$R7$	111			$F = A$	0111				
				$F = A \wedge B$	1000				
				$F = A \vee B$	1001				
				$F = A \oplus B$	1010				
				$F = \overline{A}$	1011				
				$F = B$	1100				
				$F = \text{sr } B$	1101				
				$F = \text{sl } B$	1110				

register file. The final field, RW, has the functions No Write, to prevent writing to any registers, and Write, to signify writing to a register.

The control word for a given microoperation can be derived by specifying the value of each of the control fields. For example, a subtraction given by the statement

$$R1 \leftarrow R2 + \overline{R3} + 1$$

specifies $R2$ for the A input of the ALU and $R3$ for the B input of the ALU. It also specifies function unit operation $F = A + \overline{B} + 1$ and selection of the function unit output for input into the register file. Finally, the microoperation selects $R1$ as the destination register and sets RW to 1 to cause $R1$ to be written. The control word for this microinstruction is specified by its seven fields, with the binary value for each field obtained from the encoding listed in Table 8-5. The binary control word for this subtraction microoperation, 001_010_011_0_0101_0_1 (with underline "_" used for convenience to separate the fields), is obtained as follows:

Field:	DA	AA	BA	MB	FS	MD	RW
Symbolic:	$R1$	$R2$	$R3$	Register	$F = A + \overline{B} + 1$	Function	Write
Binary:	001	010	011	0	0101	0	1

The control word for the microoperation and those for several other microoperations are given in Table 8-6 using symbolic notation and in Table 8-7 using binary codes.

The second example in Table 8-6 is a shift microoperation given by the statement

$$R4 \leftarrow \text{sl } R6$$

This statement specifies a shift left for the shifter. The content of register $R6$, shifted to the left, is transferred to $R4$. Note that because the shifter is driven by Bus B, the source for the shift is specified in the BA rather than the AA field. From the knowledge of the symbols in each field, the control word in binary is derived as shown in Table 8-7. For many microoperations, neither the A *data* nor the B *data* from the register file is used. In these cases, the respective symbolic field is marked with a dash.

☐ **TABLE 8-6**
Examples of Microoperations for the Datapath, Using Symbolic Notation

Micro-operation	DA	AA	BA	MB	FS	MD	RW
$R1 \leftarrow R2 - R3$	$R1$	$R2$	$R3$	Register	$F = A + \overline{B} + I$	Function	Write
$R4 \leftarrow \text{sl } R6$	$R4$	—	$R6$	Register	$F = \text{sl } B$	Function	Write
$R7 \leftarrow R7 + 1$	$R7$	$R7$	—	—	$F = A + 1$	Function	Write
$R1 \leftarrow R0 + 2$	$R1$	$R0$	—	Constant	$F = A + B$	Function	Write
Data out $\leftarrow R3$	—	—	$R3$	Register	—	—	No Write
$R4 \leftarrow$ Data in	$R4$	—	—	—	—	Data in	Write
$R5 \leftarrow 0$	$R5$	$R0$	$R0$	Register	$F = A \oplus B$	Function	Write

□ **TABLE 8-7**
Examples of Microoperations from Table 8-6, Using Binary Control Words

Micro-operation	DA	AA	BA	MB	FS	MD	RW
$R1 \leftarrow R2 - R3$	001	010	011	0	0101	0	1
$R4 \leftarrow$ sl R6	100	XXX	110	0	1110	0	1
$R7 \leftarrow R7 + 1$	111	111	XXX	X	0001	0	1
$R1 \leftarrow R0 + 2$	001	000	XXX	1	0010	0	1
Data out $\leftarrow R3$	XXX	XXX	011	0	XXXX	X	0
$R4 \leftarrow$ Data in	100	XXX	XXX	X	XXXX	1	1
$R5 \leftarrow 0$	101	000	000	0	1010	0	1

Since these values are unspecified, the corresponding binary values in Table 8-7 are Xs. Continuing with the last three examples in Table 8-6, to make the contents of a register available to an external destination only, we place the contents of the register on the *B data* output of the register file, with RW = No Write (0) to prevent the register file from being written. To place a small constant in a register or use a small constant as one of the operands, we place the constant on *Constant in*, set MB to Constant, and pass the value from Bus *B* through the ALU and Bus *D* to the destination register. To clear a register to 0, Bus *D* is set to all 0s by using the same register for both *A* data and *B* data with an XOR operation specified (FS = 1010) and MD = 0. The DA field is set to the code for the destination register, and RW is Write (1).

It is apparent from these examples that many microoperations can be performed by the same datapath. Sequences of such microoperations can be realized by providing a control unit that produces the appropriate sequences of control words.

To complete this section, we perform a simulation of the datapath in Figure 8-11. The number of bits in each register, *n*, is equal to 8. An unsigned decimal representation, which is most convenient for reading the simulation output, is used for all multiple-bit signals. We assume that the microoperations in Table 8-7, executed in sequence, provide the inputs to the datapath and that the initial content of each register is its number in decimal (e.g., *R5* contains $(0000\ 0101)_2 = (5)_{10}$). Figure 8-12 gives the result of this simulation. The first value displayed is the Clock with the clock cycles numbered for reference. The inputs, outputs, and state for the datapath are given roughly in the order of the flow of information through the path. The first four inputs are the primary control-word fields, which specify the register addresses that determine the register file outputs and the function selection. Next are inputs *Constant in* and MB, which control the input to Bus *B*. Following are the outputs *Address out* and *Data out*, which are the outputs from Bus *A* and Bus *B*, respectively. The next three variables—*Data in*, MD, and RW—are the final three inputs to the datapath. They are followed by the content of the eight registers and the *Status bits*, which are given as a vector (V, C, N, Z). The initial content of each register is its number in decimal. The value 2 is applied to Constant only in cycle 4, where MB equals 1. Otherwise, the value on *Constant in* is unknown, as indicated by X. Finally, *Data in* has value 18. In the simulation, this value comes from a

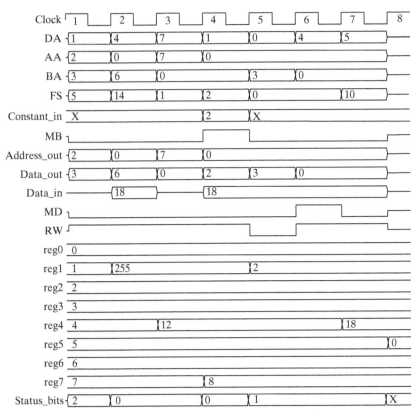

□ **FIGURE 8-12**
Simulation of the Microoperation Sequence in Table 8-7

memory that is addressed by *Address out* and that has value 18 in location 0 with unknown values in all other locations. The resulting value, except when *Address out* is 0, is represented by a line midway between 0 and 1, indicating the value is unknown.

Of note in the simulation results is that changes in registers as a result of a particular microoperation appear in the clock cycle *after* that in which the microoperation is specified. For example, the result of the subtraction in clock cycle 1 appears in register *R1* in clock cycle 2. This is because the result is loaded into flip-flops on the positive edge of the clock at the end of the clock cycle 1. On the other hand, the values on the *Status bits*, *Address out*, and *Data out* appear in the same clock cycle as the microoperation controlling them, since they do not depend on a positive clock edge occurring. Since no combinational delay is specified in the simulation, these values change at the same time as the register values. Finally, note that eight clock cycles of simulation are used for seven microoperations so that the values in the registers that result from the last microoperation executed can be observed. Although *Status bits* appear for all microoperations, they are not always meaningful. For example, for the microoperations, *R3=Data out* and *R4 ← Data in*, in clock cycles 5 and 6, respectively; the value of the status bits does not relate to the result, since the Function unit is not used in these operations. Finally, for *R5 ← R0* ⊕ *R0* in clock cycle 7, the arithmetic unit is not used, so the values of V and C from that unit are irrelevant, but the values for N and Z do represent the status of the result as a signed 2s complement integer.

8-7 A SIMPLE COMPUTER ARCHITECTURE

We introduce a simple computer architecture to obtain an initial understanding of computer design and to illustrate control designs for programmable systems. In a programmable system, a portion of the input to the processor consists of a sequence of *instructions*. Each instruction specifies an operation the system is to perform, which operands to use for the operation, where to place the results of the operation, and/or, in some cases, which instruction to execute next. For the programmable system, the instructions are usually stored in memory, which is either RAM or ROM. To execute the instructions in sequence, it is necessary to provide the address in memory of the instruction to be executed. In a computer, this address comes from a register called the *program counter* (*PC*). As the name implies, the *PC* has logic that permits it to count. In addition, to change the sequence of operations using decisions based on status information, the *PC* needs parallel load capability. So, in the case of a programmable system, the control unit contains a *PC* and associated decision logic, as well as the necessary logic to interpret the instruction in order to execute it. *Executing* an instruction means activating the necessary sequence of microoperations in the datapath (and elsewhere) required to perform the operation specified by the instruction. In contrast to the preceding, note that for a nonprogrammable system, the control unit is not responsible for obtaining instructions from memory, nor is it responsible for sequencing the execution of those instructions. There is no *PC* or similar register in such a system. Instead, the control unit determines the operations to be performed and the sequence of those operations, based on only its inputs and the status bits.

We show how the operations specified by instructions for the simple computer can be implemented by microoperations in the datapath, plus movement of information between the datapath and memory. We also show two different control structures for implementing the sequences of operations necessary for controlling program execution. The purpose here is to illustrate two different approaches to control design and the effects that such approaches have on datapath design and system performance. A more extensive study of the concepts associated with instruction sets for digital computers is presented in detail in the next chapter, and more complete CPU designs are undertaken in Chapter 10.

Instruction Set Architecture

The user specifies the operations to be performed and their sequence by the use of a *program*, which is a list of instructions that specifies the operations, the operands, and the sequence in which processing is to occur. The data processing performed by a computer can be altered by specifying a new program with different instructions or by specifying the same instructions with different data. Instructions and data are usually stored together in the same memory. By means of the techniques discussed in Chapter 10, however, they may appear to be coming from different memories. The control unit reads an instruction from memory and decodes and executes the instruction by issuing a sequence of one or more microoperations. The ability to execute a program from memory is the most important single property of a general-purpose computer. Execution of a program from memory is in sharp contrast to the nonprogrammable control units considered earlier in Examples 6-3 and 4, which execute fixed operations sequenced by inputs and status signals only.

An *instruction* is a collection of bits that instructs the computer to perform a specific operation. We call the collection of instructions for a computer its *instruction set* and a thorough description of the instruction set its *instruction set architecture* (*ISA*). Simple instruction set architectures have three major components: the storage resources, the instruction formats, and the instruction specifications.

Storage Resources

The storage resources for the simple computer are represented by the diagram in Figure 8-13. The diagram depicts the computer structure as viewed by a user programming it in a language that directly specifies the instructions to be executed. It gives the resources which the user sees available for storing information. Note that the architecture includes two memories, one for storage of instructions and the other for storage of data. These may actually be different memories, or they may be the same memory, but viewed as different from the standpoint of the CPU as discussed in Chapter 10. Also visible to the programmer in the diagram is a register file with eight 16-bit registers and the 16-bit program counter.

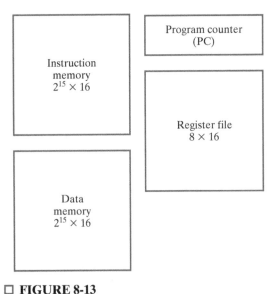

☐ **FIGURE 8-13**
Storage Resource Diagram for a Simple Computer

Instruction Formats

The format of an instruction is usually depicted by a rectangular box symbolizing the bits of the instruction, as they appear in memory words or in a control register. The bits are divided into groups or parts called *fields*. Each field is assigned a specific item, such as the operation code, a constant value, or a register file address. The various fields specify different functions for the instruction and, when shown together, constitute an instruction format.

The *operation code* of an instruction, often shortened to "opcode," is a group of bits in the instruction that specifies an operation, such as add, subtract, shift, or complement. The number of bits required for the opcode of an instruction is a function of the total number of operations in the instruction set. It must consist of at least m bits for up to 2^m distinct operations. The designer assigns a bit combination (a code) to each operation. The computer is designed to accept this bit configuration at the proper time in the sequence of activities and to supply the proper control-word sequence to execute the specified operation. As a specific example, consider a computer with a maximum of 128 distinct operations, one of them an addition operation. The opcode assigned to this operation consists of seven bits 0000010. When the opcode 0000010 is detected by the control unit, a sequence of control words is applied to the datapath to perform the intended addition.

The opcode of an instruction specifies the operation to be performed. The operation must be performed using data stored in computer registers or in memory (i.e., on the contents of the storage resources). An instruction, therefore, must specify not only the operation, but also the registers or memory words in which the operands are to be found and the result is to be placed. The operands may be specified by an instruction in two ways. An operand is said to be specified *explicitly* if the instruction contains special bits for its identification. For example, the instruction performing an addition may contain three binary numbers specifying the registers containing the two operands and the register that receives the result. An operand is said to be defined *implicitly* if it is included as a part of the definition of the operation itself, as represented by the opcode, rather than being given in the instruction. For example, in an Increment Register operation, one of the operands is implicitly +1.

The three instruction formats for the simple computer are illustrated in Figure 8-14. Suppose that the computer has a register file consisting of eight registers, $R0$ through $R7$. The instruction format in Figure 8-14(a) consists of an opcode that specifies the use of three or fewer registers, as needed. One of the registers is designated a destination for the result and two of the registers sources for operands. For convenience, the field names are abbreviated DR for "Destination Register," SA for "Source Register A," and SB for "Source Register B." The numbers of register fields and registers actually used are determined by the specific opcode. The opcode also specifies the use of the registers. For example, for a subtraction operation, suppose that the three bits in SA are 010, specifying $R2$, the three bits in SB are 011, specifying $R3$, and the three bits in DR are 001,

☐ **FIGURE 8-14**
Three Instruction Formats

specifying $R1$. Then the contents of $R3$ will be subtracted from the contents of $R2$, and the result will be placed in $R1$. As an additional example, suppose that the operation is a store (to memory). Suppose further, that the three bits in SA specify $R4$ and the three bits in SB specify $R5$. For this particular operation, it is assumed that the register specified in SA contains the address and the register specified in SB contains the operand to be stored. So the value in $R5$ is stored in the memory location given by the value in $R4$. The DR field has no effect, since the store operation prevents the register file from being written.

The instruction format in Figure 8-14(b) has an opcode, two register fields, and an operand. The operand is a constant called an *immediate operand*, since it is immediately available in the instruction. For example, for an add immediate operation with SA specified as $R7$, DR specified as $R2$, and operand OP equal to 011, the value 3 is added to the contents of $R7$, and the result of the addition is placed in $R2$. Since the operand is only three bits rather than a full 16 bits, the remaining 13 bits must be filled by using either zero fill or sign extension, as discussed in Chapter 3. In this ISA, zero fill is specified for the operand.

The instruction format in Figure 8-14(c), in contrast to the other two formats, does not change any register file or memory contents. Instead, it affects the order in which the instructions are fetched from memory. The location of an instruction to be fetched is determined by the program counter, denoted by PC. Ordinarily, the program counter fetches the instructions from sequential addresses in memory as the program is executed. But much of the power of a processor comes from its ability to change the order of execution of the instructions based on results of the processing performed. These changes in the order of instruction execution are based on the use of instructions referred to as jumps and branches.

The example format given in Figure 8-14(c) for jump and branch instructions has an operation code, one register field SA, and a split address field AD. If a branch (possibly based on the contents of the register specified) is to occur, the new address is formed by adding the current PC contents and the contents of the 6-bit address field. This addressing method is called PC relative and the 6-bit address field, referred to as an *address offset*, is treated as a signed 2s complement number. To preserve the 2s complement representation, *sign extension* is applied to the 6-bit address to form a 16-bit offset before the addition. If the leftmost bit of the address field AD is a 1, then the 10 bits to its left are filled with 1s to give a negative 2s complement offset. If the leftmost bit of the address field is 0, then the 10 bits to its left are filled with 0s to give a positive 2s complement offset. The offset is added to the contents of the *PC* to form the location from which the next instruction is to be fetched. For example, with the *PC* value equal to 55, suppose that a branch is to occur to location 35 if the contents of *R6* is equal to zero. The opcode would specify a branch-on-zero instruction, SA would be specified as *R6*, and AD would be the 6-bit, 2s complement representation of −20. If *R6* is zero, then *PC* contents becomes 55 + (−20) = 35, and the next instruction will be fetched from address 35. Otherwise, if *R6* is nonzero, the *PC* will count up to 56, and the next instruction will be fetched from address 56. This addressing method alone provides branch addresses within a small range below and above the *PC* value. The jump provides a broader range of addresses by using the unsigned contents of a 16-bit register as the jump target.

The three formats in Figure 8-14 are used for the simple computer to be discussed in this chapter. In Chapter 9, we present and discuss more generally other instruction types and formats.

Instruction Specifications

Instruction specifications describe each of the distinct instructions that can be executed by the system. For each instruction, the opcode is given along with a shorthand name called a *mnemonic*, which can be used as a symbolic representation for the opcode. This mnemonic, along with a representation for each of the additional instruction fields in the format for the instruction, represents the notation to be used in specifying all of the fields of the instruction symbolically. This symbolic representation is then converted to the binary representation of the instruction by a program called an *assembler*. A description of the operation performed by the instruction execution is given, including the status bits that are affected by the instruction. This description may be text or may use a register transfer-like notation.

The instruction specifications for the simple computer are given in Table 8-8. The register transfer notation introduced in previous chapters is used to describe the operation performed, and the status bits that are valid for each instruction are indicated. In order to illustrate the instructions, suppose that we have a memory with 16 bits per word with instructions having one of the formats in Figure 8-14.

☐ **TABLE 8-8**
Instruction Specifications for the Simple Computer

Instruction	Opcode	Mne- monic	Format	Description	Status Bits
Move A	0000000	MOVA	RD, RA	R[DR] ← R[SA]*	N, Z
Increment	0000001	INC	RD, RA	R[DR] ← R[SA] + 1*	N, Z
Add	0000010	ADD	RD, RA, RB	R[DR] ← R[SA] + R[SB]*	N, Z
Subtract	0000101	SUB	RD, RA, RB	R[DR] ← R[SA] − R[SB]*	N, Z
Decrement	0000110	DEC	RD, RA	R[DR] ← R[SA] − 1*	N, Z
AND	0001000	AND	RD, RA, RB	R[DR] ← R[SA] ∧ R[SB]*	N, Z
OR	0001001	OR	RD, RA, RB	R[DR] ← R[SA] ∨ R[SB]*	N, Z
Exclusive OR	0001010	XOR	RD, RA, RB	R[DR] ← R[SA] ⊕ R[SB]*	N, Z
NOT	0001011	NOT	RD, RA	R[DR] ← $\overline{R[SA]}$*	N, Z
Move B	0001100	MOVB	RD, RB	R[DR] ← R[SB]*	
Shift Right	0001101	SHR	RD, RB	R[DR] ← sr R[SB]*	
Shift Left	0001110	SHL	RD, RB	R[DR] ← sl R[SB]*	
Load Immediate	1001100	LDI	RD, OP	R[DR] ← zf OP*	
Add Immediate	1000010	ADI	RD, RA, OP	R[DR] ← R[SA] + zf OP*	N, Z
Load	0010000	LD	RD, RA	R[DR] ← M[SA]*	
Store	0100000	ST	RA, RB	M[SA] ← R[SB]*	
Branch on Zero	1100000	BRZ	RA, AD	if (R[SA] = 0) PC ← PC + se AD, if (R[SA] ≠ 0) PC ← PC + 1	N, Z
Branch on Negative	1100001	BRN	RA, AD	if (R[SA] < 0) PC ← PC + se AD, if (R[SA] ≥ 0) PC ← PC + 1	N, Z
Jump	1110000	JMP	RA	PC ← R[SA]*	

* For all of these instructions, PC ← PC + 1 is also executed to prepare for the next cycle.

Instructions and data, in binary, are placed in memory, as shown in Table 8-9. This stored information represents the four instructions illustrating the distinct formats. At address 25, we have a register format instruction that specifies an operation to subtract $R3$ from $R2$ and load the difference into $R1$. This operation is represented symbolically in the rightmost column of Table 8-9. Note that the 7-bit opcode for subtraction is 0000101, or decimal 5. The remaining bits of the instruction specify the three registers: 001 specifies the destination register as $R1$, 010 specifies the source register A as $R2$, and 011 specifies the source register B as $R3$.

In memory location 35 is a register format instruction to store the contents of $R5$ in the memory location specified by $R4$. The opcode is 0100000, or decimal 32, and the operation is given symbolically, again, in the rightmost column of the figure. Suppose $R4$ contains 70 and $R5$ contains 80. Then the execution of this instruction will store the value 80 in memory location 70, replacing the original value of 192 stored there.

□ **TABLE 8-9**
  Memory Representation of Instructions and Data

Decimal Address	Memory Contents	Decimal Opcode	Other Fields	Operation
25	0000101 001 010 011	5 (Subtract)	DR:1, SA:2, SB:3	$R1 \leftarrow R2 - R3$
35	0100000 000 100 101	32 (Store)	SA:4, SB:5	$M[R4] \leftarrow R5$
45	1000010 010 111 011	66 (Add Immediate)	DR:2, SA:7, OP:3	$R2 \leftarrow R7 + 3$
55	1100000 101 110 100	96 (Branch on Zero)	AD: 44, SA:6	If R6 = 0, $PC \leftarrow PC - 20$
70	0000000011000000	Data = 192. After execution of instruction in 35, Data = 80.		

At address 45, an immediate format instruction appears that adds 3 to the contents of $R7$ and loads the result into $R2$. The opcode for this instruction is 66, and the operand to be added is the value 3 (011) in the OP field, the last three bits of the instruction.

In location 55, the branch instruction previously described appears. The opcode for this instruction is 96, and source register A is specified as $R6$. Note that AD (Left) contains 101 and AD (Right) contains 100. Putting these two together and applying sign extension, we obtain 1111111111101100, which represents -20 in 2s complement. If register $R6$ is zero, then -20 is added to the PC to give 35. If register $R6$ is nonzero, the new PC value will be 56. Notice our assumption that the addition to the PC content occurs before the PC has been incremented, which would be the case in the simple computer. In real systems, however, the PC has sometimes been incremented to point to the next instruction in memory. In such a case, the value stored in AD needs to be adjusted accordingly to obtain the right branch address, in this case, -19.

The placement of instructions in memory as shown in Table 8-9 is quite arbitrary. In many computers, the word length is from 32 to 64 bits, so the instruction formats can hold much larger immediate operands and addresses than those we have given. Depending on the computer architecture, some of the instruction formats may occupy two or more consecutive memory words. Also, the number of registers is often larger, so the register fields in the instructions must contain more bits.

At this point, it is vital to recognize the difference between a computer *operation* and a hardware *microoperation*. An operation is specified by an instruction stored in binary, in the computer's memory. The control unit in the computer uses the address or addresses provided by the program counter to retrieve the instruction from memory. It then decodes the opcode bits and other information in the instruction to perform the required microoperations for the execution of the instruction. In contrast, a microoperation is specified by the bits in a control word in the hardware which is decoded by the computer hardware to execute the microoperation. The execution of a computer operation often requires a sequence or program of microoperations, rather than a single microoperation.

8-8 SINGLE-CYCLE HARDWIRED CONTROL

The block diagram for a computer that has a hardwired control unit and that fetches and executes an instruction in a single clock cycle is shown in Figure 8-15. We refer to this computer as the single-cycle computer. The storage resources, instruction formats, and instruction specifications for this computer are given in the previous section. The datapath shown is the same as that in Figure 8-11 with $m = 3$ and $n = 16$. The data memory M is attached to the Address out, Data out, and Data in by connec-

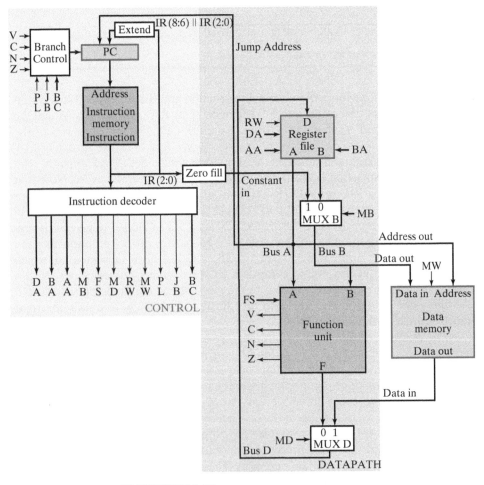

☐ **FIGURE 8-15**
Block Diagram for a Single-Cycle Computer

tions to the datapath. It has a single control signal MW, which is 1 to write the memory, and 0 otherwise.

The Control unit appears on the left in Figure 8-15. Although not usually thought of as part of the control unit, the instruction memory, together with its address inputs and instruction outputs, is shown for convenience within the control unit. We do not write to the instruction memory during the execution of a program, making it appear in this model to be a combinational rather than a sequential component. As previously discussed, the PC provides the instruction address to the instruction memory, and the instruction output from the instruction memory goes to the control logic, which in this case is the instruction decoder. The output from the instruction memory also goes to Extend and Zero fill, which provide the address offset to the PC and the constant input, Constant in, to the datapath, respectively. Extension appends the leftmost bit of the 6-bit address offset field AD to the left of AD, preserving its 2s complement representation. Zero fill appends 13 zeros to the left of the operand (OP) field of the instruction to form a 16-bit unsigned operand for use in the datapath. For example, operand value 110 becomes 0000000000000110 or +6.

The PC is updated in each clock cycle. The behavior of the PC, which is a complex register, is determined by the opcode, N, and Z, since C and V are not used in this control-unit design. If a jump occurs, the new PC value becomes the value on Bus A. If a branch is taken, then the new PC value is the sum of the previous PC value and the sign-extended address offset, which in 2s complement can be either positive or negative. Otherwise, the PC is incremented by 1. A jump occurs for bit 13 in the instruction equal to 1. For bit 13 equal to 0, a conditional branch occurs. The status bit that is the condition for the branch is selected by bit 9 of the instruction. For bit 9 equal to 1, N is selected and, for bit 9 equal to 0, Z is selected.

All parts of the computer that are sequential are shown in blue. Note that there is no sequential logic in the control part other than the PC. Thus, aside from providing the address to the instruction memory, the control logic is combinational in this case. That fact, combined with the structure of the datapath and the use of separate instruction and data memories, allows the single-cycle computer to obtain and execute an instruction from the instruction memory, all in a single clock cycle.

Instruction Decoder

The instruction decoder is a combinational circuit that provides all of the control words for the datapath, based on the contents of the fields of the instruction. A number of the fields of the control word can be obtained directly from the contents of the fields in the instruction. Looking at Figure 8-16, we see that the control-word fields DA, AA, and BA are equal to the instruction fields DR, SA, and SB, respectively. Also, control field BC for selection of the branch condition status bits is taken directly from the last bit of Opcode. The remaining control-word fields include datapath and data memory control bits MB, MD, RW, and MW. There are two added bits for the control of the PC: PL and JB. If there is to be a jump or branch, PL = 1, loading the PC. For PL = 0, the PC is incremented. With PL = 1, JB = 1 calls for a jump, and JB = 0 calls for a conditional branch. Some of the single-bit control-word fields require logic for their implementation. In order to design this logic, we divide the

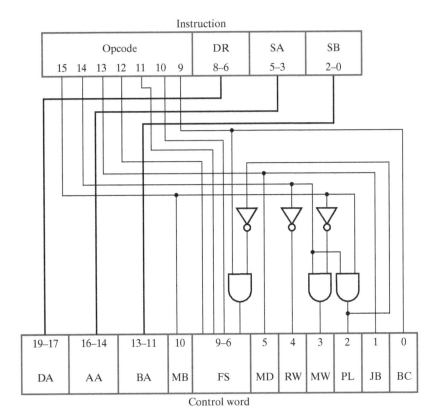

☐ **FIGURE 8-16**
Diagram of Instruction Decoder

various instructions possible for the simple computer into different function types and then assign the first three bits of the opcode to the various types. The instruction function types shown in Table 8-10 are based on the use of specific hardware resources in the computer, such as MUX B, the Function unit, the Register file, Data memory, and the *PC*. For example, the first function type uses the ALU, sets MUX B to use the Register file source, sets MUX D to use the Function unit output, and writes to the Register file. Other instruction function types are defined as various combinations of use of a constant input instead of a register, Data memory reads and writes, and manipulation of the *PC* for jumps and branches.

By looking at the relationship between the instruction function types and the necessary control-word values needed for their implementation, bits 15 through 13 and bit 9 were assigned as shown in Table 8-10. This assignment attempted to minimize the logic required to implement the decoder. To perform the design of the decoder, the values for all of the single-bit fields in the control word were determined from the function types and entered into Table 8-10. Note that there are a number of don't-care (X) entries. Treating Table 8-10 as a truth table and optimizing the logic functions, the logic for the single-bit outputs of the instruction decoder in

□ **TABLE 8-10**
   Truth Table for Instruction Decoder Logic

Instruction Function Type	Instruction Bits				Control-Word Bits						
	15	14	13	9	MB	MD	RW	MW	PL	JB	BC
Function-unit operations using registers	0	0	0	X	0	0	1	0	0	X	X
Memory read	0	0	1	X	0	1	1	0	0	X	X
Memory write	0	1	0	X	0	X	0	1	0	X	X
Function-unit operations using register and constant	1	0	0	X	1	0	1	0	0	X	X
Conditional branch on zero (Z)	1	1	0	0	X	X	0	0	1	0	0
Conditional branch on negative (N)	1	1	0	1	X	X	0	0	1	0	1
Unconditional jump	1	1	1	X	X	X	0	0	1	1	X

Figure 8-16 results. In the optimization, the four unused codes for bits 15, 14, 13, and 9 were assumed to have X values for all of the single bit fields. This implies that if one of these codes occurs in a program, the effect is unknown. A more conservative design specifies RW, MW, and PL all zero for these four codes to insure that the storage resource state is unchanged for these unused codes. The optimization results in the logic in Figure 8-16 for implementing MB, MD, RW, MW, PL, and JB.

The remaining logic in the decoder deals with the FS field. For all but the conditional branch and unconditional jump instructions, bits 9 through 12 are fed directly through to form the FS field. During conditional branch operations, such as Branch on Zero, the value in source register A must be passed through the ALU so that the status bits N and Z can be evaluated. This requires FS = 0000. The use of bit 9, however, for status-bit selection for conditional branches requires at times that bit 9, which controls the rightmost bit of FS, be a 1. The contradiction in values between bit 9 and FS is resolved by adding an enable on bit 9 that forces FS_0 to zero whenever PL = 1, as shown in Figure 8-16.

Sample Instructions and Program

Six instructions for the single-cycle computer are listed in Table 8-11. The symbolic names associated with the instructions are useful for listing programs in symbolic form rather than in binary code. Because of the importance of instruction decoding, the rightmost six columns of the table show critical control-signal values for each instruction, based on the values obtained using the logic in Figure 8-16.

Now suppose that the first instruction, "Add Immediate" (ADI), is present on the output of the instruction memory shown in Figure 8-15. Then, on the basis

☐ TABLE 8-11
Six Instructions for the Single-Cycle Computer

Operation Code	Symbolic Name	Format	Description	Function	MB	MD	RW	MW	PL	JB	BC
1000010	ADI	Immediate	Add immediate operand	$R[\text{DR}] \leftarrow R[\text{SA}] + zf\,I(2{:}0)$	1	0	1	0	0	0	0
0010000	LD	Register	Load memory content into register	$R[\text{DR}]\leftarrow M[R[\text{SA}]]$	0	1	1	0	0	0	0
0100000	ST	Register	Store register content in memory	$M[R[\text{SA}]]\leftarrow R[\text{SB}]$	0	1	0	1	0	0	0
0001110	SL	Register	Shift left	$R[\text{DR}]\leftarrow \text{sl } R[\text{SB}]$	0	0	1	0	0	1	0
0001011	NOT	Register	Complement register	$R[\text{DR}] \leftarrow \overline{R[\text{SA}]}$	0	0	1	0	0	0	1
1100000	BRZ	Jump/Branch	If $R[\text{SA}] = 0$, branch to $PC + se\,AD$	If $R[\text{SA}] = 0$, $PC \leftarrow PC$ se AD; If $R[\text{SA}] \neq 0, PC \leftarrow PC + 1$	1	0	0	0	1	0	0

of the first three bits of the opcode, 100, the outputs of the instruction decoder have the values MB = 1, MD = 0, RW = 1, and MW = 0. The last three bits of the instruction, OP_{2-0}, are extended to 16 bits by zero fill. We denote this in a register transfer statement by zf. Since MB is 1, this zero-filled value is placed on Bus B. With MD equal to 0, the function unit output is selected, and since the last four bits of the opcode, 0010, specify field FS, the operation is $A + B$. So the zero-filled value on Bus B is added to the contents of register SA, with the result presented on Bus D. Since RW = 1, the value on Bus D is written into register DR. Finally, with MW = 0, no write into memory occurs. This entire operation takes place in a single clock cycle. At the beginning of the next cycle, the destination register is written and, since PL = 0, the PC is incremented to point to the next instruction.

The second instruction, LD, is a load from memory with opcode 0010000. The first three bits of this opcode, 001, give control values MD = 1, RW = 1, and MW = 0. These values, plus the register source field SA and register destination field DR, fully specify this instruction, which loads the contents of the memory address specified by register SA into register DR. Again, since PL = 0, the PC is incremented. Note that the values of JB and BC are ignored, since this is neither a jump nor a branch instruction.

The third instruction, ST, stores the contents of a register in memory. The first three bits of the opcode, 010, give control signal values MB = 0, RW = 0, and MW = 1. MW = 1 causes a memory write operation, with the address and data from the register file. RW = 0 prevents the register file from being written. The address for the memory write comes from the register selected by field SA, and the data for the memory write comes from the register selected by SB, since MB = 0. The DR field, although present, is not used, since no write occurs to a register.

Because this computer has load and store instructions and does not combine loading and storing of data operands with other operations, it is referred to as having a *load/store* architecture. The use of such an architecture simplifies the execution of instructions.

The next two instructions use the Function unit and write to the Register file without immediate operands. The last four bits of the opcode, the value for the FS field of the control word, specify Function unit operation. For these two instructions, only one source register, $R[SA]$ for the NOT and $R[SB]$ for the shift left, and a destination register are involved.

The final instruction is a conditional branch and manipulates the PC value. It has PL = 1, causing the program counter to be loaded instead of incremented, and JB = 0, causing a conditional branch rather than a jump. Since BC = 0, register $R[SA]$ is tested for a value of zero. If $R[SA]$ equals zero, the PC value becomes $PC +$ se AD, where se stands for sign extend. Otherwise, PC is incremented. For this instruction, the DR and SB fields become the 6-bit address field AD, which is sign extended and added to the PC.

To demonstrate how instructions such as these can be used in a simple program, consider the arithmetic expression $83 - (2 + 3)$. The following program performs this computation, assuming that register $R3$ contains 248, location 248 in data memory contains 2, location 249 contains 83, and the result is to be placed in location 250:

LD	R1, R3	Load $R1$ with contents of location 248 in memory ($R1 = 2$)
ADI	R1, R1, 3	Add 3 to $R1$ ($R1 = 5$)
NOT	R1, R1	Complement $R1$
INC	R1, R1	Increment $R1$ ($R1 = -5$)
INC	R3, R3	Increment the contents of $R3$ ($R3 = 249$)
LD	R2, R3	Load $R2$ with contents of location 249 in memory ($R2 = 83$)
ADD	R2, R2,	$R1$ Add contents of $R1$ to contents of $R2$ ($R2 = 78$)
INC	R3, R3	Increment the contents of $R3$ ($R3 = 250$)
ST	R3, R2	Store $R2$ in memory location 250 ($M[250] = 78$)

The subtraction in this case is done by taking the 2s complement of $(2 + 3)$ and adding it to 83; the subtraction operation SUB could have been used as well. If a register field is not used in executing an instruction, its symbolic value is omitted. The symbolic values for the register-type instructions, when the latter are present, are in the order DR, SA, and SB. For immediate types, the fields are in the order DR, SA, and OP. To store this program in the instruction memory, it is necessary to convert all of the symbolic names and decimal numbers used to their corresponding binary codes.

Single-Cycle Computer Issues

Although there may be instances in which single-cycle computer timing and control strategy is useful, it has a number of shortcomings. One is in the area of performing complex operations. For example, suppose that an instruction is desired that executes unsigned binary multiplication using a multiplication algorithm that processes one bit of the multiplier at a time. With the given datapath, this cannot be accomplished by a microoperation that can be executed in a single clock cycle. Thus, a control organization that provides multiple clock cycles for the execution of instructions is needed.

Also, the single-cycle computer has two distinct 16-bit memories, one for instructions and one for data. For a simple computer with instructions and data in the same 16-bit memory, two read accesses of memory are required to execute an instruction that loads a data word from memory into a register. The first access obtains the instruction, and the second access, if required, reads or writes the data word. Since two different addresses must be applied to the memory address inputs, at least two clock cycles, one for each address, are required for obtaining and executing the instruction. This can also be accomplished easily with multiple-cycle control.

Finally, the single-cycle computer has a lower limit on the clock period based on a long worst-case delay path. This path is shown in blue in the simplified diagram of Figure 8-17. The total delay along the path is 9.8 ns. This limits the clock frequency to 102 MHz, which, although it may be adequate for some applications, is too slow for a modern computer CPU. In order to have a higher clock frequency, either the delays of the components on the path or the number of components in the path must be reduced. If the delays of the components cannot be reduced, reducing the number of components in the path is the only alternative. In Chapter 10, pipelining of the datapath reduces the number of components in the longest combinational delay path and

□ **FIGURE 8-17**
Worst-Case Delay Path in Single-Cycle Computer

permits the clock frequency to be increased. A pipelined datapath and control given in Chapter 10 demonstrates the improved CPU performance that can be obtained.

8-9 MULTIPLE-CYCLE HARDWIRED CONTROL

To demonstrate multiple-cycle control, we use the architecture of the simple computer, but modify its datapath, memory, and control. The goal of the modifications is to demonstrate the use of a single memory for both data and instructions and to demonstrate how more complex instructions can be implemented by using multiple clock cycles per instruction. The block diagram in Figure 8-18 shows the modifications to the datapath, memory, and control.

The changes to the single-cycle computer can be observed by comparing Figures 8-15 and 8-18. The first modification, which is possible with, but not essential to, multiple-cycle operation, replaces the separate instruction memory and data memory in Figure 8-15 with the single Memory M in Figure 8-18. To fetch instructions, the PC is the address source for the memory, and to fetch data, Bus A is the address source. At the address input to memory, multiplexer MUX M selects between these two address sources. MUX M requires an additional control signal, MM, which is added to the control-word format. Since instructions from Memory M are needed in the control unit, a path is added from its output to the instruction register IR in the control unit.

□ **FIGURE 8-18**
Block Diagram for a Multiple-Cycle Computer

In executing an instruction across multiple clock cycles, data generated during the current cycle is often needed in a later cycle. This data can be temporarily stored in a register from the time it is generated until the time it is used. Registers used for such temporary storage during the execution of the instruction are usually not visible to the user (i.e., are not part of the storage resources). The second modification provides these temporary storage registers by doubling the number of registers in the register file. Registers 0 through 7 are storage resources and registers 8 through 15 are used only for temporary storage during instruction execution, so are not part of the storage resources visible to the user. The addressing of 16 registers requires 4 bits, and becomes more complex, since addressing of the first eight registers must be controlled from the instruction, and the second eight registers, from the control unit. This is handled by the Register address logic in Figure 8-18 and by modified DX, AX, and BX fields in the control word. The details of this change will be discussed later when the control-word information is defined.

The *PC* is the only control unit component retained and it must also be modified. During the execution of a multiple-cycle instruction, the *PC* must be held at its current value for all but one of the cycles. To provide this hold capability, as well as an increment and two load operations, the *PC* is modified to be controlled by a 2-bit control-word field, PS. Since the *PC* is controlled completely by the control word, the Branch control logic previously represented by BC is absorbed into the Control Logic block in Figure 8-18.

Because of the multiple cycles of the modified computer, the instruction needs to be held in a register for use during its execution since its values are likely to be needed for more than just the first cycle. The register used for this purpose is the *instruction register IR* in Figure 8-18. Since the *IR* loads only when an instruction is being read from memory, it has a load-enable signal IL that is added to the control word. Because of the multiple-cycle operation, a sequential control circuit, which can provide a sequence of control words for microoperations used to interpret the instruction is required and replaces the Instruction decoder. The sequential control unit consists of the Control state register and the combinational Control logic. The Control logic has the state, the opcode, and the status bits as its inputs and produces the control word as its output. Conceptually, the control word is divided into two parts, one for Sequence control, which determines the next state of the overall control unit, and one for Datapath control, which controls the microoperations executed by the Datapath and Memory *M* as shown in Figure 8-18.

The 28-bit modified control word is given in Figure 8-19 and the definitions of the fields of the control word are given in Tables 8-12 and 8-13. In Table 8-12, the fields DX, AX, and BX control the register selection. If the MSB of one of these fields is 0, then the corresponding register addresses DA, AA, or BA are that given by 0 ‖ DR, 0 ‖ SA, and 0 ‖ SB, respectively. If the MSB of one of these fields is 1, then the corresponding register address is the contents of the field DX, AX, or BX. This selection process is performed by the Register address logic, which contains three multiplexers, one for each of DA, AA, and BA, controlled by the MSB of DX, AX, and BX, respectively. Table 8-12 also gives the code values for the MM field, which determines whether *Address out* or *PC* serves as the Memory *M* address. The remaining fields in Table 8-12, MB, MD, RW, and MW, have the same functions as for the single-cycle computer.

In the sequential control circuit, the State control register has a set of states, just as a set of flip-flops in any other sequential circuit has. At the level of our discussion, we assume that each state has an abstract name which can be used as both the state and the next-state value. In the design process, a state assignment needs to be made to

□ **FIGURE 8-19**
Control-Word Format for Multiple-Cycle Computer

□ **TABLE 8-12**
Control-Word Information for Datapath

DX	AX	BX	Code	MB	Code	FS	Code	MD	RW	MM	MW	Code
R[DR]	R[SA]	R[SB]	0XXX	Register	0	$F = A$	0000	FnUt	No Write	Address out	No Write		0
R8	R8	R8	1000	Constant	1	$F = A + 1$	0001	Data in	Write	PC	Write		1
R9	R9	R9	1001			$F = A + B$	0010						
R10	R10	R10	1010			Unused	0011						
R11	R11	R11	1011			Unused	0100						
R12	R12	R12	1100			$F = A+\overline{B}+1$	0101						
R13	R13	R13	1101			$F = A-1$	0110						
R14	R14	R14	1110			Unused	0111						
R15	R15	R15	1111			$F = A \wedge B$	1000						
						$F = A \vee B$	1001						
						$F = A \oplus B$	1010						
						$F = \overline{A}$	1011						
						$F = B$	1100						
						$F = \text{sr } B$	1101						
						$F = \text{sl } B$	1110						
						Unused	1111						

these abstract states. Referring to Table 8-13, the field NS in the control word provides the next state for the Control State register. We have assigned four bits for the state code, but this can be modified as necessary, depending on the number of states needed and the state assignment used in the design. This particular field could be considered as integral to the control and sequential circuit and not part of the control word, but it will appear in the state table of the control in any case. The 2-bit PS field controls the program counter, *PC*. On a given clock cycle the *PC* holds its state (00), increments its state by 1 (01), conditionally loads *PC* plus sign-extended AD (10), or unconditionally loads the contents of *R*[SA] (11). Finally, the instruction register is loaded

□ **TABLE 8-13**
Control Information for Sequence Control

NS	PS		IL	
Next State	Action	Code	Action	Code
Gives next state	Hold PC	00	No load	0
of control state	Inc PC	01	Load IR	1
register	Branch	10		
	Jump	11		

only once during the execution of an instruction. Thus, on any given cycle, either a new instruction is loaded (IL = 1) or the instruction remains unchanged (IL = 0).

Sequential Control Design

The design of the sequential control circuit can be done using techniques from Chapters 4 and 6. However, compared to the examples there, even for this comparatively simple computer, the control is quite complex. Assuming there are four state variables, the combinational Control logic has 15 input variables and 28 output variables. It turns out that a condensed state table for the circuit is not too difficult to develop, but manual design of the detailed logic is very complex, making the use of logic synthesis or a PLA (programmed logic array), as discussed in Chapter 5, more viable options. As a consequence, we focus on state table development rather than detailed logic implementation. We begin by developing a state machine diagram that represents the instructions that can be implemented with the minimum number of clock cycles. Extensions of this chart can then be developed for implementation of instructions requiring more than the minimum number of clock cycles. The state machine diagrams provide the information needed to develop the state table entries for implementing the instruction set. For instructions requiring a memory access for data as well as for the instruction itself, at least two cycles are required. It is convenient to separate the cycles into two processing steps: *instruction fetch* and *instruction execution*. On the basis of this division, the partial state machine diagram for the two-cycle instructions is given in Figure 8-20. This is called a *partial state diagram*, since there will be other pieces added to it, e.g., in Figures 8-21 and 8-22. The instruction fetch occurs in state INF at the top of the chart. The *PC* contains the address of the instruction in Memory *M*. This address is applied to the memory, and the word read from memory is loaded into the *IR* on the positive clock edge that ends

□ **FIGURE 8-20**
Partial State Machine Diagram for Multiple-Cycle Computer

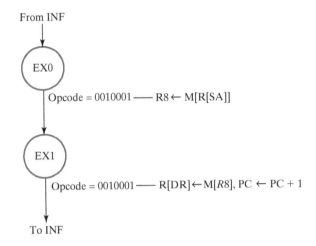

From INF

EX0

Opcode = 0010001 —— R8 ← M[R[SA]]

EX1

Opcode = 0010001 —— R[DR] ← M[R8], PC ← PC + 1

To INF

☐ **FIGURE 8-21**
Partial State Machine Diagram for Register Indirect Instruction

state INF. The same clock edge causes the new state to become EX0. In state EX0, the instruction is decoded and the microoperations executing all or part of the instruction appear in Mealy-type outputs. If the instruction can be completed in state EX0, the next state is INF in preparation for fetching of the next instruction. Further, for instructions that do not change PC contents during their execution, the PC is incremented. If additional states are required for instruction execution, the next state is EX1. In each of the execution states, 128 different input combinations are possible, based on the opcode. Many of these opcodes will be unused. An *unused opcode* is one which does not appear in any of the partial state diagrams for a particular control unit. We assume that these opcodes will never appear and so will be don't-care inputs. An alternative assumption is that if they do appear, they cause an exception that signals their presence. These and other assumptions for unused opcodes must be taken into account when evaluating constraint 2 of the transition condition constraints in Section 4-6.

Status bits are used with some operation codes, typically one at a time. In Figure 8-20, N and Z appear for the branch instructions on the lower right as output conditions and affect output actions only. In other cases, they may also affect sequencing, appearing as transition conditions.

Next, we describe a sampling of the instruction executions specified by the state machine diagram in Figure 8-20. The first opcode is 0000000 for the move A (MOVA) instruction. This instruction involves a simple transfer from the source A register to the destination register, as specified by the register transfer shown in state EX0 for the instruction opcode. Although the status bits N and Z are valid, they are not used in the execution of this instruction. The move action occurs and the PC is incremented on the clock edge, ending state EX0. The incrementing of the PC is an action that occurs for all but branch and jump instructions in the state machine diagram. Note that due to the sharing of arcs by the transitions to state INF, the incrementing of the PC can be placed on the arc shared by all transitions rather than being added to the output branch for each transition.

The third opcode is 0000010 for the ADD instruction with the register transfer for addition shown. In this case, status bits $V, C, N,$ and Z are valid, although not used.

Partial State Machine Diagram for Right-Shift and Left-Shift Multiple Instructions

The eleventh opcode, 0010000, is the load (LD) instruction, which uses the value in the register specified by SA for the address and loads the data word from Memory M into the register specified by DR. The twelfth opcode, 0100000, is for the store (ST) instruction, which stores the value in register SB into the location in Memory M specified by the address from register SA. The fourteenth opcode, 1001100, is add immediate (ADI), which adds the zero-filled value of the OP field, the rightmost three bits of the instruction, to the contents of register SA and places the result in the register DR.

The sixteenth opcode, 1100001, is the branch on negative (BRN) instruction. The decoding of this instruction causes the value in the register specified by SA to be passed through the Function unit in order to evaluate status bits N and Z. The values N and Z then propagate back to the Control logic, but no register load of the Function unit output occurs. Based on the value of N, the branch is taken or not taken by adding the extended address AD from the instruction to the value in the PC or incrementing the PC, respectively. This is represented by the output action for N shown in Figure 8-20.

From this state machine diagram, the state table for the sequential control circuit can be developed as shown in Table 8-14. The present states are given as abstract state names, and the opcodes and status bits serve as inputs. In the case of the status bits, only those bits that are used in the instruction are specified. By using combinations of bits and multiple status bit patterns, it is possible to specify functions of status bits. Note that many of the entries in Table 8-14 contain Xs, symbolizing "don't

☐ **TABLE 8-14**
State Table for Two-Cycle Instructions

	Inputs		Next State						Outputs								Comments
State	Opcode	VCNZ		IL	PS	DX	AX	BX	MB	FS	MD	RW	MM	MW		
INF	XXXXXXX	XXXX	EX0	1	00	XXXX	XXXX	XXXX	X	XXXX	X	0	1	0		$IR \leftarrow M[PC]$
EX0	0000000	XXXX	INF	0	01	0XXX	0XXX	XXXX	X	0000	0	1	X	0	MOVA	$R[DR] \leftarrow R[SA]$*
EX0	0000001	XXXX	INF	0	01	0XXX	0XXX	XXXX	X	0001	0	1	X	0	INC	$R[DR] \leftarrow R[SA]+1$*
EX0	0000010	XXXX	INF	0	01	0XXX	0XXX	0XXX	0	0010	0	1	X	0	ADD	$R[DR] \leftarrow R[SA] + R[SB]$*
EX0	0000101	XXXX	INF	0	01	0XXX	0XXX	0XXX	0	0101	0	1	X	0	SUB	$R[DR] \leftarrow R[SA] + \overline{R[SB]} + 1$*
EX0	0000110	XXXX	INF	0	01	0XXX	0XXX	XXXX	X	0110	0	1	X	0	DEC	$R[DR] \leftarrow R[SA] + (-1)$*
EX0	0001000	XXXX	INF	0	01	0XXX	0XXX	0XXX	0	1000	0	1	X	0	AND	$R[DR] \leftarrow R[SA] \wedge R[SB]$*
EX0	0001001	XXXX	INF	0	01	0XXX	0XXX	0XXX	0	1001	0	1	X	0	OR	$R[DR] \leftarrow R[SA] \vee R[SB]$*
EX0	0001010	XXXX	INF	0	01	0XXX	0XXX	0XXX	0	1010	0	1	X	0	XOR	$R[DR] \leftarrow R[SA] \oplus R[SB]$*
EX0	0001011	XXXX	INF	0	01	0XXX	0XXX	XXXX	X	1011	0	1	X	0	NOT	$R[DR] \leftarrow \overline{R[SA]}$*
EX0	0001100	XXXX	INF	0	01	0XXX	XXXX	0XXX	0	1100	0	1	X	0	MOVB	$R[DR] \leftarrow R[SB]$*
EX0	0010000	XXXX	INF	0	01	0XXX	0XXX	XXXX	X	XXXX	1	1	0	0	LD	$R[DR] \leftarrow M[R[SA]]$*
EX0	0100000	XXXX	INF	0	01	XXXX	0XXX	0XXX	0	XXXX	X	0	0	1	ST	$M[R[SA]] \leftarrow R[SB]$*
EX0	1001100	XXXX	INF	0	01	0XXX	XXXX	XXXX	1	1100	0	1	0	0	LDI	$R[DR] \leftarrow$ zf OP*
EX0	1000010	XXXX	INF	0	01	0XXX	0XXX	XXXX	1	0010	0	1	0	0	ADI	$R[DR] \leftarrow R[SA] + $ zf OP*
EX0	1100000	XXX1	INF	0	10	XXXX	0XXX	XXXX	X	0000	X	0	X	0	BRZ	$PC \leftarrow PC + $ se AD
EX0	1100000	XXX0	INF	0	01	XXXX	0XXX	XXXX	X	0000	X	0	X	0	BRZ	$PC \leftarrow PC + 1$
EX0	1100001	XX1X	INF	0	10	XXXX	0XXX	XXXX	X	0000	X	0	X	0	BRN	$PC \leftarrow PC + $se AD
EX0	1100001	XX0X	INF	0	01	XXXX	0XXX	XXXX	X	0000	X	0	X	0	BRN	$PC \leftarrow PC + 1$
EX0	1110000	XXXX	INF	0	11	XXXX	0XXX	XXXX	X	0000	X	0	X	0	JMP	$PC \leftarrow R[SA]$

* For this state and input combination, $PC \leftarrow PC+1$ also occurs.

cares." For these entries, the input or resource is not used in the given microoperation, or the specific bits of the code that are X are not used for controlling it. It is a useful exercise to determine how each of the entries in Table 8-14 is obtained, based on Tables 8-12, 8-13, and Figure 8-20.

It is interesting to briefly compare the timing of the execution of instructions in this organization with that for the single-cycle computer. Each instruction requires two clock cycles to fetch and execute, compared with one clock cycle for the single-cycle computer. Because the very long delay path from the *PC* through the Instruction memory, Instruction decoder, datapath, and branch control is broken up by the instruction register, the clock periods are somewhat shorter. Nevertheless, due to setup time requirements for the added flip-flops in the *IR* and a potential imbalance in delays for the various paths through the circuit, the overall time taken to execute an instruction could be just as long as or longer than in the single-cycle computer. So what is the benefit of this organization, other than ability to use a single memory? The next two instructions give the answer.

The first instruction to be added is a "load register indirect" (LRI), with opcode 0010001. In this instruction, the contents of register SA address a word in memory. The word, which is known as an *indirect address*, is then used to address the word in memory that is loaded into register DR. This can be represented symbolically as

$$R[DR] \leftarrow M[M[R[SA]]]$$

The partial state machine diagram for the execution of this instruction is given in Figure 8-21. Following the instruction fetch, the state becomes EX0, the same EX0 used in Figure 8-20. In this state, $R[SA]$ addresses the memory to obtain the indirect address, which is then placed in temporary register $R8$. In the next state, EX1, a new state that is added here, the next memory access occurs with the address from $R8$. The operand obtained is placed in $R[DR]$ to complete the operation, and the *PC* is incremented. The state machine diagram then returns to state INF to fetch the next instruction. The state machine diagram portion for the execution of a given instruction must have the opcode for the instruction appear on all transitions from states that have opcodes for other instructions appearing, since the same states are used by the other instructions for their execution. This applies across all of the partial state machine diagrams for the control unit. Clearly, with two accesses to Memory M, this instruction could not be executed by the single-clock-cycle computer or by using two clock cycles in the multiple-cycle computer. Also, to avoid disturbing the contents of registers $R0$ through $R7$ (except for $R[SA]$), the use of register $R8$ for temporary storage is essential. The LRI instruction requires three clock cycles for its execution. To accomplish the same operation in the single-cycle computer requires two LD instructions, taking two clock cycles. In the multiple-cycle computer, due to two instruction fetches and two data accesses, it would require two LD instructions, but would take four clock cycles. So the LRI instruction gives an improvement in execution time in the latter case.

The final two instructions to be added are "shift right multiple" (SRM) and "shift left multiple" (SLM), with opcodes 0001101 and 0001110, respectively. These two instructions can share most of the microinstruction sequence to be used. SRM specifies that the contents of register SA are to be shifted to the right by the number of positions given by the three bits of the OP field, with the result placed in register DR. The partial state machine diagram for this operation (and for SLM) is given in Figure 8-22. Register $R9$ stores the number of bit positions remaining to be shifted, and the shifting is performed in register $R8$.

Initially, the contents of $R[SA]$ to be shifted is placed in $R8$. As the contents are loaded into $R8$, it passes through the ALU and is checked to see if it is 0 to determine if shifting is needed or not. Note that this check could occur even if $R8$ was not loaded. Likewise, the shift amount being loaded into $R9$ is checked to see whether it is 0, again to determine if shifting is needed or not. If either case is satisfied, the instruction execution is complete, and the state machine flow returns to state INF. Otherwise, a right-shift operation is performed on the contents of register $R8$. $R9$ is decremented and tested to see whether it *will be* 0. If $R9 \neq 0$, then the shift and decrement are repeated. If $R9 = 0$, then the contents of $R8$ have been shifted by the number of bit positions specified by OP, so the result is transferred to $R[DR]$ to complete the instruction execution, and the state machine flow returns to state INF.

If both the operand and the shift amount are nonzero, SRM, including fetch, requires $2s + 4$ clock cycles, where s is the number of positions shifted. The range of clock cycles required, including the instruction fetch, is from 6 to 18. If the same operation were implemented by a program using the right-shift instruction plus increment and branching, then $3s + 3$ instructions would be required, giving $6s + 6$ cycles. The improvement in the required number of clock cycles is $4s + 2$, so 6 to 30 clock cycles are saved in the multiple-cycle computer for a nonzero operand and shift amount. Also, five fewer memory locations are required for storage of the SRM instruction, in contrast to that for the program.

In the state machine diagram in Figure 8-22, the states INF and EX0 are the same as those used for the two-cycle instructions in the state machine diagram in Figure 8-20, and EX1 is the same as used for the LRI instruction in Figure 8-21. Also, implementation of the left-shift multiple operation is shown in Figure 8-22, in which, based on the opcode, the left shift of $R8$ replaces the right shift of $R8$. As a consequence, the logic implementing the states used for implementation of these two instructions can be shared. Further, the logic used for the sequencing of the states can be shared between the SRM and SLM instruction implementations. The state table specification in Table 8-15 is derived by using the information from the state machine diagram in Figure 8-22, and Tables 8-12 and 8-13. The codes are derived from the register transfer and sequencing action described in the comments on the right in the same way that Table 8-14 was derived.

Implementation of the LRI and SRM instructions illustrates the flexibility achieved using multiple-cycle control. Implementation of additional instructions is explored in the problems at the end of the chapter.

8-10 CHAPTER SUMMARY

In the first part of the chapter, the concept of a computer datapath for implementing computer microoperations was introduced. Among the major components of datapaths are register files, buses, arithmetic/logic units (ALUs), and shifters. The control word provides a means of organizing the control of the microoperations performed by the datapath. These concepts were combined to serve as a basis for exploring computers in the remainder of the text.

In the second part of the chapter, control design for programmed systems was introduced by examining two different implementations of basic control units for a

□ TABLE 8-15
State Table for Illustration of Instructions Having Three or More Cycles

State	Inputs Opcode	VCNZ	Next State	L	PS	DX	AX	BX	MB	FS	MD	RW	MM	MW	Comments
EX0	0010001	XXXX	EX1	0	00	1000	0XXX	XXXX	X	0000	1	1	1	X 0	LRI $R8 \leftarrow M[R[SA]]$, → EX1
EX1	0010001	XXXX	INF	0	01	0XXX	1000	XXXX	X	0000	1	1	1	X 0	LRI $R[DR] \leftarrow M[R8]$, → INF*
EX0	0001101	XXX0	EX1	0	00	1000	0XXX	XXXX	X	0000	0	1	1	X 0	SRM $R8 \leftarrow R[SA]$, $\overline{Z}$: → EX1
EX0	0001101	XXX1	INF	0	01	1000	0XXX	XXXX	X	0000	0	1	1	X 0	SRM $R8 \leftarrow R[SA]$, Z: → INF*
EX1	0001101	XXX0	EX2	0	00	1001	XXXX	XXXX	1	1100	0	1	X	0	SRM $R9 \leftarrow$ zf OP, $\overline{Z}$: → EX2
EX1	0001101	XXX1	INF	0	01	1001	XXXX	XXXX	1	1100	0	1	X	0	SRM $R9 \leftarrow$ zf OP, Z: → INF*
EX2	0001101	XXXX	EX3	0	00	1000	XXXX	1000	0	1101	0	1	1	X 0	SRM $R8 \leftarrow$ sr $R8$, → EX3
EX3	0001101	XXX0	EX2	0	00	1001	1001	XXXX	X	0110	0	1	X	0	SRM $R9 \leftarrow R9-1$, $\overline{Z}$: → EX2
EX3	0001101	XXX1	EX4	0	00	1001	1001	XXXX	X	0110	0	1	X	0	SRM $R9 \leftarrow R9-1$, Z: → EX4
EX4	0001101	XXXX	INF	0	01	0XXX	1000	XXXX	X	0000	0	1	X	0	SRM $R[DR] \leftarrow R8$, → INF*
EX0	0001110	XXX0	EX1	0	00	1000	0XXX	XXXX	X	0000	0	1	1	X 0	SLM $R8 \leftarrow R[SA]$, $\overline{Z}$: → EX1
EX0	0001110	XXX1	INF	0	01	1000	0XXX	XXXX	X	0000	0	1	1	X 0	SLM $R8 \leftarrow R[SA]$, Z: → INF*
EX1	0001110	XXX0	EX2	0	00	1001	XXXX	XXXX	1	1100	0	1	X	0	SLM $R9 \leftarrow$ zf OP, $\overline{Z}$: → EX2
EX1	0001110	XXX1	INF	0	01	1001	XXXX	XXXX	1	1100	0	1	X	0	SLM $R9 \leftarrow$ zf OP, Z: → INF*
EX2	0001110	XXXX	EX3	0	00	1000	XXXX	1000	0	0110	0	1	1	X 0	SLM $R8 \leftarrow$ sl $R8$, → EX3
EX3	0001110	XXX0	EX2	0	00	1001	1001	XXXX	X	0110	0	1	X	0	SLM $R9 \leftarrow R9-1$, $\overline{Z}$: → EX2
EX3	0001110	XXX1	EX4	0	00	1001	1001	XXXX	X	0110	0	1	X	0	SLM $R9 \leftarrow R9-1$, Z: → EX4
EX4	0001110	XXXX	INF	0	01	0XXX	1000	XXXX	X	0000	0	1	X	0	SLM $R[DR] \leftarrow R8$, → IF*

*For this state and input combination, $PC \leftarrow PC+1$ also occurs.

simple computer architecture. We introduced the concept of instruction set architectures and defined instruction formats and operations for the simple computer. The first implementation of this computer is capable of executing any instruction in a single clock cycle. Aside from having a program counter and its logic, the control unit of this computer consists of a combinational decoder circuit.

Among the shortcomings of the single-cycle computer are limitations on the complexity of the instructions that can be executed on it, problems with the interface to a single memory, and the relatively low clock frequencies attained. To deal with the first two of these shortcomings, we examined a multiple-cycle version of the simple computer in which a single memory is used and instructions are implemented using two distinct phases: instruction fetch and instruction execution. The remaining issue of long clock cycles is dealt with in Chapter 10 by introducing pipelined datapaths and control.

REFERENCES

1. HENNESSY, J. L. AND D. A. PATTERSON. *Computer Architecture: A Quantitative Approach*, 5th ed. Amsterdam: Elsevier, 2011.

2. MANO, M. M. *Computer Engineering: Hardware Design*. Englewood Cliffs, NJ: Prentice Hall, 1988.

3. MANO, M. M. *Computer System Architecture*, 3rd ed. Englewood Cliffs, NJ: Prentice Hall, 1993.

4. PATTERSON, D. A. AND J. L. HENNESSY. *Computer Organization and Design: The Hardware/Software Interface*, 5th ed. Amsterdam: Elsevier, 2013.

PROBLEMS

The plus (+) indicates a more advanced problem and the asterisk (*) indicates that a solution is available on the Companion Website for the text.

8-1. A datapath similar to the one in Figure 8-1 has 64 registers. How many selection lines are needed for each set of multiplexers and for the decoder?

8-2. *Given an 8-bit ALU with outputs F_7 through F_0 and available carries C_8 and C_7, show the logic circuit for generating the signals for the four status bits N (sign), Z (zero), V (overflow), and C (carry).

8-3. *Design an arithmetic circuit with two selection variables S_1 and S_0 and two n-bit data inputs A and B. The circuit generates the following eight arithmetic operations in conjunction with carry C_{in}:

S_1	S_0	$C_{in} = 0$	$C_{in} = 1$
0	0	$F = A + B$ (add)	$F = A + \overline{B} + 1$ (subtract A – B)
0	1	$F = \overline{A} + B$	$F = \overline{A} + B + 1$ (subtract B – A)
1	0	$F = A - 1$ (decrement)	$F = A + 1$ (increment)
1	1	$F = \overline{A}$ (1s complement)	$F = \overline{A} + 1$ (2s complement)

Draw the logic diagram for the two least significant bits of the arithmetic circuit.

8-4. *Design a 4-bit arithmetic circuit, with two selection variables S_1 and S_0, that generates the arithmetic operations in the following table. Draw the logic diagram for a typical single-bit stage and the LSB stage.

$S_1 S_0$	$C_{in} = 0$	$C_{in} = 1$
0 0	$F = A + B$ (add)	$F = A + B + 1$
0 1	$F = A$ (transfer)	$F = A + 1$ (increment)
1 0	$F = \bar{B}$ (complement)	$F = \bar{B} + 1$ (negate)
1 1	$F = A + \bar{B}$	$F = A + \bar{B} + 1$ (subtract)

8-5. Draw the diagram of an ALU in which there are three bits allocated for selecting the following operations, for two operands. The operations are below. Draw a simple block diagram. Also, consider what should be done in the case an invalid combination of selection bits appears.

(a) Add

(b) Subtract

(c) Logical OR

(d) Logical AND

(e) Logical XOR

8-6. *Design one bit of a digital circuit that performs the four logic operations of exclusive-OR, exclusive-NOR, NOR, and NAND on register operands A and B with the result to be loaded into register A. Use two selection variables.

(a) Using a Karnaugh map, design minimum logic for one typical stage, and show the logic diagram.

(b) Repeat (a), trying different assignments of the selection codes to the four operations to see whether the logic for the stage can be simplified further.

8-7. +Design an ALU that performs the following operations:

$$A + B \qquad \text{sr } A$$
$$A + \bar{B} + 1 \qquad A \vee B$$
$$\bar{B} \qquad \text{sl } A$$
$$\bar{B} + 1 \qquad A \wedge B$$

Give the result of your design as the logic diagram for a single stage of the ALU. Your design should have one carry line to the left and one carry line to the right between stages and three selection bits. If you have access to logic optimization software, apply it to the design to obtain reduced logic. Model your ALU in an HDL and verify its operation by simulation.

8-8. *Find the output Y of the 4-bit barrel shifter in Figure 8-9 for each of the following bit patterns applied to $S_1, S_0, D_3, D_2, D_1,$ and D_0:

(a) 110101   **(b)** 101011

(c) 011010   **(d)** 001101

8-9. Specify the 16-bit control word that must be applied to the datapath of Figure 8-11 to implement each of the following microoperations:

(a) $R3 \leftarrow$ Data in
(b) $R4 \leftarrow 0$
(c) $R1 \leftarrow$ sr $R4$
(d) $R3 \leftarrow R3 + 1$
(e) $R2 \leftarrow$ sl $R2$
(f) $R1 \leftarrow R2 \oplus R4$
(g) $R7 \leftarrow R1 + R3$
(h) $R4 \leftarrow R5 -$ Constant in

8-10. *Given the following 16-bit control words for the datapath of Figure 8-11, determine (a) the microoperation that is executed and (b) the change in the contents of the register for each control word (assume that the registers are 8-bit registers and that, before the execution of a control word, they contain the value of their number (e.g., register $R5$ contains 05 in hexadecimal)). Assume that Constant in has value 6 and Data in has value 1B, both in hexadecimal.

(a) 101 100 101 0 1000 0 1
(b) 110 010 100 0 0101 0 1
(c) 101 110 000 0 1100 0 1
(d) 101 000 000 0 0000 0 1
(e) 100 100 000 1 1101 0 1
(f) 011 000 000 0 0000 1 1

8-11. Given the sequence of 16-bit control words below for the datapath in Figure 8-11 and the initial ASCII character codes in 8-bit registers, simulate the datapath to determine the alphanumeric characters in the registers after the execution of the sequence. The result is a scrambled word: what is it?

011 011 001 0 0010 0 1	R0	00000000
100 100 001 0 1001 0 1	R1	00100000
101 101 001 0 1010 0 1	R2	01000100
001 001 000 0 1011 0 1	R3	01000111
001 001 000 0 0001 0 1	R4	01010100
110 110 001 0 0101 0 1	R5	01001100
111 111 001 0 0101 0 1	R6	01000001
001 111 000 0 0000 0 1	R7	01001001

8-12. A RISC computer has a 32-bit instruction format consisting of the following:

(1) Opcode: 8 bits
(2) 3 register fields, each of 4 bits
(3) A 4 bit field for "condition"

The remaining bits are for information pertaining to the processor.

(a) What is the maximum number of operations possible?
(b) How many combinations of three registers are possible?
(c) How many conditions can be accommodated?
(d) How many registers are possible?

8-13. *A digital computer has a memory unit with a 32-bit instruction and a register file with 64 registers. The instruction set consists of 130 different operations. There is only one type of instruction format, with an opcode part, a register file address, and an immediate operand part. Each instruction is stored in one word of memory.

(a) How many bits are needed for the opcode part of the instruction?

(b) How many bits are left for the immediate part of the instruction?

(c) If the immediate operand is used as an unsigned address to memory, what is the maximum number of words that can be addressed in memory?

(d) What are the largest and the smallest algebraic values of signed 2s complement binary numbers that can be accommodated as an immediate operand?

8-14. A RISC processor has the following format for its branch instruction:

31   28 27 26 25 24   23

COND	1 0 1	L	Signed-immed_24

The figure shows the offset of the target to use a signed immediate number with 24 bits. What is the range to which control can branch to?

8-15. The single-cycle computer in Figure 8-15 executes the five instructions described by the register transfers in the table that follows.

(a) Complete the following table, giving the binary instruction decoder outputs from Figure 8-16 during execution of each of the instructions:

Instruction—Register Transfer	DA	AA	BA	BA	FS	MD	RW	MW	PL	JB
$R[0] \leftarrow R[7] \oplus R[3]$										
$R[1] \leftarrow M[R[4]]$										
$R[2] \leftarrow R[5]+2$										
$R[3] \leftarrow$ sl $R[6]$										
if $(R([4] = 0)$ $PC \leftarrow PC+$se AD else $PC \leftarrow PC+1$										

(b) Complete the following table, giving the instruction in binary for the single-cycle computer that executes the register transfer (if any field is not used, give it the value 0):

Instruction—Register Transfer	Opcode	DR	SA	SB or Operand
$R[0] \leftarrow R[7]+R[6]$				
$R[1] \leftarrow R[5]-1$				
$R[2] \leftarrow$ sl $R[4]$				
$R[3] \leftarrow \overline{R[3]}$				
$R[4] \leftarrow R[2] \lor R[1]$				

8-16. Using the information in the truth table in Table 8-10, verify that the design for the single-bit outputs in the decoder in Figure 8-16 is correct.

8-17. Manually simulate the single-cycle computer in Figure 8-15 for the following sequence of instructions, assuming that each register initially contains contents equal to its index (i.e., $R0$ contains 0, $R1$ contains 1, and so on):

ADD R0, R1, R2
SUB R3, R4, R5
SUB R6, R7, R0
ADD R0, R0, R3
SUB R0, R0, R6
ST R7, R0
LD R7, R6
ADI R0, R6, 2
ADI R3, R6, 3

Give (a) the binary value of the instruction on the current line of the results and (b) the contents of any register changed by the instruction, or the location and contents of any memory location changed by the instruction on the next line of the results. The results are positioned in this fashion because the new values do not appear in a register or memory, due to the execution of an instruction, until after a positive clock edge has occurred.

8-18. Some computers have different memory areas for storing data and instructions. The single cycle computer described here is one such computer. Obviously there are advantages as well as disadvantages of such a system.

(a) What is the name of such a type of computer architecture?

(b) What is the basic disadvantage of such a system?

(c) What is the advantage of using such a memory architecture?

8-19. List the control logic state table entries for the multiple-cycle computer (see Tables 8-12, 8-13 and 8-15) that implement the following register transfer statements. Assume that in all cases the present state is EX0. If an opcode is needed, use a symbolic name based on the problem part—e.g., for part (a), opcode_a.

(a) $R3 \leftarrow R7 - R2, \rightarrow EX1$. Assume DR = 3, SA = 7, SB = 2.

(b) $R8 \leftarrow$ sr $R8, \rightarrow INF$. Assume DR = 5, SB = 5.

(c) if $(Z = 0)$ then $(PC \rightarrow PC +$ se $AD, \rightarrow INF)$ else $(PC \rightarrow PC +1, \rightarrow INF)$.

(d) $R6 \leftarrow R6, C \leftarrow 0, \rightarrow INF$. Assume DR = SA = 6.

8-20. **(a)** What is the arithmetic operation that is the result of logical shifting left?

(b) Show what happens when the 0000 0000 1011 1000 is shifted left four times?

(c) What will the result if the above data is shifted right twice?

8-21. +In the SRM and SLM instructions, both the operand $R[SA]$ and the shift amount field OP are checked to see if either is 0 before the shifts begin.

(a) Redraw the state machine diagram for these operations with these checks removed.

(b) Use the original diagram and the new diagram to compare the number of clock cycles required for values of OP equal to 0 through 7. Assume that the probability of each OP value for 1 through 6 is 1/8, for 0 is 1/4, and for 7 is 0. Assume that the likelihood of a 0 operand is 1/8. Perform calculations to determine the best implementation (with checks or without checks) based on the given probability information and comparative number of clock cycles for the two implementations. Provide a convincing argument for your selected answer.

8-22. A new instruction is to be defined for the multiple-cycle computer with opcode 0010001. The instruction implements the register transfer

$$R[DR] \leftarrow R[SB] + M[R[SA]]$$

Find the state machine diagram for implementing the instruction, assuming that 0010001 is the opcode. Form the part of the control state table that implements this instruction.

8-23. Repeat Problem 8-22 for the two instructions: Add and check OV (AOV), described by the register transfer

$$R[DR] \leftarrow R[SA] + R[SB], \quad V{:}R8 \leftarrow 1, \quad \overline{V}{:}R8 \leftarrow 0$$

and branch on overflow (BRV), described by the register transfer

$$R8 \leftarrow R8, \quad V{:} PC \leftarrow PC + \text{se } AD, \quad V{:} PC \leftarrow PC + 1$$

The opcode for AOV is 1000101 and for BRV is 1000110. Note that register $R8$ is used as a "status" register that stores the overflow result V for the previous operation. All of the values N, Z, C and V could be stored in $R8$ to give a complete status on the prior arithmetic or logic operation.

8-24. In a multiple-cycle computer, any instruction can take more than one cycle. Delve into the different kinds of instructions available in such computers and identify the different activities for each of these operations:

(a) Fetching an opcode from memory

(b) Fetching the operand from memory

(c) Adding the content of two registers.

(d) Storing the result in memory.

8-25. The multiple-cycle computer has the capacity for multiple register loading. Take an example of 8 registers being loaded with data from 8 locations in memory. Compare this to a case of multiple instructions for loading into the 8 registers. Does this reduce the execution time to one eighth of the latter case? Substantiate with logical reasons.

8-26. +A new instruction, SMR (Store Multiple Registers), with symbolic opcode name SMR, is to be implemented for the multiple-cycle computer. The instruction stores the contents of eight registers in eight consecutive memory locations. Register $R[SA]$ specifies the address in memory M to which the first register R[SB] is to be stored. The registers to be stored are R[SB], R[(SB+1) modulo 8], . . ., R[(SB+7)modulo 8] in Memory M addresses R[SA], R[SA] +1, . . ., R[SA]+7. Design this instruction presenting your final results in the form shown in Table 8-15. [*Hint*: In order to address all eight registers, it is necessary to provide eight values of SB in the Instruction Register. Since the Instruction Register can only be loaded from memory, these "instructions" must be placed in memory temporarily during the instruction execution and loaded into the IR as data without using the usual instruction fetch.]

8-27. Using the mnemonics for the single-cycle computer, write instructions to perform the following simple operations. Assume the following:

The registers available are R1 and R2. Data memory location 120 has content 45, and address 121 has content 23. Registers R3 and R4 have the address of these data, i.e., R3 = 121 and R4 = 23.

(a) Load the two numbers in memory locations into two registers.

(b) Add the number 20 to the content of one register.

(c) Add the sum to the content of the other register.

(d) Store the sum into a memory location.

CHAPTER

9

INSTRUCTION SET ARCHITECTURE

U p to this point, much of what we have studied has focused on digital system design, with computer components serving as examples. In this chapter, we will study more specialized material, dealing with instruction set architecture for general-purpose computers. We will examine the operations that the instructions perform and focus particularly on how the operands are obtained and where the results are stored. We will contrast two distinct classes of architectures: reduced instruction set computers (RISCs) and complex instruction set computers (CISCs). We will classify elementary instructions into three categories: data transfer, data manipulation, and program control. In each of these categories, we elaborate on typical elementary instructions.

Central to the material presented here are the general-purpose parts of the generic computer at the beginning of Chapter 1, including the central processing unit (CPU) and the accompanying floating-point unit (FPU). Since a small general-purpose microprocessor may be present for controlling keyboard and monitor functions, these components are also involved. Aside from addressing used to access memory and I/O components, the concepts studied apply less to other areas of the computer. Increasingly, however, small CPUs have appeared more frequently in the I/O components.

9-1 COMPUTER ARCHITECTURE CONCEPTS

The binary language in which instructions are defined and stored in memory is referred to as *machine language*. A symbolic language that replaces binary opcodes and addresses with symbolic names and that provides other features helpful to the programmer is referred to as *assembly language*. The logical structure of computers is normally described in assembly-language reference manuals. Such manuals explain various internal elements of the computer that are of interest to the programmer, such as processor registers. The manuals list all hardware-implemented instructions, specify the symbolic names and binary code format of the instructions, and provide a precise definition of each instruction. In the past, this information represented the *architecture* of the computer. A computer was composed of its architecture, plus a specific *implementation* of that architecture. The implementation was separated into two parts: the organization and the hardware. The *organization* consists of structures such as datapaths, control units, memories, and the buses that interconnect them. *Hardware* refers to the logic, the electronic technologies employed, and the various physical design aspects of the computer.

As computer designers pushed for higher and higher performance, and as increasingly more of the computer resided within a single IC, the relationships among architecture, organization, and hardware became so intertwined that a more integrated viewpoint became necessary. According to this new viewpoint, architecture as previously defined is more restrictively called *instruction set architecture* (*ISA*), the structure of a particular hardware implementation of the ISA is referred to as the *microarchitecture* or *computer organization*, and the term *architecture* is used to encompass the whole of the computer, including instruction set architecture, organization, and hardware. This unified view enables intelligent design trade-offs to be made that are apparent only in a tightly coupled design process. These trade-offs have the potential for producing better computer designs.

In this chapter, we focus on instruction set architecture. In the next, we will look at two distinct instruction set architectures, with a focus on implementation using two somewhat different architectures.

A computer usually has a variety of instructions and multiple instruction formats. It is the function of the control unit to decode each instruction and provide the control signals needed to process it. Simple examples of instructions and instruction formats were presented in Section 8-7. We now expand this presentation by introducing typical instructions found in commercial general-purpose computers. We also investigate the various instruction formats that may be encountered in a typical computer, with an emphasis on the addressing of operands. The format of an instruction is depicted in a rectangular box symbolizing the bits of the binary instruction. The bits are divided into groups called *fields*. The following are typical fields found in instruction formats:

1. An *opcode field*, which specifies the operation to be performed.
2. An *address field*, which provides either a memory address or an address that selects a processor register.
3. A *mode field*, which specifies the way the address field is to be interpreted.

Other special fields are sometimes employed under certain circumstances—for example, a field that gives the number of positions to shift in a shift-type instruction or an operand field in an immediate operand instruction.

Basic Computer Operation Cycle

In order to comprehend the various addressing concepts to be presented in the next two sections, we need to understand the basic operation cycle of the computer. The computer's control unit is designed to execute each instruction of a program in the following sequence of steps:

1. Fetch the instruction from memory into the instruction register in the control unit.
2. Decode the instruction.
3. Locate the operands used by the instruction.
4. Fetch operands from memory (if necessary).
5. Execute the operation in processor registers.
6. Store the results in the proper place.
7. Go back to Step 1 to fetch the next instruction.

As explained in Section 8-7, a register in the computer called the *program counter* (*PC*) keeps track of the instructions in the program stored in memory. The *PC* holds the address of the instruction to be executed next and is incremented each time a word is read from the program in memory. The decoding done in Step 2 determines the operation to be performed and the addressing mode or modes of the instruction. The operands in Step 3 are located from the addressing modes and the address fields of the instruction. The computer executes the instruction, storing the result, and returns to Step 1 to fetch the next instruction in sequence.

Register Set

The *register set* consists of all registers in the CPU that are accessible to the programmer. These registers are typically those mentioned in assembly-language programming reference manuals. In the simple CPUs we have dealt with so far, the register set has consisted of the programmer-accessible portion of the register file and the *PC*. The CPUs can also contain other registers, such as the instruction register, registers in the register file that are accessible only to hardware controls and/or microprograms, and pipeline registers. These registers, however, are not directly accessible to the programmer and, as a consequence, are not a part of the register set, which represents the stored information in the CPU that is visible to the programmer through the instructions. Thus, the register set has a considerable influence on instruction set architecture.

The register set for a realistic CPU is quite complex. In this chapter, we add two registers to the set we have used thus far: the *processor status register* (*PSR*) and the *stack pointer* (*SP*). The processor status register contains flip-flops that are selectively set by status values $C, N, V,$ and Z from the ALU and shifter. These stored status bits are used to make decisions that determine the program flow, based on ALU results, shifter results, or the contents of registers. The stored status bits in the processor status register are also referred to as the *condition codes* or the *flags*. Additional bits in the *PSR* will be discussed when we cover associated concepts in this chapter.

9-2 OPERAND ADDRESSING

Consider an instruction such as ADD, which specifies the addition of two operands to produce a result. Suppose that the result of the addition is treated as just another operand. Then the ADD instruction has three operands: the addend, the augend, and the result. An operand residing in memory is specified by its address. An operand residing in a processor register is specified by a register address, a binary code of n bits that specifies one of at most 2^n registers in the register file. Thus, a computer with 16 processor registers, say, $R0$ through $R15$, has in its instructions one or more register address fields of four bits. The binary code 0101, for example, designates register $R5$.

Some operands, however, are not explicitly addressed, because their location is specified either by the opcode of the instruction or by an address assigned to one of the other operands. In such a case, we say that the operand has an *implied address*. If the address is implied, then there is no need for a memory or register address field for the operand in the instruction. On the other hand, if an operand has an address in the instruction, then we say that the operand is explicitly addressed or has an *explicit address*.

The number of operands explicitly addressed for a data-manipulation operation such as ADD is an important factor in defining the instruction set architecture for a computer. An additional factor is the number of such operands that can be explicitly addressed in memory by the instruction. These two factors are so important in defining the nature of instructions that they act a means of distinguishing different instruction set architectures. They also govern the length of computer instructions.

We begin by illustrating simple programs with different numbers of explicitly addressed operands per instruction. Since the explicitly addressed operands have up to three memory or register addresses per instruction, we label the instructions as having three, two, one, or zero addresses. Note that, of the three operands needed for an instruction such as ADD, the addresses of all operands not having an address in the instruction are implied.

To illustrate the influence of the number of operands on computer programs, we will evaluate the arithmetic statement

$$X = (A + B)(C + D)$$

using three, two, one, and zero address instructions. We assume that the operands are in memory addresses symbolized by the letters A, B, C, and D and must not be changed by the program. The result is to be stored in memory at a location with address X. The initial arithmetic operations to be used in the instructions are addition, subtraction, and multiplication, with mnemonics ADD, SUB, and MUL, respectively. Further, three operations needed to transfer data during the evaluation are move, load, and store, denoted by MOVE, LD, and ST, respectively. LD moves an operand from memory to a register and ST from a register to memory. Depending on the addresses permitted, MOVE can transfer data between registers, between memory locations, or from memory to register or register to memory.

Three-Address Instructions

A program that evaluates $X = (A + B)(C + D)$ using three-address instructions is as follows (a register transfer statement is shown for each instruction):

$$\begin{array}{ll} \text{ADD T1, A, B} & M[T1] \leftarrow M[A] + M[B] \\ \text{ADD T2, C, D} & M[T2] \leftarrow M[C] + M[D] \\ \text{MUL X, T1, T2} & M[X] \leftarrow M[T1] \times M[T2] \end{array}$$

The symbol $M[A]$ denotes the operand stored in memory at the address symbolized by A. The symbol $\times$ designates multiplication. T1 and T2 are temporary storage locations in memory.

This same program can use registers as the temporary storage locations:

$$\begin{array}{ll} \text{ADD R1, A, B} & R1 \leftarrow M[A] + M[B] \\ \text{ADD R2, C, D} & R2 \leftarrow M[C] + M[D] \\ \text{MUL X, R1, R2} & M[X] \leftarrow R1 \times R2 \end{array}$$

Use of registers reduces the data memory accesses required from nine to five. An advantage of the three-address format is that it results in short programs for evaluating expressions. A disadvantage is that the binary-coded instructions require more bits to specify three addresses, particularly if they are memory addresses.

Two-Address Instructions

For two-address instructions, each address field can again specify either a possible register or a memory address. The first operand address listed in the symbolic instruction also serves as the implied address to which the result of the operation is transferred. The program is as follows:

$$\begin{array}{ll} \text{MOVE T1, A} & M[T1] \leftarrow M[A] \\ \text{ADD T1, B} & M[T1] \leftarrow M[T1] + M[B] \\ \text{MOVE X, C} & M[X] \leftarrow M[C] \\ \text{ADD X, D} & M[X] \leftarrow M[X] + M[D] \\ \text{MUL X, T1} & M[X] \leftarrow M[X] \times M[T1] \end{array}$$

If a temporary storage register R1 is available, it can replace T1. Note that this program takes five instructions instead of the three used by the three-address instruction program.

One-Address Instructions

To perform instructions such as ADD, a computer with one-address instructions uses an implied address—such as a register called an *accumulator*, *ACC*—for obtaining one of the operands and as the location of the result. The program to evaluate the arithmetic statement is as follows:

$$
\begin{array}{lll}
\text{LD} & \text{A} & ACC \leftarrow M[A] \\
\text{ADD} & \text{B} & ACC \leftarrow ACC + M[B] \\
\text{ST} & \text{X} & M[X] \leftarrow ACC \\
\text{LD} & \text{C} & ACC \leftarrow M[C] \\
\text{ADD} & \text{D} & ACC \leftarrow ACC + M[D] \\
\text{MUL} & \text{X} & ACC \leftarrow ACC \times M[X] \\
\text{ST} & \text{X} & M[X] \leftarrow ACC \\
\end{array}
$$

All operations are done between the *ACC* register and a memory operand. In this case, the number of instructions in the program has increased to seven and the number of memory data accesses is also seven.

Zero-Address Instructions

To perform an ADD instruction with zero addresses, all three addresses in the instruction must be implied. A conventional way of achieving this goal is to use a *stack*, which is a mechanism or structure that stores information such that the item stored last is the first retrieved. Because of its "last-in, first-out" nature, a stack is also called a *last-in, first-out* (*LIFO*) queue. The operation of a computer stack is analogous to that of a stack of trays or plates, in which the last tray placed on top of the stack is the first to be taken off. Data-manipulation operations such as ADD are performed on the stack. The word at the top of the stack is referred to as TOS. The word below it is TOS_{-1}. When one or more words are used as operands for an operation, they are removed from the stack. The word below them then becomes the new TOS. When a resulting word is produced, it is placed on the stack and becomes the new TOS. Thus, TOS and a few locations below it are the implied addresses for operands, and TOS is the implied address for the result. For example, the instruction that specifies an addition is simply

ADD

The resulting register transfer action is $TOS \leftarrow TOS + TOS_{-1}$. Thus, there are no registers or register addresses used for data-manipulation instructions in a stack architecture. Memory addressing, however, is used in such architectures for data transfers. For instance, the instruction

PUSH X

results in $TOS \leftarrow M[X]$, a transfer of the word in address X in memory to the top of the stack. A corresponding operation,

$$POP\ X$$

results in $M[X] \leftarrow TOS$, a transfer of the entry at the top of the stack to address X in memory.

The program for evaluating the sample arithmetic statement for the zero-address situation is as follows:

PUSH	A	$TOS \leftarrow M[A]$
PUSH	B	$TOS \leftarrow M[B]$
ADD		$TOS \leftarrow TOS + TOS_{-1}$
PUSH	C	$TOS \leftarrow M[C]$
PUSH	D	$TOS \leftarrow M[D]$
ADD		$TOS \leftarrow TOS + TOS_{-1}$
MUL		$TOS \leftarrow TOS \times TOS_{-1}$
POP	X	$M[X] \leftarrow TOS$

This program requires eight instructions—one more than the number required by the previous one-address program. However, it uses addressed memory locations or registers only for PUSH and POP and not to execute data-manipulation instructions involving ADD and MUL. Note that memory data accesses may be necessary, however, depending upon the stack implementation. Often, stacks utilize a fixed number of registers near the top of the stack. If a given program can be executed only within these stack locations, memory data accesses are necessary for fetching the initial operands and storing the final result only. But, if the program requires more temporary, intermediate storage, additional data accesses to memory are required.

Addressing Architectures

The programs just presented change if the number of addresses to the memory in the instructions is restricted or if the memory addresses are restricted to specific instructions. These restrictions, combined with the number of operands addressed, define addressing architectures. We can illustrate such architectures with the evaluation of an arithmetic statement in a three-address architecture that has all of the accesses to memory. Such an addressing scheme is called a *memory-to-memory architecture*. This architecture has only control registers, such as the program counter in the CPU. All operands come directly from memory, and all results are sent directly to memory. The formats of data transfer and manipulation instructions contain from one to three address fields, all of which are used for memory addresses. For the previous example, three instructions are required, but if an extra word must appear in the instruction for each memory address, then up to four memory reads are required to fetch each instruction. Including the fetching of operands and storing of results, the program to perform the arithmetic operation would require 21 accesses to memory. If memory accesses take more than one clock cycle, the execution time would be in excess of 21 clock periods. Thus, even though the instruction count is low, the execution time is potentially high. Also, providing the capability for all operations to access memory increases the complexity of the control structures and may lengthen the clock cycle. Thus, this memory-to-memory architecture is typically not used in new designs.

In contrast, the three-address *register-to-register* or *load/store architecture*, which allows only one memory address and restricts its use to load and store types of instructions, is typical in modern processors. Such an architecture requires a sizeable register file, since all data manipulation instructions use register operands. With this architecture, the program to evaluate the sample arithmetic statement is as follows:

$$
\begin{array}{lll}
\text{LD} & \text{R1, A} & R1 \leftarrow M[A] \\
\text{LD} & \text{R2, B} & R2 \leftarrow M[B] \\
\text{ADD} & \text{R3, R1, R2} & R3 \leftarrow R1 + R2 \\
\text{LD} & \text{R1, C} & R1 \leftarrow M[C] \\
\text{LD} & \text{R2, D} & R2 \leftarrow M[D] \\
\text{ADD} & \text{R1, R1, R2} & R1 \leftarrow R1 + R2 \\
\text{MUL} & \text{R1, R1, R3} & R1 \leftarrow R1 \times R3 \\
\text{ST} & \text{X, R1} & M[X] \leftarrow R1 \\
\end{array}
$$

Note that the instruction count increases to eight compared to three for the three-address, memory-to-memory case. Note also that the operations are the same as those for the stack case, except for the need for register addresses. By using registers, the number of accesses to memory for instructions, addresses, and operands is reduced from 21 to 18. If addresses can be obtained from registers instead of memory, as discussed in the next section, this number can be further reduced.

Variations on the previous two addressing architectures include three-address instructions and two-address instructions with one or two of the addresses to memory. The program lengths and number of memory accesses tend to be intermediate between the previous two architectures. An example of a two-address instruction with a single memory address allowed is

$$
\text{ADD} \quad \text{R1,A} \quad R1 \leftarrow R1 + M[A]
$$

This *register-memory* type of architecture remains common among the current instruction set architectures, primarily to provide compatibility with older software using a specific architecture.

The program with one-address instructions illustrated previously gives the *single-accumulator architecture*. Since this architecture has no register file, its single address is for accessing memory. It requires 21 accesses to memory to evaluate the sample arithmetic statement. In more complex programs, significant additional memory accesses would be needed for temporary storage locations in memory. Because of its large number of memory accesses, this architecture is inefficient and consequently, is restricted to use in CPUs for simple, low-cost applications that do not require high performance.

The zero-address instruction case using a stack supports the concept of a *stack architecture*. Data-manipulation instructions such as ADD use no address, since they are performed on the top few elements of the stack. Single memory-address load and store operations, as shown in the program to evaluate the sample arithmetic statement, are used for data transfer. Since most of the stack is located in memory, as discussed earlier, one or more hidden memory accesses may be required for each stack operation. As register-register and load/store architectures have made strong performance advances, the high frequency of memory accesses in stack architectures has made them unattractive. However, stack architectures have begun to borrow technological advances from these other architectures. These architectures store substantial numbers of stack locations in the processor chip and handle transfers between these locations and the memory transparently. Stack architectures are particularly useful for rapid interpretation of high-level language programs in which the intermediate code representation uses stack operations.

Stack architectures are compatible with a very efficient approach to expression processing which uses postfix notation rather than the traditional infix notation to which we are accustomed. The infix expression

$$(A + B) \times C + (D \times E)$$

with the operators between the operands can be written as the postfix expression

$$A \ B + C \times D E \times +$$

Postfix notation is called reverse Polish notation (RPN), honoring the Polish mathematician Jan Lukasiewicz, who proposed prefix (the reverse of postfix) notation; prefix was also known as Polish notation.

Conversion of $(A + B) \times C + (D \times E)$ to RPN can be achieved graphically, as shown in Figure 9-1. When the path shown traversing the graph passes a

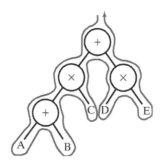

□ **FIGURE 9-1**
Graph for Example of Conversion from Infix to RPN

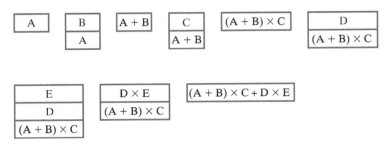

☐ **FIGURE 9-2**
Stack Activity for Execution of Example Stack Program

variable, that variable is entered into the RPN expression. When the path passes an operation for the final time, the operation is entered into the RPN expression.

It is very easy to develop a program for an RPN expression. Whenever a variable is encountered, it is pushed onto the stack. Whenever an operation is encountered, it is executed on the implicit address TOS, or addresses TOS and TOS_{-1}, with the result placed in the new TOS. The program for the example RPN expression is

```
PUSH A
PUSH B
ADD
PUSH C
MUL
PUSH D
PUSH E
MUL
ADD
```

The execution of the program is illustrated by the successive stack states shown in Figure 9-2. As an operand is pushed on the stack, the stack grows by one stack location. When an operation is performed, the operand in the TOS is popped off and temporarily stored in a register. The operation is applied to the stored operand and the new TOS operand, and the result replaces the TOS operand.

9-3 ADDRESSING MODES

The operation field of an instruction specifies the operation to be performed. This operation must be executed on data stored in computer registers or memory words. How the operands are selected during program execution is dependent on the addressing mode of the instruction. The addressing mode specifies a rule for interpreting or modifying the address field of the instruction before the operand is actually referenced. The address of the operand produced by the application of such a rule is called the *effective address*. Computers use addressing-mode techniques to accommodate one or both of the following provisions:

1. To give programming flexibility to the user via pointers to memory, counters for loop control, indexing of data, and relocation of programs.

2. To reduce the number of bits in the address fields of the instruction.

The availability of various addressing modes gives the experienced programmer the ability to write programs that require fewer instructions. The effect, however, on throughput and execution time must be carefully weighed. For example, the presence of more complex addressing modes may actually result in lower throughput and longer execution time. Also, most machine-executable programs are produced by compilers that often do not use complex addressing modes effectively.

In some computers, the addressing mode of the instruction is specified by a distinct binary code. Other computers use a common binary code that designates both the operation and the addressing mode of the instruction. Instructions may be defined with a variety of addressing modes, and sometimes two or more addressing modes are combined in one instruction.

An example of an instruction format with a distinct addressing-mode field is shown in Figure 9-3. The opcode specifies the operation to be performed. The mode field is used to locate the operands needed for the operation. There may or may not be an address field in the instruction. If there is, it may designate a memory address or a processor register. Moreover, as discussed in the previous section, the instruction may have more than one address field. In that case, each address field is associated with its own particular addressing mode.

Implied Mode

Although most addressing modes modify the address field of the instruction, one mode needs no address field at all: the implied mode. In this mode, the operand is specified implicitly in the definition of the opcode. It is the implied mode that provides the location for the two-operand-plus-result operations when fewer than three addresses are contained in the instruction. For example, the instruction "complement accumulator" is an implied-mode instruction because the operand in the accumulator register is implied in the definition of the instruction. In fact, any instruction that uses an accumulator without a second operand is an implied-mode instruction. For example, data-manipulation instructions in a stack computer, such as ADD, are implied-mode instructions, since the operands are implied to be on top of stack.

Immediate Mode

In the immediate mode, the operand is specified in the instruction itself. In other words, an immediate-mode instruction has an operand field rather than an address

Opcode	Mode	Address or operand

□ **FIGURE 9-3**
Instruction Format with Mode Field

field. The operand field contains the actual operand to be used in conjunction with the operation specified in the instruction. Immediate-mode instructions are useful, for example, for initializing registers to a constant value.

Register and Register-Indirect Modes

Earlier, we mentioned that the address field of the instruction may specify either a memory location or a processor register. When the address field specifies a processor register, the instruction is said to be in the register mode. In this mode, the operands are in registers that reside within the processor of the computer. The particular register is selected by a register address field in the instruction format.

In the register-indirect mode, the instruction specifies a register in the processor whose content gives the address of the operand in memory. In other words, the selected register contains the memory address of the operand, rather than the operand itself. Before using a register-indirect mode instruction, the programmer must ensure that the memory address is available in the processor register. A reference to the register is then equivalent to specifying a memory address. The advantage of register-indirect mode is that the address field of the instruction uses fewer bits to select a register than would have been required to specify a memory address directly.

An autoincrement or autodecrement mode is similar to the register-indirect mode, except that the register is incremented or decremented after (or before) its address value is used to access memory. When the address stored in the register refers to an array of data in memory, it is convenient to increment the register after each access to the array. This can be achieved by using a separate register-increment instruction. However, because it is such a common requirement, some computers incorporate an autoincrement mode that increments the content of the register containing the address after the memory data are accessed.

In the following instruction, an autoincrement mode is used to add the constant value 3 to the elements of an array addressed by register $R1$:

$$\text{ADD} \qquad (R1)+, 3 \qquad M[R1] \leftarrow M[R1]+3, R1 \leftarrow R1+1$$

$R1$ is initialized to the address of the first element in the array. Then the ADD instruction is repeatedly executed until the addition of 3 to all elements of the array has occurred. The register transfer statement accompanying the instruction shows the addition of 3 to the memory location addressed by $R1$ and the incrementing of $R1$ in preparation for the next execution of the ADD on the next element in the array.

Direct Addressing Mode

In the direct addressing mode, the address field of the instruction gives the address of the operand in memory in a data-transfer or data-manipulation instruction. An example of a data-transfer instruction is shown in Figure 9-4. The instruction in memory consists of two words. The first, at address 250, has the opcode for "load to ACC" and a mode field specifying a direct address. The second word of the instruction, at address 251, contains the address field, symbolized by ADRS, and is equal to 500. The PC holds the address of the instruction, which is brought from memory using two

Example Demonstrating Direct Addressing for a Data-Transfer Instruction

memory accesses. Simultaneously with or after the completion of the first access, the
PC is incremented to 251. Then the second access for ADRS occurs and the PC is
again incremented. The execution of the instruction results in the operation

$$ACC \leftarrow M[ADRS]$$

Since ADRS = 500 and M[500] = 800, the *ACC* receives the number 800. After the
instruction is executed, the *PC* holds the number 252, which is the address of the
next instruction in the program.

Now consider a branch-type instruction, as shown in Figure 9-5. If the contents
of *ACC* equal 0, control branches to ADRS; otherwise, the program continues with
the next instruction in sequence. When $ACC = 0$, the branch to address 500 is
accomplished by loading the value of the address field ADRS into the *PC*. Control
then continues with the instruction at address 500. When $ACC \neq 0$, no branch
occurs, and the *PC*, which was incremented twice during the fetch of the instruction,
holds the address 302, the address of the next instruction in sequence.

Sometimes the value given in the address field is the address of the operand,
but sometimes it is just an address from which the address of the operand is calculated. To differentiate among the various addressing modes, it is useful to distinguish
between the address part of the instruction, as given in the address field, and the
address used by the control when executing the instruction. Recall that we refer to
the latter as the effective address.

Indirect Addressing Mode

In the indirect addressing mode, the address field of the instruction gives the address
at which the effective address is stored in memory. The control unit fetches the
instruction from memory and uses the address part to access memory again in order

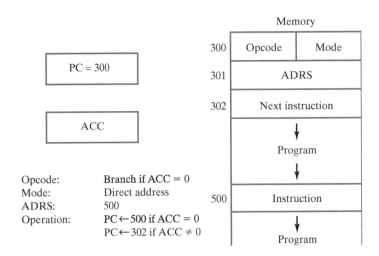

□ **FIGURE 9-5**
Example Demonstrating Direct Addressing in a Branch Instruction

to read the effective address. Consider the instruction "load to *ACC*" given in Figure 9-4. If the mode specifies an indirect address, the effective address is stored in M[ADRS]. Since ADRS = 500 and M[ADRS] = 800, the effective address is 800. This means that the operand loaded into the *ACC* is the one found in memory at address 800 (not shown in the figure).

Relative Addressing Mode

Some addressing modes require that the address field of the instruction be added to the content of a specified register in the CPU in order to evaluate the effective address. Often, the register used is the *PC*. In the relative addressing mode, the effective address is calculated as follows:

Effective address = Address part of the instruction + Contents of *PC*

The address part of the instruction is considered to be a signed number that can be either positive or negative. When this number is added to the contents of the *PC*, the result produces an effective address whose position in memory is relative to the address of the next instruction in the program.

To clarify this with an example, let us assume that the *PC* contains the number 250 and the address part of the instruction contains the number 500, as in Figure 9-6, with the mode field specifying a relative address. The instruction at location 250 is read from memory during the fetch phase of the operation cycle, and the *PC* is incremented by 1 to 251. Since the instruction has a second word, the control unit reads the address field into a control register, and the *PC* is incremented to 252. The computation of the effective address for the relative addressing mode is 252 + 500 = 752. The result is that the operand associated with the instruction is 500 locations away, relative to the location of the next instruction.

Relative addressing is often used in branch-type instructions when the branch address is in a location close to the instruction word. Relative addressing produces

Memory

250	Opcode	Mode
251	ADRS or NBR = 500	
252	Next instruction	
400	700	
500	800	
752	600	
800	300	
900	200	

PC = 250

R1 = 400

ACC

Opcode: Load to ACC

□ **FIGURE 9-6**
Numerical Example for Addressing Modes

more compact instructions, since the relative address can be specified with fewer bits than are required to designate the entire memory address. This permits the relative address field to be included in the same instruction word as the opcode.

Indexed Addressing Mode

In the indexed addressing mode, the content of an index register is added to the address part of the instruction to obtain the effective address. The index register may be a special CPU register or simply a register in a register file. We illustrate the use of indexed addressing by considering an array of data in memory. The address field of the instruction defines the beginning address of the array. Each operand in the array is stored in memory relative to the beginning address. The distance between the beginning address and the address of the operand is the index value stored in the register. Any operand in the array can be accessed with the same instruction, provided that the index register contains the correct index value. The index register can be incremented to facilitate access to consecutive operands.

Some computers dedicate one CPU register to function solely as an index register. This register is addressed implicitly when an index-mode instruction is used. In computers with many processor registers, any CPU register can be used as an index register. In such a case, the index register to be used must be specified with a register field within the instruction format.

A specialized variation of the index mode is the base-register mode. In this mode, the contents of a base register are added to the address part of the instruction to obtain the effective address. This is similar to indexed addressing, except that the register is called a base register instead of an index register. The difference between the two modes is in the way they are used rather than in the way addresses are computed: an index register is assumed to hold an index number that is relative to the address field of the instruction; a base register is assumed to hold a base address, and the address field of the instruction gives a displacement relative to the base address.

Summary of Addressing Modes

In order to show the differences among the various modes, we investigate the effect of the addressing mode on the instruction shown in Figure 9-6. The instruction in addresses 250 and 251 is "load to ACC," with the address field ADRS (or an operand NBR) equal to 500. The PC has the number 250 for fetching this instruction. The content of a processor register $R1$ is 400, and the ACC receives the result after the instruction is executed. In the direct mode, the effective address is 500, and the operand to be loaded into the ACC is 800. In the immediate mode, the operand 500 is loaded into the ACC. In the indirect mode, the effective address is 800, and the operand is 300. In the relative mode, the effective address is $500 + 252 = 752$, and the operand is 600. In the index mode, the effective address is $500 + 400 = 900$, assuming that $R1$ is the index register. In the register mode, the operand is in $R1$, and 400 is loaded into the ACC. In the register-indirect mode, the effective address is the contents of $R1$, and the operand loaded into the ACC is 700.

Table 9-1 lists the value of the effective address and the operand loaded into the ACC for the seven addressing modes. The table also shows the operation with a

□ **TABLE 9-1**
Symbolic Convention for Addressing Modes

Addressing Mode	Symbolic Convention	Register Transfer	Refers to Figure 9-6	
			Effective Address	Contents of ACC
Direct	LDA ADRS	$ACC \leftarrow M[ADRS]$	500	800
Immediate	LDA #NBR	$ACC \leftarrow NBR$	251	500
Indirect	LDA [ADRS]	$ACC \leftarrow M[M[ADRS]]$	800	300
Relative	LDA $ADRS	$ACC \leftarrow M[ADRS + PC]$	752	600
Index	LDA ADRS (R1)	$ACC \leftarrow M[ADRS + R1]$	900	200
Register	LDA R1	$ACC \leftarrow R1$	—	400
Register-indirect	LDA (R1)	$ACC \leftarrow M[R1]$	400	700

register transfer statement and a symbolic convention for each addressing mode. LDA is the symbol for the load-to-accumulator opcode. In the direct mode, we use the symbol ADRS for the address part of the instruction. The # symbol precedes the operand NBR in the immediate mode. The symbol ADRS enclosed in square brackets symbolizes an indirect address, which some compilers or assemblers designate with the symbol @. The symbol $ before the address makes the effective address relative to the *PC*. An index-mode instruction is recognized by the symbol of a register placed in parentheses after the address symbol. The register mode is indicated by giving the name of the processor register following LDA. In the register-indirect mode, the name of the register that holds the effective address is enclosed in parentheses.

9-4 INSTRUCTION SET ARCHITECTURES

Computers provide a set of instructions to permit computational tasks to be carried out. The instruction sets of different computers differ in several ways from each other. For example, the binary code assigned to the opcode field varies widely for different computers. Likewise, although a standard exists (see Reference 2), the symbolic name given to instructions varies for different computers. In comparison to these minor differences, however, there are two major types of instruction set architectures that differ markedly in the relationship of hardware to software: *Complex instruction set computers* (CISCs) provide hardware support for high-level language operations and have compact programs; *reduced instruction set computers* (RISCs) emphasize simple instructions and flexibility that, when combined, provide higher throughput and faster execution. These two architectures can be distinguished by considering the properties that characterize their instruction sets.

A *RISC architecture* has the following properties:

1. Memory accesses are restricted to load and store instructions, and data manipulation instructions are register-to-register.
2. Addressing modes are limited in number.
3. Instruction formats are all of the same length.
4. Instructions perform elementary operations.

The goal of a RISC architecture is high throughput and fast execution. To achieve these goals, accesses to memory, which typically take longer than other elementary operations, are to be avoided, except for fetching instructions. A result of this view is the need for a relatively large register file. Because of the fixed instruction length, limited addressing modes, and elementary operations, the control unit of a RISC is comparatively simple and is typically hardwired. In addition, the underlying organization is universally a pipelined design, as covered in Chapter 10.

A purely *CISC architecture* has the following properties:

1. Memory access is directly available to most types of instructions.
2. Addressing modes are substantial in number.
3. Instruction formats are of different lengths.
4. Instructions perform both elementary and complex operations.

The goal of the CISC architecture is to match more closely the operations used in programming languages and to provide instructions that facilitate compact programs and conserve memory. In addition, efficiencies in performance may result through a reduction in the number of instruction fetches from memory, compared with the number of elementary operations performed. Because of the high memory accessibility, the register files in a CISC may be smaller than in a RISC. Also, because of the complexity of the instructions and the variability of the instruction formats, microprogrammed control is more likely to be used. In the quest for speed, the microprogrammed control in newer designs is likely to be controlling a pipelined datapath. CISC instructions are converted to a sequence of RISC-like operations that are processed by the RISC-like pipeline, as discussed in detail in Chapter 10.

Actual instruction set architectures range between those which are purely RISC and those which are purely CISC. Nevertheless, there is a basic set of elementary operations that most computers include among their instructions. In this chapter, we will focus primarily on elementary instructions that are included in both CISC and RISC instruction sets. Most elementary computer instructions can be classified into three major categories: (1) data-transfer instructions, (2) data-manipulation instructions, and (3) program-control instructions.

Data-transfer instructions cause transfer of data from one location to another without changing the binary information content. Data-manipulation instructions perform arithmetic, logic, and shift operations. Program-control instructions provide decision-making capabilities and change the path taken by the program when executed in the computer. In addition to the basic instruction set, a computer may have other instructions that provide special operations for particular applications.

9-5 DATA-TRANSFER INSTRUCTIONS

Data-transfer instructions move data from one place in the computer to another without changing the data. Typical transfers are between memory and processor registers, between processor registers and input and output registers, and among the processor registers themselves.

Table 9-2 gives a list of eight typical data-transfer instructions used in many computers. Accompanying each instruction is a mnemonic symbol, the assembly-language abbreviation recommended by an IEEE standard (Reference 2). Different computers, however, may use different mnemonics for the same instruction name. The load instruction is used to designate a transfer from memory to a processor register. The store instruction designates a transfer from a processor register into a memory word. The move instruction is used in computers with multiple processor registers to designate a transfer from one register to another. It is also used for data transfer between registers and memory and between two memory words.

The exchange instruction exchanges information between two registers, between a register and a memory word, or between two memory words. The push and pop instructions are for stack operations described next.

Stack Instructions

The stack architecture introduced earlier possesses features that facilitate a number of data-processing and control tasks. A stack is used in some electronic calculators

□ **TABLE 9-2**
Typical Data Transfer Instructions

Name	Mnemonic
Load	LD
Store	ST
Move	MOVE
Exchange	XCH
Push	PUSH
Pop	POP
Input	IN
Output	OUT

and computers for the evaluation of arithmetic expressions. Unfortunately, because of the negative effects on performance of having the stack reside primarily in memory, a stack in a computer typically handles only state information related to procedure calls and returns and interrupts, as explained in Sections 9-8 and 9-9.

The stack instructions push and pop transfer data between a memory stack and a processor register or memory. The *push* operation places a new item onto the top of the stack. The *pop* operation removes one item from the stack so that the stack pops up. However, nothing is really physically pushed or popped in the stack. Rather, the memory stack is essentially a portion of a memory address space accessed by an address that is always incremented or decremented before or after the memory access. The register that holds the address for the stack is called a *stack pointer* (*SP*) because its value always points to TOS, the item at the Top Of Stack. Push and pop operations are implemented by decrementing or incrementing the stack pointer.

Figure 9-7 shows a portion of a memory organized as a stack that grows from higher to lower addresses. The stack pointer, *SP*, holds the binary address of the item that is currently on top of the stack. Three items are presently stored in the stack: *A*, *B*,

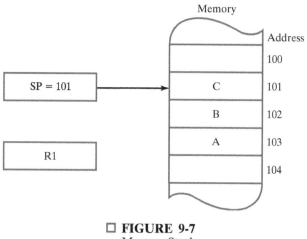

□ **FIGURE 9-7**
Memory Stack

and C, in consecutive addresses 103, 102, and 101, respectively. Item C is on top of the stack, so SP contains 101. To remove the top item, the stack is popped by reading the item at address 101 and incrementing SP. Item B is now on top of the stack, since SP contains address 102. To insert a new item, the stack is pushed by first decrementing SP and then writing the new item on top of the stack using SP as the memory address. Note that item C has been read out of the stack, but is not physically removed from it. This does not matter as far as the stack operation is concerned, because when the stack is pushed, a new item is written over it regardless of what was there before.

We assume that the items in the stack communicate with a data register $R1$ or a memory location X. A new item is placed on the stack with the push operation sequence:

$$SP \leftarrow SP - 1$$

$$M[SP] \leftarrow R1$$

The stack pointer is decremented so that it points at the address of the next word. A memory write microoperation inserts the word from $R1$ onto the top of the stack. Note that SP holds the address of the top of the stack and that $M[SP]$ denotes the memory word specified by the address presently in SP. An item is deleted from the stack with the pop operation pair:

$$R1 \leftarrow M[SP]$$

$$SP \leftarrow SP + 1$$

The top item is read from the stack into $R1$, and the stack pointer is incremented to point at the next item in the stack, which is the new top of the stack. The two microoperations described in this case can be in parallel.

The two microoperations needed for either the push or the pop operation are an access to memory through SP and an update of SP. In Figure 9-7, the stack grows by decreasing the memory address. By contrast, a stack may be constructed to grow by increasing the memory address. In such a case, SP is incremented for the push operation and decremented for the pop operation. A stack may also be constructed so that SP points to the next empty location above the top of the stack. In that case, the order of execution of the microoperations must be modified.

A stack pointer is loaded with an initial value, which must be the bottom address of an assigned stack in memory. From then on, SP is automatically decremented or incremented with every push or pop operation. The advantage of a memory stack is that the processor can refer to it without having to specify an address, since the address is always available and automatically updated in the stack pointer.

The final pair of data transfer instructions, input and output, depend on the type of input-output used, as described next.

Independent versus Memory-Mapped I/O

Input and output (I/O) instructions transfer data between processor registers and input and output devices. These instructions are similar to load and store instructions, except that the transfers are to and from external registers instead of memory words. The computer has a number of input and output ports, with one or more ports dedicated to communication with a specific input or output device. A *port* is typically a register with input and/or output lines attached to the device. The particular port is chosen by an address, in a manner similar to the way an address selects a word in memory. Input and output instructions include an address field in their format, for specifying the particular port selected for the transfer of data.

Port addresses are assigned in two ways. In the *independent I/O system*, the address ranges assigned to memory and I/O ports are independent from each other. The computer has distinct input and output instructions, as listed in Table 9-2, containing a separate address field that is interpreted by the control and used to select a particular I/O port. Independent I/O addressing isolates memory and I/O selection, so that the memory address range is not affected by the port address assignment. For this reason, the method is also referred to as an *isolated I/O configuration*.

In contrast to independent I/O, *memory-mapped I/O* assigns a subrange of the memory addresses for addressing I/O ports. There are no separate addresses for handling input and output transfers, since I/O ports are treated as memory locations in one common address range. Each I/O port is regarded as a memory location, similar to a memory word. Computers that adopt the memory-mapped scheme have no distinct input or output instructions, because the same instructions are used for manipulating both memory and I/O data. For example, the load and store instructions used for memory transfer are also used for I/O transfer, provided that the address associated with the instruction is assigned to an I/O port and not to a memory word. The advantage of this scheme is the simplicity that results with the same set of instructions serving for both memory and I/O access.

9-6 DATA-MANIPULATION INSTRUCTIONS

Data-manipulation instructions perform operations on data and provide the computational capabilities of the computer. In a typical computer, they are usually divided into three basic types:

1. Arithmetic instructions.
2. Logical and bit-manipulation instructions.
3. Shift instructions.

A list of elementary data-manipulation instructions looks very much like the list of microoperations given in Chapter 8. However, an instruction is typically processed by executing a *sequence* of one or more microinstructions. A microoperation is an elementary operation executed by the hardware of the computer under the control of the control unit. In contrast, an instruction may involve several elementary operations that fetch the instruction, bring the operands from appropriate processor registers, and store the result in the specified location.

Arithmetic Instructions

The four basic arithmetic instructions are addition, subtraction, multiplication, and division. Most computers provide instructions for all four operations. A list of typical arithmetic instructions is given in Table 9-3. The increment instruction adds one to the value stored in a register or memory word. A common characteristic of the increment operation, when executed on a computer word, is that a binary number of all 1s produces a result of all 0s when incremented. The decrement instruction subtracts one from a value stored in a register or memory word. When decremented, a number of all 0s produces a number of all 1s.

The add, subtract, multiply, and divide instructions may be available for different types of data. The data type assumed to be in processor registers during the execution of these arithmetic operations is included in the definition of the opcode. An arithmetic instruction may specify unsigned or signed integers, binary or decimal numbers, or floating-point data. The arithmetic operations with binary integers were presented in Chapters 1 and 3. The floating-point representation is used for scientific calculations and is presented in the next section.

The number of bits in any register is finite; therefore, the results of arithmetic operations are of finite precision. Most computers provide special instructions to facilitate double-precision arithmetic. A carry flip-flop is used to store the carry from an operation. The instruction "add with carry" performs the addition with two operands plus the value of the carry from the previous computation. Similarly, the "subtract with borrow" instruction subtracts two operands and a borrow that may have resulted from a previous operation.

The subtract reverse instruction reverses the order of the operands, performing $B - A$ instead of $A - B$. The negate instruction performs the 2s complement of a signed number, which is equivalent to multiplying the number by -1.

Logical and Bit-Manipulation Instructions

Logical instructions perform binary operations on words stored in registers or memory words. They are useful for manipulating individual bits or a group of bits that represent binary-coded information. Logical instructions consider each bit of the operand separately and treat it as a binary variable. By proper application of the logical

☐ **TABLE 9-3**
Typical Arithmetic Instructions

Name	Mnemonic
Increment	INC
Decrement	DEC
Add	ADD
Subtract	SUB
Multiply	MUL
Divide	DIV
Add with carry	ADDC
Subtract with borrow	SUBB
Subtract reverse	SUBR
Negate	NEG

instructions, it is possible to change bit values, to clear a group of bits, or to insert new bit values into operands stored in registers or memory.

Some typical logical and bit-manipulation instructions are listed in Table 9-4. The clear instruction causes the specific operand to be replaced by 0s. The set instruction causes the operand to be replaced by 1s. The complement instruction inverts all the bits of the operand. The AND, OR, and XOR instructions produce the corresponding logical operations on individual bits of two operands. Although logical instructions perform Boolean operations, when used on words they often are viewed as performing bit-manipulation operations. Three bit-manipulation operations are possible. A selected bit can be cleared to 0, set to 1, or complemented. The three logical instructions are usually applied to do just that.

The AND instruction is used to clear a bit or a selected group of bits of an operand to 0. For any Boolean variable X, the relationship $X \cdot 0 = 0$ dictates that a binary variable ANDed with a 0 produces a 0; and similarly, the relationship $X \cdot 1 = X$ dictates that the variable does not change when ANDed with a 1. Therefore, the AND instruction is used to selectively clear bits of an operand by ANDing the operand with a word that has 0s in the bit positions that must be cleared and 1s in the bit positions that must remain the same. The AND instruction is also called a *mask* because, by inserting 0s, it masks a selected portion of an operand. AND is also sometimes referred to as a *bit clear* instruction.

The OR instruction is used to set a bit or a selected group of bits of an operand to 1. For any Boolean variable X, the relationship $X + 1 = 1$ dictates that a binary variable ORed with a 1 produces a 1; similarly, the relationship $X + 0 = X$ dictates that the variable does not change when ORed with a 0. Therefore, the OR instruction can be used to selectively set bits of an operand by ORing the operand with a word with 1s in the bit positions that must be set to 1. The OR instruction is sometimes called a *bit set* instruction.

The XOR instruction is used to selectively complement bits of an operand. This is because of the Boolean relationships $X \oplus 1 = \overline{X}$ and $X \oplus 0 = X$. A binary variable is complemented when XORed with a 1, but does not change value when

□ **TABLE 9-4**
   Typical Logical and Bit-Manipulation Instructions

Name	Mnemonic
Clear	CLR
Set	SET
Complement	NOT
AND	AND
OR	OR
Exclusive-OR	XOR
Clear carry	CLRC
Set carry	SETC
Complement carry	COMC

XORed with a 0. The XOR instruction is sometimes called a *bit complement* instruction.

Other bit-manipulation instructions included in Table 9-4 can clear, set, or complement the carry bit. Additional instructions can clear, set, or complement other status bits or flag bits in a similar manner.

Shift Instructions

Instructions to shift the content of a single operand are provided in several varieties. Shifts are operations in which the bits of the operand are moved to the left or to the right. The incoming bit shifted in at the end of the word determines the type of shift. Instead of using just a 0, as for sl and sr in Chapter 8, here we add further possibilities. The shift instructions may specify either logical shifts, arithmetic shifts, or rotate-type operations.

Table 9-5 lists four types of shift instructions, both right and left versions. The small diagrams shown in the right column show the bit movement for each of the shifts in the Intel IA-32 ISA. In all cases, the outgoing bit is copied into the carry status bit C. The logical shifts insert 0 into the incoming bit position during the shift. Arithmetic shifts conform to the rules for shifting 2s complement signed numbers. The arithmetic shift right instruction uses sign extension, filling the leftmost position with its own value during the shift. The arithmetic shift left instruction inserts 0 into the incoming bit in the rightmost position and is identical to the logical shift left instruction.

The rotate instructions produce a circular shift: the values shifted out of the outgoing bit are rotated back into the incoming bit. The rotate-with-carry instructions treat the carry bit as an extension of the register whose word is being rotated.

☐ **TABLE 9-5**
Typical Shift Instructions

Name	Mnemonic	Diagram
Logical shift right	SHR	
Logical shift left	SHL	
Arithmetic shift right	SHRA	
Arithmetic shift left	SHLA	
Rotate right	ROR	
Rotate left	ROL	
Rotate right with carry	RORC	
Rotate left with carry	ROLC	

Thus, a rotate left with carry transfers the carry bit into the incoming bit in the rightmost bit position of the register, transfers the outgoing bit from the leftmost bit of the register into the carry, and shifts the entire register to the left.

Most computers have a multiple-field format for the shift instruction that provides for shifting multiple, rather than just one, bit positions. One field contains the opcode, and another contains the number of positions that an operand is to be shifted. A shift instruction may include the following five fields:

OP   REG   TYPE   RL   COUNT

OP is the opcode field for specifying a shift, and REG is a register address that specifies the location of the operand. TYPE is a 2-bit field that specifies one of the four types of shifts (logical, arithmetic, rotate, and rotate with carry), while RL is a 1-bit field that specifies whether a shift is to the right or the left. COUNT is a k-bit field that specifies shifts of up to $2^k - 1$ positions. With such a format, it is possible to specify the type of shift, the direction of the shift, and the number of positions to be shifted, all in one instruction.

Note that for shifts of greater than one position, the filling of the positions vacated by the shift is consistent with the diagrams shown in Table 9-5. In the Intel IA-32 ISA, in addition to the use of the carry bit C, the N and Z condition code bits are also set based on the shift results. The overflow bit, V, is defined only for 1-bit shifts.

9-7 FLOATING-POINT COMPUTATIONS

In many scientific calculations, the range of numbers is very large. In a computer, the way to express such numbers is in floating-point notation. The floating-point number has two parts, one containing the sign of the number and a *fraction* (sometimes called a *mantissa*) and the other designating the position of the radix point in the number and called the *exponent*. For example, the decimal number +6132.789 is represented in floating-point notation as

Fraction	Exponent
+.6132789	+04

The value of the exponent indicates that the actual position of the decimal point is four positions to the right of the indicated decimal point in the fraction. This representation is equivalent to the scientific notation $+.6132789 \times 10^{+4}$. Decimal floating-point numbers are interpreted as representing a number in the form

$$F \times 10^E$$

where F is the fraction and E the exponent. Only the fraction and the exponent are physically represented in computer registers; radix 10 and the decimal point of the fraction are assumed and are not shown explicitly. A floating-point binary number is represented in a similar manner, except that it uses radix 2 for the exponent. For example, the binary number +1001.11 is represented with an 8-bit fraction and 6-bit exponent as

Fraction	Exponent
01001110	000100

The fraction has a 0 in the leftmost position to denote a plus. The binary point of the fraction follows the sign bit, but is not shown in the register. The exponent has the equivalent binary number +4. The floating-point number is equivalent to

$$F \times 2^E = +(0.1001110)_2 \times 2^{+4}$$

A floating-point number is said to be *normalized* if the most significant digit of the fraction is nonzero. For example, the decimal fraction 0.350 is normalized, but 0.0035 is not. Normalized numbers provide the maximum possible precision for the floating-point number. A zero cannot be normalized because it does not have a non-zero digit; it is usually represented in floating-point by all 0s in both the fraction and the exponent.

Floating-point representation increases the range of numbers that can be accommodated in a given register. Consider a computer with 48-bit registers. Since one bit must be reserved for the sign, the range of signed integers will be $\pm (2^{47} - 1)$, which is approximately $\pm 10^{14}$. The 48 bits can be used to represent a floating-point number, with one bit for the sign, 35 bits for the fraction, and 12 bits for the exponent. The largest positive or negative number that can be accommodated is thus

$$\pm (1 - 2^{-35}) \times 2^{+2047}$$

This number is derived from a fraction that contains 35 1s, and an exponent with a sign bit and 11 1s. The maximum exponent is $2^{11} - 1$, or 2047. The largest number that can be accommodated is approximately equivalent to decimal 10^{615}. Although a much larger range is represented, there are still only 48 bits in the representation. As a consequence, exactly the same number of numbers are represented. Hence, the range is traded for the precision of the numbers, which is reduced from 48 bits to 35 bits.

Arithmetic Operations

Arithmetic operations with floating-point numbers are more complicated than with integer numbers, and their execution takes longer and requires more complex hardware. Adding and subtracting two numbers require that the radix points be aligned, since the exponent parts must be equal before adding or subtracting the fractions. The alignment is done by shifting one fraction and correspondingly adjusting its exponent until it is equal to the other exponent. Consider the sum of the following floating-point numbers:

$$.5372400 \times 10^2$$

$$+ \ .1580000 \times 10^{-1}$$

It is necessary that the two exponents be equal before the fractions can be added. We can either shift the first number three positions to the left or shift the second number three positions to the right. When the fractions are stored in registers, shifting to the left causes a loss of the most significant digits. Shifting to the right causes a loss of the least significant digits. The second method is preferable because it only reduces the precision, whereas the first method may cause an error. The usual alignment procedure is to shift the fraction with the smaller exponent to the right by a number of places equal to the difference between the exponents. After this is done, the fractions can be added:

$$
\begin{array}{r}
.5372400 \times 10^2 \\
+ \,.0001580 \times 10^2 \\
\hline
.5373980 \times 10^2
\end{array}
$$

When two normalized fractions are added, the sum may contain an overflow digit. An overflow can be corrected by shifting the sum once to the right and incrementing the exponent. When two numbers are subtracted, the result may contain most significant zeros in the fraction, as shown in the following example:

$$
\begin{array}{r}
.56780 \times 10^5 \\
- \,.56430 \times 10^5 \\
\hline
.00350 \times 10^5
\end{array}
$$

A floating-point number that has a 0 in the most significant position of the fraction is not normalized. To normalize the number, it is necessary to shift the fraction to the left and decrement the exponent until a nonzero digit appears in the first position. In the preceding example, it is necessary to shift left twice to obtain $.35000 \times 10^3$. In most computers, a normalization procedure is performed after each operation to ensure that all results are in normalized form.

Floating-point multiplication and division do not require an alignment of the fractions. Multiplication can be performed by multiplying the two fractions and adding the exponents. Division is accomplished by dividing the fractions and subtracting the exponents. In the examples shown, we used decimal numbers to demonstrate arithmetic operations on floating-point numbers. The same procedure applies to binary numbers, except that the base of the exponent is 2 instead of 10.

Biased Exponent

The sign and fraction part of a floating-point number is usually a signed-magnitude representation. The exponent representation employed in most computers is known as a *biased exponent*. The bias is an excess number added to the exponent so that, internally, all exponents become positive. As a consequence, the sign of the exponent is removed from being a separate entity.

Consider, for example, the range of decimal exponents from -99 to $+99$. This is represented by two digits and a sign. If we use an excess 99 bias, then the biased exponent e will be equal to $e = E + 99$, where E is the actual exponent. For $E = -99$, we have $e = -99 + 99 = 0$; and for $E = +99$, we have $e = 99 + 99 = 198$. In this way, the biased exponent is represented in a register as a positive number in the range from 000 to 198. Positive-biased exponents have a range of numbers from 099 to 198. Subtraction of the bias, 99, gives the positive values from 0 to $+99$. Negative-biased exponents have a range from 098 to 000. Subtraction of 99 gives the negative values from −1 to −99.

The advantage of biased exponents is that the resulting floating-point numbers contain only positive exponents. It is then simpler to compare the relative magnitude between two numbers without being concerned with the signs of their exponents. Another advantage is that the most negative exponent converts to a biased exponent with all 0s. The floating-point representation of zero is then a zero fraction and a zero biased exponent, which is the smallest possible exponent.

Standard Operand Format

Arithmetic instructions that perform operations with floating-point data often use the suffix F. Thus, ADDF is an add instruction with floating-point numbers. There are two standard formats for representing a floating-point operand: the single-precision data type, consisting of 32 bits, and the double-precision data type, consisting of 64 bits. When both types of data are available, the single-precision instruction mnemonic uses an FS suffix, and the double precision uses FL (for "floating-point long").

The format of the IEEE standard (see Reference 3) single-precision floating-point operand is shown in Figure 9-8. It consists of 32 bits. The sign bit s designates the sign for the fraction. The biased exponent e contains 8 bits and uses an excess 127 number. The fraction f consists of 23 bits. The binary point is assumed to be immediately to the left of the most significant bit of the f field. In addition, an implied 1 bit is inserted to the left of the binary point, which in effect expands the number to 24 bits representing a value from 1.0_2 to $1.11 \ldots 1_2$. The component of the binary floating-point number that consists of a leading bit to the left of the implied binary point, together with the fraction in the field, is called the *significand*. Following are some examples of field values and the corresponding significands:

f Field	Significand	Decimal Equivalent
100...0	1.100...0	1.50
010...0	1.010...0	1.25
000...0	1.000...0*	1.00*

* Assuming the exponent is not equal to 00...0.

Even though the f field by itself may not be normalized, the significand is always normalized, because it has a nonzero bit in the most significant position. Since normalized numbers must have a nonzero most significant bit, this 1 bit is not included explicitly in the format, but must be inserted by the hardware during arithmetic computations. The exponent field uses an excess 127 bias value for

1	8	23
s	e	f

☐ **FIGURE 9-8**
IEEE Floating-Point Operand Format

normalized numbers. The range of valid exponents is from -126 (represented as 00000001) through $+127$ (represented as 11111110). The maximum (11111111) and minimum (00000000) values for the e field are reserved to indicate exceptional conditions. Table 9-6 shows the biased and actual values of some exponents.

Normalized numbers are numbers that can be expressed as floating-point operands in which the e field is neither all 0s nor all 1s. The value of the number is derived from the three fields in the format of Figure 9-8 using the formula

$$(-1)^s 2^{e-127} \times (1.f)$$

The most positive normalized number that can be obtained has a 0 for the sign bit for a positive sign, a biased exponent equal to 254, and an f field with 23 1s. This gives an exponent $E = 254 - 127 = 127$. The significand is equal to $1 + 1 - 2^{-23} = 2 - 2^{-23}$. The maximum positive number that can be accommodated is

$$+2^{127} \times (2 - 2^{-23})$$

The smallest positive normalized number has a biased exponent equal to 00000001 and a fraction of all 0s. The exponent is $E = 1 - 127 = -126$, and the significand is equal to 1.0. The smallest positive number that can be accommodated is $+2^{-126}$. The corresponding negative numbers are the same, except that the sign bit is negative. As mentioned before, exponents with all 0s or all 1s (decimal 255) are reserved for the following special conditions:

1. When $e = 255$ and $f = 0$, the number represents plus or minus infinity. The sign is determined from the sign bit s.

2. When $e = 255$ and $f \neq 0$, the representation is considered to be *not a number*, or NaN, regardless of the sign value. NaNs are used to signify invalid operations, such as the multiplication of zero by infinity.

3. When $e = 0$ and $f = 0$, the number denotes plus or minus zero.

□ **TABLE 9-6**
Evaluating Biased Exponents

Exponent E in decimal	Biased exponent $e = E + 127$	
	Decimal	Binary
-126	$-126 + 127 = 1$	00000001
-001	$-001 + 127 = 126$	01111110
000	$000 + 127 = 127$	01111111
$+001$	$001 + 127 = 128$	10000000
$+126$	$126 + 127 = 253$	11111101
$+127$	$127 + 127 = 254$	11111110

4. When $e = 0$ and $f \neq 0$, the number is said to be denormalized. This is the name given to numbers with a magnitude less than the minimum value that is represented in the normalized format.

9-8 PROGRAM CONTROL INSTRUCTIONS

The instructions of a program are stored in successive memory locations. When processed by the control, the instructions are read from consecutive memory locations and executed one by one. Each time an instruction is fetched from memory, the *PC* is incremented so that it contains the address of the next instruction in sequence. In contrast, a program control instruction, when executed, may change the address value in the *PC* and cause the flow of control to be altered. The change in the *PC* as a result of the execution of a program control instruction causes a break in the sequence of execution of instructions. This is an important feature of digital computers, since it provides control over the flow of program execution and a capability of branching to different program segments, depending on previous computations.

Some typical program control instructions are listed in Table 9-7. The branch and jump instructions are often used interchangeably to mean the same thing, although sometimes they are used to denote different addressing modes. For example, the jump may use direct or indirect addressing, whereas the branch uses relative addressing. The branch (or jump) is usually a one-address instruction. When executed, the branch instruction causes a transfer of the effective address into the *PC*. Since the *PC* contains the address of the instruction to be executed next, the next instruction will be fetched from the location specified by the effective address.

Branch and jump instructions may be conditional or unconditional. An unconditional branch instruction causes a branch to the specified effective address without any conditions. The conditional branch instruction specifies a condition that must be met in order for the branch to occur, such as the value in a specified register being negative. If the condition is met, the *PC* is loaded with the effective address, and the next instruction is taken from this address. If the condition is not met, the *PC* is not changed, and the next instruction is taken from the next location in sequence.

The call and return instructions are used in conjunction with procedures. Their performance and implementation are discussed later in this section.

□ **TABLE 9-7**
Typical Program Control Instructions

Name	Mnemonic
Branch	BR
Jump	JMP
Call procedure	CALL
Return from procedure	RET
Compare (by subtraction)	CMP
Test (by ANDing)	TEST

The compare instruction performs a comparison via a subtraction, with the difference not retained. Instead, the comparison causes a conditional branch, changes the contents of a register, or sets or resets stored status bits. Similarly, the test instruction performs the logical AND of two operands without retaining the result and executes one of the actions listed for the compare instruction.

Based on their three possible actions, compare and test instructions are viewed to be of three distinct types, depending upon the way in which conditional decisions are handled. The first type executes the entire decision as a single instruction. For example, the contents of two registers can be compared and a branch or jump taken if the contents are equal. Since two register addresses and a memory address are involved, such an instruction requires three addresses. The second type of compare and test instruction also uses three addresses, all of which are register addresses. Considering the same example, if the contents of the first two registers are equal, a 1 is placed in the third register. If the contents are not equal, a 0 is placed in the third register. These two types of instructions avoid the use of stored status bits. In the first case, no such bit is required, and in the second case, a register is used to simulate its presence. The third type of compare and test has compare and test operations that set or reset stored status bits. Branch or jump instructions are then used to conditionally change the program sequence. This third type of compare and test instruction is discussed in the next subsection.

Conditional Branch Instructions

A conditional branch instruction is a branch instruction that may or may not cause a transfer of control, depending on the value of stored bits in the processor status register, *PSR*. Each conditional branch instruction tests a different combination of status bits for a condition. If the condition is true, control is transferred to the effective address. If the condition is false, the program continues with the next instruction.

Table 9-8 gives a list of conditional branch instructions that depend directly on the bits in the *PSR*. In most cases, the instruction mnemonic is constructed with the letter B (for "branch") and a letter for the name of the status bit. The letter N (for

□ **TABLE 9-8**
Conditional Branch Instructions Relating to Status Bits in the PSR

Branch Condition	Mnemonic	Test Condition
Branch if zero	BZ	$Z = 1$
Branch if not zero	BNZ	$Z = 0$
Branch if carry	BC	$C = 1$
Branch if no carry	BNC	$C = 0$
Branch if minus	BN	$N = 1$
Branch if plus	BNN	$N = 0$
Branch if overflow	BV	$V = 1$
Branch if no overflow	BNV	$V = 0$

"not") is included if the status bit is tested for a 0 condition. Thus, BC is a branch if carry $= 1$, and BNC is a branch if carry $= 0$.

The zero status bit Z is used to check whether the result of an ALU operation or shift is equal to zero. The carry bit C is used to check the carry after the addition or the borrow after the subtraction of two operands in the ALU. It is also used in conjunction with shift instructions to check the value of the outgoing bit. The sign bit N reflects the state of the leftmost bit of the output from the ALU or shift. $N = 0$ denotes a positive sign and $N = 1$ a negative sign. These instructions can be used to check the value of the leftmost bit, whether it represents a sign or not. The overflow bit V is used in conjunction with arithmetic and shift operations with both signed and unsigned numbers.

As stated previously, the compare instruction performs a subtraction of two operands, say, $A - B$. The result of the operation is not transferred into a destination register, but the status bits are affected. The status bits provide information about the relative magnitude between A and B. Some computers provide special branch instructions that can be applied after the execution of a compare instruction. The specific conditions to be tested depend on whether the two numbers are considered to be unsigned or signed.

The relative magnitude between two unsigned binary numbers A and B can be determined by subtracting $A - B$ and checking the C and Z status bits. Most commercial computers consider the C status bit as a carry after addition and a borrow after subtraction. A borrow occurs when $A < B$, because the most significant position must borrow a bit to complete the subtraction. A borrow does not occur if $A \geq B$, because the difference $A - B$ is positive. The condition for borrowing is the inverse of the condition for carrying when the subtraction is done by taking the 2s complement of B. Computers that use the C status bit as a borrow after a subtraction, complement the output carry after adding the 2s complement of the subtrahend and call this bit a borrow. The technique is typically applied to all instructions that use subtraction within the functional unit, not just the subtract instruction. For example, it applies to compare instructions.

The conditional branch instructions for unsigned numbers are listed in Table 9-9. It is assumed that a previous instruction has updated status bits C and Z after a subtraction $A - B$ or some other similar instruction. The words "above," "below," and

☐ **TABLE 9-9**
Conditional Branch Instructions for Unsigned Numbers

Branch Condition	Mnemonic	Condition	Status Bits*
Branch if above	BA	$A > B$	$C + Z = 0$
Branch if above or equal	BAE	$A \geq B$	$C = 0$
Branch if below	BB	$A < B$	$C = 1$
Branch if below or equal	BBE	$A \leq B$	$C + Z = 1$
Branch if equal	BE	$A = B$	$Z = 1$
Branch if not equal	BNE	$A \neq B$	$Z = 0$

*Note that C here is a borrow bit.

□ **TABLE 9-10**
Conditional Branch Instructions for Signed Numbers

Branch Condition	Mnemonic	Condition	Status Bits
Branch if greater	BG	$A > B$	$(N \oplus V) + Z = 0$
Branch if greater or equal	BGE	$A \geq B$	$N \oplus V = 0$
Branch if less	BL	$A < B$	$N \oplus V = 1$
Branch if less or equal	BLE	$A \leq B$	$(N \oplus V) + Z = 1$
Branch if equal	BE	$A = B$	$Z = 1$
Branch if not equal	BNE	$A \neq B$	$Z = 0$

"equal" are used to denote the relative magnitude between two unsigned numbers. The two numbers are equal if $A = B$. This is determined from the zero status bit Z, which is equal to 1 because $A = B$. A is below B and the borrow $C = 1$ when $A - B = 0$. For A to be below or equal to B ($A < B$), we must have $C = 1$ or $Z = 1$. The relationship ($A \leq B$), is the inverse of $A > B$ and is detected from the complemented condition of the status bits. Similarly, $A \leq B$ is the inverse of $A \geq B$, and $A \neq B$ is the inverse of $A = B$.

The conditional branch instructions for signed numbers are listed in Table 9-10. Again, it is assumed that a previous instruction has updated the status bits N, V, and Z after a subtraction $A - B$. The words "greater," "less," and "equal" are used to denote the relative magnitude between two signed numbers. If $N = 0$, the sign of the difference is positive, and A must be greater than or equal to B, provided that $V = 0$, indicating that no overflow occurred. An overflow causes a sign reversal, as discussed in Section 3-11. This means that if $N = 1$ and $V = 1$, there was a sign reversal, and the result should have been positive, which makes A greater than or equal to B. Therefore, the condition $A \geq B$ is true if both N and V are equal to 0 or both are equal to 1. This is the complement of the exclusive-OR operation.

For A to be greater than but not equal to B ($A > B$), the result must be positive and nonzero. Since a zero result gives a positive sign, we must ensure that the Z bit is 0 to exclude the possibility that $A = B$. Note that the condition $(N \oplus V) + Z = 0$ means that both the exclusive-OR operation and the Z bit must be equal to 0. The other two conditions in the table can be derived in a similar manner. The conditions BE (branch on equal) and BNE (branch on not equal) given for unsigned numbers apply to signed numbers as well and can be determined from $Z = 1$ and $Z = 0$, respectively.

Procedure Call and Return Instructions

A *procedure* is a self-contained sequence of instructions that performs a given computational task. During the execution of a program, a procedure may be called to perform its function many times at various points in the program, a procedure may be called to perform its function many times at various points in the program. Each time the procedure is called, a branch is made to the beginning of the procedure to start executing its set of instructions. After the procedure has been executed, a branch is made again to return to the main program. A procedure is also referred to as a *subroutine*.

The instruction that transfers control to a procedure is known by different names, including call procedure, call subroutine, jump to subroutine, branch to subroutine, and branch and link. We will refer to the routine containing the procedure call as the *calling procedure*. The calling procedure is often referred to as the *caller*, and the procedure being called is often referred to as the *callee*. The call procedure instruction has a one-address field and performs two operations. First, it stores the value of the *PC*, which is the address following that of the call procedure instruction, in a temporary location. This address is called the *return address*, and the corresponding instruction is the *continuation point* in the calling procedure. Second, the address in the call procedure instruction—the address of the first instruction in the procedure—is loaded into the *PC*. When the next instruction is fetched, it comes from the called procedure.

The final instruction in every procedure must be a return to the calling procedure. The return instruction takes the address that was stored by the call procedure instruction and places it back in the *PC*. This results in a transfer of program execution back to the continuation point in the calling procedure.

Different computers use different temporary locations for storing the return address. Some computers store it in a fixed location in memory, some store it in a processor register, and some store it in a memory stack. The advantage of using a stack for the return address is that, when a succession of procedures are called, the sequential return address can be pushed onto the stack. The return instruction causes the stack to pop, and the contents of the top of the stack are then transferred to the *PC*. In this way, a return is always to the program that last called the procedure. A procedure call instruction using a stack is implemented with the following microoperation sequence:

$$SP \leftarrow SP - 1 \qquad \text{Decrement stack pointer}$$
$$M[SP] \leftarrow PC \qquad \text{Store return address on stack}$$
$$PC \leftarrow \text{Effective address} \qquad \text{Transfer control to procedure}$$

The return instruction is implemented by popping the stack and transferring the return address to the *PC*:

$$PC \leftarrow M[SP] \qquad \text{Transfer return address to } PC$$
$$SP \leftarrow SP + 1 \qquad \text{Increment stack pointer}$$

By using a procedure stack, all return addresses are automatically stored by the hardware in the memory stack. Thus, the programmer does not have to be concerned about managing the return addresses for procedures called from within procedures.

In addition to storing the return address, the program must also properly manage any parameter values transferred to the procedure and result values returned to the calling procedure, as well as temporary values stored in registers required by either the procedure or calling procedure. The method used by a programming language or compiler to ensure that the values are properly managed is commonly known as a *calling convention*. The calling convention will typically specify how parameter values are provided to the procedure, how result values are returned to the calling procedure, which registers may be overwritten by the procedure, and which registers must be preserved by the procedure so that their values can be used by the calling procedure after the procedure returns control to it. A combination of registers and the stack is often used as part of the calling convention to pass parameter values to the procedure and return values to the calling procedure. The stack can also be used to preserve register values across the procedure call.

9-9 PROGRAM INTERRUPT

A program interrupt is used to handle a variety of situations that require a departure from the normal program sequence. A program interrupt transfers control from a program that is currently running to another service program as a result of an externally or internally generated request. Control returns to the original program after the service program is executed. In principle, the interrupt procedure is similar to a call procedure, except in three respects:

1. The interrupt is usually initiated at an unpredictable point in the program by an external or internal signal, rather than the execution of an instruction.

2. The address of the service program that processes the interrupt request is determined by a hardware procedure, rather than the address field of an instruction.

3. In response to an interrupt, it is necessary to store information that defines all or part of the contents of the register set, rather than storing only the program counter.

After the computer has been interrupted and the appropriate service program executed, the computer must return to exactly the same state that it was in before the interrupt occurred. Only if this happens will the interrupted program be able to resume exactly as if nothing had happened. The state of the computer at the end of an execution of an instruction is determined from the contents of the register set. In addition to containing the condition codes, the *PSR* can specify what interrupts are allowed to occur and whether the computer is operating in user or system mode. Most computers have a resident operating system that controls and supervises all other programs. When the computer is executing a program that is part of the operating system, the computer is placed in system mode, in which certain instructions are privileged and can be executed in the system mode only. The computer is in user mode when it executes user programs, in which case it cannot execute the privileged instructions. The mode of the computer at any given time is determined from a special status bit or bits in the *PSR*.

Some computers store only the program counter when responding to an interrupt. In such computers, the program that performs the data processing for servicing the interrupt must include instructions to store the essential contents of the register set. Other computers store the entire register set automatically in response to an interrupt. Some computers have two sets of processor registers, so that when the program switches from user to system mode in response to an interrupt, it is not necessary to store the contents of processor registers, because each computer mode employs its own set of registers.

The hardware procedure for processing interrupts is very similar to the execution of a procedure call instruction. The contents of the register set of the processor are temporarily stored in memory, typically by being pushed onto a memory stack, and the address of the first instruction of the interrupt service program is loaded into the *PC*. The address of the service program is chosen by the hardware. Some computers assign one memory location for the beginning address of the service program:

the service program must then determine the source of the interrupt and proceed to service it. Other computers assign a separate memory location for each possible interrupt source. Sometimes, the interrupt source hardware itself supplies the address of the service routine. In any case, the computer must possess some form of hardware procedure for selecting a branch address for servicing the interrupt.

Most computers will not respond to an interrupt until the instruction that is in the process of being executed is completed. Then, just before going to fetch the next instruction, the control checks for any interrupt signals. If an interrupt has occurred, control goes to a hardware interrupt cycle. During this cycle, the contents of some part or all of the register set are pushed onto the stack. The branch address for the particular interrupt is then transferred to the *PC*, and the control goes to fetch the next instruction, which is the beginning of the interrupt service routine. The last instruction in the service routine is a return from the interrupt instruction. When this return is executed, the stack is popped to retrieve the return address, which is transferred to the *PC* as well as any stored contents of the rest of the register set, which are transferred back to the appropriate registers.

Types of Interrupts

The three major types of interrupts that cause a break in the normal execution of a program are as follows:

1. External interrupts.
2. Internal interrupts.
3. Software interrupts.

External interrupts come from input or output devices, from timing devices, from a circuit monitoring the power supply, or from any other external source. Conditions that cause external interrupts are an input or output device requesting a transfer of data, an external device completing a transfer of data, the time-out of an event, or an impending power failure. A time-out interrupt may result from a program that is in an endless loop and thus exceeds its time allocation. A power-failure interrupt may have as its service program a few instructions that transfer the complete contents of the register set of the processor into a nondestructive memory such as a disk in the few milliseconds before power ceases.

Internal interrupts arise from the invalid or erroneous use of an instruction or data. Internal interrupts are also called *traps*. Examples of interrupts caused by internal conditions are an arithmetic overflow, an attempt to divide by zero, an invalid opcode, a memory stack overflow, and a protection violation. A *protection violation* is an attempt to address an area of memory that is not supposed to be accessed by the currently executing program. The service programs that process internal interrupts determine the corrective measure to be taken in each case.

External and internal interrupts are initiated by the hardware of the computer. By contrast, a *software interrupt* is initiated by executing an instruction. The software interrupt is a special call instruction that behaves like an interrupt rather than a procedure call. It can be used by the programmer to initiate an interrupt procedure at any desired point in the program. Typical use of the software interrupt is associated with a system call instruction. This instruction provides a means for switching from user mode to system mode. Certain operations in the computer may be performed by the operating system only in system mode. For example, a complex input or output procedure is done in system mode. In contrast, a program written by a user must run in user mode. When an input or output transfer is required, the user program causes a software interrupt, which stores the contents of the *PSR* (with the mode bit set to "user"), loads new *PSR* contents (with the mode bit set to "system"), and initiates the execution of a system program. The calling program must pass information to the operating system in order to specify the particular task that is being requested.

An alternative term for an interrupt is an *exception*, which may apply only to internal interrupts or to all interrupts, depending on the particular computer manufacturer. As an illustration of the use of the two terms, what one programmer calls interrupt-handling routines may be referred to as exception-handling routines by another programmer.

Processing External Interrupts

External interrupts may have single or multiple interrupt input lines. If there are more interrupt sources than there are interrupt inputs in the computer, two or more sources are ORed to form a common line. An interrupt signal may originate at any time during program execution. To ensure that no information is lost, the computer usually acknowledges the interrupt only after the execution of the current instruction is completed and only if the state of the processor warrants it.

Figure 9-9 shows a simplified external interrupt configuration. Four external interrupt sources are ORed to form a single interrupt input signal. Within the CPU is an enable-interrupt flip-flop (*EI*) that can be set or reset with two program instructions: enable interrupt (ENI) and disable interrupt (DSI). When *EI* is 0, the interrupt signal is neglected. When *EI* is 1 and the CPU is at the end of executing an instruction, the computer acknowledges the interrupt by enabling the interrupt acknowledge output *INTACK*. The interrupt source responds to *INTACK* by providing an interrupt vector address *IVAD* to the CPU. The program-controlled *EI* flip-flop allows the programmer to decide whether to use the interrupt facility. If a DSI instruction to reset *EI* has been inserted in the program, it means that the programmer does not want the program to be interrupted. The execution of an ENI instruction to set *EI* indicates that the interrupt facility will be active while the program is running.

The computer responds to an interrupt request signal if $EI = 1$ and execution of the present instruction is completed. Typical microinstructions that implement the interrupt are as follows:

$SP \leftarrow SP - 1$	Decrement stack pointer
$M[SP] \leftarrow PC$	Store return address on stack
$SP \leftarrow SP - 1$	Decrement stack pointer
$M[SP] \leftarrow PSR$	Store processor status word on stack
$EI \leftarrow 0$	Reset enable – interrupt flip – flop
$INTACK \leftarrow 1$	Enable interrupt acknowledge
$PC \leftarrow IVAD$	Transfer interrupt vector address to *PC*
	Go to fetch phase.

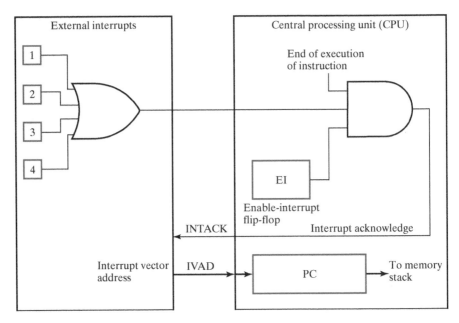

☐ **FIGURE 9-9**
Example of External Interrupt Configuration

The return address available in the *PC* is pushed onto the stack, and the *PSR* contents are pushed onto the stack. *EI* is reset to disable further interrupts. The program that services the interrupt can set *EI* with an instruction whenever it is appropriate to enable other interrupts. The CPU assumes that the external source will provide an *IVAD* in response to an *INTACK*. The *IVAD* is taken as the address of the first instruction of the program that services the interrupt. Obviously, a program must be written for that purpose and stored in memory.

The return from an interrupt is done with an instruction at the end of the service program that is similar to a return from a procedure. The stack is popped, and the return address is transferred to the *PC*. Since the *EI* flip-flop is usually included in the *PSR*, the value of *EI* for the original program is returned to *EI* when the old value of the *PSR* is returned. Thus, the interrupt system is enabled or disabled for the original program, as it was before the interrupt occurred.

9-10 CHAPTER SUMMARY

In this chapter, we defined the concepts of instruction set architecture and the components of an instruction and explored the effects on programs of the maximum address count per instruction, using both memory addresses and register addresses. This led to the definitions of four types of addressing architecture: memory-to-memory, register-to-register, single-accumulator, and stack. Addressing modes specify how the information in an instruction is interpreted in determining the effective address of an operand.

Reduced instruction set computers (RISCs) and complex instruction set computers (CISCs) are two broad categories of instruction set architecture. A RISC has as its goals high throughput and fast execution of instructions. In contrast, a CISC attempts to closely match the operations used in programming languages and facilitates more compact programs.

Three categories of elementary instructions are data transfer, data manipulation, and program control. In elaborating data transfer instructions, the concept of the memory stack appears. Transfers between the CPU and I/O are addressed by two different methods: independent I/O, with a separate address space, and memory-mapped I/O, which uses part of the memory address space. Data manipulation instructions fall into three classes: arithmetic, logical, and shift. Floating-point formats and operations handle broader ranges of operand values for arithmetic operations.

Program control instructions include basic unconditional and conditional transfers of control, the latter may or may not use condition codes. Procedure calls and returns permit programs to be broken up into procedures that perform useful tasks. Interruption of the normal sequence of program execution is based on three types of interrupts: external, internal, and software. Also referred to as exceptions, interrupts require special processing actions upon the initiation of routines to service them and upon returns to execution of the interrupted programs.

References

1. HENNESSY, J. L. AND D. A. PATTERSON. *Computer Architecture: A Quantitative Approach*, 5th ed. Amsterdam: Elsevier, 2011.

2. *IEEE Standard for Microprocessor Assembly Language* (IEEE Std 694-1985). New York: The Institute of Electrical and Electronics Engineers.

3. *IEEE Standard for Binary Floating-Point Arithmetic* (ANSI/IEEE Std 754-1985). New York: The Institute of Electrical and Electronics Engineers.

4. *The Intel 64 and IA-32 Architectures Software Developer's Manual*, Vols. 2A and 2B. Intel Corporation, 1997–2006.

5. MANO, M. M. *Computer Engineering: Hardware Design*. Englewood Cliffs, NJ: Prentice Hall, 1988.

6. MANO, M. M. *Computer System Architecture*, 3rd ed. Englewood Cliffs, NJ: Prentice Hall, 1993.

7. PATTERSON, D. A. AND J. L. HENNESSY. *Computer Organization and Design: The Hardware/Software Interface*, 5th ed. Amsterdam: Elsevier, 2013.

Problems

 The plus (+) indicates a more advanced problem and the asterisk (*) indicates that a solution is available on the Companion Website for the text.

9-1. Based on operations illustrated in Section 9-2, write a program to evaluate the arithmetic expression

$$X = (A + B - C) \times (D - E)$$

Make effective use of the registers to minimize the number of MOVE or LD instructions where possible.

(a) Assume a register-to-register architecture with three-address instructions. The operand order for subtraction, SUB, is difference, minuend, subtrahend.

(b) Assume a memory-to-memory architecture with two-address instructions.

(c) Assume a single-accumulator computer with one-address instructions.

9-2. *Repeat Problem 9-1 for

$$Y = (A + B) \times C \div (D - E \times F)$$

All operands are initially in memory. The operand order for divide, DIV, is quotient, dividend, divisor.

9-3. *A program is to be written for a stack architecture for the arithmetic expression

$$X = (A - B) \times (A + C) \times (B - D)$$

(a) Find the corresponding RPN expression.

(b) Write the program using PUSH, POP, ADD, MUL, SUB, and DIV instructions as appropriate for the operators in the expression.

(c) Show the contents of the stack after the execution of each instruction.

9-4. Repeat Problem 9-3 for the arithmetic expression

$$Y = (((A \times B) + C) \times D) \div (E - (A \times F))$$

9-5. **(a)** There are different ways of address calculation for instructions in which one of the operands is in memory. Consider the case of address being calculated before getting the second operand from memory (assuming that the first operand is in one of the registers). How is the second operand's address calculated in the indexed and relative modes?

(b) The length of an instruction is shortest if both operands are in registers. Why?

9-6. *A two-word relative mode branch-type instruction is stored in memory at locations 207 and 208 (decimal). The branch is made to an address equivalent to decimal 195. Let the address field of the instruction (stored at address 208) be designated by X.

(a) Determine the value of X in decimal.

(b) Determine the value of X in binary, using 16 bits. (Note that the number is negative and must be in 2s complement notation. Why?)

9-7. Repeat Problem 9-6 for a branch instruction in locations 143 and 144 and a branch address equivalent to 1000. All values are in decimal.

9-8. Consider the case of the following "two operand" instructions where the first operand is the destination and the second is the source. "M" refers to an address in memory.

(a) ADD $R1, M$

(b) ADD $M, R1$

Illustrate the difference in the actions needed to get these instructions executed.

9-9. Do address calculations (in hex format) for the following modes of addressing:

(a) Relative

(b) Relative Indexed

The relative number is 1214H. The index register contains the number 0078H. The instruction contains one constituent of the address in $R1$ as $R1 = 5600$H.

9-10. *A computer has a 32-bit word length, and all instructions are one word in length. The register file of the computer has 16 registers.

(a) For a format with no mode fields and three register addresses, what is the maximum number of opcodes possible?

(b) For a format with two register address fields, one memory field, and a maximum of 100 opcodes, what is the maximum number of memory address bits available?

9-11. Stacks are of two types: ascending and descending. Consider two stacks: one which is descending and the other which is ascending. The value of SP for both the stacks is 124. Refer to the figure below for the SP values for the two kinds of stacks and where it points to.

Ascending stack

Descending stack

Draw the figures of the stack with the value of SP and where it points after the following operations:

(a) Two PUSH operations where XX and YY are the data that are pushed in.

(b) One POP operation.

9-12. It is required to swap the data of two registers $R1$ and $R2$, which are part of the architected set of registers.

(a) Write the code to do it using only PUSH and POP operations

(b) Write the code to do it by register transfer instructions.

(c) Compare the two methods and explain why one method is superior to the other in terms of time expended.

9-13. In I/O mapped input-output, the address of the port is needed to be specified in the instruction. It uses only the IN and OUT instructions for accessing peripherals.

(a) Write the code for inputting data from an input device with address 89.

(b) Write the code for outputting data to an output device with address 95.

(c) Write the code for doing both these operations using memory-mapped I/O.

9-14. *Assume a computer with 8-bit words for the multiple-precision addition of two 32-bit unsigned numbers,

$$1F\ C6\ 24\ 7B\ +\ 00\ 57\ ED\ 4B$$

(a) Write a program to execute the addition, using add and add with carry instructions.

(b) Execute the program for the given operands. Each byte is expressed as a 2-digit hexadecimal number.

9-15. How many operands does each of these instructions have at the minimum?

(a) Add with carry

(b) Increment

9-16. **(a)** What is the importance of "Arithmetic right shifting"?

(b) Given the data 1001 0000 1100 1101, perform each of the below operations on it. The carry flag is reset.

(1) Arithmetic right shift once.

(2) Rotate Right with carry once.

(3) Logical shift left once.

9-17. *An 8-bit register contains the value 01101001, and the carry bit is equal to 1. Perform the eight shift operations given by the instructions listed in Table 9-5 as a sequence of operations on this register.

9-18. Represent the following two numbers in two exponential forms of representation.

(a) 6567

(b) 0.006789

9-19. *A 36-bit floating-point number consists of 26 bits plus sign for the fraction and 8 bits plus sign for the exponent. What are the largest and smallest positive nonzero quantities for normalized numbers?

9-20. *A 4-bit exponent uses an excess 7 number for the bias. List all biased binary exponents from +8 through −7.

9-21. Floating point numbers are represented in single precision or in double precision as the following figures show.

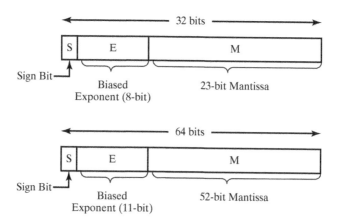

Convert the number 230.25 into single precision and –6765.1875 into double precision.

9-22. Convert the following double- and single-precision numbers to normal decimal representation:

(a) Double precision
(1) 40AB0F8000000000
(2) 4056480000000000
(3) 416110027C000000

(b) Single precision
(1) 45587C00H
(2) 42B24000H
(3) 4B088013H

9-23. What is meant by the "fixed point" representation of floating point numbers? How will the number 7.0301678 be rounded off if it is decided to have four digits after the decimal point?.

9-24. The IEEE standard single-precision floating-point format shown in Figure 9-8 uses 32 bits.

(a) What is the 8-digit hexadecimal representation of the decimal number −9.359375?

(b) What decimal number is represented by the hexadecimal value 41CBA000?

9-25. *It is necessary to branch to ADRS if the bit in the least significant position of the operand in a 16-bit register is equal to 1. Show how this can be done with the TEST (Table 9-7) and BNZ (Table 9-8) instructions.

9-26. (a) Find the status of the carry and sign flags after adding the following 8-bit numbers, i.e., 0011 0101 and 1100 1111.

(b) What is sum obtained? What is the size of the result?

(c) Find the sum obtained adding the following 16-bit numbers 0100 0101 1110 1100 and 0111 0111 0010 0011.

(d) What is the status of the carry, overflow, and Zero flags after the 16-bit addition?

(e) Write a few instructions that use the condition of flags as criteria for their operation.

9-27. *The program in a computer compares two unsigned numbers A and B by performing a subtraction $A - B$ and updating the status bits. For operands let $A = 01011101$ and $B = 01011100$,

(a) Evaluate the difference and interpret the binary result.

(b) Determine the values of status bits C (borrow) and Z (zero).

(c) List the conditional branch instructions from Table 9-9 that will have a true condition.

9-28. The program in a computer compares two signed 2s complement numbers A and B by performing subtraction $A - B$ and updating the status bits. For operands let $A = 11011010$ and $B = 01110110$,

(a) Evaluate the difference and interpret the binary result.

(b) Determine the value of status bits N (sign), Z (zero), and V (overflow).

(c) List the conditional branch instructions from Table 9-10 that will have a true condition.

9-29. Repeat Problem 9-28 with $A = 10100100$ and $B = 10101001$.

9-30. *The top of a memory stack contains 5000. The stack pointer SP contains 4000. A two-word procedure call instruction is located in memory at address 2000, followed by the address field of 502 at location 2001. All of these are decimal values. What are the contents of PC, SP, and the top of the stack **(a)** before the call instruction is fetched from memory, **(b)** after the call instruction is executed, and **(c)** after the return from the procedure?

9-31. In computer architecture literature, it is found that very few computers use the concept of a link register. A link register saves the "return" address on the event of a procedure calls.

(a) How is the idea of using a "link register" superior compared to architectures that don't have such a register?

(b) In architectures that don't have a link register, the last instruction in a procedure is RET. What is the last instruction for the case when a link register is present?

9-32. "A procedure call has more overheads than a jump instruction." Explain the concept behind this statement.

9-33. *Give five examples of external interrupts and five examples of internal interrupts. What is the difference between a software interrupt and a procedure call?

9-34. Interrupts are very important in the scheme of computer activity. Answer the following questions regarding interrupts:

(a) How are software interrupts initiated?

(b) Error induced interrupts are named "exceptions". Give an example of an exception.

(c) When the current program is interrupted, a new program is to be started. What is this new program called?

(d) Where is this new program available?

(e) Does the stack have a role in interrupt processing?

9-35. The program counter (PC) is an important register for any computer. Answer the following questions regarding the program counter:

(a) On what aspect of the computer's architecture does the size of the PC depend on?

(b) Can a computer with an 8-bit data bus have a 16-bit PC?

(c) When a call instruction is encountered, what happens to the value in PC?

(d) How does the PC get a new value when a jump instruction is encountered?

CHAPTER

10

RISC AND CISC CENTRAL PROCESSING UNITS

The central processing unit (CPU) is the key component of a digital computer. Its purpose is to decode instructions received from memory and perform transfer, arithmetic, logic, and control operations with data stored in internal registers, memory, or I/O interface units. Externally, the CPU provides one or more buses for transferring instructions, data, and control information to and from components connected to it.

In the generic computer at the beginning of Chapter 1, the CPU is a part of the processor. CPUs, however, may also appear elsewhere in computers. Small, relatively simple computers called microcontrollers are used in computers and in other digital systems to perform limited or specialized tasks. For example, a microcontroller is present in the keyboard and in the monitor in the generic computer. In such microcontrollers, the CPU may be quite different from those discussed in this chapter. The word lengths may be short (e.g., eight bits), the number of registers small, and the instruction sets limited. Performance, relatively speaking, is low, but adequate. Most important, the cost of these microcontrollers is very low, making their use cost effective.

The approach in this chapter builds upon and parallels that in Chapter 8. It begins by converting the datapath in Chapter 8 to a pipelined datapath and then adding a pipelined control unit to form a reduced instruction set computer (RISC) analogous to the single-cycle computer. Problems due to the use of pipelining are introduced and solutions are offered for the RISC design. Next, the control unit is expanded to form a complex instruction set computer (CISC) that is analogous to the multiple-cycle computer. A brief overview of techniques to enhance pipelined processor performance is presented. Finally, we consider PC microprocessors that use multiple processors on a single chip.

10-1 PIPELINED DATAPATH

Figure 8-17 was used to illustrate the long delay path present in the single-cycle computer and the resultant clock frequency limit. With a narrower focus, Figure 10-1(a) illustrates maximum delay values for each of the components of a typical datapath. A maximum of 0.8 ns (0.6 ns + 0.2 ns) is required to read two operands from the register file or to read one operand from the register file and obtain a constant from MUX *B*. A maximum of 0.8 ns is required to execute an operation in the functional unit. Also, a maximum of 0.8 ns is required to write the result back into the register file, including the delay of MUX *D*. Adding these delays, we find that 2.4 ns is required to perform a single microoperation. The maximum rate at which the microoperations can be performed is the inverse of 2.4 ns (i.e., 416.7 MHz). This is the maximum frequency at which the clock can be operated, since 2.8 ns is the smallest clock period that will allow each microoperation to be completed with certainty. As illustrated in Figure 8-17, delay paths that pass through both the datapath and the control unit limit the clock frequency to an even smaller value. For the datapath

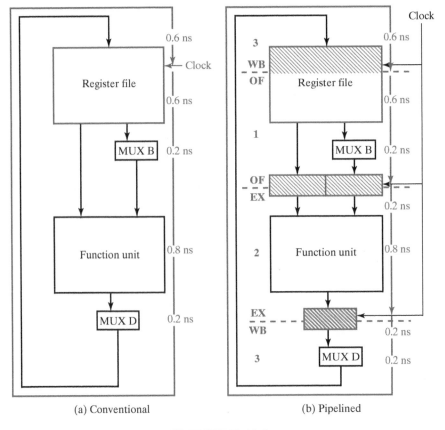

(a) Conventional   (b) Pipelined

☐ **FIGURE 10-1**
Datapath Timing

alone and for the combination of the datapath and control unit in the single-cycle computer, the execution of a microoperation constitutes the execution of an instruction. Thus, the rate of execution of instructions equals the clock frequency.

Now suppose that the datapath execution rate is not adequate for a particular application, and that no faster components are available with which to reduce the 2.8 ns required to complete a microoperation. Still, it may be possible to reduce the clock period and increase the clock frequency. This can be done by breaking up the 2.8 ns delay path with registers. The resulting datapath, sketched in Figure 10-1(b), is referred to as a *pipelined datapath*, or just a *pipeline*.

Three sets of registers break the delay of the original datapath into three parts. These registers are shown crosshatched in blue. The register file contains the first set of registers. Cross-hatching covers only the top half of the register file, since the lower half is viewed as the combinational logic that selects the two registers to be read. The two registers that store the *A* data from the register file and the output of MUX *B* constitute the second set of registers. The third set of registers stores the inputs to MUX *D*.

The term "pipeline," unfortunately, does not provide the best analogy for the corresponding datapath structure. A better analogy is a production line. A common example is an automated car wash in which cars are pulled through a series of stations at which a particular step is performed:

1. Wash—Flush with hot, soapy water,
2. Rinse—Flush with plain warm water, and
3. Dry—Blow air over the surface.

The processing of a vehicle through the car wash consists of three steps and requires a certain amount of time to complete. Analogously, the processing of an instruction by a pipeline consists of $n > 1$ steps and requires a certain amount of time to complete. The length of time required to process an instruction is called the *latency time*. In the car wash, the latency time is the length of time it takes for a car to pass through the three stations performing the three steps of the process. This time remains the same regardless of whether a single car or three cars are in the car wash at a given time.

Continuing this analogy, with the pipelined datapath corresponding to the car wash, what corresponds to the nonpipelined datapath? It would be a car wash with all of the steps available at a single station, with the steps performed serially. We now can compare the analogies, thereby comparing the pipelined and nonpipelined datapaths. For the multiple-station car wash and the single-station car wash, the latencies are approximately the same. So, going to the multiple-station car wash does not, decrease the time required to wash a car. However, suppose that we consider the frequency at which a washed car emerges from the two types of car washes. For the single-station car wash, this frequency is the inverse of the latency time. In contrast, for the multiple-station car wash with three stages, a washed car emerges at a frequency of three times the inverse of the latency time. Thus, there is a factor-of-three improvement in the frequency or rate of delivery of washed cars. Based on the analogy to pipelined datapaths with n stages and nonpipelined datapaths, the former has a processing rate or *throughput* for instructions that is n times that of the latter.

The desired structure, based on the nonpipelined, conventional datapath described in Chapter 8, is sketched in Figure 10-1(b). The operand fetch (OF) is stage 1, the execution (EX) is stage 2, and the write-back (WB) is stage 3. These stages are labeled at their boundaries with appropriate abbreviations. At this point the analogy breaks down somewhat, because the cars move smoothly through the car wash while the data within the pipeline moves synchronously with a clock, which controls the movement from stage to stage. This has some interesting implications. First of all, the movement of the data through the pipeline is in discrete steps rather than continuous. Second, the length of time in each of the stages must be the clock period and is the same for all stages. To provide the mechanism separating the stages in the pipeline, registers are placed between the stages. These registers provide temporary storage for data passing through the pipeline and are called *pipeline platforms*.

Returning to the pipelined datapath example in Figure 10-1(b), Stage 1 of the pipeline has the delay required for reading the register file followed by selection by MUX B. This delay is 0.6 plus 0.2 ns, or 0.8 ns. Stage 2 of the pipeline has the 0.2 ns delay of the platform plus the 0.8 ns delay of the functional unit, giving 1.0 ns. Stage 3 has the 0.2 ns delay of the platform, the delay for the selection by MUX D, and the delay for writing back into the register file. This delay is 0.2 + 0.2 + 0.6, for a total of 1.0 ns. Thus, all flip-flop-to–flip-flop delays are at most 1.0 ns, allowing a minimum clock period of 1.0 ns (assuming that the setup times for the flip-flops are zero) and a maximum clock frequency of 1.0 GHz, compared with the 416.7 MHz for the single-stage datapath. This clock frequency corresponds to the maximum throughput of the pipeline, which is 1 billion instructions per second, about 2.4 times that of the nonpipelined datapath. Even though there are three stages, the improvement factor is not three — for two reasons: (1) the additional delay contributed by the pipeline platforms and (2) the differences between the delay of the logic assigned to each stage. The clock period is governed by the longest delay, rather than the average delay assigned to any stage.

A more detailed diagram of the pipelined datapath appears in Figure 10-2. In this diagram, rather than showing the path from the output of MUX D to the register file input, the register file is shown *twice* — once in the OF stage, where it is read, and once in the WB stage, where it is written.

The first stage, OF, is the operand fetch stage. The operand fetch consists of reading register values to be used from the register file and, for Bus B, selecting between a register value or a constant by using MUX B. Following the OF stage is the first pipeline platform. The pipeline registers store the operand or operands for use in the next stage during the next clock cycle.

The second stage of the pipeline is the execute stage, denoted EX. In this stage, a function unit operation occurs for most microoperations. The results produced from this stage are captured by the second pipeline platform.

The third and final stage of the pipeline is the write-back stage, denoted WB. In this stage, the result saved from the EX stage, or the value on Data in, is selected by MUX D and written back into the register file at the end of the stage. In this case, the write part of the register file is the pipeline platform. The WB stage completes the execution of each microoperation that requires writing to a register.

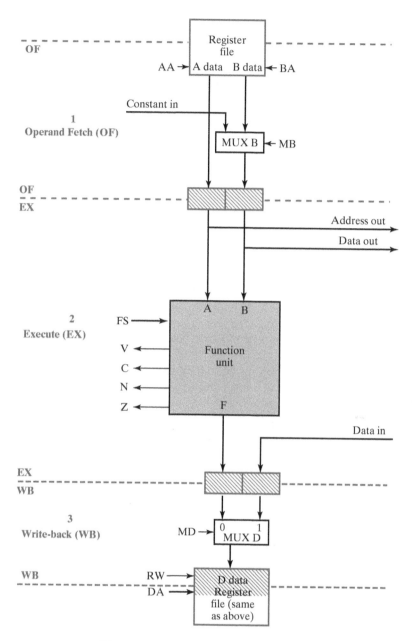

□ **FIGURE 10-2**
Block Diagram of Pipelined Datapath

Before leaving the car-wash analogy, we examine the cost of the single-stage versus that of the three-stage car wash. First, even though the three-stage facility washes vehicles three times as fast as the single-stage one, it costs three times as much in terms of space. Plus, it has the overhead of the mechanism to move the cars through the stages. So it, would appear to be less cost effective than three single-stage wash stations operating in parallel. Nevertheless, from a business standpoint, it has proven to be cost effective. In terms of the car wash, can you figure out why? In contrast, for the pipelined datapath, pipeline platforms cut a single datapath into three pieces. Thus, a first-order estimate of the cost increase is mainly that of the pipeline platforms.

Execution of Pipeline Microoperations

There are up to three operations at some stage of completion in the car wash at any given time. By analogy, we should be able to have three microoperations at some stage of completion in the pipelined datapath at any given time.

We now examine the execution of this sequence of microoperations with respect to the stages of the pipeline in Figure 10-2. In clock period 1, microoperation 1 is in the OF stage. In clock period 2, microoperation 1 is in the EX stage, and microoperation 2 is in the OF stage. In clock period 3, microoperation 1 is in the WB stage, microoperation 2 is in the EX stage, and microoperation 3 is in the OF stage. So at the end of the third clock period, microoperation 1 has completed execution, microoperation 2 is two-thirds finished, and microoperation 3 is one-third finished. So we have completed $1 + 2/3 + 1/3 = 2.0$ microoperations in three clock periods, or 3 ns. In the conventional datapath, we would have completed microoperation 1 only. So, indeed, the pipelined datapath performance is superior in this example.

The procedure we have been using so far is somewhat tedious. So to finish analyzing the timing of the sequence, we will use a *pipeline execution pattern* diagram, as shown in Figure 10-3. Each vertical position in this diagram represents a microoperation to be performed, and each horizontal position represents a clock cycle. An entry in the diagram represents the stage of processing of the microoperation. So, for example, the execution (EX) stage of microoperation 4, which adds the constant 2 to $R0$, occurs in clock cycle 5.

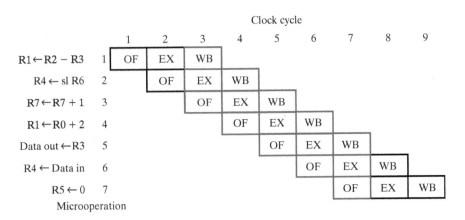

☐ **FIGURE 10-3**
Pipeline Execution Pattern for Microoperation Sequence

We can see from the overall diagram that the sequence of seven microoperations requires nine clock cycles to execute completely. The time required for execution is $9 \times 1 = 9$ ns, compared to $7 \times 2.4 = 16.8$ ns for the conventional datapath. Thus, the sequence of microoperations is executed about 1.9 times faster using the pipeline.

Now let us examine the pipeline execution pattern carefully. In the first two clock cycles, not all of the pipeline stages are active, since the pipeline is *filling*. In the next five clock cycles, all stages of the pipeline are active, as indicated in blue, and the pipeline is fully utilized. In the last two clock cycles, not all stages of the pipeline are active, since the pipeline is *emptying*. If we want to find the maximum possible improvement of the pipelined datapath over the conventional one, we compare the two when the pipeline is fully utilized. Over these five clock cycles, 3 through 7, the pipeline executes $(5 \times 3) \div 3 = 5$ microoperations in 5 ns. In the same time, the conventional datapath executes $5/2.4 = 2.083$ microoperations. So the pipelined datapath executes at best $5 \div 2.083 = 2.4$ times as many microoperations in a given time as the conventional datapath. In this ideal situation, we say that the throughput of the pipelined datapath is 2.4 times that of the conventional one. Note that filling and emptying reduce the pipeline speed below the maximum of 2.4. Additional topics associated with pipelines—in particular, providing a control unit for a pipelined datapath and dealing with pipeline hazards—are covered in the next two sections.

10-2   PIPELINED CONTROL

In this section, a control unit is specified to produce a CPU by using the datapath from the last section. Since the instruction must be fetched from a memory as well as executed, we add a stage to the analogous car wash used for illustration in that section. Analogous to the instruction fetch from the instruction memory, the operations in the car wash are specified by order sheets, produced by an attendant, that permit the functions performed in the stages of the car wash to vary. The order sheet, which is analogous to an instruction, accompanies the car as it moves down the line.

Figure 10-4 shows the block diagram of a pipelined computer based on the single-cycle computer. The datapath is that of Figure 10-2. The control has an added stage for instruction fetch that includes the *PC* and instruction memory. This becomes stage 1 of the combined pipeline. The instruction decoder and register file read are now in stage 2, the function unit and data memory read and write are in stage 3, and the register file write is in stage 4. These stages are labeled at their boundaries with appropriate abbreviations. In the figure, we have added registers to the pipeline platforms between stages, as necessary, to pass the decoded instruction information through the pipeline along with the data being processed. These additional registers serve to pass along the instruction information, just as order information was passed along in the car wash.

The added first stage is the instruction fetch stage, denoted by IF, which lies wholly in the control. In this stage, the instruction is fetched from the instruction memory, and the value in the *PC* is updated. Due to additional complexities of handling jumps and branches in a pipelined design, *PC* update is restricted here to an

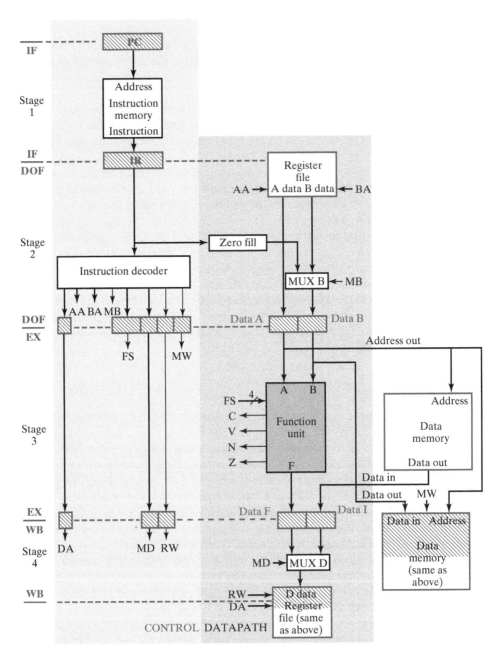

☐ **FIGURE 10-4**
Block Diagram of Pipelined Computer

increment, with a more complete treatment provided in the next section. Between the first stage and the second stage is an interstage pipeline platform that plays the role of instruction register, so it has been labeled *IR*.

In the second stage, DOF (decode and operand fetch), decoding of the *IR* into control signals takes place. Among the decoded signals, the register file addresses AA and BA and the multiplexer control signal MB are used in this stage for operand fetch. All other decoded control signals are passed on to the next pipeline platform, to be used later. Following the DOF stage is the second pipeline platform, whose registers store control signals to be used later. The third stage of the pipeline is the execution stage, denoted EX. In this stage, an ALU operation, a shift operation, or a memory operation is executed for most instructions. Thus, the control signals used in this stage are FS and MW. The read part of the data memory *M* is considered a part of the stage. For a memory read, the value of the word addressed is read to Data out from the data memory. All of the results produced from this stage, plus the control signals for the last stage, are captured by the third pipeline platform. The write part of data memory *M* is considered a part of this platform, so a memory write may occur here. The control information held in the final pipeline platform consists of DA, MD, and RW, which are used in the final write-back stage, WB.

The location of the pipeline platforms has balanced the partitioning of the delays, so that the delays per stage are no more than 1.0 ns. This gives a potential maximum clock frequency of 1 GHz, 3.4 times that of the single-cycle computer. Note, however, that an instruction takes $4 \times 1 = 4$ ns to execute. This latency of 4 ns compares to that of 3.4 ns for the single-cycle computer. So if only one instruction at a time is being executed, even fewer instructions are executed per second than for the single-cycle computer.

Pipeline Programming and Performance

If our hypothetical car wash is extended to four stages, there are up to four operations at some stage of completion at any given time. By analogy, then, we should be able to have four instructions at some stage of completion in the pipeline of our computer at any given time. Suppose we consider a simple calculation: Load the constants 1 through 7 into the seven registers $R1$ through $R7$, respectively. The program to do this is as follows (the number on the left is a number to identify the instruction):

1	LDI R1, 1
2	LDI R2, 2
3	LDI R3, 3
4	LDI R4, 4
5	LDI R5, 5
6	LDI R6, 6
7	LDI R7, 7

Let us examine the execution of this program with respect to the stages of the pipeline in Figure 10-4. We employ the pipeline execution pattern diagram shown in Figure 10-5. In clock period 1, instruction 1 is in the IF stage of the pipeline. In clock period 2, instruction 1 is in the DOF stage and instruction 2 is the IF stage. In clock period 3, instruction 1 is in the EX stage, instruction 2 is in the DOF stage, and

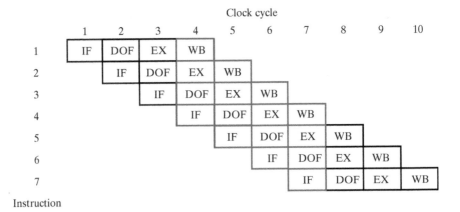

☐ **FIGURE 10-5**
Pipeline Execution Pattern of Register Number Program

instruction 3 is in the IF stage. In clock period 4, instruction 1 is in the WB stage, instruction 2 is in the EX stage, instruction 3 is in the DOF stage, and instruction 4 is in the IF stage. So at the end of the fourth clock period, instruction 1 has completed execution, instruction 2 is three-fourths finished, instruction 3 is half finished, and instruction 4 is one-fourth finished. So we have completed $1 + 3/4 + 1/2 + 1/4 = 2.5$ instructions in four clock periods, or 4 ns. We can see from the overall diagram that the complete program of seven instructions requires 10 clock cycles to execute. Thus, the time required is 10 ns, compared to 23.8 ns for the single-cycle computer, and the program is executed about 2.4 times faster.

Now suppose that we examine the pipeline execution pattern carefully. In the first three clock cycles, not all of the pipeline stages are active, since the pipeline is *filling*. In the next four clock cycles, all stages of the pipeline are active, as indicated in blue, and the pipeline is fully utilized. In the last three clock cycles, not all stages of the pipeline are active, since the pipeline is *emptying*. If we want to find the maximum possible improvement of the pipelined computer over the single-cycle computer, we compare the two in the situation in which the pipeline is fully utilized. Over these four clock cycles, or 4 ns, the pipeline executes $4 \times 4 \div 4 = 4.0$ instructions. In the same time, the single-cycle computer executes $4 \div 3.4 = 1.18$ instructions. So in the best case, the pipelined computer executes $4 \div 1.18 = 3.4$ times as many instructions in a given time as the single-cycle computer does. In this ideal situation, we say that the throughput of the pipelined computer is 3.4 times that of the single-cycle computer.

Note that even though the pipeline has four stages, the pipelined computer is not four times as fast as the single-cycle computer, because the delays of the latter cannot be divided exactly into four equal pieces and because of the delays of the added pipeline platforms. Also, filling and emptying the pipeline reduces its speed enough that the speed of the pipelined computer is less than the ideal maximum speed of 3.4 times as fast as the single-cycle computer.

The study of the pipelined computer here, along with the single-cycle computer and multiple-cycle computer in Chapter 8, completes our examination of three computer control organizations. Both the pipelined datapaths and the controls we have studied here are simplified and have elements missing. Next we present two CPU designs that illustrate combinations of architectural characteristics of the instruction set, the datapath, and the control unit. The designs are top down, but reuse prior component designs, illustrating the influence of the instruction set architecture on the datapath and control units, and the influence of the datapath on the control unit. The material makes extensive use of tables and diagrams. Although we reuse and modify component designs from Chapter 8, background information from these chapters is not repeated here. Pointers, however, are given to earlier sections of the book, where detailed information can be found.

The two CPUs presented are for a RISC using a pipelined datapath with a hardwired pipelined control unit and a CISC based on the RISC using an auxiliary microprogrammed control unit. These two designs represent two distinct instruction set architectures with architectures using a common pipelined core that contributes enhanced performance.

10-3 THE REDUCED INSTRUCTION SET COMPUTER

The first design we examine is for a reduced instruction set computer with a pipelined datapath and control unit. We begin by describing the RISC instruction set architecture, which is characterized by load/store memory access, four addressing modes, a single instruction format length, and instructions that require only elementary operations. The operations, resembling those that can be performed by the single-cycle computer, can be performed by a single pass through the pipeline. The datapath for implementing the ISA is based on the single-cycle datapath initially described in Figure 8-11 and converted to a pipeline in Figure 10-2. In order to implement the RISC instruction set architecture, modifications are made to the register file and the function unit. These modifications represent the effects of a longer instruction-word length and the desire to include multiple position shifts among the elementary operations. The control unit is based on the pipelined control unit in Figure 10-4. Modifications include support for the 32-bit instruction word and a more extensive program counter structure for dealing with branches in the pipeline environment. In response to data and control hazards associated with pipelined designs, additional changes will be made to both the control and datapath to sustain the performance gain achieved by using a pipeline.

Instruction Set Architecture

Figure 10-6 shows the CPU registers accessible to the programmer in this RISC. All registers are 32 bits. The register file has 32 registers, $R0$ through $R31$. $R0$ is a special register that supplies the value zero when used as a source and discards the result when used as a destination. The size of the programmer-accessible register file is comparatively large in the RISC because of the load/store instruction set architecture. Since the data-manipulation operations can use only register operands, many active operands need to be present in the register file. Otherwise, numerous stores and loads would be needed to temporarily save operands in the data memory between data-manipulation operations. In addition, in many real

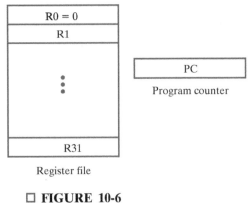

☐ **FIGURE 10-6**
CPU Register Set Diagram for RISC

pipelines, these stores and loads require more than one clock cycle for their execution. To prevent these factors from degrading RISC performance, a larger register file is required.

In addition to the register file, only a program counter, *PC*, is provided. If stack pointer-based or processor status register-based operations are required, they are simply implemented by sequences of instructions using registers.

Figure 10-7 gives the three instruction formats for the RISC CPU. The formats use a single word of 32 bits. This longer word length is needed to hold realistic address values, since additional instruction words for holding addresses are difficult to accommodate in the RISC CPU. The first format specifies three registers. The two registers addressed by the 5-bit source register fields SA and SB contain the two operands. The third register, addressed by a 5-bit destination register field DR, specifies the register location for the result. A 7-bit OPCODE provides for a maximum of 128 operations.

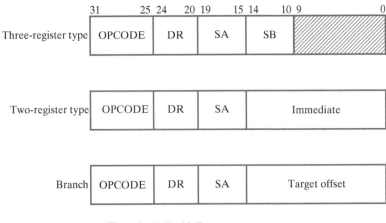

☐ **FIGURE 10-7**
RISC CPU Instruction Formats

The remaining two formats replace the second register with a 15-bit constant. In the two-register format, the constant acts as an immediate operand, and in the branch format, the constant is a *target offset*. The *target address* is another name for the effective address, particularly if the address is used in a branch instruction. The target address is formed by adding the target offset to the contents of the *PC*. Thus, branching uses relative addressing based on the updated value of the *PC*. In order to branch backward from the current *PC* location, the offset, regarded as a 2s complement number with sign extension, is added to the *PC*. The branch instructions specify source register SA. Whether the branch or jump is taken is based on whether the source register contains zero. The DR field is used to specify the register in which to store the return address for the procedure call. Finally, the rightmost 5 bits of the 15-bit constant are also used as the shift amount SH for multiple bit shifts.

Table 10-1 contains the 27 operations to be performed by the instructions. A mnemonic, an opcode, and a register transfer description are given for each operation. All of the operations are elementary and can be described by a single register transfer statement. The only operations that can access memory are Load and Store. A significant number of immediate instructions help to reduce data memory accesses and speed up execution when constants are employed. Since the immediate field of the instruction is only 15 bits, the leftmost 17 bits must be filled to form a 32-bit operand. In addition to using zero fill for logical operations, a second method used is called *sign extension*. The most significant bit of the immediate operand, bit 14 of the instruction, is viewed as a sign bit. To form a 32-bit 2s complement operand, this bit is copied into the 17 bits. In Table 10-1, the sign extension of the immediate field is denoted by se *IM*. The same notation, se *IM*, also represents the sign extension of the target offset field discussed previously.

The absence of stored versions of status bits is handled by the use of three instructions: Branch if Zero (BZ), Branch if Nonzero (BNZ), and Set if Less Than (SLT). BZ and BNZ are single instructions that determine whether a register operand is zero or nonzero and branch accordingly. SLT stores a value in register $R[DR]$ that acts like a negative status bit. If $R[SA]$ is less than $R[SB]$, a 1 is placed in register $R[DR]$; if $R[SA]$ is greater than or equal to $R[SB]$, a 0 is placed in $R[DR]$. The register $R[DR]$ can then be examined by a subsequent instruction to see whether it is zero (0) or nonzero (1). Thus, using two instructions, the relative values of two operands or the sign of one operand (by letting $R[SB]$ equal $R0$) can be determined.

The Jump and Link (JML) instruction provides a mechanism for implementing procedures. The value in the *PC* after updating is stored in register $R[DR]$, and then the sum of the *PC* and the sign-extended target offset from the instruction is placed in the *PC*. The return from a called procedure can use the Jump Register instruction with *SA* equal to *DR* for the calling procedure. If a procedure is to be called from within a called procedure, then each successive procedure that is called will need its own register for storing the return value. A software stack that moves return addresses from $R[DR]$ to memory at the beginning of a called procedure and restores them to $R[SA]$ before the return can also be used, as was explained in Chapter 9.

☐ **TABLE 10-1**
RISC Instruction Operations

Operation	Symbolic Notation	Opcode	Action
No Operation	NOP	0000000	None
Move A	MOVA	1000000[1]	$R[DR] \leftarrow R[SA]$
Add	ADD	0000010	$R[DR] \leftarrow R[SA] + R[SB]$
Subtract	SUB	0000101	$R[DR] \leftarrow R[SA] + \overline{R[SB]} + 1$
AND	AND	0001000	$R[DR] \leftarrow R[SA] \wedge R[SB]$
OR	OR	0001001	$R[DR] \leftarrow R[SA] \vee R[SB]$
Exclusive-OR	XOR	0001010	$R[DR] \leftarrow R[SA] \oplus R[SB]$
Complement	NOT	0001011	$R[DR] \leftarrow \overline{R[SA]}$
Add Immediate	ADI	0100010	$R[DR] \leftarrow R[SA] + $ se IM
Subtract Immediate	SBI	0100101	$R[DR] \leftarrow R[SA] + \overline{(\text{se } IM)} + 1$
AND Immediate	ANI	0101000	$R[DR] \leftarrow R[SA] \wedge (0 \parallel IM)$
OR Immediate	ORI	0101001	$R[DR] \leftarrow R[SA] \vee (0 \parallel IM)$
Exclusive-OR Immediate	XRI	0101010	$R[DR] \leftarrow R[SA] \oplus (0 \parallel IM)$
Add Immediate Unsigned	AIU	1000010	$R[DR] \leftarrow R[SA] + (0 \parallel IM)$
Subtract Immediate Unsigned	SIU	1000101	$R[DR] \leftarrow R[SA] + \overline{(0 \parallel IM)} + 1$
Move B	MOVB	0001100	$R[DR] \leftarrow R[SB]$
Logical Right Shift by SH Bits	LSR	0001101	$R[DR] \leftarrow$ lsr $R[SA]$ by SH
Logical Left Shift by SH Bits	LSL	0001110	$R[DR] \leftarrow$ lsl $R[SA]$ by SH
Load	LD	0010000	$R[DR] \leftarrow M[R[SA]]$
Store	ST	0100000	$M[R[SA]] \leftarrow R[SB]$
Jump Register	JMR	1110000	$PC \leftarrow R[SA]$
Set if Less Than[2]	SLT	1100101	If $R[SA] < R[SB]$ then $R[DR] = 1$
Branch if Zero	BZ	1100000	If $R[SA] = 0$, then $PC \leftarrow PC + 1 +$ se IM
Branch if Nonzero	BNZ	1001000	If $R[SA] \neq 0$, then $PC \leftarrow PC + 1 +$ se IM
Jump	JMP	1101000	$PC \leftarrow PC + 1 +$ se IM
Jump and Link	JML	0110000	$PC \leftarrow PC + 1 +$ se IM, $R[DR] \leftarrow PC + 1$

[1]In the CISC, beginning with MOVA and ending with LSL, each instruction has an additional opcode having a 1 in position 4 (with opcode bits numbered 0 through 6 from right to left). In addition to causing the usual operation to occur, these codes update the condition code bits.

[2]In the CISC, the SLT instruction is removed. Its function is replaced by branching on the status bits.

Addressing Modes

The four addressing modes in the RISC are register, register indirect, immediate, and relative. The mode is specified by the operation code, rather than by a separate mode field. As a consequence, the mode for a given operation is fixed and cannot be varied.

The three-operand data-manipulation instructions use register-mode addressing. Register indirect, however, applies only to the load and store instructions, the only instructions that access data memory. Instructions using the two-register format have an immediate value that replaces register address SB. Relative addressing applies exclusively to branch and jump instructions and so produces addresses only for the instruction memory.

When programmers want to use an addressing mode not provided by the instruction set architecture, such as indexed addressing, they must use a sequence of RISC instructions. For example, for an indexed address for a load operation, the desired transfer is

$$R15 \leftarrow M[R5 + 0 \,\|\, I]$$

This transfer can be accomplished by executing two instructions:

> AIU R9, R5, I
>
> LD R15, R9

The first instruction, Add Immediate Unsigned, forms the address by appending 17 0s to the left of I and adding the result to $R5$. The resulting effective address is then temporarily stored in $R9$. Next, the Load instruction uses the contents of $R9$ as the address at which to fetch the operand and places the operand in the destination register $R15$. Since, for indexed addressing, I is regarded as a positive offset in memory, the use of unsigned addition is appropriate. Sequences of operations for implementing addressing modes are the primary justification for having unsigned immediate addition available.

Datapath Organization

The pipelined datapath in Figure 10-2 serves as the basis for the datapath here, and we deal only with modifications. These modifications affect the register file, the function unit, and the bus structure. The reader should also refer to the datapath in Figure 10-2 and the new datapath shown in Figure 10-8 in order to understand fully the discussion that follows. We treat each modification in turn, beginning with the register file.

In Figure 10-2, there are 16 16-bit registers, and all registers are identical in function. In the new datapath, there are 32 32-bit registers. Also, reading register $R0$ gives a constant value of zero. If a write is attempted into $R0$, the data will be lost. These changes are implemented in the new register file in Figure 10-8. All data inputs and the data output are 32 bits. To correspond to the 32 registers, the address inputs are five bits. The fixed value of 0 in $R0$ is implemented by replacing the storage elements for $R0$ with open circuits on the lines that were their inputs, and with constant zero values on the lines that were their outputs.

A second major modification to the datapath is the replacement of the single-bit position shifter with a barrel shifter to permit multiple-position shifting. This barrel shifter can perform a logical right or logical left shift of from 0 to 31

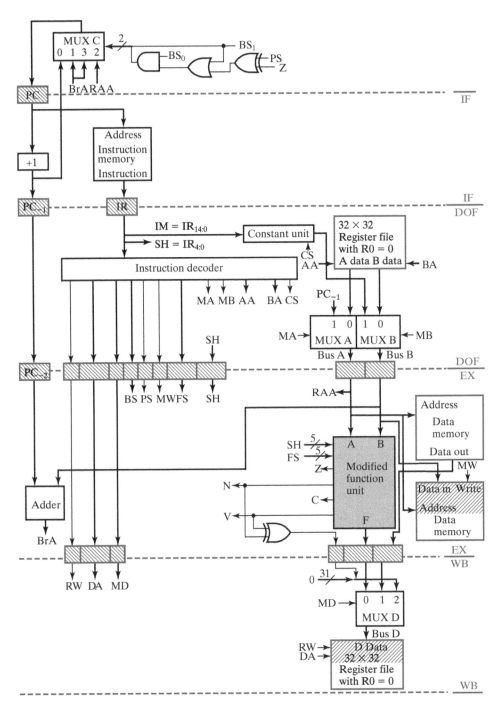

□ **FIGURE 10-8**
Pipelined RISC CPU

positions. A block diagram for the barrel shifter appears in Figure 10-9. The data input is 32-bit operand A, and the output is 32-bit result G. Left/$\overline{\text{right}}$, a control signal decoded from OPCODE, selects a left or right shift. The shift amount field $SH = IR$ (4:0) specifies the number of bit positions to shift the data input and takes on values from 0 through 31. A logical shift of p bit positions involves inserting p zeros into the result. In order to provide these zeros and simplify the design of the shifter, we will perform both the left and right shift by using a right rotate. The input to this rotate will be the input data A with 32 zeros concatenated to its left. A right shift is performed by rotating the input p positions to the right; a left shift is performed by rotating $64 - p$ positions to the right. This number of positions can be obtained by taking the 2s complement of the 6-bit value of $0 \| SH$.

The 63 different rotates can be obtained by using three levels of 4-to-1 multiplexers, as shown in Figure 10-8. The first level shifts by 0, 16, 32, or 48 positions, the second level by 0, 4, 8, or 12 positions, and the third level by 0, 1, 2, or 3 positions. The number of positions for A to be shifted, 0 through 63, can be implemented by representing $0 \| SH$ as a three-digit base-4 integer. From left to right, the digits have weights $4^2 = 16$, $4^1 = 4$, and $4^0 = 1$. The digit values in each of the positions are 0, 1, 2, and 3. Each digit controls a level of the 4-to-1 multiplexers, the most significant digit controlling the first level, the least significant the third level. Due to the presence of 32 zeros in the 64-bit input, fewer than 64 multiplexers can be used in each level. A level requires the number of multiplexers to be 32 plus the total number of positions its output can be shifted by subsequent levels. The output of the first level can be shifted at most $12 + 3 = 15$ positions to the right. Thus, this level requires $32 + 15 = 47$ multiplexers. The output of the second level can be shifted at most three positions, giving $32 + 3 = 35$ multiplexers. The final level cannot be shifted further and so needs just 32 multiplexers.

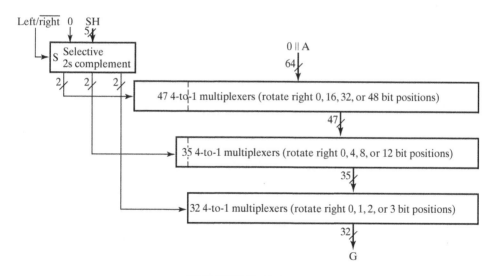

□ **FIGURE 10-9**
32-Bit Barrel Shifter

In the function unit, the ALU is expanded to 32 bits, and the barrel shifter replaces the single-position shifter. The resulting modified function unit uses the same function codes as in Chapter 8, except that the two codes for shifts are now labeled as logical shifts, and some codes are not used. The shift amount SH is a new 5-bit input to the modified function unit in Figure 10-8.

The remaining datapath changes are shown in Figure 10-8. Beginning at the top of the datapath, zero fill has been replaced by the constant unit. The constant unit performs zero fill for $CS = 0$ and sign extension for $CS = 1$. MUX A is added to provide a path for the updated PC, PC_{-1}, to the register file for implementation of the Jump and Link (JML) instruction.

One other change in the figure helps implement the Set if Less Than (SLT) instruction. This logic provides a 1 to be loaded into $R[DA]$ if $R[AA] - R[BA] < 0$ and a 0 to be loaded into $R[DA]$ if $R[AA] - R[BA] \geq 0$. It is implemented by adding an additional input to MUX D. The leftmost 31 bits of the input are 0; the rightmost bit is 1 if N is 1 and V is 0 (i.e., if the result of the subtraction is negative and there is no overflow). It is also 1 if N is 0 and V is 1 (i.e., if the result of the subtraction is positive and there is an overflow). These represent all cases in which $R[AA]$ is greater than $R[BA]$ and can be implemented using an exclusive-OR of N and V.

A final difference in the datapath is that the register file is no longer edge triggered and is no longer a part of a pipeline platform at the end of the write-back (WB) stage. Instead, the register file uses latches and is written much earlier than the positive clock edge. Special timing signals are provided that permit the register file to be written in the first half and to be read in the last half of the cycle. In particular, in the second half of the cycle, it is possible to read data written into the register file during the first half of the same clock cycle. This is called a *read-after-write* register file, and it both avoids added complexity in the logic used for handling hazards and reduces the cost of the register file.

Control Organization

The control organization in the RISC is modified from that in Figure 10-4. The modified instruction decoder is essential to deal with the new instruction set. In Figure 10-8, SH is added as an *IR* field, a 1-bit *CS* field is added to the instruction decoder, and MD is expanded to two bits. There is a new pipeline platform for SH, and expanded 2-bit platforms for MD.

The remaining control signals are included to handle the new control logic for the PC. This logic permits the loading of addresses into the PC for implementing branches and jumps. MUX C selects from three different sources for the next value of PC. The updated PC is used to move sequentially through a program. The branch target address BrA is formed from the sum of the updated PC value for the branch instruction and the sign-extended target offset. The value in $R[AA]$ is used for the register jump. The selection of these values is controlled by the field BS. The effects of BS are summarized in Table 10-2. If $BS_0 = 0$, then the updated PC is selected by $BS_1 = 0$, and $R[AA]$ is selected by $BS_1 = 1$. If $BS_0 = 1$ and $BS_1 = 1$, then BrA is selected unconditionally. If $BS_0 = 1$ and $BS_1 = 0$, then, for $PS = 0$, a branch to

□ **TABLE 10-2**
Definition of Control Fields BS and PS

Register Transfer	BS Code	PS Code	Comments
$PC \leftarrow PC + 1$	00	X	Increment PC
$Z: PC \leftarrow \text{BrA}, \overline{Z}: PC \leftarrow PC + 1$	01	0	Branch on Zero
$\overline{Z}: PC \leftarrow \text{BrA}, Z: PC \leftarrow PC + 1$	01	1	Branch on Nonzero
$PC \leftarrow R[AA]$	10	X	Jump to Contents of $R[AA]$
$PC \leftarrow \text{BrA}$	11	X	Unconditional Branch

BrA occurs for $Z = 1$, and for $PS = 1$, a branch to BrA occurs for $Z = 0$. This implements the two conditional branch instructions BZ and BNZ.

In order to have the value of the updated PC for the branch and jump instructions when they reach the execution stage, two pipeline registers, PC_{-1} and PC_{-2}, are added. PC_{-2} and the value from the constant unit are inputs to the dedicated adder that forms BrA in the execution stage. Note that MUX C and the attached control logic are in the EX stage, although shown above the PC. The related clock-cycle difference causes problems with instructions following branches, which we will deal with in later subsections.

The heart of the control unit is the instruction decoder. This is combinational circuitry that converts the operation code in the IR into the control signals necessary for the datapath and control unit. In Table 10-3, each instruction is identified by its mnemonic. A register transfer statement and the opcode are given for the instruction. The opcodes are selected such that the least significant four of the seven bits match the bits in the control field FS whenever it is used. This leads to simpler decoding. The register file addresses AA, BA, and DA come directly from SA, SB, and DR, respectively, in the IR.

Otherwise, to determine the control codes, the CPU is viewed much as is the single-cycle CPU in Figure 8-15. The pipeline platforms can be ignored in this determination—however, it is important to examine the timing carefully to be sure that various parts of the register transfer statement for the operation take place in the right stage of the pipeline. For example, note that the adder for the PC is in stage EX. This adder is connected to MUX C and its attached control logic, and to the incrementer +1 for the PC. Thus, all of this logic is in the EX stage, and the loading of the PC that begins the IF stage is controlled from the EX stage. Likewise, the input $R[AA]$ is in the same combinational block of logic and comes not from the A Data output of the register file, but from Bus A in the EX stage, as shown.

Table 10-3 can serve as the basis for the design of the instruction decoder. It contains the values for all control signals, except the register addresses from IR. In contrast to the instruction decoder in Section 8-8, the logic is complex and is most easily designed by using a computer-based logic synthesis program.

☐ **TABLE 10-3**
Control Words for Instructions

Symbolic Notation	Action	Op Code	RW	MD	BS	PS	MW	FS	MB	MA	CS
NOP	None	0000000	0	xx	00	x	0	xxxx	x	x	x
MOVA	$R[DR] \leftarrow R[SA]$	1000000	1	00	00	x	0	0000	x	0	x
ADD	$R[DR] \leftarrow R[SA] + R[SB]$	0000010	1	00	00	x	0	0010	0	0	x
SUB	$R[DR] \leftarrow R[SA] + \overline{R[SB]} + 1$	0000101	1	00	00	x	0	0101	0	0	x
AND	$R[DR] \leftarrow R[SA] \wedge R[SB]$	0001000	1	00	00	x	0	1000	0	0	x
OR	$R[DR] \leftarrow R[SA] \vee R[SB]$	0001001	1	00	00	x	0	1001	0	0	x
XOR	$R[DR] \leftarrow R[SA] \oplus R[SB]$	0001010	1	00	00	x	0	1010	0	0	x
NOT	$R[DR] \leftarrow \overline{R[SA]}$	0001011	1	00	00	x	0	1011	x	0	x
ADI	$R[DR] \leftarrow R[SA] + \text{se IM}$	0100010	1	00	00	x	0	0010	1	0	1
SBI	$R[DR] \leftarrow R[SA] + \overline{(\text{se IM})} + 1$	0100101	1	00	00	x	0	0101	1	0	1
ANI	$R[DR] \leftarrow R[SA] \wedge \text{zf IM}$	0101000	1	00	00	x	0	1000	1	0	0
ORI	$R[DR] \leftarrow R[SA] \vee \text{zf IM}$	0101001	1	00	00	x	0	1001	1	0	0
XRI	$R[DR] \leftarrow R[SA] \oplus \text{zf IM}$	0101010	1	00	00	x	0	1010	1	0	0
AIU	$R[DR] \leftarrow R[SA] + \text{zf IM}$	1000010	1	00	00	x	0	0010	1	0	0
SIU	$R[DR] \leftarrow R[SA] + \overline{(\text{zf IM})} + 1$	1000101	1	00	00	x	0	0101	1	0	0
MOVB	$R[DR] \leftarrow R[SB]$	0001100	1	00	00	x	0	1100	0	x	x
LSR	$R[DR] \leftarrow \text{lsr } R[SA] \text{ by SH}$	0001101	1	00	00	x	0	1101	x	0	x
LSL	$R[DR] \leftarrow \text{lsl } R[SA] \text{ by SH}$	0001110	1	00	00	x	0	1110	x	0	x
LD	$R[DR] \leftarrow M[R[SA]]$	0010000	1	01	00	x	0	xxxx	x	0	x
ST	$M[R[SA]] \leftarrow R[SB]$	0100000	0	xx	00	x	1	xxxx	0	0	x
JMR	$PC \leftarrow R[SA]$	1110000	0	xx	10	x	0	xxxx	x	0	x
SLT	If $R[SA] < R[SB]$, then $R[DR] = 1$	1100101	1	10	00	x	0	0101	0	0	x
BZ	If $R[SA] = 0$, then $PC \leftarrow PC+1+\text{se IM}$	1100000	0	xx	01	0	0	0000	1	0	1
BNZ	If $R[SA] \neq 0$, then $PC \leftarrow PC+1+\text{se IM}$	1001000	0	xx	01	1	0	0000	1	0	1
JMP	$PC \leftarrow PC+1+\text{se IM}$	1101000	0	xx	11	x	0	xxxx	1	x	1
JML	$PC \leftarrow PC+1+\text{se IM}, R[DR] \leftarrow PC+1$	0110000	1	00	11	x	0	0000	1	1	1

Data Hazards

In Section 10-1, we examined a pipeline execution diagram and found that filling and flushing of the pipeline reduced the throughput below the maximum level achievable. Unfortunately, there are other problems with pipeline operation that reduce throughput. In this and the next subsection, we will examine two such problems: data hazards and control hazards. Hazards are timing problems that arise because the execution of an operation in a pipeline is delayed by one or more clock cycles from the time at which the instruction containing the operation was fetched. If a subsequent instruction tries to use the result of the operation as an operand before the result is available, it uses the old or stale value, which is very likely to give a wrong result. To deal with data hazards, we present two solutions, one that uses software and another that uses hardware.

Two data hazards are illustrated by examining the execution of the following program:

```
1  MOVA  R1, R5
2  ADD   R2, R1, R6
3  ADD   R3, R1, R2
```

The execution diagram of this program appears in Figure 10-10(a). The MOVA instruction places the contents of R5 into R1 in the first half of WB in cycle 4. But, as shown by the blue arrow, the first ADD instruction reads R1 in the last half of DOF in cycle 3, one cycle before it is written. Thus, the ADD instruction uses the stale value in R1. The result of this operation is placed in R2 in the first half of WB in cycle 5. The second ADD instruction, however, reads both R1 and R2 in the second half of DOF in cycle 4. In the case of R1, the value read was written in the first half of WB in cycle 4. So the value read in the second half of cycle 4 is the new value. The write-back of R2, however, occurs in the first half of cycle 5, after it is read by the next instruction during cycle 4. So R2 has not been updated to the new value at the time it is read. This gives two data hazards, as indicated by the blue arrows in the figure. The registers that are not properly updated to new values are highlighted in blue in the program and in the register transfer statements, both in the figure. In each of these cases, the read of the involved register occurs one clock cycle too soon with respect to the write of that register.

(a) The data-hazard problem

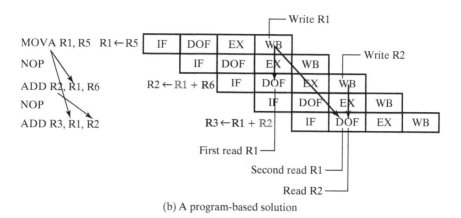

(b) A program-based solution

□ **FIGURE 10-10**
Example of Data Hazard

One possible remedy for data hazards is to have the compiler or programmer generate the machine code to delay instructions so that new values are available. The program is written so that any pending write to a register occurs in the same or an earlier clock cycle than a subsequent read from the register. To accomplish this, the programmer or compiler needs to have detailed information on how the pipeline operates. Figure 10-10(b) illustrates a modification of the simple three-line program that solves the problem. No-operation (NOP) instructions are inserted between the first and second instructions and between the second and third instructions to delay the respective reads relative to the writes by one clock cycle. The execution diagram shows that, at worst, this approach has writes and subsequent reads in the same clock cycle. This is indicated by the pairs consisting of a register write and a subsequent register read connected by a black arrow in the diagram. Because of the read-after-write assumption for the register file, the timing shown permits the program to be executed on correct operands.

This approach solves the problem, but what is the cost? First of all, the program is obviously longer, although it may be possible to place other, unrelated instructions in the NOP positions instead of just wasting them. Also, the program takes two clock cycles longer and reduces the throughput from 0.5 instruction per cycle to 0.375 instruction per cycle with the NOPs in place.

Figure 10-11 illustrates an alternative solution involving added hardware. Instead of the programmer or compiler putting NOPs in the program, the hardware inserts the NOPs automatically. When an operand is found at the DOF stage that has not been written back yet, the associated execution and write-back are delayed by stalling the pipeline flow in IF and DOF for one clock cycle. Then the flow resumes with completion of the instruction when the operand becomes available, and a new instruction is fetched as usual. The delay of one cycle is enough to permit the result to be written before it is read as an operand.

When the actions associated with an instruction flowing through the pipe are prevented from happening at a given point, the pipeline is said to contain a

☐ **FIGURE 10-11**
Example of Data Hazard Stall

bubble in subsequent clock cycles and stages for that instruction. In Figure 10-11, when the flow for the first ADD instruction is prevented beyond the DOF stage, in the next two clock cycles a bubble passes through the EX and the WB stages, respectively. The holding of the pipeline flow in the IF and DOF stages delays the microoperations taking place in these stages for one clock cycle. In the figure, this delay is represented by two diagonal blue arrows from the initial location in which the completion of the microoperation is prevented to the location one clock cycle later in which the microoperation is performed. When the pipeline flow is held in IF and DOF for an extra clock cycle, the pipeline is said to be *stalled*, and if the cause of the stall is a data hazard, then the stall is referred to as a *data hazard stall*.

An implementation of data-hazard handling for the pipelined RISC that uses data-hazard stalls is presented in Figure 10-12. The added or modified hardware is shown in the areas shaded in light blue. For this particular pipeline stage arrangement, a data hazard will occur for a register file read if there is a destination register at the execution stage that is to be written back in the next clock cycle and that is to be read at the current DOF stage as either of the two operands. So we have to determine whether such a register exists. This is done by evaluating the Boolean equations

$$HA = \overline{MA_{\mathrm{DOF}}} \cdot (DA_{\mathrm{EX}} = AA_{\mathrm{DOF}}) \cdot RW_{\mathrm{EX}} \cdot \sum_{i=0}^{4} (DA_{\mathrm{EX}})_i$$

$$HB = \overline{MB_{\mathrm{DOF}}} \cdot (DA_{\mathrm{EX}} = BA_{\mathrm{DOF}}) \cdot RW_{\mathrm{EX}} \cdot \sum_{i=0}^{4} (DA_{\mathrm{EX}})_i$$

and

$$DHS = HA + HB$$

The following events must all occur for *HA*, which represents a hazard for the *A* data, to equal 1:

1. *MA* in the DOF stage must be 0, meaning that the *A* operand is coming from the register file.

2. *AA* in the DOF stage equals *DA* in the EX stage, meaning that there is potentially a register being read in the DOF stage that is to be written in the next clock cycle.

3. *RW* in the EX stage is 1, meaning that register *DA* in the EX stage will definitely be written in WB during the next clock cycle.

4. The OR (Σ) of all bits of *DA* is 1, meaning that the register to be written is not *R0* and so is a register that must be written before being read. (*R0* has the same value 0 regardless of any writes to it.)

If all these conditions hold, there is a write pending for the next clock cycle to a register that is the same as one being read and used on Bus *A*. Thus, a data hazard exists for the *A* operand from the register file. *HB* represents the same combination of events for the *B* data. If either of the *HA* or *HB* terms equals 1, there is a data hazard and *DHS* is 1, meaning that a data-hazard stall is required.

☐ **FIGURE 10-12**
Pipelined RISC: Data Hazard Stall

The logic implementing the preceding equations is shown in the shaded area in the center of Figure 10-12. The blocks marked "Comp" are equality comparators that have output 1 if and only if the two 5-bit inputs are equal. The OR gate with *DA* entering it ORs together the five bits of *DA* and has output 1 as long as *DA* is not 00000 (*R*0).

DHS is inverted and the inverted signal is used to initiate a bubble in the pipeline for the instruction currently in the *IR*, as well as to stop the *PC* and *IR* from changing. The bubble, which prevents actions from occurring as the instruction passes through the EX and WB stages, is produced by using AND gates to force *RW* and *MW* to 0. These 0s prevent the instruction from writing the register file and the memory. AND gates also force *BS* to 0, causing the *PC* to be incremented instead of loaded during the EX stage for a jump register or branch instruction affected by a data hazard. Finally, to prevent the data stall from continuing for the next and subsequent clock cycles, AND gates force *DA* to 0 so that it appears that *R0* is being written, giving a condition which does not cause a stall. The registers to remain unchanged in the stall are the *PC*, the PC_{-1}, PC_{-2}, and the *IR*. These registers are replaced with registers with load control signals driven by $\overline{DHS}$. When $\overline{DHS}$ goes to 0, requesting a stall, the load signals become 0 and these pipeline platform registers hold their contents unchanged for the next clock cycle.

Returning to Figure 10-12, we see that in cycle 3 the data hazard for *R1* is detected, so that $\overline{DHS}$ goes to 0 before the next clock edge. *RW*, *MW*, *BS*, and *DA* are set to 0, and at the clock edge, a bubble is launched into the EX stage for the ADD. At the same clock edge, the IF and DOF stages are stalled, so the information in them now is associated with clock cycle 4 instead of 3. In clock cycle 4, since DA_{EX} is 0, there is no stall, so the execution of the stalled ADD instruction proceeds. The same sequence of events occurs for the next ADD. Note that the execution diagram is identical to that in Figure 10-10(b), except that the NOPs are replaced by stalled instructions, shown in parentheses. Thus, although it removes the need for programming NOPs into the software, the data-hazard stall solution has the same throughput penalty as the program with the NOPs.

A second hardware solution, *data forwarding*, does not have this penalty. Data forwarding is based on the answer to the following question: When a data hazard is detected, is the result available somewhere else in the pipeline, so that it can be used immediately in the operation having the data hazard? The answer is "almost." The result will be on Bus *D*, but it is not available until the next clock cycle. The result is to be written into the destination register during that clock cycle. The information needed to form the result, however, is available on the inputs to the pipeline platform that provides the inputs to MUX *D*. All that is needed to form the result during the current clock cycle is a multiplexer to select from the three values, just as MUX *D* does. MUX *D'* is accordingly added to produce the result on Bus *D'*. In Figure 10-13, instead of reading the operand from the register file, we use data forwarding to replace the operand with the value on Bus *D'*. This replacement is implemented with an additional input to MUX *A* and to MUX *B* from Bus *D'* as shown. Essentially the same logic as before is used to detect the data hazard, except that the separate detection signals *HA* and *HB* are used directly for *A* data and *B* data, respectively, so that the replacement occurs for the operand that has the data hazard.

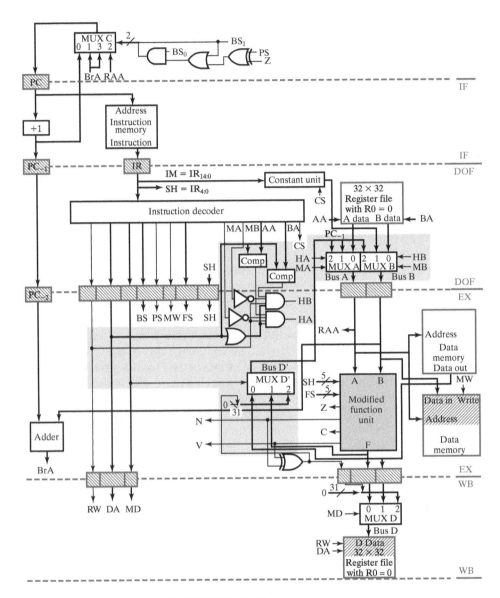

☐ **FIGURE 10-13**
Pipeline RISC: Data Forwarding

The data-forwarding execution diagram for the three-instruction example appears in Figure 10-14. The data hazard for $R1$ is detected in cycle 3. This causes the value to go into $R1$ in the next cycle, to be forwarded from the EX stage of the first instruction in cycle 3. The correct value of $R1$ enters the DOF/EX platform at the next clock edge so that execution of the first ADD can proceed normally. The data hazard for $R2$ is detected in cycle 4, and the correct value is forwarded from the EX stage of the second instruction in that cycle. This gives the correct value in the

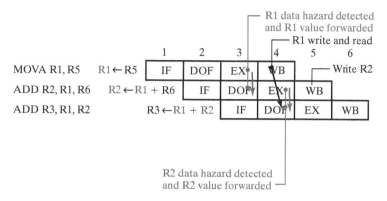

□ **FIGURE 10-14**
Example of Data Forwarding

DOF/EX platform needed for the second ADD to proceed normally. In contrast to the data-hazard stall method, data forwarding does not increase the number of clock cycles required to execute the program and hence does not affect the throughput in terms of the number of clock cycles required. It may, however, add combinational delay, causing the clock period to be somewhat longer.

Data hazards can also occur with memory access, as well as with register access. For the ST and LD instructions, it is not likely that a data memory read can be performed after a write in a single clock cycle. Further, some memory reads may take more than one clock cycle, in contrast to what we have assumed here. Thus, the reduction in throughput for a data hazard may be increased due to a longer delay before the data is available.

Control Hazards

Control hazards are associated with branches in the control flow of the program. The following program containing a conditional branch illustrates a control hazard:

1	BZ	R1, 18
2	MOVA	R2, R3
3	MOVA	R1, R2
4	MOVA	R4, R2
20	MOVA	R5, R6

The execution diagram for this program is given in Figure 10-15(a). If $R1$ is zero, then a branch to the instruction in location 20 (recall that addressing is PC relative) is to occur, skipping the instructions in locations 2 and 3. If $R1$ is nonzero, then the instructions in locations 2 and 3 are to be executed in sequence. Assume that the branch is taken to location 20 because $R1$ is equal to zero. The fact that $R1$ equals 0 is not detected until EX in cycle 3 of the first instruction in Figure 10-15(a). So the

☐ **FIGURE 10-15**
Example of Control Hazard

PC is set to 20 on the clock edge at the end of cycle 3. But the MOVA instructions in locations 2 and 3 are into the EX and DOF stages, respectively, after the clock edge. Thus, unless corrective action is taken, these instructions will complete execution, even though the programmer's intention was for them to be skipped. This situation is one form of a *control hazard*.

NOP instructions can be used to deal with control hazards just as they were with data hazards. The insertion of NOPs is performed by the programmer or compiler generating the machine-language program. The program must be written so that only operations intended to be performed, regardless of whether the branch is taken, are introduced into the pipeline before the branch execution actually occurs. Figure 10-15(b) illustrates a modification of the simple three-line program that satisfies this condition. Two NOPs are inserted after the branch instruction BZ. These two NOPs can be performed regardless of whether the branch is taken in the EX stage of BZ in cycle 3, with no adverse effects on the correctness of the program. When control hazards in the CPU are handled in this manner by programming, the branch hazard dealt with by the NOPs is referred to as a *delayed branch*. Branch execution is delayed by two clock cycles in this CPU.

The NOP solution in Figure 10-15(b) increases the time required to process the simple program by two clock cycles, regardless of whether the branch is taken. Note, however, that these wasted cycles can sometimes be avoided by rearranging the order of instructions. Suppose that those instructions to be executed regardless of whether the branch is taken can be placed in the two locations following the branch instruction. In this situation, the lost throughput is completely recovered.

Just as in the case of the data hazard, a stall can be used to deal with the control hazard. But, also as in the case of the data hazard, the reduction in throughput will be the same as with the insertion of NOPs. This solution is referred to as a *branch-hazard stall* and will not be presented here.

A second hardware solution is to use *branch prediction.* In its simplest form, this method predicts that branches will never be taken. Thus, instructions will be fetched and decoded and operands fetched on the basis of the addition of 1 to the value of the *PC.* These actions occur until it is known during the execution cycle whether the branch in question will be taken. If the branch is not taken, the instructions already in the pipeline due to the prediction will be allowed to proceed. If the branch is taken, the instructions following the branch instruction need to be canceled. Usually, the cancellation is done by inserting bubbles into the execution and write-back stages for these instructions. This is illustrated for the four instruction program in Figure 10-16. On the basis of the prediction that the branch will not be taken, the two MOVA instructions after BZ are fetched, the first one is decoded, and its operands are fetched. These actions take place in cycles 2 and 3. In cycle 3, the condition upon which the branch is based has been evaluated, and it is found that $R1 = 0$. Thus, the branch is to be taken. At the end of cycle 3, the *PC* is set to 20, and the instruction fetch in cycle 4 is performed using the new value of the *PC.* In cycle 3, the fact that the branch is taken has been detected, and bubbles are inserted into the pipeline for instructions 2 and 3. Proceeding through the pipeline, these bubbles have the same effect as two NOP instructions. However, because the NOPs are not present in the program, there is no delay or performance penalty when the branch is not taken.

□ **FIGURE 10-16**
Example of Branch Prediction with Branch Taken

The branch-prediction hardware is shown in Figure 10-17. Whether a branch is taken is determined by looking at the selection values on the inputs to MUX C. If the pair of inputs is 01, then a conditional branch is being taken. If the pair is 10, then

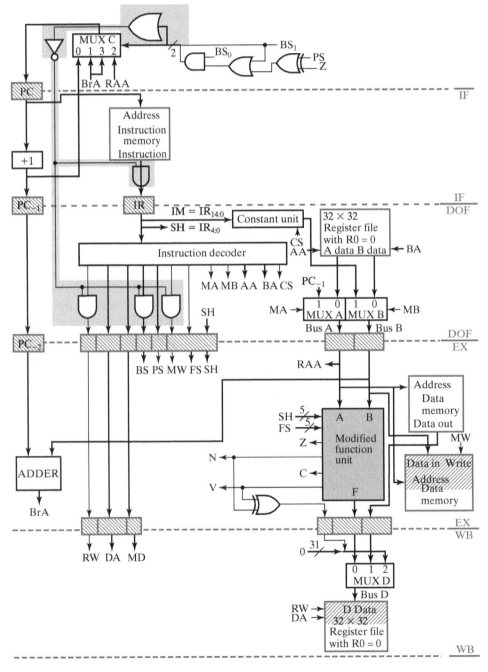

☐ **FIGURE 10-17**
Pipelined RISC: Branch Prediction

an unconditional JMR is occurring. If the pair is 11, then an unconditional JMP or JML is taking place. On the other hand, if the pair of inputs is 00, then no branch is occurring. Thus, a branch occurs for all combinations other than 00 (i.e., for at least one 1) on the pair of lines. Logically, this corresponds to the OR of the lines, as shown in the figure. The output of the OR is inverted and then ANDed with the *RW* and *MW* fields, so that the register file and the data memory cannot be written for the instruction following the branch instruction if the branch is taken. The inverted output is also ANDed with the *BS* field, so that a branch in the next instruction is not executed. In order to cancel the second instruction following the branch, the inverted OR output is ANDed with the *IR* output. This gives an instruction of all 0s, for which the OPCODE field is defined as NOP. If the branch is not taken, however, the inverted OR output is 1, and the *IR* and the three control fields remain unchanged, giving normal execution of the two instructions following the branch.

Branch prediction can also be done on the assumption that the branch is taken. In this case, the instructions and operands must be fetched down the path of the branch target. Thus, the branch target address must be computed and used for fetching the instruction in the branch target location. In case the branch does not take place, however, the updated value of the *PC* must also be saved. As a consequence, this solution will require additional hardware to compute and store the branch target address. Nevertheless, if branches are more likely to be taken than not, the "branch taken" prediction may yield a more favorable cost–performance trade-off than the "branch not taken" prediction.

For simplicity of presentation, we have treated the hardware solutions for dealing with hazards one at a time. In an actual CPU, these solutions need to be combined. In addition, other hazards, such as those associated with writing and reading memory locations, need to be handled.

10-4 THE COMPLEX INSTRUCTION SET COMPUTER

CISC instruction set architectures are characterized by complex instructions that are, at worst, impossible, and, at best, difficult to implement using a single-cycle computer or a single pass through a pipeline. A CISC ISA often employs a sizable number of addressing modes. Further, the ISA often employs variable-length instructions. The support for decision making via conditional branching is also more sophisticated than the simple concepts of branch on zero register contents and setting a register bit to 1 based on a comparison of two registers. In this section, a basic architecture for a CISC is developed with the high-performance of a RISC for simple instructions and most of the characteristics of a CISC ISA as just described.

Suppose that we are to implement a CISC architecture, but we are interested in approaching a throughput of one instruction per short RISC clock cycle for simple, frequently used instructions. To accomplish this goal, we use a pipelined datapath and a combination of pipelined and microprogrammed control as shown in Figure 10-18. An instruction is fetched into the IR and enters the Decode and Operand Fetch stage. If it is a simple instruction that executes completely in a single pass through the normal RISC pipeline, it is decoded and operand fetch occurs as usual. On the other hand, if the instruction requires multiple microoperations or multiple

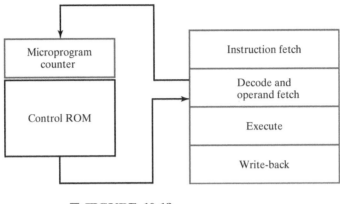

☐ **FIGURE 10-18**
Combined CISC–RISC Organization

memory accesses in sequence, the decode stage produces a microcode address for the microcode ROM and replaces the usual decoder outputs with control values from the microcode ROM. Execution of microinstructions from the ROM, selected by the microprogram counter, continues until the execution of the instruction is completed.

Recall that to execute a sequence of microinstructions, it is often necessary to have temporary registers in which to store information. An organization of this type will frequently supply temporary registers with a convenient mechanism for switching between temporary registers and the usual programmer-accessible register resources.

The preceding organization supports an architecture that has combined CISC–RISC properties. It illustrates that pipelines and microprograms can be compatible and need not be viewed as mutually exclusive. The most frequent use of such a combined architecture allows existing software designed for a CISC to take advantage of a RISC architecture while preserving the existing ISA. The CISC–RISC architecture is a combination of concepts from the multiple-cycle computer in Chapter 8, the RISC CPU in the previous section, and the microprogramming concept introduced briefly in Chapter 8. This combination of concepts makes sense, since the CISC CPU executes instructions using multiple passes through the RISC datapath pipeline. To sequence these multiple-pass instruction implementations, a sequential control of considerable complexity is needed, so microprogrammed control is chosen.

The development of the architecture begins with some minor modifications to the RISC ISA to obtain some capabilities desirable in the CISC ISA. Next, the datapath is modified to support the ISA changes. These include modification of the Constant Unit, addition of a Condition Code register CC, and deletion of the hardware for supporting the SLT instruction. Further, the Register file addressing logic is modified to provide addressing for 16 temporary registers for multiple-pass use of the datapath, with 16 registers remaining in the storage resources. This is in contrast to the 32 registers in the storage resources for the RISC. The next step is to adapt the

RISC control to work with the microprogrammed control in implementing the multiple pass instructions. Finally, the microprogrammed control itself is developed and its operation is illustrated by the implementation of three CISC instructions that characterize a CISC ISA.

ISA Modifications

The first modification to the RISC ISA is the addition of a new format for branch instructions. In terms of the instructions provided in the CISC, it is desirable to have the capability to compare the contents of two source registers and branch, indicating the relationship between the contents of the two registers. To perform such a comparison, a format with two source register fields SA and SB and a target offset are required. Referring to Figure 10-7, addition of the SB field to the branch format reduces the length of the target offset from 15 bits to 10 bits. The resulting Branch 2 format added for the CISC instructions is shown in Figure 10-19. This format is used by an illustration in Example 10-2 of a BLE instruction that compares the contents of registers $R[SA]$ and $R[SB]$.

The second modification is to partition the Register file to provide addressing for 16 temporary registers for multiple-pass use of the datapath. With the partition, only 16 registers remain in the storage resources. Rather than modify all of the register address fields in the instruction formats, we will simply ignore the most significant bit of these fields. For example, only the rightmost four bits of the field DR will be used. DR_4 will be ignored.

The third modification to the RISC ISA is the addition of condition codes (also called flags) as discussed in Chapter 9. The condition codes provided are designed

□ **FIGURE 10-19**
CISC CPU Instruction Formats

specifically to be used in combination with branch on zero and branch on nonzero in implementing instructions that will provide a wide spectrum of decisions, such as greater than, less than, less than or equal to, and so on for both signed and unsigned integers. The codes are zero (Z), negative (N), carry (C), overflow (V), and less than (L). The first four are stored versions of the status outputs of the Function Unit. The less than (L) bit is the exclusive OR of Z and V, which is useful in easily implementing particular decisions. The inclusion of the L bit in the condition codes eliminates the need for the SLT instruction.

To make the most effective use of these condition codes, it is useful to control whether or not they are modified for a particular microoperation execution from the instructions. Examination of the RISC instruction codes in Table 10-1 shows that bit 4 (third from the left) of the opcode is 0 for the operations MOVA down through instruction LSL. This bit can be used for these instructions to control whether the condition codes are affected by the instruction. If the bit is 1, then the condition-code values are affected by the execution of the instruction. If it is 0, then the condition codes will not be affected. This adds an additional 17 new operation codes with a 1 in opcode position 4 and 17 new mnemonic codes to the architecture. These opcodes must not overlap the existing operation codes, and the mnemonics are formed by appending C to the current mnemonics in Table 10-1. These modifications permit flexible use of the condition codes in making decisions at both the ISA level and in the microcode. In both cases, the actual control of condition-code loading is passed through a bit LD in the control words for the RISC pipeline.

Datapath Modifications

Several changes to the datapath are required to support the ISA modifications. These changes will be covered beginning with the datapath components in the DOF stage in Figure 10-20.

First, modifications are made to the Constant unit to handle the change in the length of the target offset. Logic added to the Constant unit extracts a constant, $IM_S = IR_{9:0}$, from constant IM. Sign extension is applied to IM_S to obtain a 32-bit word. Also, for use in comparisons with condition-code values, an 8-bit constant CA is provided from the microinstruction register, MIR, in the microprogrammed control. This constant is zero filled to form a 32-bit word. The CS control field for the Constant unit is expanded to two bits to perform selection from among the four possible constant sources.

Second, the Register address logic from the multiple-cycle computer in Chapter 8 is added to the address inputs of the Register file. The purpose of this change is to support the ISA modification that provides 16 temporary registers and 16 registers that are a part of the storage resources. An additional mode supports the use of DX as a register-file source address with BX as the corresponding register-file destination address. This is necessary to capture the contents for $R[DR]$ for use in destination address mode calculations.

☐ **FIGURE 10-20**
Pipelined CISC CPU

Third, a number of changes are made to support the modification adding condition codes. In the DOF stage, an additional port is added on MUX *A* in order to provide access to *CC*, the stored condition codes, for storage in temporary registers or comparison to constant values. In the EX stage, the condition-code bit L (less than) is implemented and the condition-code register *CC* is added to the pipeline platform. The new control signal LC determines whether *CC* is loaded for the execution of a specific microoperation using a function unit operation. In the WB stage, the logic for support of the SLT instruction is replaced by a zero-filled *CC* value, which is passed to the new port on MUX *A*. Since the new condition-code structure provides support for the same decision making as SLT did and more, support for SLT is no longer needed.

Control Unit Modifications

The addition of a microprogrammed control to the control unit to support instruction implementation using multiple passes through the pipeline causes significant changes to the existing control, as shown in Figure 10-20. The microprogrammed control is a part of the instruction decoding hardware in the DOF stage, but it interacts with other parts of the control as well. For convenience, it will be described separately.

A quick overview of the execution of a multiple-pass instruction provides a perspective for the control unit changes. The *PC* points to the instruction in the Instruction memory. The instruction is fetched in the IF stage, and on the next clock edge it is loaded into the *IR* and the *PC* is updated. The instruction is identified as a multiple-pass instruction from its opcode. Decoding of the opcode changes signal MI to 1 to indicate that this instruction is to use the microprogrammed control. The decoder also produces an 8-bit starting address, SA, that identifies the beginning of the microprogram in the Microcode ROM. Since multiple passes through the pipeline are needed to implement the instruction, the loading of subsequent instructions into the *IR* and further updating of the *PC* must be prevented. A signal MS produced by the microprogrammed control logic becomes 1 and stalls the *PC* and the *IR*. This prevents the *PC* from incrementing, but permits $PC + 1$ to continue down the pipeline into PC_{-1} and PC_{-2} for use in a branch. This stall remains until the multiple-pass instruction has been executed or until there is branch or jump action on the *PC*. Also, when MI = 1, most of the fields of the decoded instruction are replaced with fields of the current microinstruction, which is a decoded NOP (no operation). This 31-bit field replacement, performed by MUX I, prevents the instruction itself from causing any direct actions. Some changes have been made to the control word to control modified datapath resources. Fields CS and MA have been expanded to two bits each, and field LC has been added. At this point, the microprogrammed control is now controlling the pipeline and supplies a series of microinstructions (control words) to implement the instruction execution. The control word format follows that for the multiple cycle computer and includes fields such as SH, AX, BX, and DX. DX is modified to match the register address changes described for the datapath. In addition, the microprogrammed control has to interact with the datapath in order to perform decisions. This interaction includes application of the constant CA, use of the condition codes *CC*, and use of the zero detect signal *Z*.

To support the operations just discussed, the following changes are made to the control unit:

1. the addition of the stall signal MS to the *PC*, PC_{-1}, and *IR*,

2. changes in the instruction decoder to produce MI and ST,

3. expansion of the fields CS and MA to two bits,

4. addition of MUX I, and

5. addition of control fields AX, BX, and DX, and LC.

The definitions of new and modified control fields are given in Table 10-4.

Except for the addition of the microprogrammed control discussed in the next section, this completes the changes to the control unit.

Microprogrammed Control

A block diagram for the microprogrammed control and the format for microinstructions appear in Figure 10-21. The control is centered about the Microcode ROM, which has an 8-bit address and stores up to 256 41-bit microinstructions. The microprogram counter MC stores the address corresponding to the current microinstruction stored in the microinstruction register, MIR. The address for the ROM is provided by MUX E, which selects from the incremented MC, the jump address obtained from the microinstruction, CA, the prior value of the jump address, CA_{-1}, and the starting address from the instruction decoder in the control unit, SA. Table 10-5 defines the 2-bit select input ME for MUX E and stall bit, MS, in terms of the new control field MZ plus other variables. This function is implemented by the Microaddress Control logic. To set the context for the discussion, in location 0 of

□ **TABLE 10-4**
   Added or Modified Control Word (Microinstruction) Fields for CISC

Control Fields				Register Fields		CS		MA		LC	
MZ 2b	CA 8h	BS 2b	P S	Action	Code 5h	Action	Code 2b	Action	Code 2b	Action	Code
See Table 10-5	Next Address or Constant	See Table 10-2		**AX, BX**		zf IM	00	A Data	00	Hold CC	0
						se IM	01	PC_{-1}	01	Load CC	1
				R[SA], R[SB]	0X	se IM$_S$	10	$0 \parallel CC$	10		
				R_{16}	10	zf CA	11				
				...	...						
				R_{31}	1F '						
				DX							
				Source R[DR] and Dest. R[SB]	00						
				Dest R[DR] with X $\ne$ 0	0X						
				R_{16}	10						
				...	...						
				R_{31}	1F						

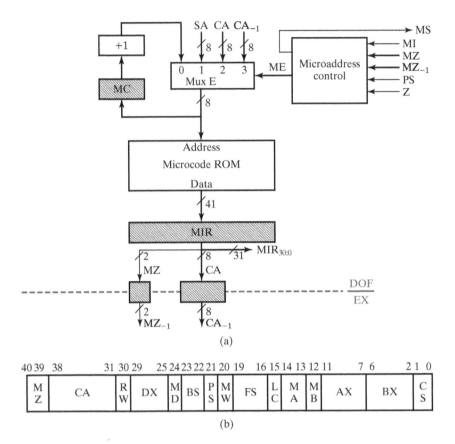

☐ **FIGURE 10-21**
Pipelined CISC CPU: Microprogrammed Control

the ROM, the IDLE state 0 for the microprogrammed control contains a microinstruction that is a NOP consisting of all zeros. This microinstruction has $MZ = 0$ and $CA = 0$. From Table 10-5, with $MI = 0$, the microprogram address is $CA = 0$, causing the control to remain in this state until $MI = 1$. With $MI = 1$, starting address SA is applied to fetch the first microinstruction of the microprogram for the complex instruction being held in IR. In the control unit, $MI = 1$ also switches MUX I from the normal control word coming from the decoder to the 31-bit MIR portion that is a NOP instruction. In addition, the output MS from the Microaddress control becomes 1, stalling the PC, PC_{-1}, and the IR in the main control. At the next clock edge, the microinstruction fetched from the starting address SA enters the MIR, and the pipeline is now controlled by the microprogram.

In Figure 10-21, two pipeline registers are required as a part of the microprogrammed control. The stored pipeline values, MZ_{-1} and CA_{-1}, are required for the execution of a conditional microbranch, since the value of Z to be tested occurs during the execution cycle for the microbranch instruction, one clock cycle after it enters the MIR.

During the execution of the microprogram, the microaddress is controlled by MZ, MZ_{-1}, MI, PS, and Z. For $MZ_{-1} = 11$, $MZ = 01$ since the microinstruction following a

□ **TABLE 10-5**
   Address Control

Inputs					Outputs			
MZ_{-1}	MZ	MI	PS	Z	ME_1	ME_0	MS	Register Transfer Due to ME
11	01	X	0	0	0	0	1	$\overline{PS}\cdot\overline{Z}: MC \leftarrow MC + 1$
11	01	X	0	1	0	1	1	$\overline{PS}\cdot Z: MC \leftarrow CA_{-1}$
11	01	X	1	0	0	0	1	$PS\cdot\overline{Z}: MC \leftarrow CA_{-1}$
11	01	X	1	1	0	0	0	$PS\cdot Z: MC \leftarrow MC + 1$
0X	01	X	X	X	0	0	1	$MC \leftarrow MC + 1$
X0	01	X	X	X	0	0	1	$MC \leftarrow MC + 1$
XX	00	0	X	X	1	0	0	$MC \leftarrow CA$
XX	00	1	X	X	0	1	1	$MC \leftarrow ST$
XX	10	X	0	X	1	0	0	$\overline{PS}: MC \leftarrow CA$
XX	10	X	1	X	1	0	1	$PS: MC \leftarrow CA$
XX	11	X	X	X	0	0	1	$MC \leftarrow MC + 1$

conditional microbranch must be a NOP. Under these conditions, the ME values are controlled by PS and Z with MS = 1. For PS and Z having opposite values, a conditional branch to the microaddress value from CA_{-1} occurs. Otherwise, for $MZ_{-1} = 11$ and MZ = 01, the next microaddress becomes the incremented value of MC.

For $MZ_{-1} \neq 11$, MZ, MI, and PS control the microaddress. For MZ = 00, the values of ME and MS are controlled by MI. For MI = 0, the next microaddress is CA and MS = 0, corresponding to the idle state for the microprogrammed control. For MI = 1, the next microaddress is SA and MS = 1, selecting the next microinstruction from the Microcode ROM and stalling the first two pipeline platforms. For MZ = 01, the next microaddress is the incremented value of MC, advancing execution to the next microinstruction in sequence. For MZ = 10, an unconditional jump is performed in the microcode control and the value of MS is controlled by PS. PS = 1 causes MS = 1, continuing microprogram execution. PS = 0 forces MS = 0, removing the stall, and returning control to the pipeline. This causes MI to become 0 (if the new instruction is not also a complex one). If CA = 0, the microprogrammed control is locked the IDLE state until MI = 1. In order for this to happen, the final instruction in the microprogram must have MZ = 10, PS = 0, and CA = 0.

Microprograms for Complex Instructions

Three examples illustrate complex instructions implemented by using the CISC capabilities provided by the design just completed. The resulting microprograms are given in Table 10-6.

☐ **TABLE 10-6**
Example Microprograms for CISC Architecture

				Microinstructions												
				R	M		PM				L	M				
Action	Address	MZ	CA	W	DX	D	BS	S	W	FS	C	MA	B	AX	BX	CS
Shared Microinstructions																
MI: $MC \leftarrow ST$, $\overline{MI}: MC \leftarrow 00$	IDLE	00	00	0	00	0	00	0	0	0	0	00	0	00	00	00
$MC \leftarrow MC + 1$ (NOP)	Arbitrary	01	XX	0	00	0	00	0	0	0	0	00	0	00	00	00
Load Indirect Indexed (LII)																
$R_{16} \leftarrow R[SA] +$ zf IM_L	LII0	01	00	1	10	0	00	0	0	2	0	00	1	00	00	00
$MC \leftarrow MC + 1$ (NOP)	LII1	01	00	0	00	0	00	0	0	0	0	00	0	00	00	00
$R_{17} \leftarrow M[R_{16}]$	LII2	01	00	1	11	1	00	0	0	0	0	00	0	10	00	00
$MC \leftarrow MC + 1$ (NOP)	LII3	01	00	0	00	0	00	0	0	0	0	00	0	00	00	00
$R[DR] \leftarrow M[R_{17}]$	LII4	10	IDLE	1	01	1	00	0	0	0	0	00	0	11	00	00
Compare Less Than or Equal To (BLE)																
$R[SA]-R[SB]$, $CC \leftarrow L\|Z\|N\|C\|V$	BLE0	01	00	0	01	0	00	0	0	5	1	00	0	00	00	00
$MC \leftarrow MC + 1$ (NOP)	BLE1	01	00	0	00	0	00	0	0	0	0	00	0	00	00	00
$R_{31} \leftarrow CC \wedge 11000$	BLE2	01	18	1	1F	0	00	0	0	8	0	10	1	00	00	11
$MC \leftarrow MC + 1$ (NOP)	BLE3	01	00	0	00	0	00	0	0	0	0	00	0	00	00	00
if $(R_{31} \neq 0)\ MC \leftarrow$ BLE7 else $MC \leftarrow MC + 1$	BLE4	11	BLE7	0	00	0	00	1	0	0	0	00	0	1F	00	00
$MC \leftarrow MC + 1$ (NOP)	BLE5	01	00	0	00	0	00	0	0	0	0	00	0	00	00	00
$MC \leftarrow$ IDLE	BLE6	00	IDLE	0	00	0	00	0	0	0	0	00	0	00	00	00
$PC \leftarrow (PC_{-1}) +$ se IM_L, $MC \leftarrow$ IDLE	BLE7	10	IDLE	0	00	0	11	0	0	0	0	01	1	00	00	00
Move Memory Block (MMB)																
$R_{16} \leftarrow R[SB]$	MMB0	01	00	1	10	0	00	0	0	C	0	00	0	00	00	00
$MC \leftarrow MC + 1$ (NOP)	MMB1	01	00	0	00	0	00	0	0	0	0	00	0	00	00	00
$R_{16} \leftarrow R_{16} -1$	MMB2	01	01	1	10	0	00	0	0	5	0	00	1	00	00	11
$R_{17} \leftarrow R[DR]$	MMB3	01	00	1	00	0	00	0	0	C	0	00	0	00	11	00
$R_{18} \leftarrow R[SA] + R_{16}$	MMB4	01	00	1	12	0	00	0	0	2	0	00	0	00	10	00
$R_{19} \leftarrow R_{17} + R_{16}$	MMB5	01	00	1	13	0	00	0	0	2	0	00	0	11	10	00
$R_{20} \leftarrow M[R_{18}]$	MMB6	01	00	1	14	1	00	0	0	0	0	00	0	12	00	00
$MC \leftarrow MC + 1$ (NOP)	MMB7	01	00	0	00	0	00	0	0	0	0	00	0	00	00	00
$M[R_{19}] \leftarrow R_{20}$	MMB8	01	00	0	00	0	00	0	1	0	0	00	0	13	14	00
if $(R_{16} \neq 0)MC \leftarrow$ MMB2	MMB9	11	MMB2	0	00	0	00	1	0	0	1	00	0	10	00	00
$MC \leftarrow MC + 1$ (NOP)	MMB10	01	00	0	00	0	00	0	0	0	0	00	0	00	00	00
$MC \leftarrow$ IDLE	MMB11	10	IDLE	0	00	0	00	0	0	0	0	00	0	00	00	00

EXAMPLE 10-1   LD Instruction with Indirect Indexed Addressing (LII)

The LII instruction adds the target offset to the contents of a register that is being used as an index register. In the indirection step, the indexed address formed is then used to fetch the effective address from memory. Finally, the effective address is used to fetch the operand from memory. The opcode for this instruction is 0110001, and the instruction uses the Immediate format with the SA register field and a 15-bit target offset. When the LII instruction is fetched and appears in the *IR*, the instruction decoder sets MI equal to 1 and provides the microcode address symbolically represented by LII0 in Table 10-6. The first microinstruction to be executed is the one appearing in the IDLE address. This microoperation executes a NOP in the datapath and memory, but in the presence of MI = 1, the address control selects SA as the next microinstruction address, thereby leaving the IDLE state. The LII0 microinstruction forms the indexed address and increments the address in *MC* to fetch the next microinstruction LII1. This causes the NOP microinstruction in address LII1 to be fetched for execution in the pipeline. This NOP has been inserted, since the result of the microinstruction in LII0 is not placed in R_{16} until the WB stage. The next microinstruction in LII2 fetches the effective address from memory. A NOP is required next, due to the clockcycle delay in writing the effective address to R_{17}. The microinstruction in LII4 applies the effective address to the memory to obtain the operand and place it in the destination register *R*[DR]. Since this completes the LII implementation, the microprogrammed control state in *MC* returns to IDLE and the next instruction following LII is fetched from the instruction memory by using the address in the *PC*. ■

In Table 10-6, this sequence of microinstructions is described in the Action column by register transfer statements, and symbolic names are provided for the addresses of the microinstructions in the Microcode ROM. The remainder of the columns in the table provides the coding of the microinstruction fields. These codes are selected from Tables 8-12, 10-2, 10-3, and 10-5, to implement the register transfers. Of particular note is the appearance of MC = 10, PS = 0, and CA = IDLE (00) in microinstruction LII4, causing the microprogram control to return to IDLE and program control to return to the pipeline control.

EXAMPLE 10-2   Branch on Less Than or Equal to (BLE)

The BLE instruction compares the contents of registers *R*[SA] and *R*[SB]. If *R*[SA] is less than or equal to *R*[SB], then the *PC* branches to *PC* + 1 plus the sign-extended Short Target Offset (IM$_S$). Otherwise, the incremented *PC* is used. The opcode for the instruction is 1100101.

The register transfers for the instruction are given in the Action column of Table 10-6. In microinstruction BLE0, *R*[SB] is subtracted from *R*[SA] and the condition codes *L* through *V* are captured in register *CC*. Due to the one-cycle delay in writing to *CC*, a NOP is required in microinstruction BLE1. *R*[SA] is less than or equal to *R*[SB] if $(L + Z) = 1$ (+ is OR in this expression). Thus, of the five condition-code bits, only *L* and *Z* are of interest. So in microinstruction BLE2, the least significant three bits of *CC* are masked out using the mask 11000 ANDed with *CC*. The result is placed in register R_{31}, and, in BLE3, another NOP is required waiting for R_{31} to be written. In BLE4, a microbranch on R_{31} nonzero occurs. If R_{31} is nonzero, then $L + Z = 1$, giving *R*[SA] less than or equal to *R*[SB]. Otherwise, both *L* and *Z* are 0, indicating *R*[SA] is not less than or equal to *R*[SB]. Due to the micro-branch, a NOP is required in BLE5. The connections to MUX E require only one

NOP after a microbranch instead of the two NOPs needed for the conditional branch in the main control. If the branch is not taken, the next microinstruction BLE6 executes, returning *MC* to IDLE and reactivating the pipeline control to execute the next instruction. If the branch is taken, microinstruction BLE7 is executed, placing *PC* + 1 + BrA into the *PC* for fetching the next instruction when the microinstruction reaches the EX stage. Note that such a branch on the *PC* can take place only after MS becomes 0 and the pipeline is reactivated. In this regard, a control hazard exists for this instruction in the main control, so it must be followed by a NOP. The codes for the microinstruction fields appear in Table 10-6. ■

EXAMPLE 10-3 Move Memory Block (MMB)

The MMB instruction copies a block of information from one set of contiguous locations in memory to another. It has opcode 0100011 and uses the three-register type format. Register *R*[SA] specifies address A, the beginning location of the source block in memory, and register *R*[DR] specifies address B, the beginning location of the destination block. *R*[SB] gives the number *n* of words in the block.

The register transfers for the instruction are given in the Action column of Table 10-6. In microinstruction MMB0, *R*[SB] is loaded into R_{16}. MMB1 contains a NOP waiting for R_{16} to be written. In MMB2, R_{16} is decremented, providing an index with *n* values, *n* − 1 down to 0, for use in addressing the copying of *n* words. Since *R*[DR] is a destination register, it is ordinarily not available as a source. But to do address manipulation for the destination locations, it is necessary for its value to be placed in a register that can act as a source. Thus, in MMB3, the value of *R*[DR] is copied to register R_{17} by using the register code DX = 00000, which treats *R*[DR] as the source and the register specified in the BX field, R_{17}, as the destination. In microinstructions MMB4 and MMB5, R_{16} is added to *R*[SA] and to *R*[SB] to serve as pointers to the addresses in the blocks. Due to these operations, the words in the blocks are transferred from the highest location first. In MMB6, the first word is transferred from the first source address in memory to temporary register R_{20}. In MMB7, a NOP appears to permit the writing of the value in R_{20} by MMB6 before the use of the value by MMB8. In MMB8, the first word is transferred from R_{20} to the first destination address in memory. In MMB9, a branch on zero is done on the contents of R_{16} to determine if all of the words in the block have been transferred. If not, then MM2 is the next microaddress in which the next word transfer begins. If R_{16} equals zero, the next microinstruction is the NOP placed in MMB10 due to the branch. The final microinstruction in MMB11 returns *MC* to IDLE and returns execution back to the pipeline control.

The codes for the microinstructions appear in Table 10-6. The code consists of simple register and memory transfers with a single branch to provide the looping capability and NOPs to deal with data and control hazards. ■

10-5 MORE ON DESIGN

The two designs considered in this chapter represent two different ISAs and two different supporting CPU architectures. The RISC architecture matches well with the pipelined control organization because of the simplicity of the instructions. Due to the need for high performance, the modern CISC architecture presented is built upon the RISC foundation. In this section, we will deal with additional features for speeding up the fundamental RISC pipeline.

Advanced CPU Concepts

Among the various methods used to design advanced CPUs are multiple units organized as a pipeline-parallel structure, superpipelines, and superscalar architectures.

Consider the case in which an operation takes multiple clock cycles to execute, but the instruction fetch and write-back operations can be handled in a single cycle. Then it is possible to initiate an instruction every clock cycle, but not possible to complete the execution of an instruction every cycle. In such a situation, the performance of the CPU can be substantially improved by having multiple execution units in parallel. A high-level block diagram for this kind of system is shown in Figure 10-22. The instruction fetch, decoding, and operand fetch, and branches are carried out in the I-unit

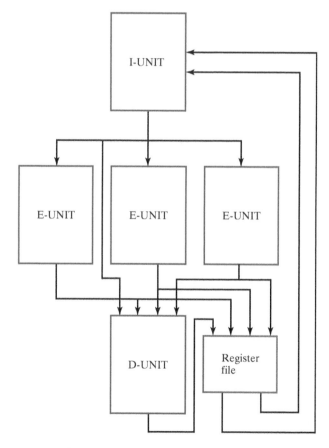

☐ **FIGURE 10-22**
Multiple Execution Unit Organization

pipeline. When decoding of a nonbranch instruction has been completed, the instruction and operands are *issued* to the appropriate E-unit. When execution of the instruction is completed by the E-unit, the write-back to the register file occurs. If a memory access is required, then the D-unit is used to execute the memory operation. If the operation is a store, it goes immediately to the D-unit.

In all of the methods considered thus far, the peak throughput possible is one instruction per clock cycle. With this limitation, it is desirable to maximize the clock rate by minimizing the maximum pipeline stage delay. If, as a consequence, a large number of pipeline stages is used, the CPU is said to be *superpipelined*. A superpipelined CPU will generally have a very high clock frequency, in the range of a few to several GHz. In such an organization, however, handling hazards effectively is critical, since any stalling or reinitialization of the pipeline will degrade the performance of the CPU significantly. Also, as more pipeline stages are added, further dividing up the combinational logic, the setup and propagation delay times of the flip-flops begin to dominate the platform-to-platform delay and the speed of the clock. The improvement achieved is less, and when hazards are taken into account, the performance may actually become worse rather than better.

For fast execution, an alternative to superpipelining is the use of a *superscalar* architecture. Its goal is to have a peak rate of issuing instructions for execution in excess of one instruction per clock cycle. A superscalar CPU that fetches a pair of instructions simultaneously by using a double-word wide path from instruction memory is illustrated in Figure 10-23. The processor checks for hazards among the instructions, as well as available execution units in the instruction issue stage of the pipeline. If there are hazards or busy execution units corresponding to the first instruction, then both instructions are held for later issuing. If the first instruction has no hazard and its E-unit is available, but there is a hazard or no available E-unit for the second instruction, then only the first instruction is issued. Otherwise, both instructions are issued in parallel. If a given superscalar architecture is triple issue, then it has the ability to issue up to three instructions simultaneously, and a peak execution rate of three instructions per clock cycle. Note that the hazard checking for instructions in both the issue and execution stages becomes very complex as the maximum number of instructions issued simultaneously is increased.

Following are three methods for preventing hazards from stalling the pipeline in superpipelined and superscalar processors.

Instead of waiting for a branch to be taken, a processor predicts which way a branch is expected to go and proceeds to speculatively execute down that path. In addition, execution continues in order to determine the path the branch actually takes. When the result of the branch becomes available, if it does not match the speculated direction, the speculated results are quashed and the actual branch taken is followed. If the speculated direction is correct, then the pipeline delay waiting for the branch to occur is eliminated, significantly improving performance. *Branch predictors* must achieve a high rate of correct speculation in order to achieve performance improvement. Branch prediction is based on various approaches to recording the recent history of branches taken/not taken. In sophisticated prediction schemes, results from multiple predictors are often combined

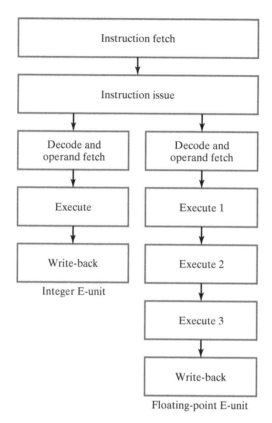

□ **FIGURE 10-23**
Superscalar Organization

to achieve high rates of correct speculation, even with complex, and sometimes irregular, branching patterns.

Instead of waiting to load data from memory until it is known that the data is needed, *speculative loading* of data from memory is performed. The purpose is to avoid the relatively long delay required to fetch an operand from memory. If the data that is speculatively fetched turns out to be the data needed, then it will be available and the computation can proceed immediately with no waiting for a memory access to get the data.

Extending this further, *data speculation* uses methods to predict data values and use the predicted values to proceed with computation. When the actual value becomes known and matches the predicted value, then the result produced from the predicted value can be used to carry forward the computation. If the actual value and the predicted value differ, then the result based on the predicted value is discarded and the actual value is used to continue computation. An example of data speculation is permitting a value to be loaded from memory before a store into the same memory location occurring earlier in the program has been executed. In this case, it is predicted that the store will not change the value of the data loaded from memory. If, at the time the store executes, the loaded value is not valid, the result of computation using it is discarded. Data speculation is often used in *prefetching*—executing loads before stores upon which the loaded values may depend have been completed.

All of these techniques perform operations or sequences of operations for which results are discarded with some frequency. Thus, there is "wasted" computation. To be able to do large amounts of useful computation, as well as the wasted computation, more parallel resources, as well as specialized hardware for implementing the techniques, are required. The payoff in return for the cost of these resources is higher performance.

Recent Architectural Innovations

The techniques in the previous section all have the goal of exploiting *instruction level parallelism* (*ILP*), which in conjunction with advancements in integrated circuit technology resulted in the sustained rise in microprocessor performance over the last three decades of the 20th century. All of the ILP advances, however, have come with an increase in complexity, and, most notably, a seemingly never-ending increase in power needs. Around the millennium, it became very apparent that further increases in performance due to ILP were diminishing. This recognition, along with the continuing advancements in IC technology, have combined to set a new direction for performance improvement to begin the 21st century, namely, the use of multiple-CPU-processors on a single chip in servers and desktop and laptop PCs. This section covers two of the directions in this changing approach to performance, targeting two somewhat differing goals: general-purpose applications and digital media applications.

MIMD AND SYMMETRIC ON-CHIP CORE MULTIPROCESSORS   Multiple cores have appeared in microprocessors for servers and, more recently, for the PC market. These products resemble shared-memory symmetric (identical) multiprocessors, and are categorized as multiple-instruction-stream, multiple-data-stream (MIMD) microprocessors. In such systems, advantages can be achieved by executing in parallel (1) multiple programs and/or (2) multiple threads. (A thread is a process that has its own data, instructions, and processor state.) Multiple cores can execute a program by dedicating one of the CPUs to its execution or by executing the program's threads on multiple CPUs to improve performance over single-CPU microprocessors. For example, a complex image-processing program can run on a single CPU while word processing or web browsing takes place on a second CPU. Alternatively, the image-processing program can be spread over two cores by running the threads of the program distributed across two CPUs. We use the Intel Core 2 Duo and the more recent Core i7 as an illustration of a multicore microprocessor. These designs not only achieve performance improvements via multiple CPUs, but also advancements in instruction-level parallelism as well.

EXAMPLE 10-4   The Intel Core 2 Duo and Core i7 Microprocessors

The Core 2 Duo is a microprocessor product introduced by Intel in July 2006. The dual symmetric processors each have their own level 1 (L1) instruction and data caches[1] and share a common unified level 2 (L2) cache of either 2 or 4 MB capacity, depending on the particular Core 2 Duo product. The L2 cache is the pair of large dark blocks at the bottom of the cover background. Each core is a superscalar processor with a quad-issue 14-stage pipeline, a pipeline length decreased by 35 percent from recent Intel microprocessor designs, showing a move away from focus on an increase in clock rate based on a superpipeline. In addition, the number of execution units in each processor has been increased significantly to support the four-issue strategy and multimedia performance. Intel has also introduced *macrofusion*, in which multiple machine-level instructions are issued within a single microinstruction (called a µop by Intel), providing an increase in maximum instruction issue rate of one beyond that achieved by the broader issue path alone. In order to achieve a high memory bandwidth, the path from the L2 cache to each core is 256 bits wide. Further, there is an elaborate data prefetch mechanism to improve the performance of all three data caches. Prefetch is used to load data before it is needed for computation by predicting what data will be needed and whether or not the data will change after it has been prefetched. If the latter is the case, then the data will need to be loaded again after the store affecting its value has occurred. *Memory disambiguation* is the term applied to doing prefetch and cleaning up the situation in the event that stale data has been loaded into any of the caches.

Technologically, the Core 2 Duo has been fabricated using a 65 nm technology (gate lengths of 35 nm) and has embedded temperature sensors in the chip that are used to control the fan speed, power voltage values, and clock frequencies. Power reduction is also achieved by clock and power gating of entire blocks and unused portions of buses. These techniques have little impact on performance, while providing significantly reduced power consumption.

More recently, Intel has introduced a range of multicore microprocessors called Core i3, Core i5, and Core i7, targeting different price-performance breakpoints, with Core i3 intended for entry-level applications, Core i5 intended for midrange applications, and Core i7 intended for high-performance applications. Even within each line, there are variants intended for desktop and mobile (low power) markets. As of mid-2014, the Core i7 is available in 2-, 4-, and 6-core versions, with an 8-core version soon to be released. Unlike the Core 2 Duo, each Core i7 has its own L2 cache and all of the processors share a common unified level 3 (L3) cache. The Core i7 is currently constructed using a 22 nm technology.   ■

SIMD AND VECTOR PROCESSING   The history of single-instruction-stream, multiple-data-stream (SIMD) processors and vector processing goes back to the 1960s and 70s, with the beginnings of the Illiac IV project at the University of Illinois,

---

[1]For the basics on caches and multilevel caches, see Section 12-3.

and with two commercial vector-processing products announced in 1972. These were followed over the next two decades by a number of supercomputers targeted primarily at scientific applications. In response to the need for vector processing in PC microprocessors for multimedia applications, Intel introduced the MMX extensions to the Pentium instruction set in 1997 and Advanced Micro Devices (AMD) added 3DNow! to the Athalon instruction set in 1998. Multiple sets of SSE (streaming SIMD extensions) have been added over time by Intel and AMD. IBM/Motorola (Freescale) also introduced Altivec extensions in its PowerPC line. The basic approach in current microprocessors uses a set of 128-bit registers dedicated to these SIMD/vector operations, with each instruction performing the same operations on bytes, half-words, words, or double words within the 128-bit registers. Most recently, SIMD has been central to the collaborative development by IBM, Sony, and Toshiba of the Broadband Processor Architecture and its first-generation product, the Cell processor for Sony's Playstation 3 launched in November 2006. The following example summarizes briefly the architecture of the Cell processor.

EXAMPLE 10-5   The STI Cell Processor

The Cell processor is based on the PowerPC architecture. It consists of nine cores plus a very fast RAMBUS on-chip memory controller and a controller for a configurable I/O interface. One of the cores is a 64-bit Power Processor Element (PPE) with first-level instruction and data caches and 512 KB second-level caches. It supports execution of two instruction threads by use of a dual multiprocessor with shared dataflow. The integer pipeline has 23 stages. There are 128 128-bit registers per thread for SIMD instructions handling 2×64, 4×32, 8×16, 16×8, and 128×1 element widths. The remaining eight processors are Synergistic Processor Elements (SPEs), each with (1) 128×128 bit register files with same element sizes as the PPE and (2) a local store implemented in SRAM of 256 KB. The number of parallel actions of the set of SPEs permits from 16 simultaneous parallel operations on 64-bit operands to 1024 simultaneous parallel operations on 1-bit operands. The PPE and SPEs are connected by a coherent on-chip Element Interconnection Bus (EIB) using Direction Memory Access (DMA) communication on a very highspeed set of four 128-bit wide bus rings. In the original Playstation 3, the chip is constructed with an advanced high-speed, low-voltage, low-power, 90 nm silicon-on-insulator (SOI) CMOS technology. Due to the need to carefully control the thermal environment of the Cell chip, 11 temperature sensors are built into the chip that are used to provide thermal protection and control the cooling system in the Playstation 3. The more recent "slim" versions of the Playstation 3 use a Cell processor constructed using a 45 nm CMOS technology, resulting in power consumption that is less than 40% of the original 90 nm version. To form a symmetric multiprocessor system, two Cell processors can be connected together directly. Four Cell processors require a broadband switch to handle the four bidirectional broadband device interfaces. ∎

GRAPHICS PROCESSING UNITS   Related to the introduction of SIMD capabilities to CPUs is the development of graphics processing units (GPUs), which grew from the addition of functions for accelerating 2D and 3D graphics to video graphics controllers. GPUs are a distinct category from the CPUs that are the focus of this text, with their own nomenclature and a narrower focus on graphics- and video-related applications. GPUs are not intended to replace CPUs but rather to serve as a co-processor for improved graphics. Despite this distinction, they are worthy of note because, much as the increased vector functionality of CPUs has permitted them to better handle graphics applications, the increased scalar functionality of GPUs has allowed them to be used for non-graphics applications that can benefit from high-performance vector processing, particularly in the area of scientific computing. Using GPUs for non-graphics applications, typically referred to as *general-purpose computing on graphics processing units* (GPGPU), has benefited from several efforts to develop general purpose programming languages for GPUs instead of relying on graphics languages and application programming interfaces. In terms of architectural approaches, GPUs do not fit cleanly into the MIMD/SIMD categories described earlier in this section. GPUs exploit both thread-level and data-level parallelism. For example, the GPU manufacturer Nvidia has introduced the term Single Instruction Multiple Thread (SIMT) to describe the style of program execution on their GPU architecture, in which multiple independent threads concurrently execute the same instruction.

10-6 CHAPTER SUMMARY

The focus of this chapter was the design of two processors—one for a reduced instruction set computer (RISC) and one for a complex instruction set computer (CISC). As a prelude to the design of these processors, the chapter began with an illustration of a pipelined datapath. The pipeline concept enables operations to be performed with clock frequencies and throughput not achievable with the same processing components in a conventional datapath. The pipeline execution pattern diagram was introduced for visualizing the behavior of a pipeline and estimating its peak performance. The problem of the low clock frequency of the single-cycle computer was addressed by adding a pipelined control unit to the datapath.

Next, we examined a RISC design with a pipelined datapath and control unit. Based on the single-cycle computer in Chapter 8, the RISC ISA is characterized by a single instruction length, a limited number of instructions with only a few addressing modes, and memory access restricted to load and store operations. Most RISC operations are simple in the sense that, in a conventional architecture, they can be executed using a single microoperation.

The RISC ISA is implemented by using a modified version of the pipelined datapath in Figure 10-2. Likewise, a modified version of the control unit in Figure 10-4 is used. Control changes were performed to accommodate the datapath changes and to handle branches and jumps in a pipeline environment. After completion of the basic design, consideration was given to data hazard and control hazard problems. We examined each type of hazard, as well as software and hardware solutions for each.

The ISA of the CISC has the potential for performing many distinct operations, with memory access supported by several addressing modes. The CISC also has operations that are complex in the sense that they require many clock cycles for their execution. The CISC also has complex conditional branching supported by condition codes (status bits). Although, in general, a CISC ISA permits multiple instruction lengths, this feature is not provided by the example architecture.

To provide high throughput, the RISC architecture serves as the core of the CISC architecture. Simple instructions can be executed at the RISC throughput, with complex instructions, executed by multiple passes through the RISC pipeline. RISC datapath modification provided registers for temporary operand storage and condition code storage. Changes to the control unit were required to support these datapath changes. The primary control unit modification, however, was the addition of the microprogram control for execution of complex instructions. Added changes to the RISC control unit were required to integrate the microprogram control into the control pipeline. Examples of microprograms for three complex instructions were provided.

After completing the CISC and RISC designs, we touched on some advanced concepts, including parallel execution units, superpipelined CPUs, superscalar CPUs, and predictive and speculative techniques for high performance. Finally, we considered, and illustrated with real-world examples, a recent major turn in PC microprocessor design toward the use of multiple CPUs and elements rather than increased clock frequencies and more aggressive instruction-level parallelism.

REFERENCES

1. DE GELAS, J. *Intel Core versus AMD's K8 Architecture.* AnandTech (http://www.anandtech.com), May 1, 2006.

2. HENNESSY, J. L. AND D. A. PATTERSON. *Computer Architecture: A Quantitative Approach,* 5th ed. Amsterdam: Elsevier, 2011.

3. KAHLE, J. A. et al. "Introduction to the Cell Multiprocessor", *IBM J. Res. & Dev.,* Vol. 49, No. 4/5 July/September 2005, pp. 589–604.

4. KANE, G. AND J. HEINRICH. *MIPS RISC Architecture.* Englewood Cliffs, NJ: Prentice Hall, 1992.

5. LINDHOLM, E. et al. "NVIDIA Tesla: A Unified Graphics and Computing Architecture," *IEEE Micro,* Vol. 28, No. 2, March–April 2008, pp. 39–55.

6. MANO, M. M. *Computer System Architecture,* 3rd ed. Englewood Cliffs, NJ: Prentice Hall, 1993.

7. PATTERSON, D. A. AND J. L. HENNESSY. *Computer Organization and Design: The Hardware/Software Interface,* 5th ed. Amsterdam: Elsevier, 2013.

8. PHAM, D. et al. "The Design and Implementation of the CELL Processor," *Digest of Technical Papers–2005 IEEE International Solid State Circuits Conf.,* IEEE, 2005, pp. 184–185.

9. SHEN, J. P. and M. H. LIPASTI. *Modern Processor Design: Fundamentals of Superscalar Processors.* New York: McGraw-Hill, 2005.

10. SPARC INTERNATIONAL, INC. *The SPARC Architecture Manual: Version 8.* Englewood Cliffs, NJ: Prentice Hall, 1992.

11. WECHLER, O. *Inside Intel Core Microarchitecture.* White Paper, Intel Corporation, 2006 (www.intel.com).

12. WEISS, S. AND J. E. SMITH. *POWER and PowerPC.* San Mateo, CA: Morgan Kaufmann, 1994.

PROBLEMS

The plus (+) indicates a more advanced problem and the asterisk (*) indicates that a solution is available on the Companion Website for the text.

10-1. A pipelined datapath is similar to that in Figure 10-1(b), but with the delays from the top to the bottom replaced by the following values: 0.5 ns, 0.5 ns, 0.1 ns, 0.1 ns, 0.7 ns, 0.1 ns, and 0.1 ns. Determine (a) the maximum clock frequency, (b) the latency time, and (c) the maximum throughput for this datapath.

10-2. *A program consisting of a sequence of ten instructions without branch or jump instructions is to be executed in an 8-stage pipelined RISC computer with a clock period of 0.5 ns. Determine (a) the latency time for the pipeline, (b) the maximum throughput for the pipeline, and (c) the time required for executing the program.

10-3. Consider an unpipelined processor with a clock period of 2 ns. This processor is remodeled with a five-stage pipeline that adds a latency of 0.3 ns to the clock period. The five stages of the pipeline are Fetch(IF), Decode (ID), Execute(EX), Memory Read(MEM), and Write back (WB).

   (a) Draw the five-stage pipeline.

   (b) What is the ideal speedup obtained by pipelining?

   (c) What is the actual speedup?

10-4. For each of the RISC operations in Table 10-1, list the addressing mode or modes used.

10-5. Simulate the operation of the barrel shifter in Figure 10-9 for each of the following shifts and $A = 3DF3CB4A_{16}$. List the hexadecimal values on the 47 lines, 35 lines, and 32 lines out of the three levels of the shifter.

   (a) Right, $SH = 0F$

   (b) Left, $SH = 1D$

10-6. *For the RISC CPU in Figure 10-8, manually simulate, in hexadecimal, the processing of the instruction ADI R1 R16 2F01 located in $PC = 10F$. Assume that $R16$ contains 0000001F. Show the contents of each of the pipeline platforms and of the register file (the latter only when a change in value occurs) for each of the clock cycles.

10-7. Repeat Problem 10-6 for the instruction LSR R6 R2 001D with $R6$ containing 00000000 and $R2$ containing 01ABCDEF.

10-8. Repeat Problem 10-6 for the instruction SLT R7 R3 R5 with $R3$ containing 0000F001 and $R5$ containing 0000000F.

10-9. Refer to the five-stage pipeline introduced in Problem 10-3. Give an example, with explanation, of a set of instructions that can cause a data hazard in this pipeline.

10-10. +Use a computer-based logic minimization program to design the instruction decoder for a RISC from Table 10-3. Create an HDL model of your design and verify its correctness in simulation.

10-11. *For the RISC design, draw the execution diagram for the following RISC program, and indicate any data hazards that are present:

$$
\begin{array}{lll}
1 & \text{MOVA} & R7, R6 \\
2 & \text{SUB} & R8, R8, R6 \\
3 & \text{AND} & R8, R8, R7
\end{array}
$$

10-12. For the RISC design, draw the execution diagram for the following RISC program (with the contents of $R7$ nonzero after the subtraction), and indicate any data or control hazards that are present:

$$
\begin{array}{lll}
1 & \text{SUB} & R7, R7, R2 \\
2 & \text{BNZ} & R7, 000F \\
3 & \text{AND} & R8, R7, R4 \\
4 & \text{OR} & R4, R8, R2
\end{array}
$$

10-13. *Rewrite the RISC programs in Problems 10-11 and 10-12, using NOPs to avoid all data and control hazards, and draw the new execution diagrams.

10-14. Draw the execution diagrams for the program in Problem 10-11, assuming

(a) RISC CPU with data stall given in Figure 10-12.

(b) RISC CPU with data forwarding in Figure 10-13.

10-15. Simulate the processing of the program in Problem 10-12 using the RISC CPU with data-hazard stall in Figure 10-12. Give the contents of each pipeline platform and the register file (the latter only whenever a change occurs) for each clock cycle. Initially, $R2$ contains 00000010_{16}, $R4$ contains 00000020_{16}, $R7$ contains 00000030_{16}, and the PC contains 00000001_{16}. Is the data hazard avoided?

10-16. *Repeat Problem 10-15 using the RISC CPU with data forwarding in Figure 10-13.

10-17. Draw the execution diagram for the program in Problem 10-12, assuming the combination of the RISC CPU with branch prediction in Figure 10-17 and the RISC CPU with data forwarding in Figure 10-13.

10-18. Design the constant unit in the pipelined CISC CPU by using the information given in Table 10-4 and multiple-bit multiplexers, AND gates, OR gates, and inverters. Create an HDL model of your design and verify its correctness in simulation.

10-19. *Design the register address logic in the pipelined CISC CPU by using information given in the register fields of Table 10-4 plus multiple-bit multiplexers, AND gates, OR gates, and inverters.

10-20. Design the address control logic described by Table 10-5 by using AND gates, OR gates, and inverters.

10-21. Write microcode for the execution part of each of the following CISC instructions. Give both a register transfer description and binary or hexadecimal representations similar to those shown in Table 10-6 for the binary code for each microinstruction.

(a) Branch if overflow

(b) Branch if greater than zero

(c) Compare less than

10-22. Repeat Problem 10-21 for the following CISC instructions that are specified by register transfer statements.

(a) Push: $R[SA] \leftarrow R[SA] + 1$ followed by $M[R[SA]] \leftarrow R[SB]$. Assume DR=SA.

(b) Pop: $R[DR] \leftarrow M[R[SA]]$ followed by $R[SA] \leftarrow R[SA] - 1$. Assume SB=SA.

10-23. *Repeat Problem 10-22 for the following CISC instructions.

(a) Add with carry: $R[DR] \leftarrow R[SA] + R[SB] + C$

(b) Subtract with borrow: $R[DR] \leftarrow R[SA] - R[SB] - B$

Borrow B is defined as the complement of the carry out, C.

10-24. Repeat Problem 10-22 for the following CISC instructions.

(a) Add Memory Indirect: $R[DR] \leftarrow R[SA] + M[M[R[SB]]]$

(b) Add to Memory: $M[R[DR]] \leftarrow M[R[SA]] + R[SB]$

10-25. *Repeat Problem 10-21 for the CISC instruction, Memory Scalar Add. This instruction uses the contents of $R[SB]$ as the vector length. It adds the elements of the vector with its least significant element in memory pointed to by $R[SA]$ and places the result in the memory location pointed to by $R[DR]$.

10-26. Repeat Problem 10-21 for the CISC instruction, Memory Vector Add. This instruction uses the contents of $R[SB]$ as the vector length. It adds the vector with its least significant element in memory pointed to by $R[SA]$ to the vector with its least significant element in memory pointed to by $R[DR]$. The result of the addition replaces the vector with its least significant element pointed to by $R[DR]$.

10-27. PADDB (Add Packed Byte Integers) is the mnemonic for an SSE SIMD instruction in the IA-32 architecture. In the RISC computer in this chapter, the equivalent instruction would add two 32-bit operands by adding the corresponding pairs of four bytes independently, one byte taken from each operand, with the result returned to the third operand, and without setting any condition codes.

(a) For operands $R[SA]$ and $R[SB]$ and destination $R[DR]$, write a register transfer description of this instruction.

(b) What modifications would need to be made to the ALU in the RISC/CISC computer to support this instruction?

10-28. **(a)** In the Core 2 Duo, each core can perform a PMINSW (Minimum of Packed Signed Word Integers) instruction with two 128-bit operands, placing the result back in the first operand. For 16-bit words, how many minimum words can be determined in parallel in the Core 2 Duo?

(b) In the Cell processor, each SPE can perform an "average bytes" instruction on a pair of 128-bit registers RA and RB, with the resulting average byte placed in register RT. How many byte averages can be produced in parallel for all SPEs executing the same instruction?

INPUT–OUTPUT AND COMMUNICATION

I n this chapter, we give an overview of selected aspects of computer input–output (I/O) and communication between the CPU and external I/O devices. Because of the wide variety of different I/O devices and the quest for faster handling of programs and data, I/O is one of the most complex areas of computer design. As a consequence, we are able to present only selected pieces of the I/O puzzle. We illustrate in detail just three devices: a keyboard, a hard drive, and an LCD screen. We then introduce the I/O bus and the I/O interfaces that connect to I/O devices. We look at the Universal Serial Bus (USB), one of many solutions to the problem of accessing I/O devices. Finally, we discuss three modes for performing data transfers: program-controlled transfer, interrupt-initiated transfer, and direct memory access.

Interms of the generic computer at the beginning of Chapter 1, it is apparent that I/O involves a very large part of the computer. Only the processor, external cache, and RAM are not as highly involved, although they, too, are used extensively in directing and performing I/O transfers. Even the generic computer, which has fewer I/O devices than most PC systems, has a diverse set of such devices requiring significant digital electronic hardware for support.

11-1 COMPUTER I/O

The input and output subsystem of a computer provides an efficient mode of communication between the CPU and the outside environment. Programs and data must be entered into the memory for processing, and results obtained from computations must be recorded or displayed. Among the input and output devices commonly found in computer systems are keyboards, displays, printers, magnetic drives, compact disc read-only memory (CD-ROM), and digital video disc read-only memory

(DVD-ROM) drives. Other input and output devices frequently encountered are network devices or other communication interfaces, scanners, and sound cards with speakers and microphones. Significant numbers of computers, such as those used in automobiles, have analog-to-digital converters, digital-to-analog converters, and other data-acquisition and control components.

The I/O facility of a computer is a function of its intended application. This results in a wide diversity of attached devices and corresponding differences in the needs for interacting with them. Since each device behaves differently, it would be time consuming to dwell on the detailed interconnections needed between the computer and each peripheral. We will, therefore, examine just three peripherals that appear in most computers. In addition, we present some of the common characteristics found in the I/O subsystem of computers, as well as the various techniques available for transferring data either in parallel, using many conducting paths, or serially, through communication lines.

11-2 SAMPLE PERIPHERALS

Devices that the CPU controls directly are said to be connected *online*. These devices communicate directly with the CPU or transfer binary information into or out of the memory upon command from the CPU. Input or output devices attached to the computer online are called *peripherals*. In this section, we examine three peripheral devices: a keyboard, a hard drive, and a graphics display. We also use the keyboard as an example to illustrate I/O concepts in a later section. We introduce the hard drive both to motivate the need for direct memory access and to provide background for the role of the device in Chapter 12 as a component in a memory hierarchy. We include the graphics display to illustrate the very high potential transfer-rate requirements of contemporary applications.

Keyboard

The keyboard is among the simplest of the electromechanical devices attached to the typical computer. Since it is manually controlled, it has one of the slowest data rates of any peripheral.

The keyboard consists of a collection of keys that can be depressed by the user. It is necessary to detect which of the keys have been depressed. To do this, a *scan matrix* that lies beneath the keys is used, as shown in Figure 11-1. This two-dimensional matrix is conceptually similar to the matrix used in RAM. The matrix shown in the figure is 8×16, giving 128 intersections, so it can handle up to 128 keys. A decoder drives the X lines of the matrix, which are analogous to the word lines of a RAM. A multiplexer is attached to the Y lines of the matrix, which are analogous to the bit lines of a RAM. The decoder and the multiplexer are controlled by a microcontroller, a tiny computer that contains RAM, ROM, a timer, and simple I/O interfaces.

The microcontroller is programmed to periodically scan all intersections in the matrix by manipulating the control inputs of the decoder and multiplexer. If the key is depressed at an intersection, a signal path is closed from an output of the X

□ **FIGURE 11-1**
Keyboard Scan Matrix

decoder to an input of the Y multiplexer. The existence of this path is sensed at an input to the microcontroller. The 7-bit control code applied to the decoder and multiplexer at the time identifies the key. To allow for "rollover" in typing, in which multiple keys are depressed before any of them is released, the microcontroller actually identifies the depressing and release of the keys. Whether a key is depressed or released, the control code at the time of the event is sensed and is translated by the microcontroller into a *K-scan code*. When a key is depressed, a *make code* is produced; when a key is released, a *break code* is produced. Thus, there are two codes for each key, one for when the key is depressed and one for when it is released. Note that the scanning of the entire keyboard occurs hundreds of times per second, so there is no danger of missing any depression or release of a key.

After presenting a number of I/O interface concepts, we will revisit the keyboard to see what happens to the K-scan codes before they are finally translated to ASCII characters.

Hard Drive

The hard drive is the primary intermediate-speed, nonvolatile, writable storage medium for most computers. The typical hard drive stores information serially on a nonremovable disk, as shown in the upper right of the generic computer at the beginning of Chapter 1. Each platter is magnetizable on one or both surfaces. There are one or more read/write *heads* per recording surface. Each disk is divided into concentric *tracks*, as illustrated in Figure 11-2. The set of tracks that are at the same distance from the center of all disk surfaces is referred to as a *cylinder*. Each track is divided into *sectors* containing a fixed number of bytes. The number of bytes per sector typically ranges from 256 to 4K. In older hard drives, up to the mid-1990s, a typical byte address included the cylinder number, head number, sector number, and word offset within the sector. The addressing assumes that the number of sectors per track is fixed. In modern, high-capacity drives, more sectors are included in the longer outer tracks than in the shorter inner tracks, referred to as *zone bit recording*. In addition, a number of spare sectors are reserved to take the place of defective sectors. Currently available hard drives use logical block addressing (LBA) in which

☐ **FIGURE 11-2**
Hard Disk Format

each sector is addressed using a single integer, with sectors numbered sequentially. The mapping from this address to the physical address is typically accomplished in the drive controller or drive electronics.

To enable information to be accessed, the set of heads is mounted on an actuator that can move the heads radially over the disks, as shown in the generic computer drawing. The time required to move the heads from the current cylinder to the desired cylinder is called the *seek time*. The time required to rotate the disk from its current position to that having the desired sector under the heads is called the *rotational delay*. In addition, a certain amount of time is required by the drive controller to access and output information. This is the *controller time*. The time required to locate a word on the disk is the *disk access time*, which is the sum of the controller time, the seek time, and the rotational delay. Average values over all possibilities are used for these four parameters. Words may be transferred singly, but as we will see in Chapter 12, they are often accessed in blocks. The transfer rate for a block of words, once the block has been located, is the *disk transfer rate*, typically specified in megabytes/second (MB/s). The transfer rate required by the CPU-memory bus to transfer a sector from the drive is the number of bytes in the sector divided by the length of time taken to read a sector from the drive. The length of time required to read a sector is equal to the proportion of the cylinder occupied by the sector divided by the rotational speed of the disks. For example, with 63 sectors, 512 B per sector, a rotational speed of 5400 rpm, and allowance for the gap between sectors, this time is about 0.15 ms, giving a transfer rate of 512/0.15 ms = 3.4 MB/s. The controller will store the information read from the sector in its memory. The sum of the disk access time and the disk transfer rate times the number of bytes per sector gives an estimate of the time required to transfer the information in a sector to or from the hard drive.

EXAMPLE 11-1 Hard Drive Parameters

This example presents parameters for an advanced desktop hard drive in 2014. The drive is 4 TB (with 4 T = 4×10^{12}, not 4×2^{40}). The drive has four disks and eight heads. There are 4096 bytes per sector, and there is a 64 MB buffer in the drive. The average read seek time is <8.5 ms, and the average write seek time is <9.5 ms. The maximum sustained I/O transfer rate is 180 MB per second, with an average rate of 146 MB per second. ■

Liquid Crystal Display Screen

The Liquid Crystal Display (LCD) screen is the primary interactive output device for both laptop and desktop computers. The display screen is defined in terms of picture elements called *pixels*. As this page is being written, it is displayed on a laptop with an LCD screen array of 1366 × 768 pixels. The color display has three subpixels associated with each pixel on the screen. These subpixels correspond to the primary colors red, green, and blue (RGB). A drawing of one pixel for this LCD screen is shown in Figure 11-3(a). The three subpixels are side-by side rectangles with a black mask filling the space between them.

Initially, we examine the liquid crystal display technology by exploring a small square portion of a pixel shown in Figures 11-3(b) and 11-3(c). In a temperature range around room temperature, liquid crystals used in LCDs are in a state between the usual solid and liquid states. In this state, they have crystal properties but are also movable and can be bent, twisted, and so on. The specific liquid crystals used in LCDs, called *nematic liquid crystals*, have limitations on the movements of the molecules. They can be moved in any direction, but can only rotate or wiggle in a single plane. In Figure 11-3(b) a one-molecule thick layer of liquid crystals is illustrated. The molecules are elongated and rod shaped. The axis through the center of the molecules about which they can rotate is shown. The particular display illustrated uses *twisted nematic* (TN) *liquid crystals*. The liquid crystal material is contained in a gap between two substrates (glass plates) that are sealed at the panel edges. Crystal properties are used to align the rod-shaped liquid crystal molecules. The inner surfaces of the substrates are coated and the coating is rubbed with a cloth to produce fine grooves. The direction of the rubbing and the resulting grooves fixes the orientation of the molecules in contact with the coating. In Figure 11-3(b), the rear substrate coating has vertical grooves (as illustrated by the small area at its lower left), and the front substrate coating has horizontal grooves, as likewise illustrated. The liquid crystal molecules align with the grooves they contact on the two substrates. Due to the surrounding molecule structure, the molecules in between the contact layers form a helix with a twist of 90 degrees, as shown in Figure 11-3(b).

To understand how the TN crystal can be used in a display, we need to consider liquid crystal optics, particularly in the presence of polarized light. In general, light waves vibrate in many planes perpendicular to their direction of propagation. Light passing through a filter called a linear polarizer emerges as waves that propagate in a single plane that aligns with the axis of the polarizer. In Figure 11-3(b), beginning at the back of the display, light waves that vibrate in various directions are produced by the backlight panel. The light passes through a linear polarizer with a vertical axis of

(a) LCD screen pixel

(b) Twisted nematic LCD technology

(c) Twisted nematic LCD with maximum voltage applied

☐ **FIGURE 11-3**
Liquid Crystal Screen Details

polarization on the back of the rear substrate. All light emitted from the polarizer has its waves vibrating in the direction of the polarization axis, i.e., vertically. The molecules at the rear of the liquid crystal are likewise oriented vertically. Optically, a liquid crystal layer causes the plane of polarization of light to align with the orientation of its molecules around the axis of rotation. The liquid crystal helix rotates the plane of polarization by 90 degrees, so that the light emerging from the liquid crystal is now horizontal instead of vertical. These horizontal waves align with axis of polarization of the front polarizer located on the front face of the front substrate and are able to pass through it. Thus, the light appears, although much dimmer than the original source, on the face of the display. In each subpixel area, the light has also been colored by passing through a color filter positioned beneath the grooved coating on the front substrate.

The liquid crystal molecules can be rotated by an electric field produced by an applied voltage between electrodes deposited beneath the coatings on the two substrates. In turn, the rotated molecules rotate the plane of polarization of the light passing through the crystal. The total amount of rotation from the rear substrate to the front substrate depends on the value of the voltage applied. In Figure 11-3(c), the maximum voltage necessary has been applied to produce a full 90-degree rotation. At the upper substrate, the plane of polarization is vertical, i.e., perpendicular to the axis of polarization of the polarizer, which is horizontal. In this situation, none of the light waves will pass through the polarizer, giving a black pixel value. Assuming that the voltage applied to each subpixel is obtained from an 8-bit digital signal using a D-to-A converter, 256 voltage values are available to determine the brightness of the subpixel color. Since there are three subpixels per pixel, $2^{8 \times 3} = 2^{24} = 16,777,216$ different colors available for each pixel.

In Figure 11-4, three pixels consisting of nine subpixels are shown with the necessary electronic circuitry within the LCD panel. Ignoring the liquid crystal sandwich for a moment, the remaining circuitry including the capacitance C, the transistor, the gate lines, and the data lines looks exactly like a DRAM using coincident selection via rows and columns. The differences are: (a) there is the liquid crystal subpixel connected across the storage capacitor C, (b) the input to the transistors is a discrete analog signal rather than a digital signal, and (c) the entire circuit is constructed between the two glass substrates using thin film technology rather than a silicon substrate. The circuitry, is placed in a corner of each pixel on the surface of the rear substrate facing the liquid crystal. The transistor, conductors and so on, are separated from the liquid crystal by coating layers including the final one with the fine grooves in it.

In terms of operation, the circuitry behaves much like a DRAM. To write the lower row of elements, the voltage values to be applied are placed on Data Lines m, $m + 1, m + 2$, and so on, a high voltage is placed on Gate Line $n + 3$, and 0 volts is placed on all other Gate Lines. The voltage values are placed on the storage capacitor C and on the upper surface of the subpixel. For technical reasons, the applied

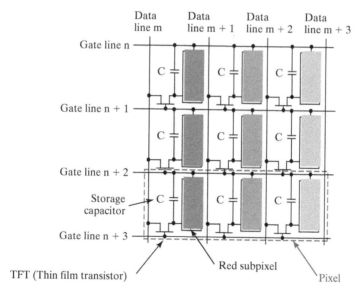

☐ **FIGURE 11-4**
Liquid Crystal Subpixel Array

voltages are inverted each time a row is written. When Gate Line 3 is returned to 0 volts, the transistor turns off and the voltage is stored on capacitance C. The rows of the LCD are successively written one at a time, with a full panel write taking less than a sixtieth of a second.

The inputs to the Data Lines and Gate Lines are provided by the driver circuitry for the LCD panel. In addition, there is a display controller that may be combined with the driver circuitry. The display driver may be driven by digital inputs or analog RGB inputs as used for the older cathode ray tube display technology.

I/O Transfer Rates

An indicated earlier, the three peripheral devices discussed in this section give a sense of the range of peak I/O transfer rates. The keyboard data transfer rate is less than 10 bytes/s. For the hard drive, while the drive controller is capturing the data arriving rapidly from the disc in the sector buffer, the transfer of data from the buffer to main memory is impossible. Thus, in the case in which the next sector is to be read immediately, all of the data from the sector buffer needs to be stored in main memory during the time the gap on the disc between the sectors passes under the disc head. For current desktop hard drives, the peak sustained transfer rate is about 150 MB/s to 180 MB/s. For a 1366 × 768 display using 32-bit color (8 bits for each RGB channel, plus 8 bits for an alpha channel for transparency effects), if the display is to be changed entirely every sixtieth of a second, 4 MB of data must be delivered to the video RAM from the CPU in that amount of time. This requires a data rate of 4 MB × 60 = 240 MB/s. Based on the preceding examples, we can conclude that the peak data rates required by the particular peripherals we have considered have a wide range. The bus system must be designed to handle the highest transfer rates between peripherals and memory.

11-3   I/O INTERFACES

Peripherals connected to a computer need special communication links to interface them with the CPU. The purpose of these links is to resolve the differences in the properties of the CPU and memory and the properties of each peripheral. The major differences are as follows:

1. Peripherals are often electromechanical devices whose manner of operation is different from that of the CPU and memory, which are electronic devices. Therefore, a conversion of signal values may be required.

2. The data-transfer rate of peripherals is usually different from the clock rate of the CPU. Consequently, a synchronization mechanism may be needed.

3. Data codes and formats in peripherals differ from the word format in the CPU and memory.

4. The operating modes of peripherals differ from each other, and each must be controlled in a way that does not disturb the operation of other peripherals connected to the CPU.

To resolve these differences, computer systems include special hardware components between the CPU and the peripherals to supervise and synchronize all input and output transfers. These components are called *interface units*, because they interface between the bus from the CPU and the peripheral device. In addition, each device has its own controller to supervise the operations of the particular mechanism of that peripheral. For example, the controller in a printer attached to a computer controls the motion of the paper, the timing of the printing, and the selection of the characters to be printed.

I/O Bus and Interface Unit

A typical communication structure between the CPU and several peripherals is shown in Figure 11-5. Each peripheral has an interface unit associated with it. The common bus from the CPU is attached to all peripheral interfaces. To communicate with a particular device, the CPU places a device address on the address bus. Each interface attached to the common bus contains an address decoder that monitors the address lines. When the interface detects its own address, it activates the path between the bus lines and the device that it controls. All peripherals with addresses that do not correspond to the address on the bus ignore the bus activity. At the same time that the address is made available on the address bus, the CPU provides a function code on the control lines. The selected interface responds to the function code and proceeds to execute it. If data must be transferred, the interface communicates with both the device and the CPU data bus to synchronize the transfer.

In addition to communicating with the I/O devices, the CPU of a computer must communicate with the memory unit through an address and data bus. There are two ways that external computer buses communicate with memory and I/O. One method uses common data, address, and control buses for both memory and I/O. We

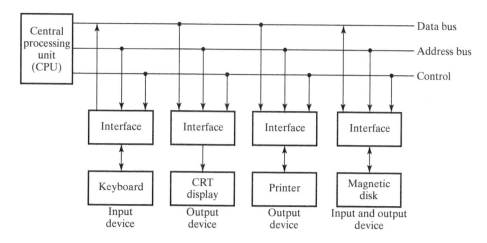

□ **FIGURE 11-5**
Connection of I/O Devices to CPU

have referred to this configuration as *memory-mapped I/O*. The common address space is shared between the interface units and memory words, each having distinct addresses. Computers that adopt the memory-mapped scheme read and write from interface units as if they were assigned memory addresses by using the same instructions that read from and write to memory.

The second alternative is to share a common address bus and data bus, but use different control lines for memory and I/O. Such computers have separate read and write lines for memory and I/O. To read or write from memory, the CPU activates the memory read or memory write control. To perform input to or output from an interface, the CPU activates the read I/O or write I/O control, using special instructions. In this way, the addresses assigned to memory and I/O interface units are independent from each other and are distinguished by separate control lines. This method is referred to as the *isolated I/O configuration*.

Example of I/O Interface

A typical I/O interface unit is shown in block diagram form in Figure 11-6. It consists of two data registers called *ports*, a control register, a status register, a bidirectional data bus, and timing and control circuits. The function of the interface is to translate the signals between the CPU buses and the I/O device and to provide the needed hardware to satisfy the two sets of timing constraints.

The I/O data from the device can be transferred into either port A or port B. The interface may operate with an output device, with an input device, or with a device that requires both input and output. If the interface is connected to a printer, it will only output data; if it services a scanner, it will only input data. A hard drive transfers data in both directions, but not at the same time—so the interface needs only one set of I/O bidirectional data lines.

The *control register* receives control information from the CPU. By loading appropriate bits into this register, the interface and the device can be placed in a variety of operating modes. For example, a printer may be set in a mode that permits cartridges to be changed. The bits in the status register are used for status conditions and for recording errors that may occur during data transfer. For example, a status bit may indicate that port A has received a new data item from the device, while another bit in the status register may indicate that a parity error has occurred during the transfer.

The interface registers communicate with the CPU through the bidirectional data bus. The address bus selects the interface unit through the chip select input and the two register select inputs. A circuit (usually a decoder or a gate) detects the address assigned to the interface registers. This circuit sets the chip select (*CS*) input when the interface is selected by the address bus. The two *register select inputs RS*1 and *RS*0 are usually connected to the two least significant lines of the address bus. These two inputs select one of the four registers in the interface, as specified in the table accompanying the diagram in Figure 11-6. The contents of the selected register are transferred into the CPU via the data bus when the I/O read signal is set. The CPU transfers binary information into the selected register via the data bus when the I/O write input is set.

CS	RS1	RS0	Register selected
0	X	X	None: data bus in high-impedance state
1	0	0	Port A register
1	0	1	Port B register
1	1	0	Control register
1	1	1	Status register

☐ **FIGURE 11-6**
Example of I/O Interface Unit

The CPU, interface, and I/O device are likely to have different clocks that are not synchronized with each other. Thus, these units are said to be *asynchronous* with respect to each other. Asynchronous data transfer between two independent units requires that control signals be transmitted between the units to indicate the time at which data is being transmitted. In the case of CPU-to-interface communication, control signals must also indicate the time at which the address is valid. We will look at two methods for performing this timing: strobing, as it is called, and handshaking. Initially, we will consider generic cases in which no addresses are involved—subsequently, we will add addressing. The communicating units for the generic case will be referred to as the source unit and destination unit.

Strobing

Data transfers using *strobing* are shown in Figure 11-7. The data bus between the two units is assumed to be made bidirectional by the use of three-state buffers.

The transfer in Figure 11-7(a) is initiated by the destination unit. In the shaded area of the data signal, the data is invalid. Also, a change in Strobe at the tail of each arrow causes a change on the data bus at the head of the arrow. The destination unit

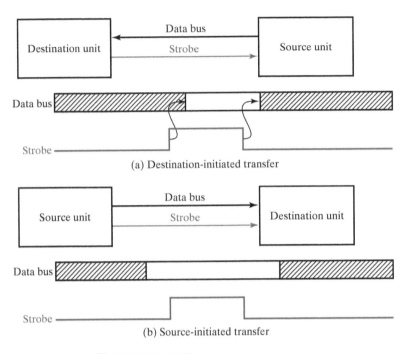

☐ **FIGURE 11-7**
Asynchronous Transfer Using Strobing

changes Strobe from 0 to 1. When the value 1 on Strobe reaches the source unit, the unit responds by placing the data on the data bus. The destination unit expects the data to be available, at worst, a fixed amount of time after Strobe goes to 1. At that time, the destination unit captures the data in a register and changes Strobe from 1 to 0. In response to the 0 value on Strobe, the source unit removes the data from the bus.

The transfer in Figure 11-7(b) is initiated by the source unit. In this case, the source unit places the data on the data bus. After a short time required for the data to settle on the bus, the source unit changes Strobe from 0 to 1. In response to Strobe equal to 1, the destination unit sets up the transfer to one of its registers. The source then changes Strobe from 1 to 0, which triggers the transfer into the register at the destination. Finally, after a short time required to ensure that the register transfer is done, the source removes the data from the data bus, completing the transfer.

Although simple, the strobe method of transferring data has several disadvantages. First, when the source unit initiates the transfer, there is no indication to it that the data was ever captured by the destination unit. It is possible, due to a hardware failure, that the destination unit did not receive the change in Strobe. Second, when the destination unit performs the transfer, there is no indication to it that the source has actually placed the data on the bus. Thus, the destination unit could be reading arbitrary values from the bus rather than actual data. Finally, the speeds at which the various units respond may vary. If there are multiple units, the unit initiating a transfer must wait for the delay of the slowest of the attached communicating units before changing Strobe to 0. Thus, the time taken for every transfer is determined by the slowest unit with which a given unit initiates transfers.

Handshaking

The *handshaking* method uses two control signals to deal with the timing of transfers. In addition to the signal from the unit initiating the transfer, there is a second control signal from the other unit involved in the transfer.

The basic principle of a two-signal handshaking procedure for data transfer is as follows. One control line from the initiating unit is used to request a response from the other unit. The second control line from the other unit is used to reply to the initiating unit that the response is occurring. In this way, each unit informs the other of its status, and the result is an orderly transfer through the bus.

Figure 11-8 shows data transfer procedures using handshaking. In Figure 11-8(a), the transfer is initiated by the destination unit. The two handshaking lines are called Request and Reply. In the initial state both Request and Reply are reset and in the 00 state. Subsequent states are 10, 11, and 01. The destination unit initiates the transfer by enabling Request. The source unit responds by placing the data on the bus. After a short

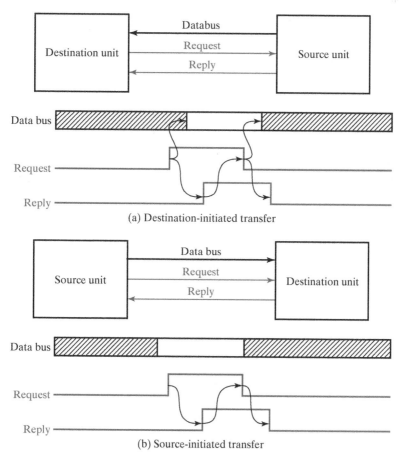

(a) Destination-initiated transfer

(b) Source-initiated transfer

□ **FIGURE 11-8**
Asynchronous Transfer Using Handshaking

time for settling of the data on the bus, the source unit activates Reply, to signal the presence of the data. In response to Reply, the destination unit captures the data in a register and resets Request. The source unit then resets Reply, and the system goes to the initial state. The destination unit may not make another request until the source unit has shown its readiness to provide new data by disabling Reply. Figure 11-8(b) represents handshaking for the source-initiated transfer. In this case, the source controls the interval between when the data is applied and when Request changes to 1 and between when Request changes to 0 and when the data is removed.

The handshaking scheme provides a high degree of flexibility and reliability, because the successful completion of a data transfer relies on active participation by both units. If one unit is faulty, the data transfer will not be completed. Such an error can be detected by means of a time-out mechanism, which produces an alarm if the data transfer is not completed within a predetermined time interval. The time-out is implemented by means of an internal clock that starts counting time when the unit sets one of its handshaking control signals. If the return handshake does not occur within a given period, the unit assumes that an error occurred. The time-out signal can be used to interrupt the CPU and execute a service routine that takes appropriate error recovery action. Also, the timing is controlled by both units, not just the initiating unit. Within the time-out limits, the response of each unit to a change in the control signal of the other unit can take an arbitrary amount of time, and the transfer will still be successful.

The examples of transfers in Figures 11-7 and 11-8 represent transfers between an interface and an I/O device and between a CPU and an interface. In the latter case, however, an address will be necessary to select the interface with which the CPU wishes to communicate and a register within the interface. In order to ensure that the CPU addresses the correct interface, the address must have settled on the address bus before the Strobe or Request signal changes from 0 to 1. Further, the address must remain stable until the change in the strobe or request from 1 to 0 has settled to 0 at the interface logic. If either of these conditions is violated, another interface may be falsely activated, causing an incorrect data transfer.

11-4 SERIAL COMMUNICATION

The transfer of data between two units may be parallel or serial. In parallel data transfer, each bit of the message has its own path, and the entire message is transmitted at one time. This means that an n-bit message is transmitted in parallel through n separate conductor paths. In serial data transmission, each bit in the message is sent in sequence, one at a time. This method requires the use of one or two signal lines. Parallel transmission is faster, because multiple signal lines operate in parallel. It is used for short distances and when speed is important. Serial transmission is slower, but less expensive, since it requires only one conductor. Serial connections are becoming increasingly important because of the ease of connecting smaller cables and because as data rates increase, signal skew from line-to-line becomes more problematic. For the serial case, there are just one or two signals, so that skew is less of a problem. As an example of the trend toward serial interfaces, in the last decade, the typical hard drive interface for desktop computers has changed from the parallel ATA (PATA) interface with 40 wires to the serial ATA (SATA) with only seven wires.

One way that computers and terminals that are remote from each other are connected is via telephone lines. Since telephone lines were originally designed for voice communication, but computers communicate in terms of digital signals, some form of conversion is needed. The devices that do the conversion are called *data sets* or *modems* (modulator–demodulators). There are various modulation schemes, as well as several different grades of communication media and transmission speeds. Serial data can be transmitted between two points in three different modes: simplex, half duplex, or full duplex. A *simplex* line carries information in one direction only. This mode is seldom used in data communication, because the receiver cannot communicate with the transmitter to indicate whether errors have occurred. Examples of simplex transmission are radio and television broadcasting.

A *half-duplex* transmission system is capable of transmitting in both directions, but in only one direction at a time. A pair of wires is needed for this mode. A common situation is for one modem to act as the transmitter and the other as the receiver. When transmission in one direction is completed, the roles of the modems are reversed to enable transmission in the opposite direction. The time required to switch a half-duplex line from one direction to the other is called the *turnaround time*.

A *full-duplex* transmission system can send and receive data in both directions simultaneously. This can be achieved by means of a two-wire plus ground link, with a different wire dedicated to each direction of transmission. Alternatively, a single-wire circuit can support full-duplex communication if the frequency spectrum is subdivided into two nonoverlapping frequency bands to create separate receiving and transmitting channels in the same physical pair of wires.

The serial transmission of data can be synchronous or asynchronous. In *synchronous transmission*, the two units share a common clock frequency, and bits are transmitted continuously at that frequency. In long-distance serial transmission, the transmitter and receiver units are each driven by separate clocks of the same frequency. Synchronization signals are transmitted periodically between the two units to keep their clock frequencies in step with each other. In *asynchronous* transmission, binary information is sent only when it is available, and the line remains idle when there is no information to be transmitted. This is in contrast to synchronous transmission, in which bits must be transmitted continuously to keep the clock frequencies in both units synchronized.

 ASYNCHRONOUS TRANSMISSION   A supplement containing the subsection on asynchronous transmission, a serial port protocol used less frequently in new designs, is available on the Companion Website.

Synchronous Transmission

The modems employed in synchronous transmission have internal clocks that are set to the frequency at which bits are being transmitted. For proper operation, the clocks of the transmitter and receiver modems must remain synchronized at all times. The communication line, however, carries only the data bits, from which information on the clock frequency must be extracted. Frequency synchronization is achieved by the receiving modem from the signal transitions that occur in the data that is received. Any frequency shift that may occur between the transmitter and receiver clocks is continuously adjusted by maintaining the receiver clock at the frequency of the incoming bit stream. In this way, the same rate is maintained in both the transmitter and the receiver.

Contrary to asynchronous transmission, in which each character can be sent separately, synchronous transmission must send a continuous message in order to maintain synchronism. The message consists of a group of bits that form a block of data. The entire block is transmitted with special control bits at the beginning and the end, in order to frame the block into one unit of information.

The Keyboard Revisited

To this point, we have covered the basic nature of the I/O interface and serial transmission. With these two concepts available, we are now ready to continue with the example of the keyboard and its interface, as shown in Figure 11-9. The K-scan code produced by the keyboard microcontroller is to be transferred serially from the keyboard through the keyboard cable to the keyboard controller in the computer. In this case, however, a signal Keyboard clock is also sent through the cable. Thus, the transmission is synchronous with a transmitted clock signal, rather than asynchronous. These same signals are used to transmit control commands to the keyboard. In the keyboard controller, the microcontroller converts the K-scan code to a more standard *scan code*, which it then places in the Input register, at the same time sending an interrupt signal to the CPU indicating that a key has been pressed and a code is available. The interrupt-handling routine reads the scan code from the input register into a special area in memory. This area is manipulated by software stored in the Basic Input/Output System (BIOS) that can translate the scan code into an ASCII character code for use by applications.

The Output register in the interface receives data from the CPU. The data can be passed on to control the keyboard—for example, setting the repetition rate when a key is held down. The Control register is used for commands to the keyboard controller. Finally, the Status register reports specific information on the status of the keyboard and the keyboard controller.

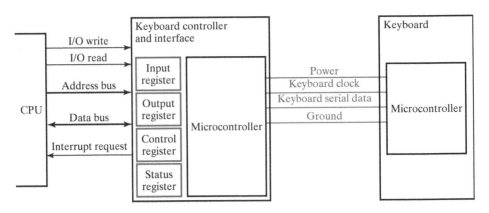

□ **FIGURE 11-9**
Keyboard Controller and Interface

An interesting aspect of keyboard I/O is its high complexity. It involves two microcontrollers executing different programs, plus the main processor executing BIOS software (i.e., three different computers executing three distinct programs).

A Packet-Based Serial I/O Bus

Serial I/O, as described for the keyboard, uses a serial cable specifically dedicated to communicating between the computer and the keyboard. Whether parallel or serial, external I/O connections are typically dedicated. The use of these dedicated paths often requires that the computer case be opened and cards inserted with electronics and connectors specific to the particular I/O standard used for a given I/O device.

In contrast, packet-based serial I/O permits many different external I/O devices to use a shared communication structure that is attached to the computer through just one or two connectors. The types of devices supported include keyboards, mice, joysticks, printers, scanners, and speakers. The particular packet-based serial I/O we will describe here is the Universal Serial Bus (USB), which is becoming commonplace as the connection approach of choice for slow-speed to medium-speed I/O devices.

The interconnection of I/O devices by using USB is shown in Figure 11-10. The computer and attached devices can be classified as hubs, devices, or compound

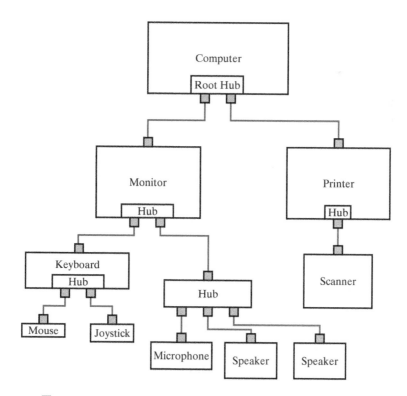

□ **FIGURE 11-10**
I/O Device Connection Using the Universal Serial Bus (USB)

devices. A hub provides attachment points for USB devices and other hubs. A hub contains a USB interface for control and status handling, and a repeater for transferring information through the hub.

The computer contains a USB controller and the root hub. Additional hubs may be a part of the USB I/O structure. If a hub is combined with a device such as the keyboard shown in Figure 11-10, then the keyboard is referred to as a *compound device*. Aside from such compound devices, a USB device contains only one USB port to serve its function alone. The scanner is an example of a regular USB device. Without USB, the monitor, keyboard, mouse, joystick, microphone, speakers, printer, and scanner shown would all have separate I/O connections directly on the computer. The monitor, printer, scanner, microphone, and speakers might all require special cards to be inserted, as discussed previously. With USB, only two connections are required.

The USB cables contain four wires: ground, power, and two data lines (D+ and D−) used for differential signaling. The power wire is used to provide small amounts of power to devices such as keyboards so that they do not need their own power supplies. To provide immunity to signal variation and noise, 0s and 1s are transmitted by using the difference in voltage between D+ and D−. If the voltage on D+ exceeds the voltage on D− by 200 millivolts or more, then the logic value is a 1. If the voltage on D− exceeds the voltage on D+ by 200 millivolts or more, the logic value is a 0. Other voltage relationships between D+ and D− are used as special signal states as well.

The logic values used for signaling are not the actual logic values of the information being transmitted. Instead, a Non-Return-to-Zero Inverted (NRZI) signaling convention is used. A zero in the data being transmitted is represented by a transition from 1 to 0 or 0 to 1 and a 1 is represented by a fixed value of 1 or 0. The relationship between the data being transmitted and the NRZI representation is illustrated in Figure 11-11. As is typical for I/O devices, there is no common clock serving both the computer and the device. NRZI encoding of the data provides edges that can be used to maintain synchronization between the arriving data and the time at which each bit is sampled at the receiver. If there are a large number of 1s in series in the data, there will be no transitions for some time in the NRZI encoding. To prevent loss of synchronization, a 0 is "stuffed" in before every seventh bit position in a string of 1s prior to NRZI encoding so that no more than six 1s appear in series. The receiver must be able to remove these extra zeros when converting NRZI data to normal data.

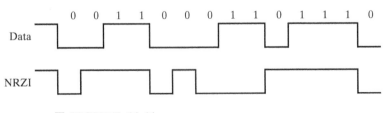

☐ **FIGURE 11-11**
Non-Return-to-Zero Inverted Data Representation

USB information is transmitted in packets. Each packet contains a specific set of fields, depending on the packet type. Logical strings of packets are used to compose USB transactions. For example, an output transaction consists of an Out packet followed by a Data packet and a Handshake packet. The Out packet comes from the USB controller in the computer and notifies the device that it is to receive data. The computer then sends the Data packet. If the Data packet is received without error, then the device responds with the Acknowledge Handshake packet. Next, we detail the information contained in each of these packets.

Figure 11-12(a) shows a general format for USB packets and the formats for each of the three packets involved in an output transaction. Note that each packet begins with a synchronization pattern SYNC. This pattern is 00000001. Because of the sequence of zeros, the corresponding NRZI pattern contains seven edges, which provide a pattern to which the receiving clock can be synchronized. Since this pattern is preceded by a specific signal voltage state referred to as Idle, the pattern also signals the beginning of a new packet.

Following the SYNC, each packet format contains eight bits called the packet identifier (PID). In the PID, the packet type is specified by four bits, with an additional four bits that are complements of the first four to provide an error check on the type. A very large class of type errors will be detected by the repetition of the type as its complement. The type is optionally followed by information specific to the packet, which varies depending upon the packet type. Optionally, a CRC field appears next. The CRC pattern consisting of five or 16 bits is a Cyclic Redundancy

SYNC	PID	Packet-specific data	CRC	EOP

(a) General packet format

SYNC 8 bits	Type 4 bits 1001	Check 4 bits 0110	Device address 7 bits	Endpoint address 4 bits	CRC	EOP

(b) Output packet

SYNC 8 bits	Type 4 bits 1100	Check 4 bits 0011	Data (Up to 1024 bytes)	CRC	EOP

(c) Data packet (Data0 type)

SYNC 8 bits	Type 4 bits 0100	Check 4 bits 1011	EOP

(d) Handshake packet (Acknowledge type)

☐ **FIGURE 11-12**
USB Packet Formats

Check pattern. This pattern is calculated at transmission of the packet from the packet-specific data. The same calculation is performed when the data is received. If the CRC pattern does not match the newly calculated pattern, then an error has been detected. In response to the error, the packet can be ignored and retransmitted. In the last field of the packet, an End of Packet (EOP) appears. This consists of D+ and D−, both low for two bit times, followed by the Idle state for a bit time. As its name indicates, this sequence of signal states identifies the end of the current packet. It should be noted that all fields are presented least significant bit first.

Referring to Figure 11-12(b), for the Output packet, the Type and Check fields are followed by a Device Address, an Endpoint Address, and a CRC pattern. The Device Address consists of seven bits and defines the device that is to input data. The Endpoint Address consists of four bits and defines which port of the device is to receive the information in the Data packet to follow. For example, there may be a port for data and one for control on a given device.

For the Data packet, the packet-specific data consists of 0 to 1024 data bytes. Due to the length of the packet, complex errors are more likely, so the CRC pattern is increased in length to 16 bits to improve its error-detection capability.

In the Handshake packet, the packet-specific data is empty. The response to the receipt of the data packet is carried by the PID. PID 01001011 is an Acknowledge (ACK) indicating that the packet was received without any errors detected. Absence of any HANDSHAKE packet when one would normally appear is an indication of an error. PID 01011010 is a No Acknowledge, indicating that the target is temporarily unable to accept or return data. PID 01111000 is a Stall (STALL), indicating that the target is unable to complete the transfer and that software intervention is required to recover from the stall condition.

The preceding concepts illustrate the general principles underlying a packet-based serial I/O bus and are specific to USB. USB supports other packet types and many different kinds of transactions. In addition, the attachment and detachment of devices is sensed and can trigger various software reactions. In general, there is substantial software in the computer to support the details of the control and operation of the USB.

11-5 MODES OF TRANSFER

Binary information received from an external device is usually stored in memory for later processing. Information transferred from the central computer into an external device originates in the memory. The CPU merely executes the I/O instructions and may accept the data temporarily, but the ultimate source or destination is the memory. Data transfer between the central computer and I/O devices may be handled in a variety of modes, some of which use the CPU as an intermediate path, while others transfer the data directly to and from the memory. Data transfer to and from peripherals may be handled in one of three possible modes:

1. Data transfer under program control.

2. Interrupt-initiated data transfer.

3. Direct memory access transfer.

Program-controlled operations are the result of I/O instructions written in the computer program. Each transfer of data is initiated by an instruction in the program. Usually, the transfer is to and from a CPU register and peripheral. Other instructions are needed to transfer the data to and from the CPU and memory. Transferring data under program control requires constant monitoring of the peripheral by the CPU. Once a data transfer is initiated, the CPU is required to monitor the interface to see when a transfer can again be made. It is up to the programmed instructions executed in the CPU to keep close tabs on everything that is taking place in the interface unit and the external device.

In the program-controlled transfer, the CPU stays in a program loop called a *busy-wait loop* until the I/O unit indicates that it is ready for data transfer. This is a time-consuming process, since it keeps the processor busy needlessly. The loop can be avoided by using the interrupt facility and special commands to inform the interface to issue an interrupt request signal when the data is available from the device. This allows the CPU to proceed to execute another program. The interface, meanwhile, keeps monitoring the device. When the interface determines that the device is ready for data transfer, it generates an interrupt request to the computer. Upon detecting the external interrupt signal, the CPU momentarily stops the task it is performing, branches to a service program to process the data transfer, and then returns to the original task. This interrupt-initiated transfer is the type used for the keyboard controller shown in Figure 11-9.

Transferring of data under program control is performed through the I/O bus and between the CPU and a peripheral interface unit. In *direct memory access* (DMA), the interface unit transfers data into and out of the memory unit through the memory bus. The CPU initiates the transfer by supplying the interface with the starting address and the number of words needing to be transferred and then proceeds to execute other tasks. When the transfer is made, the interface requests memory cycles through the memory bus. When the request is granted by the memory controller, the interface transfers the data directly into memory. The CPU merely delays memory operations to allow the direct memory I/O transfer. Since the speed of a peripheral is usually slower than that of a processor, I/O memory transfers are infrequent compared with processor access to memory. DMA transfer is discussed in more detail in Section 11-7.

Many computers combine the interface logic with the requirements for DMA into one unit called an *I/O processor* (IOP). The IOP can handle many peripherals through a DMA-and-interrupt facility. In such a system, the computer is divided into three separate modules: the memory unit, the CPU, and the IOP.

Example of Program-Controlled Transfer

A simple example of data transfer from an I/O device through an interface into the CPU is shown in Figure 11-13. The device transfers bytes of data one at a time as they are available. When a byte is available, the device places it on the I/O bus and sets Ready. The interface accepts the byte into its data register and sets Acknowledge. The interface sets a bit in the status register, which we will refer to as a *flag*. The device can now reset Ready, but it will not transfer another byte

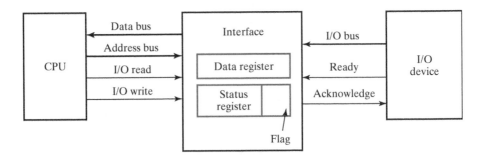

□ **FIGURE 11-13**
Data Transfer from I/O Device to CPU

until Acknowledge is reset by the interface, according to the handshaking procedure established in Section 11-3.

Under program control, the CPU must check the flag to determine whether there is a new byte in the interface data register. This is done by reading the contents of the status register into a CPU register and checking the value of the flag. If the flag is equal to 1, the CPU reads the data from the data register. The flag is then cleared to 0 either by the CPU or the interface, depending on how the interface circuits are designed. Once the flag is cleared, the interface resets Acknowledge, and the device can transfer the next data byte.

A flowchart of a program written for the preceding transfer is shown in Figure 11-14. The flowchart assumes that the device is sending a sequence of bytes that must be stored in memory. The program continually examines the status of the interface until the flag is set to 1. Each byte is brought into the CPU and transferred to memory until all of the data have been transferred.

The program-controlled data transfer is used only in systems that are dedicated to monitor a device continuously. The difference in information transfer rate between the CPU and the I/O device makes this type of transfer inefficient. To see why, consider a typical computer that can execute the instructions to read the status register and check the flag in 100 ns. Assume that the input device transfers its data at an average rate of 100 bytes/s. This is equivalent to one byte every 10,000 µs, meaning that the CPU will check the flag 100,000 times between each transfer. Thus, the CPU is wasting time checking the flag instead of doing a useful processing task.

Interrupt-Initiated Transfer

An alternative to having the CPU constantly monitor the flag is to let the interface inform the computer when it is ready to transfer data. This mode of transfer uses the interrupt facility. While the CPU is running a program, it does not check the flag. However, when the flag is set, the computer is momentarily interrupted from proceeding with the current program and is informed that the flag has been set. The CPU drops what it is doing to take care of the input or output transfer.

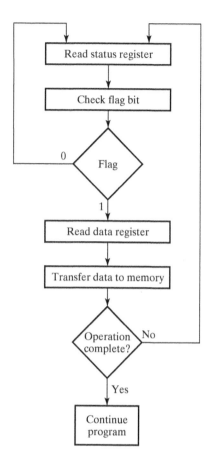

Flowchart for CPU Program to Input Data

After the transfer is completed, the computer returns to the previous program to continue what it was doing before the interrupt. The CPU responds to the interrupt signal by storing the return address from the program counter into a memory stack or register, and then control branches to a service routine that processes the required I/O transfer. The way that the processor chooses the branch address of the service routine varies from one unit to another. In principle, there are two methods for accomplishing this: *vectored interrupt* and *nonvectored interrupt*. In a nonvectored interrupt, the branch address is assigned to a fixed location in memory. In a vectored interrupt, the source that interrupts supplies the branch address to the computer. This information is called the *vector address*. In some computers, the vector address is the first address of the service routine; in other computers, the vector address is an address that points to a location in memory where the first address of the service routine is stored. The vectored interrupt procedure was presented in Section 9-9 in conjunction with Figure 9-9.

11-6 PRIORITY INTERRUPT

A typical computer has a number of I/O devices attached to it that are able to originate an interrupt request. The first task of the interrupt system is to identify the source of the interrupt. There is also the possibility that several sources will request service simultaneously. In this case, the system must decide which device to service first.

A priority interrupt system establishes a priority over the various interrupt sources to determine which interrupt request to service first when two or more are pending simultaneously. The system may also determine which requests are permitted to interrupt the computer while another interrupt is being serviced. Higher levels of priority are assigned to requests that, if delayed or interrupted, could have serious consequences. Devices with high-speed transfers such as hard drives are given high priority, and slow devices such as keyboards receive the lowest priority. When two devices interrupt the computer at the same time, the computer services the device with the higher priority first.

Establishing the priority of simultaneous interrupts can be done by software or hardware. Software uses a polling procedure to identify the interrupt source of highest priority. In this method, there is one common branch address for all interrupts. The program at the branch address takes care of interrupts by polling the interrupt sources in sequence. The priority of each interrupt source determines the order in which it is polled. The source with the highest priority is tested first, and if its interrupt signal is on, control branches to a routine which services that source. Otherwise, the source with the next lower priority is tested, and so on. Thus, the initial service routine for all interrupts pending consists of a program that tests the interrupt sources in sequence and branches to one of many possible service routines. The particular service routine that is reached belongs to the highest-priority device among all devices that interrupted the computer. The disadvantage of the software method is that if there are many interrupts, the time required to poll all the sources can exceed the time available to service the I/O device. In this situation, a hardware priority interrupt unit can be used to speed up the operation of the system.

A hardware priority interrupt unit functions as an overall manager in an interrupt system environment. The unit accepts interrupt requests from many sources, determines which request has the highest priority, and issues an interrupt request to the computer based on this determination. To speed up the operation, each interrupt source has its own interrupt vector address to access its own service routine directly. Thus, no polling is required, because all the decisions are made by the hardware priority interrupt unit. The hardware priority function can be established either by a serial or parallel connection of interrupt lines. The serial connection is also known as the daisy chain method.

Daisy Chain Priority

The *daisy chain* method of establishing priority consists of a serial connection of all devices that request an interrupt. The device with the highest priority is placed in the first position, followed by devices of priority in descending order, down to the device with the lowest priority, which is placed last in the chain. This method of connection

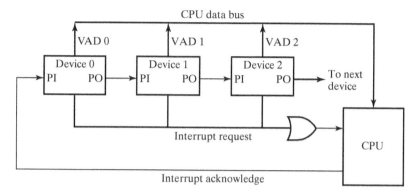

□ **FIGURE 11-15**
Daisy Chain Priority Interrupt

between three devices and the CPU is shown in Figure 11-15. Interrupt request lines from all devices are ORed to form the interrupt line to the CPU. If any device has its Interrupt request at 1, the interrupt line goes to 1 and enables the interrupt input of the CPU. When no interrupts are pending, the interrupt line stays at 0, and no interrupts are recognized by the CPU. The CPU responds to an interrupt request by enabling Interrupt acknowledge. The signal produced is received by device 0 at its *PI* (priority in) input. The signal then passes on to the next device through the *PO* (priority out) output only if device 0 is not requesting an interrupt. If device 0 has a pending interrupt, it blocks the acknowledge signal from the next device by placing a 0 on the *PO* output and proceeds to insert its own interrupt vector address (*VAD*) onto the data bus for the CPU to use during the interrupt cycle.

A device with a 0 on its *PI* input generates a 0 on its *PO* output to inform the device with next lower priority that the acknowledge signal has been blocked. A device that is requesting an interrupt and has a 1 on its *PI* input will intercept the acknowledge signal by placing a 0 on its *PO* output. If the device does not have pending interrupts, it transmits the acknowledge signal to the next device by placing a 1 on its *PO* output. Thus, the device with *PI* = 1 and *PO* = 0 is the one with the highest priority that is requesting an interrupt, and this device places its *VAD* on the data bus. The daisy chain arrangement gives the highest priority to the device that receives the Interrupt acknowledge signal from the CPU. The farther the device is from the first position, the lower is its priority.

Figure 11-16 shows the internal logic that must be included within each device connected in the daisy chain scheme. The device sets its *RF* latch when it is about to interrupt the CPU. The output of the latch functionally enters the OR that drives the interrupt line. If *PI* = 0, both *PO* and the enable line to *VAD* are equal to 0, irrespective of the value of *RF*. If *PI* = 1 and *RF* = 0, then *PO* = 1, the vector address is disabled, and the acknowledge signal passes to the next device through *PO*. The device is active when *PI* = 1 and *RF* = 1, which places a 0 on *PO* and enables the vector address onto the data bus. It is assumed that each device has its own distinct vector address. The *RF* latch is reset after a sufficient delay to ensure that the CPU has received the vector address.

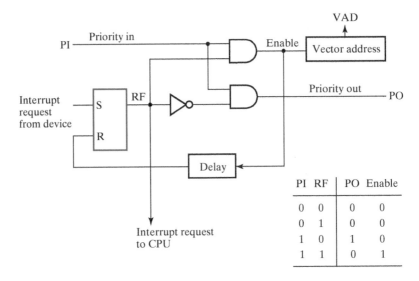

☐ **FIGURE 11-16**
One Stage of the Daisy Chain Priority Arrangement

Parallel Priority Hardware

The parallel priority interrupt method uses a register with bits set separately by the interrupt signal from each device. Priority is established according to the position of the bits in the register. In addition to the interrupt register, the circuit may include a mask register to control the status of each interrupt request. The mask register can be programmed to disable lower-priority interrupts while a higher-priority device is being serviced. It can also allow a high-priority device to interrupt the CPU while a lower-priority device is being serviced.

The priority logic for a system with four interrupt sources is shown in Figure 11-17. The logic consists of an interrupt register with individual bits set by external conditions and cleared by program instructions. Interrupt input 3 has the highest priority, input 0 the lowest. The mask register has the same number of bits as the interrupt register. By means of program instructions, it is possible to set or reset any bit in the mask register. Each interrupt bit and its corresponding mask bit are applied to an AND gate to produce the four inputs to a priority encoder. In this way, an interrupt is recognized only if its corresponding mask bit is set to 1 by the program. The priority encoder generates two bits of the vector address, which is transferred to the CPU via the data bus. Output V of the encoder is set to 1 if an interrupt request that is not masked has occurred. This provides the interrupt signal for the CPU.

The priority encoder is a circuit that implements the priority function. The logic of the priority encoder is such that, if two or more inputs are 1 at the same time, the input having the highest priority takes precedence. The circuit of a 4-input priority encoder can be found in Section 3-6, and its truth table is listed in Table 3-6. Input D_3 has the highest priority, so, regardless of the values of other inputs, when this input is 1 the output is $A_1A_0 = 11$. D_2 has the next lower priority. The output is 10 if

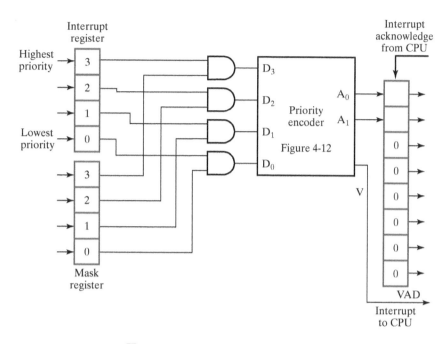

□ **FIGURE 11-17**
Parallel Priority Interrupt Hardware

$D_2 = 1$, provided that $D_3 = 0$, regardless of the values of the other two lower-priority inputs. The output is 01 when $D_1 = 1$, provided that the two higher-priority inputs are equal to 0, and so on down the priority levels. The interrupt output labeled V is equal to 1 when one or more inputs are equal to 1. If all inputs are 0, V is 0, and the other two outputs of the encoder are not used. This is because the vector address is not transferred to the CPU when $V = 0$.

The output of the priority encoder is used to form part of the vector address of the interrupt source. The other bits of the vector address can be assigned any values. For example, the vector address can be found by appending six zeros to the outputs of the encoder. With this choice, the interrupt vectors for the four I/O devices are assigned the 8-bit binary numbers equivalent to decimal 0, 1, 2, and 3.

11-7 DIRECT MEMORY ACCESS

The transfer of blocks of information between a fast storage device such as a hard drive and the CPU can preoccupy the CPU and permit little, if any, other processing to be accomplished. Removing the CPU from the path and letting the peripheral device manage the memory buses directly relieves the CPU from many I/O operations and allow it to proceed with other processing. In this transfer technique, called direct memory access (DMA), the DMA controller takes over the buses to manage the transfer directly between the I/O device and memory. As a consequence, the CPU is temporarily deprived of access to memory and control of the memory buses.

☐ **FIGURE 11-18**
CPU Bus Control Signals

DMA may capture the buses in a number of ways. One common method extensively used in microprocessors is to disable the buses through special control signals. Figure 11-18 shows two control signals in a CPU that facilitate the DMA transfer. The bus request (*BR*) input is used by the DMA controller to request the CPU to relinquish control of the buses. When *BR* input is active, the CPU places the address bus, the data bus, and the read and write lines into a high-impedance state. After this is done, the CPU activates the bus granted (*BG*) output to inform the external DMA that it can take control of the buses. As long as the *BG* line is active, the CPU is unable to proceed with any operations requiring access to the buses.

When the bus request input is reset by the DMA, the CPU returns to its normal operation, resets the *BG* output, and takes control of the buses. When the *BG* line is set, the external DMA controller takes control of the bus system in order to communicate directly with memory. The transfer can be made for an entire block of memory words, suspending operation of the CPU until the entire block is transferred, a process referred to as *burst transfer*. Or the transfer can be made one word at a time between executions of CPU instructions, a process called *single-cycle transfer* or *cycle stealing*. The CPU merely delays its bus operations for one memory cycle to allow the direct memory-I/O transfer to steal one memory cycle.

DMA Controller

The DMA controller needs the usual circuits of an interface to communicate with the CPU and the I/O device. In addition, it needs an address register, a word-count register, and a set of address lines. The address register and address lines are used for direct communication with memory. The word-count register specifies the number of words that must be transferred. The data transfer may be done directly between the device and memory under control of the DMA.

Figure 11-19 shows the block diagram of a typical DMA controller. The unit communicates with the CPU via the data bus and control lines. The registers in the DMA are selected by the CPU through the address bus by enabling the *DS* (DMA select) and *RS* (register select) inputs. The *RD* (read) and *WR* (write) inputs are bidirectional. When the *BG* (bus granted) input is 0, the CPU can communicate with the DMA registers through the data bus to read from or write to those registers. When *BG* = 1, the CPU has relinquished the buses, and the DMA can communicate directly with memory by specifying an address on the address bus and activating the *RD* or *WR* control. The DMA communicates with the external peripheral

□ **FIGURE 11-19**
Block Diagram of a DMA Controller

through the DMA request and DMA acknowledge lines by a prescribed handshaking procedure.

The DMA controller has three registers: an address register, a word-count register, and a control register. The address register contains an address to specify the desired location of a word in memory. The address bits go through bus buffers onto the address bus. The address register is incremented after each word is transferred to memory. The word-count register holds the number of words to be transferred. This register is decremented by one after each word transfer and internally tested for zero. The control register specifies the mode of transfer. All registers in the DMA appear to the CPU as I/O interface registers. Thus, the CPU can read from or write to the DMA registers under program control via the data bus.

After initialization by the CPU, the DMA starts and continues to transfer data between memory and the peripheral unit until an entire block is transferred. The initialization process is essentially a program consisting of I/O instructions that include the address for selecting particular DMA registers. The CPU initializes the DMA by sending the following information through the data bus:

1. The starting address of the memory block in which data is available (for reading) or data is to be stored (for writing).

2. The word count, which is the number of words in the memory block.

3. A control bit to specify the mode of transfer, such as read or write.

4. A control bit to start the DMA transfer.

The starting address is stored in the address register, the word count in the word-count register, and the control information in the control register. Once the DMA is initialized, the CPU stops communicating with it unless the CPU receives an interrupt signal or needs to check how many words have been transferred.

DMA Transfer

The position of the DMA controller among the other components in a computer system is illustrated in Figure 11-20. The CPU communicates with the DMA through the address and data buses, as with any interface unit. The DMA has its own address, which activates the *DS* and *RS* lines. The CPU initializes the DMA through the data bus. Once the DMA receives the start control bit, it can begin transferring data between the peripheral device and memory. When the peripheral device sends a DMA request, the DMA controller activates the *BR* line, informing the CPU that it is to relinquish the buses. The CPU responds with its *BG* line, informing the DMA that the buses are disabled. The DMA then puts the current value of its address register onto the address bus, initiates the *RD* or *WR* signal, and sends a DMA acknowledge to the peripheral device.

When the peripheral device receives a DMA acknowledge, it puts a word on the data bus (for writing) or receives a word from the data bus (for reading). Thus, the DMA controls the read or write operation and supplies the address for memory. The peripheral unit can then communicate with memory through the data bus for a direct transfer of data between the two units while the CPU access to the data bus is momentarily disabled.

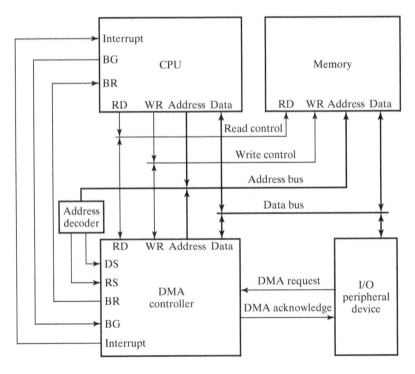

□ **FIGURE 11-20**
DMA Transfer in a Computer System

For each word that is transferred, the DMA increments its address register and decrements its word-count register. If the word count has not reached zero, the DMA checks the request line coming from the peripheral. In a high-speed device, the line will be activated as soon as the previous transfer is completed. A second transfer is then initiated, and the process continues until the entire block is transferred. If the speed of the peripheral is slower, the DMA request line may be activated somewhat later. In this case, the DMA resets the bus request line so that the CPU can continue to execute its program. When the peripheral requests a transfer, the DMA requests the buses again.

If the word count reaches zero, the DMA stops any further transfer and removes its bus request. It also informs the CPU of the termination of the transfer by means of an interrupt. When the CPU responds to the interrupt, it reads the contents of the word-count register. A value of zero indicates that all the words were successfully transferred. The CPU can read the word-count register at any time, as well, to check the number of words already transferred.

A DMA controller may have more than one channel. In this case, each channel has a request and acknowledge pair of control signals that are connected to separate peripheral devices. Each channel also has its own address register and word-count register so that channels with high priority are serviced before channels with lower priority.

DMA transfer is very useful in many applications, including the fast transfer of information between hard drives and memory, and between memory and graphic displays.

11-8 CHAPTER SUMMARY

In this chapter, we introduced I/O devices, typically called peripherals, and their associated digital support structures, including I/O buses, interfaces, and controllers. We studied the structure of a keyboard, a hard drive, and a graphics display. We looked at an example of a generic I/O interface and examined the interface and I/O controller for the keyboard. We introduced USB as an alternative solution to the attachment of many I/O devices. We considered timing problems between systems with different clocks and the parallel and serial transmission of information.

We also looked at modes of transferring information and saw how the more complex modes came about, principally to relieve the CPU from extensive, performance-robbing handling of I/O transfers. Interrupt-initiated transfers with multiple I/O interfaces lead to means of establishing priority between interrupt sources. Priority can be handled by software, serial daisy chain logic, or parallel interrupt-priority logic. Direct memory access accomplishes the transfer of data directly between an I/O interface and memory, with little CPU involvement.

REFERENCES

1. HENNESSY, J. L. AND D. A. PATTERSON. *Computer Architecture: A Quantitative Approach*, 5th ed. Amsterdam: Elsevier, 2011.
2. Fundamentals of Liquid Crystal Displays — How They Work and What They Do. Fujitsu Microelectronics America, Inc., 2006. (http://www.fujitsu.com/downloads/MICRO/fma/pdf/LCD_Backgrounder.pdf)

3. MESSMER, H. P. *The Indispensable PC Hardware Book*, 2nd ed. Reading, MA: Addison-Wesley, 1995.

4. MindShare, Inc. (Don Anderson). *Universal Serial Bus System Architecture.* Reading, MA: Addison-Wesley Developers Press, 1997.

5. VAN GILLUWE, F. *The Undocumented PC.* Reading, MA: Addison-Wesley, 1994.

6. *What is TFT LCD?* Avdeals America, 2006, (http://www.plasma.com/classroom/what_is_tft_lcd.htm)

PROBLEMS

The plus (+) indicates a more advanced problem and the asterisk (*) indicates that a solution is available on the Companion Website for the text.

11-1. *Find the formatted capacity of the hard drives described in the following table:

Drive	Heads	Cylinders	Sectors/ Track	Bytes/ Sector
A	1	1023	63	512
B	4	8191	63	512
C	16	16383	63	512

11-2. Estimate the time required to transfer a block of 1 MB (2^{20} B) from a hard drive to memory given the following drive parameters: seek time, 8.5 ms; rotational delay, 4.17 ms; controller time, negligible; transfer rate, 150 MB/s.

11-3. Assume that your LCD screen has a maximum resolution of 1600 × 1200 by virtue of its hardware capability. Your settings (done by the OS or manually by you) denote a resolution of 800 × 600 resolution. What will be the effect on a 1600 × 1200 picture displayed on it?

11-4. The addresses assigned to the four registers of the I/O interface of Figure 11-6 are equal to hexadecimal CA, CB, CC, and CD. Show the external circuit that must be connected between an 8-bit I/O address from the CPU and the CS, $RS0$, and $RS1$ inputs of the interface.

11-5. *How many I/O interface units of the type shown in Figure 11-6 can be addressed by using a 16-bit address, assuming

(a) each of the chip select (CS) lines is attached to a different address line?

(b) address bits are fully decoded to form the chip select inputs?

11-6. Interface units of the type shown in Figure 11-6 are connected to a CPU that uses an I/O address of eight bits. Each one of the six chip select (CS) inputs is connected to a different address line. Specifically, address line 0 is connected to the CS input of the first interface unit, and address line 4 is connected to the CS input of the sixth interface unit. Address lines 7 and 6 are connected to the $RS1$ and $RS0$ inputs, respectively, of all six interface units. Determine the 8-bit address of each register in each interface (a total of 24 addresses).

11-7. *A different type of I/O interface does not have the *RS*1 and *RS*0 inputs. Up to two registers can be addressed by using a separate I/O read signal and I/O write signal for each address available. Assume that 25 percent of the registers at the interface with the CPU are read only, 25 percent of the registers are write only, and 50 percent of the registers are both read and write (bidirectional). How many registers can be addressed if the address contains eight bits?

11-8. A commercial interface unit uses names different from those appearing in this text for the handshake lines associated with the transfer of data from the I/O device to the interface unit. The interface input handshake line is labeled *STB* (strobe), and the interface output handshake line is labeled *IBF* (input buffer full). A low-level signal on *STB* loads data from the I/O bus into the interface data register. A high-level signal on *IBF* indicates that the data has been accepted by the interface. *IBF* goes low after an I/O read signal from the CPU when it reads the contents of the data register.

(a) Draw a block diagram showing the CPU, the interface, and the I/O device, along with the pertinent interconnections between the three units.

(b) Draw a timing diagram for the handshaking transfer.

11-9. *Assume that the transfers with strobing shown in Figure 11-7 are between a CPU on the left and an I/O interface on the right. There is an address coming from the CPU for each of the transfers, both of which are initiated by the CPU.

(a) Draw block diagrams showing the interconnections for the transfers.

(b) Draw the timing diagrams for the two transfers, assuming that the address must be applied some time before the strobe becomes 1 and removed some time after the strobe becomes 0.

11-10. Assume that the transfers with handshaking shown in Figure 11-8 are between a CPU on the left and an I/O interface on the right. There is an address coming from the CPU for each of the transfers, both of which are initiated by the CPU.

(a) Draw block diagrams, showing interconnections for the transfers.

(b) Draw the timing diagrams, assuming that the address must be applied some time before the request becomes 1 and removed some time after the request becomes 0.

11-11. *Sketch the waveforms for the SYNC pattern used for USB and the corresponding NRZI waveform. Explain why the pattern selected is a good choice for achieving synchronization.

11-12. **(a)** Draw the NRZI waveform corresponding to the raw data 10100110001, which is to be sent using the USB protocol.

(b) The USB system has a host and devices. Differentiate between the two.

(c) List two input and two output devices that use the USB protocol.

11-13. *The 8-bit ASCII word "Bye" is to be transmitted to a device address 39 and endpoint 2. List the Output and Data 0 packets and the Handshake packet for a Stall for this transmission prior to NRZI encoding.

11-14. Repeat Problem 11-13 for the word "Hlo" and a Handshake packet of type No Acknowledge.

11-15. Explain why interrupt driven data transfer is preferred over the polling method, even though the latter is simpler in concept and application.

11-16. *What happens in the daisy chain priority interrupt shown in Figure 11-15 when device 0 requests an interrupt after device 2 has sent an interrupt request to the CPU, but before the CPU responds with the interrupt acknowledge?

11-17. **(a)** When there are many sources for interrupts, there is an extra hardware to take care of interrupt processing. What are the capabilities needed for this extra hardware?

   (b) What is the concept of an interrupt vector?

   (c) What is the idea behind the term "interrupt masking"?

11-18. *What changes are needed in Figure 11-17 to make the four VAD values equal to the binary equivalent of 024, 025, 026, and 027?

11-19. Repeat Problem 11-18 for VAD values 122, 123, 124, and 125.

11-20. *Design parallel priority interrupt hardware for a system with six interrupt sources.

11-21. A priority structure is to be designed that provides vector addresses.

   (a) Obtain the condensed truth table of a 16 × 4 priority encoder.

   (b) The four outputs w, x, y, z from the priority encoder are used to provide an 8-bit vector address in the form $10wxyz01$. List the 16 addresses, starting from the one with the highest priority.

11-22. **(a)** What is meant by DMA? Draw a conceptual diagram of DMA and explain the role of the control signals used therein.

   (b) What does a DMA controller do?

11-23. It is necessary to transfer 2048 words from a hard drive to a section of memory starting from address 4096. The transfer is by means of DMA, as shown in Figure 11-20.

   (a) Give the initial values that the CPU must transfer to the DMA controller.

   (b) Give the step-by-step account of the actions taken during the input of the first two words.

MEMORY SYSTEMS

In Chapter 7, we discussed basic RAM technology for implementing memory systems, including SRAMs and DRAMs. In the current chapter, we probe more deeply into what really constitutes a computer memory system. We begin with the premise that a fast, large memory is desirable, and demonstrate that a straightforward implementation of such a memory for the typical computer is too costly and too slow. As a consequence, we study a more elegant solution in which most accesses to memory are fast (but some are slow) and the memory appears to be large. This solution employs two concepts: cache memory and virtual memory. A cache memory is a small, fast memory with special control hardware that permits it to handle a significant proportion of all accesses required by the CPU with an access time of the order of several CPU clock periods. Virtual memory, implemented in software and hardware, using an intermediate-sized main memory (typically, DRAM), gives the appearance of a large main memory with access time similar to the main memory for the vast majority of accesses. The actual storage medium for most of the code and data in the virtual memory is a hard drive. Because there is a progression of components in the memory system having larger and larger storage capability, but slower and slower access (one or more cache levels, main memory, and hard drive), the term *memory hierarchy* is applied.

In the generic computer presented at the beginning of Chapter 1, a number of components are heavily involved in the memory hierarchy. Within the processor, there is the memory management unit (MMU), which is hardware provided to support virtual memory. Also in the processor, one or more internal caches appear. A larger cache often appears outside the processor. Of course, the RAM is involved, and due to the presence of virtual memory, the hard drive, the bus interface, and the drive controller all have a role as parts of the memory system.

12-1 MEMORY HIERARCHY

Figure 12-1 shows a generic block diagram for a memory hierarchy. The lowest level of the hierarchy is a small, fast memory called a *cache*. For the hierarchy to function well, a very large proportion of the CPU instruction and operand fetches are

□ **635**

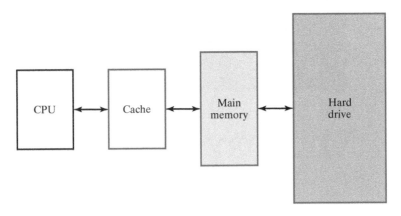

☐ **FIGURE 12-1**
Memory Hierarchy

expected to be from the cache. At the next level upward in the hierarchy is the *main memory*. The main memory serves directly most of the CPU instructions and operand fetches not satisfied by the cache. In addition, the cache fetches all of its data, some portion of which is passed on to the CPU, from the main memory. At the top level of the hierarchy is the *hard drive*, which is accessed only in the very infrequent cases where a CPU instruction or a operand fetch is not found in main memory.

With this memory hierarchy, since the CPU fetches most of the instructions and operands from the cache, it "sees" a fast memory, most of the time. Occasionally, when a word must come from main memory, a fetch takes somewhat longer. Very infrequently, when a word must be fetched from the hard drive, the fetch takes a very long time. In this last case, the CPU is likely to experience an interrupt that passes execution to a program which brings in a block of words from the hard drive. On balance, the situation is usually satisfactory, providing an average fetch time close to that of the cache. Moreover, the CPU sees a memory address space considerably larger than that of main memory.

Keeping in mind this general notion of a memory hierarchy, we will proceed to consider an example that illustrates the potential power of such a hierarchy. However, there is one issue to be clarified first. In most instruction set architectures, the smallest of the objects that are addressed is a byte rather than a word. For a given load or store operation, whether a byte or word is affected is typically determined by the opcode. Addressing to bytes brings with it some assumptions and hardware details that are important, but, if used up to this point in the text, would have unnecessarily complicated much of the material covered. Consequently, for simplicity, we have assumed up to now that an addressed location contains a word. By contrast, in this chapter we will assume that addresses are defined for bytes, to match current practice. Nevertheless, we will still assume that data is moved around outside of the CPU as words or sets of words, to avoid messy explanations relating to the manipulation of bytes. This assumption simply hides some hardware details that would distract from the main focus of our discussion, but nevertheless must be handled by the hardware designer. To accomplish the simplification, if there are 2^b bytes per word, we will ignore the last *b* bits of the address. Since these bits are not needed to address a word, we show their values as 0s. For the examples we will present, a word is 4 bytes and *b* is always equal to 2, so two 0s are shown.

In Section 10-3, the pipelined CPU had a memory address with 32 bits and was able to access an instruction and data, if necessary, in each of the 1-ns clock cycles. Also, we assumed that the instruction and the data were, in effect, fetched from two different memories. To support this assumption in this chapter, we will suppose initially that the memory is divided in half—one-half for instructions and one-half for data. Each half of the memory must have an access time of 1 ns. In addition, if we utilize all the bits in the 32-bit address, then the memory can contain up to 2^{32} bytes, or 4 gigabytes (GB), of information. So the goal is to have two 2-GB memories, each with an access time of 1 ns.

Is such a memory realistic in terms of, say, 2014 computer technology? The typical memory is constructed of DRAM modules ranging in size from 256 MB to 8 GB. The typical access time is about 10 ns. Thus, our two 2-GB memories would have an access time of somewhat more than 10 ns per word. This kind of memory is both too costly and too slow, operating at only one-tenth the desired speed. So our goal must be achieved another way, leading us to explore a memory hierarchy.

We begin by assuming a hierarchy with two caches, one for instructions and one for data, as shown in Figure 12-2. The use of these two caches permits one instruction and one operand to be fetched, or one instruction to be fetched and one result to be stored, in a single clock cycle if the caches are fast enough. In terms of the generic computer, we assume that the caches are internal, so that they can operate at speeds comparable to that of the CPU. Thus, fetches from the instruction cache, and fetches from and stores to the data cache can be accomplished in 2 ns. Hence, most of the fetches and stores for the CPU are from or to these caches and will take 2 CPU clock cycles. Suppose, then, that we are satisfied with most—say, 95 percent—of the memory accesses taking 2 ns. Suppose further that most of the remaining 5 percent of the memory accesses take 10 ns. Then the average access time is

$$0.95 \times 2 + 0.05 \times 10 = 2.4 \text{ ns}$$

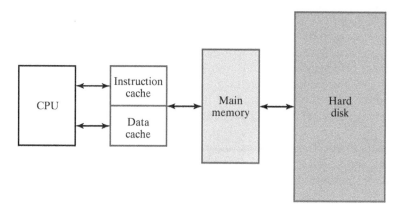

□ **FIGURE 12-2**
Example of Memory Hierarchy

This means that, on 19 out of every 20 memory accesses, the CPU operates at full speed, while the CPU will have to wait for 10 clock cycles for 1 out of every 20 memory accesses. This wait can be accomplished by stalling the CPU pipeline. Thus, we have accomplished our goal of "most" memory accesses taking 2 ns. But there is still the problem of the cost of the large memory.

Now suppose that, in addition to infrequently accepting a wait for a word from main memory that will take more than 10 ns, we are also willing to accept a very infrequent wait for a hard disk access taking $13 \text{ ms} = 1.3 \times 10^7$ ns. Suppose that we have data indicating that about 95 percent of the fetches will be from a cache and about 4.999995 percent of the fetches will be from main memory. With this information, we can estimate the average access time as

$$0.95 \times 2 + 0.04999995 \times 10 + 5 \times 10^{-8} \times 1.3 \times 10^7 = 3.05 \text{ ns}$$

Thus, the average access time is about 3 times the 1 ns CPU clock period, but is about one-third of the 10 ns access time for main memory, again with 19 out of 20 of the accesses taking place in 2 ns. So we have achieved an average access time of about 3.05 ns for a memory structure with a capacity of 2^{32} bytes, not far from the original goal. Further, the cost of this memory hierarchy is tens of times smaller than the large, fast memory approach.

It therefore appears that the original goal of the appearance of a fast, large memory has been approached by the memory hierarchy at a reasonable cost. But along the way, we made some assumptions, namely, that 95 percent of the time the word desired would come from what we are now calling the cache and that 99.999995 percent of the time the words would come from either cache or main memory, with the remainder from hard disk. In the rest of this chapter, we will explore why assumptions similar to these usually hold, and we will examine the hardware and associated software components needed to achieve the goals of the memory hierarchy.

12-2 LOCALITY OF REFERENCE

In the previous section, we indicated that the success of the memory hierarchy is based on assumptions that are critical to achieving the appearance of a large, fast memory. We now deal with the foundation for making these assumptions, which is called *locality of reference*. Here "reference" means reference to memory for accessing instructions and for reading or writing operands. The term "locality" refers to the relative times at which instructions and operands are accessed (*temporal locality*) and the relative locations at which they reside in main memory (*spatial locality*).

Let us consider first the nature of the typical program. A program frequently contains many loops. In a loop, a sequence of instructions is executed many times before the program exits the loop and moves on to another loop or straight-line code not in a loop. In addition, loops are often nested in a hierarchy in which loops are contained in loops, and so on. Suppose we have a loop of eight instructions that is to be executed 100 times. Then for 800 executions, all instruction fetches will occur from just eight addresses in memory. Thus, each of the eight addresses is visited 100 times during the time the loop is executed. This is an example of temporal locality in the sense that an address which is accessed is likely to be accessed many times in the near future. Also, it is likely that the addresses of the instructions will be in sequential order. Thus, if an address is accessed for an instruction, nearby addresses are going to be addressed during the execution of the loop. This is an example of spatial locality.

In terms of accessing operands, similar temporal and spatial localities also occur. For example, in a computation on an array of numbers, there are multiple visits to the locations of many of the operands, giving temporal locality. Also, as the computation proceeds, when a particular address is accessed for a number, sequential addresses near it are likely to be accessed for other numbers in the array, giving spatial locality.

From the prior discussion, we can conjecture that there is significant locality of reference in computer programs. To verify this decisively, we need to study the patterns of execution of real programs. Such studies have demonstrated the presence of significant temporal and spatial locality of reference and play an important role in the design of caches and virtual memory systems.

The next question to answer is: What is the relation of locality of reference to the memory hierarchy? To examine this issue, we consider again the instruction fetch within a loop and look at the relationship between the cache and main memory. Initially, we assume that instructions are present only in main memory and that the cache is empty. When the CPU fetches the first instruction in a loop, it obtains the instruction from main memory. But the instruction and a portion of its address called the *address tag* are also placed in the cache. What then happens for the next 99 executions of this instruction? The answer is that the instruction can be fetched from the cache, which provides a much faster access. This is temporal locality at work: The instruction that was fetched once will tend to be used again and is now present in the cache for fast access.

Additionally, when the CPU fetches the instruction from main memory, the cache fetches nearby instructions into its SRAM. Now suppose that the nearby instructions include the entire loop of eight instructions presented in our example. Then all of the instructions are in the cache. By bringing in such a block of instructions, the cache is able to exploit spatial locality: It takes advantage of the fact that the execution of the first instruction implies the execution of instructions with nearby addresses by making the latter instructions available for fast access.

In our example, each of the instructions is fetched from main memory exactly once for the 100 executions of the loop. All other instruction fetches come from the cache. Thus, in this particular example, at least 99 percent of the instructions being executed are fetched from the cache, so that the rate of execution of instructions is governed almost completely by the cache access time and CPU speed, and very little by the main memory access time. Without temporal locality, many more accesses to main memory would occur, slowing down the system.

A relationship similar to that between cache and the main memory can exist between main memory and the hard drive. Again, both temporal and spatial locality of reference are of interest, except this time on a much larger scale. Programs and data are fetched from the hard drive, and data is written to the hard drive in blocks that range from kilowords to megawords. Ideally, once the code and initial data for a program reside in main memory, the hard drive need not be accessed except for storing final results of the program. But this can happen only if all of the code and data, including intermediate data used by the program, reside fully in main memory. If not, then it will be necessary to bring in code from the hard drive and to read and write data from and to the hard drive during program execution. Words are read from and written to the drive in blocks referred to as *pages*. If the movement of pages between main memory and hard drive is transparent to the programmer, then it will appear as if main memory is large enough to hold the entire program and all of the data. Hence, this automated arrangement is referred to as *virtual memory*. During the execution of the program, if an instruction to be executed is not in main memory, the CPU program flow is diverted to bring the page containing the instruction into main memory. Then the instruction can be read from main memory and executed. The details of this operation and the hardware and software actions required for it will be covered in Section 12-4.

In summary, locality of reference is absolutely key to the success of the concepts of cache memory and virtual memory. In the case of most programs, locality of reference is present to a fairly high degree. But occasionally, one does encounter a program that, for example, requires frequent access to a large body of data that cannot be accommodated in main memory. In such a case, the computer spends almost all of its time moving information between main memory and the hard drive and does little other computation. Emanation of continuous sounds from the hard drive as the heads move from track to track is a telltale sign of this phenomenon, referred to as *thrashing*.

12-3 CACHE MEMORY

To illustrate the concept of cache memory, we assume a very small cache of eight 32-bit words and a small main memory with 1 KB (256 words), as shown in Figure 12-3. Both of these are too small to be realistic, but their size makes illustration of the concepts easier. The cache address contains 3 bits, the memory address 10. Out of the 256 words in main memory, only 8 at a time may lie in the cache. In order for the CPU to address a word in the cache, there must be information in the cache to identify the address of the word in main memory. Clearly, if we consider the example of the loop in the last section, we find it desirable to contain the entire loop within the cache, so that all of the instructions can be fetched from the cache while the program is executing most of the passes through the loop. The instructions in the loop lie in consecutive word addresses. Thus, it is desirable for the cache to have words from consecutive addresses in main memory present simultaneously. A simple way to facilitate this feature is to make bits 2 through 4 of the main memory address be the cache address. We refer to these bits as the *index*, as shown in Figure 12-3. Note that the data from address 0000001100 in main memory must be stored in cache address 011. The upper 5 bits of the main memory address, called the *tag*, are stored in the cache along with the data. Continuing the example, we find that for main memory address 0000001100, the tag is 00000. The tag combined with the index (or cache address) and 00 byte field identify an address in main memory.

Suppose that the CPU is to fetch an instruction from location 000001100 in main memory. This instruction may actually come from either the cache or main

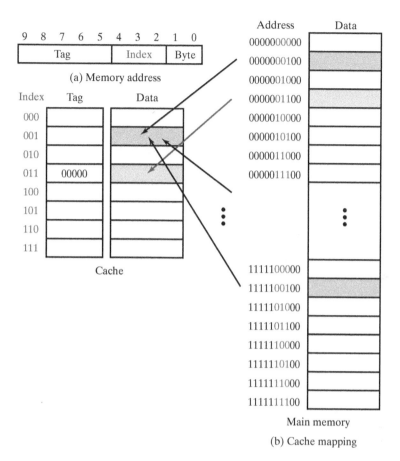

9 8 7 6 5 4 3 2 1 0

| Tag | Index | Byte |

(a) Memory address

□ FIGURE 12-3
Direct Mapped Cache

memory. The cache separates the tag 00000 from the cache address 011, internally fetches the tag and the stored word from location 011 in the cache memory, and compares the tag fetched with the tag portion of the address from the CPU. If the tag fetched is 00000, then the tags match, and the stored word fetched from cache memory is the desired instruction. Thus, the cache control places this word on the bus to the CPU, completing the fetch operation. This case in which the memory word is fetched from cache is called a *cache hit*. If the tag fetched from cache memory is not 00000, then there is a tag mismatch, and the cache control notifies main memory that it must provide the memory word, which is not available in the cache. This situation is called a *cache miss*. For a cache to be effective, the slower fetches from main memory must be avoided as much as possible, making considerably more cache hits than cache misses necessary.

When a cache miss occurs on a fetch, the word from main memory is not placed just on the bus for the CPU. The cache also captures the word and its tag and stores them for future access. In our example, the tag 00000 and the word from memory will be written in cache location 011 in anticipation of future accesses to the same memory address. The handling of writes to memory will be dealt with later in the chapter.

Cache Mappings

The example we just considered uses a particular association or mapping between the main memory address and the cache address; namely, the last three bits of the main memory word address are the cache address. Additionally, there is only one location in the cache for the 2^5 locations in main memory that have their last three bits in common. This mapping in Figure 12-3, in which only one specific location in the cache can contain the word from a particular main memory location, is called *direct mapping*.

Direct mapping for a cache, however, does not always produce the most desirable situation. In our loop instruction fetch example, suppose that instructions and data are in the same cache and that data from location 1111101100 is frequently used. Then when the instruction in 0000001100 is fetched, location 011 in the cache is likely to contain the data from 1111101100 and tag 11111. A cache miss occurs and causes tag 11111 to be replaced in the cache with tag 00000 and the data to be replaced with the instruction. But the next time the data is needed, another cache miss occurs, since the location in the cache is now occupied by the instruction. Throughout the execution of the loop, both instruction fetch and data fetch cause many cache misses, significantly slowing CPU processing. To solve this problem, we explore alternative cache mappings.

In direct mapping, 2^5 addresses in main memory map to the single address in the cache that matches their last three bits. These locations are highlighted in gray in Figure 12-3 for index 001. As is illustrated, only one of the 2^5 addresses can have its word in cache address 001 at any time. In contrast, suppose that we let locations in main memory map into an arbitrary location in the cache. Then any location in memory can be mapped to any one of the eight addresses in the cache. This means that the tag will now be the full main memory word address. We examine the operation of such a cache having a *fully associative* mapping in Figure 12-4. Note that in this case there are two main memory addresses, 0000010000 and 1111110000, with bits 2 through 4 equal to 100 among the cache tags. These two addresses cannot be present simultaneously in the direct-mapped cache, as they would both occupy the cache address 100. Thus, a succession of cache misses due to alternate fetching of an instruction and data with the same index is avoided here, since both can be in the cache.

Now suppose that the CPU is to fetch an instruction from location 0000010000 in main memory. This instruction may actually be returned from either the cache or main memory. Since the instruction might lie in the cache, the cache must compare 00000100 to each of its eight tags. One way to do this is to successively read each tag and the associated word from the cache memory and compare the tag to 00000100. If a match occurs, as it will for the given address and cache location 000 in Figure 12-4, a cache hit occurs. The cache control then places the word on the bus to the CPU, completing the fetch operation. If the tag fetched from the cache is not 00000100, then there is a tag mismatch, and the cache control fetches the next successive tag and word.

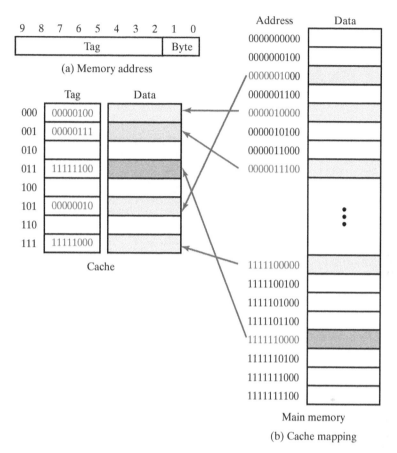

□ **FIGURE 12-4**
Fully Associative Cache

In the worst case, for a match on the tag in cache address 111, eight fetches from the cache are required before the cache hit occurs. At 2 ns a fetch, this requires at least 16 ns, about half the time it would take to obtain the instruction from main memory. So successive reads of tags and words from the cache memory to find a match is not a very desirable approach. Instead, a structure called *associative memory* implements the tag portion of the cache memory.

Figure 12-5 shows an associative memory for a cache with 4-bit tags. The mechanism for writing tags into the memory uses a conventional write. Likewise, the tags can be read from the memory using the conventional memory read. Thus, the associative memory can use the bit-slice model for RAM presented in Chapter 7. In addition, each tag storage row has match logic. The implementation of this logic and its connection to the RAM cells are shown in the figure. The match logic does an equality comparison or match between the tag T and the applied address A from the CPU. The match logic for each tag is composed of an exclusive-OR gate for each bit and a

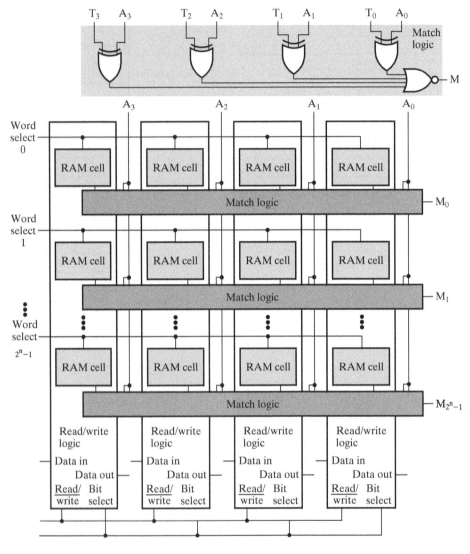

☐ **FIGURE 12-5**
Associative Memory for 4-Bit Tags

NOR gate that combines the outputs of the exclusive-ORs. If all of the bits of the tag and the address match, then the outputs of all the exclusive-ORs are 0 and the NOR output is a 1, indicating a match. If there is a mismatch between any of the bits in the tag and the address, then at least one exclusive-OR has a 1 output, which causes the output of the NOR gate to be 0, indicating a mismatch.

Since all tags are unique, only two situations can arise in the associative memory: there will be a match, with a 1 on the output of the match logic for one matching tag and a 0 on the remaining match logic outputs; or there will be no match, and all of the match logic outputs will be 0. With an associative memory holding the cache tags, the outputs of the match logic drive the word lines for the data memory words to be read. A signal must indicate whether a hit or a miss has occurred. If this signal is 1 for a hit and 0 for a miss, then it can be generated by using the OR of the match outputs. In the case of a hit, a 1 on Hit/$\overline{miss}$ places the word on the memory bus to the CPU; in the case of a miss, a 0 on Hit/$\overline{miss}$ tells the main memory that it is to provide the word addressed.

As in the case of the direct-mapped cache discussed earlier, the fully associative cache must capture the data word and its address tag and store them for future accesses. But now a new problem arises: Where in the cache are the tag and data to be placed? In addition to selecting a cache mapping, the cache designer must select a replacement approach that determines the location in the cache to be used for the incoming tag and data. One possibility is to select a *random replacement* location. The 3-bit address can be read from a simple hardware structure that generates a number which satisfies certain properties of random numbers. A somewhat more thoughtful approach is to use a first-in, first-out (FIFO) location. In this case, the location selected for replacement is the one that has occupied the cache for the longest time, based on the notion that the use of this oldest entry is likely to be finished. An approach that appears to attack the replacement problem even more directly is the *least recently used* (LRU) location approach. The goal of this approach is to replace the entry that has been unused for the longest time—hence the least recently used entry. The reason is that a cache entry that has not been used for the longest time is least likely to be used in the future. Thus, it can be replaced by a new cache entry. Although the LRU approach yields better results for caches, the difference between it and the other approaches is not large, and full implementation is costly. As a consequence, if used at all, the LRU approach is often only approximated.

There are also performance and cost issues surrounding the fully associative cache. Although such a cache provides maximum flexibility and good performance, it is not clear that the cost is justified. In fact, an alternative mapping that has better performance and eliminates the cost of most of the matching logic is a compromise between a direct-mapped cache and a fully associative cache. For such a mapping, lower-order address bits act much as they do in direct mapping—however, for each combination of lower-order address bits, instead of having one location, there is a *set* of *s* locations. As with direct mapping, the tags and words are read from the cache memory locations addressed by the lower-order address bits. For example, if the *set size s* equals two, then two tags and the two accompanying data words are read simultaneously. The tags are then simultaneously compared to the CPU-supplied address using just two matching logic structures. If one of the tags matches the address, then the associated word is returned to the CPU on the memory bus. If neither tag matches the address, then the two 0 matching values are used to send a miss signal to the CPU and main memory. Since there are sets of locations, and associativity is used on sets, this technique is called *set-associative mapping*. Such a mapping with a set size *s* is an *s-way* set-associative mapping.

Figure 12-6 shows a two-way set-associative cache. Eight cache locations are arranged in four rows of two locations each. The rows are addressed by a 2-bit index and contain tags made up of the remaining six bits of the main memory address. The cache entry for a main memory address must lie in a specific row of

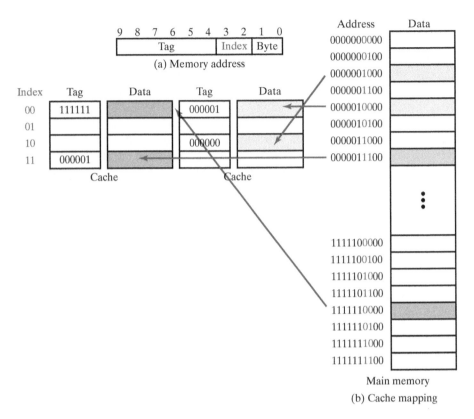

☐ **FIGURE 12-6**
Two-Way Set-Associative Cache

the cache, but can be in either of the two columns. In the figure, the addresses are the same as they are in the fully associative cache in Figure 12-4. Note that no mapping is shown for main memory address 1111100000, since the two cache cells in set 00 are already occupied by addresses 0000010000 and 1111110000. In order to accommodate 1111100000, the set size would need to be at least three. This example illustrates a case in which the reduced flexibility of a set-associative cache, compared to a fully associative cache, has an impact. The impact declines as the set size increases.

Figure 12-7 is a section of a hardware block diagram for the set-associative cache of Figure 12-6. The index is used to address each row of the cache memory. The two tags read from the tag memories are compared to the tag part of the address on the address bus from the CPU. If a match occurs, then the three-state buffer on the corresponding data memory output is activated, placing the data onto the data bus to the CPU. In addition, the match signal causes the output of the Hit/miss OR gate to become 1, indicating a hit. If a match does not occur, then Hit/miss is 0, informing the main memory that it must supply the word to the CPU, and informing the CPU that the word will be delayed.

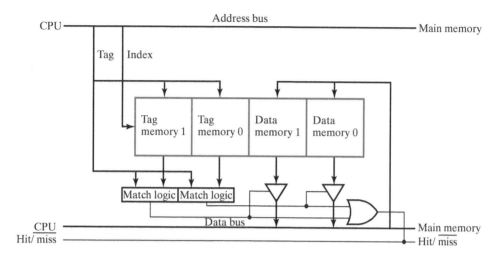

□ **FIGURE 12-7**
Partial Hardware Block Diagram for Set-Associative Cache

Line Size

To this point, we have assumed that each cache entry consists of a tag and a single memory word. In real caches, spatial locality is to be exploited, so additional words close to the one addressed are included in the cache entry. Then, rather than a single word being fetched from main memory when a cache miss occurs, a block of l words called a *line* is fetched. The number of words in a line is a power of two, and the words are aligned on address boundaries. For example, if four words are included in a line, then the addresses of the words in the line differ only in bits 2 and 3. The use of a block of words changes the makeup of the fields into which the cache divides the address. The new field structure is shown in Figure 12-8(a). Bits 2 and 3, the Word field, are used to address the word within the line. In this case, two bits are used, so there are four words per line. The next field, Index, identifies the set. Here two bits are used, so there are four sets of tags and lines. The remainder of the address word is the Tag field, which contains the remaining four bits of the 10-bit memory address.

The resulting cache structure is shown in Figure 12-8(b). The tag memory has eight entries, two in each of the four sets. Corresponding to each of the tag entries is a line of four data words. To ensure fast operation, Index is applied to the tag memory to read two tags, one for each of the set entries, simultaneously. At the same time, Index and the Word address are applied to read out two words from the cache data memory that correspond to the two tags. Matching logic provided for each of the two set elements compares each tag to the CPU-supplied address. If a match occurs, then the associated cache data word already read is placed on the memory bus to the CPU. Otherwise, a cache miss is signaled, and the word addressed is returned from main memory to the CPU. The line containing the word and its tag is also loaded into the cache. To facilitate loading the entire line of words, the width of the memory bus between main memory and the cache, as well as the cache load path, is made more than one word wide. Ideally, for our example the path is $4 \times 32 = 128$ bits wide. This

9 8 7 6 5 4 3 2 1 0

	Tag	Index	Word	Byte

(a) Memory address

Cache

(b) Cache mapping

□ **FIGURE 12-8**
Set-Associative Cache with 4-Word Lines

allows the entire line to be placed in the cache in a single main memory read cycle. If the path is narrower, then a sequence of several reads from main memory is required.

An additional decision that the cache designer has to make is to determine the line size. A wide path to memory can affect both cost and performance, and a narrower path can slow transfer of the line to the cache. These features encourage a smaller cache line size, while spatial locality of reference encourages a larger line. In current systems, however, use of synchronous DRAM facilitates reading or writing large cache lines without the cost and performance issues associated with wide path. The rapid writing to and reading from memory of consecutive words achieved by using synchronous DRAM matches well the needs for transferring cache lines.

Cache Loading

Before any words and tags have been loaded into the cache, all locations contain invalid information. If a hit occurs on the cache at this time, then the word fetched and sent to the CPU cannot have come from main memory and is invalid. As lines are fetched from main memory into the cache, cache entries become valid, but there is no way to distinguish valid from invalid entries. To deal with this problem, in addition to the tag, a bit is added to each cache entry. This *valid bit* indicates that the associated cache line is valid (1) or invalid (0). It is read out of the cache along with the tag. If the valid bit is 0, then a cache miss occurs, even if the tag matches the address from the CPU, requiring the addressed word to be taken from main memory.

Write Methods

We have focused so far on reading instructions and operands from the cache. What happens when a write occurs? Recall that, up to now, the words in a cache have been viewed simply as copies of words from main memory that are read from the cache to provide faster access. Now that we are considering writing results, this viewpoint changes somewhat. Following are three possible write actions from which we can select:

1. Write the result into main memory.
2. Write the result into the cache.
3. Write the result into both main memory and the cache.

Various realistic cache write methods employ one or more of these actions. Such methods fall into two main categories: write-through and write-back.

In *write-through*, the result is always written to main memory. This uses the main memory write time and can slow down processing. The slowdown can be partially avoided by using *write buffering*, a technique in which the address and word to be written are stored in special registers called write buffers by the CPU so that it can continue processing during the write to main memory. In most cache designs, the result is also written into the cache if the word is present there—that is, if there is a cache hit.

In the *write-back* method, also called *copy-back*, the CPU performs a write only to the cache in the case of a cache hit. If there is a miss, the CPU performs a write to main memory. There are two possible design choices for when a cache miss occurs. One is to read the line containing the word to be written from main memory into the cache, with the new word written into both the cache and main memory. This is referred to as *write-allocate*. It is done with the hope that there will be additional writes to the same block which will result in write hits and thus avoid writes to main memory. The other choice on a write miss is simply to write to main memory. In what follows, we will assume that write-allocate is used.

The goal of a write-back cache is to be able to write at the writing speed of the cache whenever there is a cache hit. This avoids having all writes performed at the slower writing speed of main memory. In addition, it reduces the number of accesses to main memory, making it more accessible to DMA, an I/O processor, or another CPU in the system. A disadvantage of write-back is that main memory entries corresponding to words in the cache that have been written are invalid. Unfortunately, this can cause a problem with respect to I/O processors or another CPU in the system accessing the same main memory, due to "stale" data in the memory.

The implementation of the write-back concept requires a write-back operation from the cache location to be used to store a new line being brought from main memory on a read miss. If the location in the cache contains a word that has been written into, then the entire line from the cache must be written back into main memory in order to release the location for the new line. This write-back requires additional time whenever a read miss occurs. To avoid a write-back on every read miss, an additional bit is added to each cache entry. This bit, called the *dirty bit*, is a 1 if the line in the cache has been written and a 0 if it has not been written. Write-back must be performed only if the dirty bit is a 1. With write-allocate used in a write-back cache, a write-back operation may also be required on a write miss.

Many other issues affect the choice of cache design parameters, particularly in the case of caches in a system in which the main memory may be read or written by a device other than the CPU for which the cache is provided.

Integration of Concepts

We now put together the basic concepts we have examined to determine the block diagram for a 256 KB, two-way set-associative cache with write-through. The memory address shown in Figure 12-9(a) contains 32 bits using byte addressing with line size $l = 16$ bytes. The index contains 13 bits. Since four bits are used for addressing words and bytes, and 13 bits are used for the index, the tag contains the remaining 15 bits of the 32-bit address. The cache contains 16,384 entries consisting of $2^{13} = 8192$ sets. Each cache entry contains 16 bytes of data, a 15-bit tag, and a valid bit. The replacement strategy is random replacement.

Figure 12-9(b) gives the block diagram for the cache. There are two data memories and two tag memories, since the cache is two-way set associative. Each of these memories contains $2^{13} = 8192$ entries. Each entry in the data memory consists of 16 bytes. Since 32-bit words are assumed, there are four words in each data memory entry. Thus, each of the data memories consists of four 8192×32 memories in parallel with the index as their common address. In order to read a single word from these four memories on a cache hit, a 4-to-1 selector using three-state memory outputs selects the word, based on the two bits in the Word field of the address. The two tag memories are 8192×15 — in addition to them, a valid bit is associated with each cache entry. These bits are stored in an 8192×2 memory and read out during a cache access with the data and tags. Note that the path between the cache and main memory is 128 bits wide. This allows us to assume that an entire cache line can be read from main memory in a single main memory cycle. To understand the elements of the cache and how they work together, we will look at three possible cases of reading and writing. For each of these cases, we assume that the address from the CPU is $0F3F4024_{16}$. This gives Tag $= 000011110011111_2 = 079F_{16}$, Index $= 1010000000010_2 = 1402_{16}$, and Word $= 01_2$.

(a) Memory address

(b) Cache diagram

□ **FIGURE 12-9**
Detailed Block Diagram for 256K Cache

First we assume a read hit—a read operation in which the data word lies in a cache entry, as in Figure 12-10. The cache uses the Index field to read out two tag entries from location 1402_{16} in Tag memory 1 and Tag memory 0. The match logic compares the tags of the entries, and in this case we assume that Tag 0 matches, causing Match 0 to be 1. This does not necessarily mean that we have a hit, since the cache entry may be invalid. Thus, the Valid 0 from location 1402_{16} bit is ANDed with Match 0. Also, the data can be placed on the CPU data bus only if the operation is a read. Thus, Read is ANDed with the Match 0 bit and the Valid 0 bit to form the control signal for three-state buffer 0. In this case, the control signal for the buffer 0 is 1. The data memories have used the Index field to read out eight words from location 1402_{16} at the same times the tags were read. The Word field selects the two of the eight words with word = 01_2 to place on the data buses going into the three-state buffers 1 and 0. Finally, with three-state buffer 0 turned on, the word addressed is placed on the CPU data bus. Also, the Hit/miss signal sends a 1 to the CPU and the main memory, notifying them of the hit.

In the second case, also shown in Figure 12-10, we assume a read miss—a read operation in which the data word is not in a cache entry. As before, the Index field

☐ **FIGURE 12-10**
256K Cache: Read and Write Operations

address reads out the tag and valid entries, two tag comparisons are made, and two valid bits are checked. For both entries, a miss has occurred and is signaled by Hit/miss at 0. This means that the word must be fetched from main memory. Accordingly, the cache control selects the cache entry to be replaced, and four words read from main memory are applied simultaneously by the memory data bus to the cache inputs and are written into the cache entry. At the same time, the 4-to-1 multiplexer selects the word addressed by the Word field and places it on the CPU data bus using the three-state buffer 3.

In the third case in Figure 12-10, we assume a write operation. The word from the CPU is fanned out to appear in all four of the word positions of the 128-bit memory data bus. The address to which the word is to be written is provided by the address bus to main memory for the write operation into the addressed word only. If the address causes a hit on the cache, the word addressed is also written into the cache.

Instruction and Data Caches

In most of the designs in previous chapters, we assumed that it was possible to fetch an instruction and to read an operand or write a result in the same clock cycle. To do this, however, we need a cache that can provide access to two distinct addresses in a single clock cycle. In response to this need, we discussed in a prior subsection an *instruction cache* and a *data cache*. In addition to easily providing multiple accesses per clock, the use of two caches permits caches that have different design parameters. The design parameters for each cache can be selected to fit the different characteristics of access for fetching instructions or reading and writing data. Because the demands on each of these caches are typically less than those on a single cache, a simpler design can be used. For example, a single cache may require a four-way set-association structure, whereas an instruction cache needs only direct mapping, and a data cache may need only a two-way set-associative structure.

In other instances, a single cache for both instructions and data may be used. Such a *unified cache* is typically as large as the instruction and data caches combined. The unified cache allows cache entries to be shared by instructions and data freely. Thus, at one time more entries can be occupied by instructions, and at another time more entries can be occupied by data. This flexibility has the potential for increasing the number of cache hits. This higher hit rate may be misleading, however, since the unified cache supports only one access at a time, and separate caches support two simultaneous accesses as long as one is for instructions and one is for data.

Multiple-Level Caches

It is possible to extend the depth of the memory hierarchy by adding additional levels of cache. Two levels of cache, often referred to as L1 and L2, with L1 closest to the CPU, are often used. In order to satisfy the demand of the CPU for instruction and operands, a very fast L1 cache is needed. To achieve the necessary speed, the delay that occurs when crossing IC boundaries is intolerable. Thus, the L1 cache is placed in the processor IC together with the CPU and is referred to as the *internal cache*, as in the generic computer processor. If the area in the IC is limited, L1 cache is typically small and not fully adequate as the only cache. Thus, a larger L2 cache is added outside the processor IC. If more space is available in the IC, then the L2 cache can also be an internal cache.

The design of a two-level cache is more complex than that of a single-level cache. Two sets of parameters are specified. The L1 cache can be designed to specific CPU access needs including the possibility of separate instruction and data caches. Also, the constraint of external pins between the CPU and L1 cache is removed. In addition to permitting faster reads, the path between the CPU and the L1 cache can be quite wide, allowing, for example, multiple instructions to be fetched simultaneously. On the other hand, the L2 cache may occupy the typical external cache environment. It differs, however, from the typical external cache in that, rather than providing instructions and operands to a CPU, it primarily provides instructions and operands to the first-level cache L1. Since the L2 cache is accessed only on L1 misses, the access pattern is considerably different than that for a CPU, and the design parameters are accordingly different.

12-4   VIRTUAL MEMORY

In our quest for a large, fast memory, we have achieved the appearance of a fast, medium-sized memory through the use of a cache. In order to have the appearance of a large memory, we now explore the relationship between main memory and hard drive. Because of the complexity of managing transfers between these two media, the control of such transfers involves the use of data structures and programs. Initially, we will discuss the most basic data structure used and the necessary hardware and software actions. Then we will deal with special hardware used to implement time-critical hardware actions.

With respect to large memory, not only do we want the entire virtual address space to appear to be main memory, but in most cases we would also like this complete space to appear to be available to each program that is executing. Thus, each program will "see" a memory the size of the virtual address space. Equally important to the programmer is the fact that real address space in main memory and real drive addresses are replaced by a single address space that has no restrictions on its use. With this arrangement, virtual memory can be used not only to provide the appearance of large main memory, but also to free up the programmer from having to consider the actual locations of the program and data in main memory and on the hard drive. The job of the software and hardware that implement virtual memory is to map each *virtual address* for each program into a *physical address* in the main memory. In addition, with a virtual address space for each program, it is possible for a virtual address from one program and a virtual address from another program to map to the same physical address. This allows code and data to be shared by multiple programs, thereby reducing the size of the main memory space and drive space required.

To permit the software to map virtual addresses to physical addresses, and to facilitate the transfer of information between main memory and hard drive, the virtual address space is divided into blocks of addresses, typically of a fixed size. These blocks, called *pages*, are larger than, but analogous to, lines in a cache. The physical address space in memory is divided into blocks called *page frames* that are the same size as the pages. When a page is present in the physical address space, it occupies a page frame. For purposes of illustration, we assume that a page consists of 4 KB (1K words of 32 bits). Further, we assume that there are 32 address bits in the virtual address space. There are 2^{20} pages, maximum, in the virtual address space, and assuming a main memory of 16 MB, there are 2^{12} page frames in main memory. Figure 12-11 shows the fields of virtual and physical addresses. The portion of the virtual address used to address words or bytes within a page is the *page offset*, which is the only part of the address that the virtual and physical addresses share. Note that words are assumed to be aligned in terms of their location with respect to their byte addresses such that each word address ends in binary 00. Likewise, pages are assumed to be aligned with respect to the byte addresses, such that the page offset of the first byte in the page is 000_{16} and that of the last byte in the page is FFF_{16}. The 20-bit portion of the virtual address used to select pages from the virtual address space is the *virtual page number*. The 12-bit portion of the physical address used to select pages in main memory is the *page frame number*. The figure shows a hypothetical mapping from the virtual address space into the physical address space. The virtual and physical page numbers are given in hexadecimal. A virtual page can be mapped to any physical page frame. Six mappings of pages from virtual memory to physical memory are shown. These pages constitute a total of 24 KB. Note that no virtual pages are mapped to physical page frames FFC and FFE. Thus, any data present in these pages is invalid.

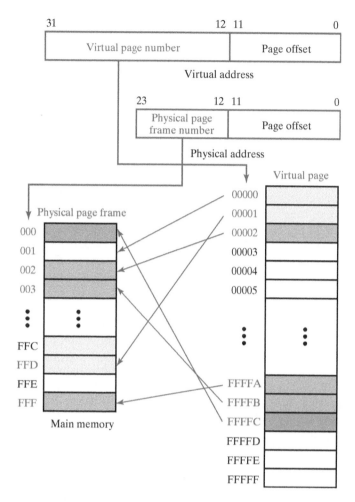

□ **FIGURE 12-11**
Virtual and Physical Address Fields and Mapping

Page Tables

In general, there may be a very large number of virtual pages, each of which must be mapped to either main memory or hard drive. The mappings are stored in a data structure called a *page table*. There are many ways to structure page tables and access them; we assume that page tables themselves are also kept in pages. Assuming that the representation of each mapping requires one word, 2^{10}, or 1K, mappings can be contained in a 4 KB page. Thus, the mappings for the entire address space for a program of 2^{22} bytes (4 MB) can be contained in one 4 KB page. A special table for each program called a *directory page* provides the mappings used to locate the 4 KB program page tables.

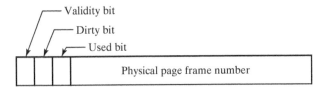

☐ **FIGURE 12-12**
Format for Page Table Entries

A sample format for a page table entry is given in Figure 12-12. Twelve bits are used for the page frame number in which the page is located in main memory. In addition, there are three single-bit fields: Valid, Dirty, and Used. If Valid is 1, then the page frame in memory is valid; if Valid is 0, the page frame in memory is invalid, meaning that it does not correspond to correct code or data. If Dirty is 1, then there has been a write to at least one byte in the page since it was placed in main memory. If Dirty is 0, there have been no writes to the page since it entered main memory. Note that the Valid and Dirty bits correspond exactly to those in a cache which uses write-back. When it is necessary for a page to be removed from main memory and the Dirty bit is 1, then the page is copied back to the hard drive. If the Dirty bit is 0, indicating that the page in main memory has not been written into, then the page coming into the same page frame is simply written over the present page. This can be done because the drive version of the present page is still correct. In order to use this feature, the software keeps a record of the location of the page on the drive elsewhere when it places the page in main memory. The Used bit is a simple mechanism for implementing a crude approximation to an LRU replacement scheme. Some additional bit positions in a page entry may be reserved for flags used by the computer operating system. For example, a few flags might represent the read and write protection status of a page and whether the page can be accessed in user mode or supervisor mode.

The page table structure we have just described is shown in Figure 12-13. The *directory page pointer* is a register that points to the location of the directory page in main memory. The directory page contains the locations of up to 1K page tables associated with the program that is executing. These page tables may be in main memory or on the hard drive. The page table to be accessed is derived from the most significant ten bits of the virtual page number, which we call the *directory offset*. Assuming that the page table selected is in main memory, it can be accessed by the *page table page number*. The least significant ten bits of the virtual page number, which we call the *page table offset*, can be used to access the entry for the page to be accessed. If the page is in main memory, the page offset is used to locate the physical location of the byte or word to be accessed. If either the page table or the desired page is not in main memory, it must first be fetched by software from the hard drive to main memory before the word within it is accessed. Note that combining the offsets with register or table entries is done by simply setting the offset to the right of the page frame number, rather than adding the two together. This approach requires no delay, whereas addition would cause significant delay.

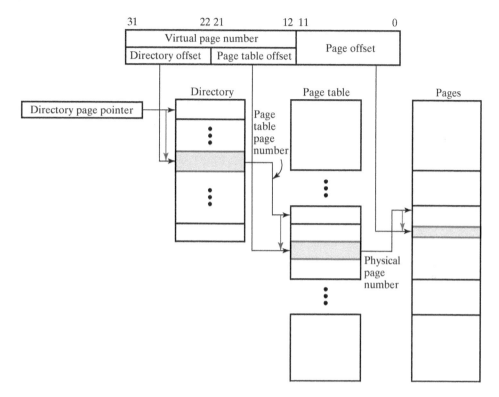

□ **FIGURE 12-13**
Example of Page Table Structure

Translation Lookaside Buffer

From the preceding discussion, we note that virtual memory has a considerable performance penalty even in the best case, when the directory, the page table, and the page to be accessed are in main memory. For our assumed page table approach, three successive accesses to main memory occur in order to fetch a single operand or instruction:

1. Access for the directory entry.
2. Access for the page table entry.
3. Access for the operand or instruction.

Note that these accesses are performed automatically by hardware that is part of the MMU in the generic computer. Thus, to make virtual memory feasible, we need to drastically reduce accesses to main memory. If we have a cache, and if all of the entries are in the cache, then the time for each access is reduced. Nevertheless, three accesses to the cache are needed. To reduce the number of accesses, we will employ yet another cache for the purpose of translating the virtual address directly into a physical address. This new cache is called a *translation lookaside buffer* (TLB). It holds the locations of recently addressed pages to speed access to cache or main memory. Figure 12-14 gives an example of a TLB, which is typically fully associative or set associative, since it is necessary to compare the virtual page number from the CPU with a number of virtual page number tags. In addition to the latter, a cache entry includes the physical page number for those pages in main memory and a Valid bit. If the page is in main memory, the Dirty bit also appears. The Dirty bit serves the same function for a page in main memory as discussed previously for a line in a cache.

We now briefly look at a memory access using the TLB in Figure 12-14. The virtual page number is applied to the page number input to the cache. Within the cache, this page number is compared simultaneously with all of the virtual page number tags. If a match occurs and the Valid bit is a 1, then a TLB hit has occurred, and the physical page frame number appears on the page number output of the cache. This operation can be performed very quickly and produces the physical address required to access memory or a cache. On the other hand, if there is a TLB miss, then it is necessary to access main memory for the directory table entry and the page table entry. If there is a physical page in main memory, then the page table entry is brought into the TLB cache and replaces one of the entries there. Overall, three memory accesses are required, including the one for the operand. If the physical page does not exist in main memory, then a *page fault* occurs. In this case, a software-implemented action fetches the page

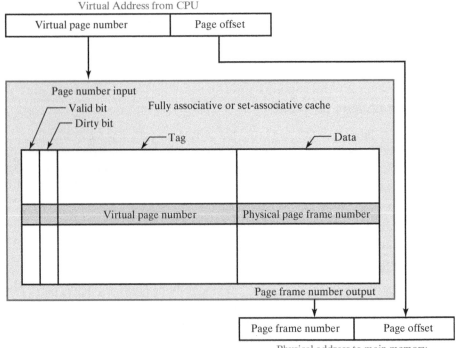

☐ **FIGURE 12-14**
Example of Translation Lookaside Buffer

from its hard drive location to main memory. During the time required to complete this action, the CPU may execute a different program rather than waiting until the page has been placed in main memory.

Noting the prior hierarchy of actions based on the presentation of a virtual address, we see that the effectiveness of virtual memory depends on temporal and spatial locality. The fastest response is possible when the virtual page number is present in the TLB. If the hardware is fast enough and a hit also occurs on the cache, the operand can be available in as little as one or two CPU clock cycles. Such an event is likely to happen frequently if the same virtual pages tend to get accessed over time. Because of the size of the pages, if one operand is accessed from a page, then, due to spatial locality, it is likely that another operand will be accessed on the same page. With the limited capacity of the TLB, the next fastest action requires three accesses to main memory and slows processing considerably. In the worst of all situations, the page table and the page to be accessed are not in main memory. Then, lengthy transfers of two pages—the page table and the page from hard drive—are required.

Note that the basic hardware for implementing virtual memory, the TLB, and other optional features for memory access are included in the MMU in the generic computer. Among the other features is hardware support for an additional layer of virtual addressing called *segmentation* and for protection mechanisms to permit appropriate isolation and sharing of programs and data.

Virtual Memory and Cache

Although we have considered the cache and virtual memory separately, in an actual system they are both very likely to be present. In that case, the virtual address is converted to the physical address, and then the physical address is applied to the cache. Assuming that the TLB takes one clock cycle and the cache takes one clock cycle, in the best of cases fetching an instruction or operand requires two CPU clock cycles. As a consequence, in many pipelined CPU designs, two or more clock cycles are allowed for an operand fetch. Since instruction fetch addresses are more predictable, it is possible to modify the CPU pipeline and consider the TLB and cache to be a two-stage pipeline segment, so that an instruction fetch appears to require only one clock cycle.

12-5 CHAPTER SUMMARY

In this chapter, we examined the components of a memory hierarchy. Two concepts fundamental to the hierarchy are cache memory and virtual memory.

Based on the concept of locality of reference, a cache is a small, fast memory that holds the operands and instructions most likely to be used by the CPU. Typically, a cache gives the appearance of a memory the size of main memory with a speed close to that of the cache. A cache operates by matching the tag portion of the CPU address with the tag portions of the addresses of the data in the cache. If a match occurs and other specific conditions are satisfied, a cache hit occurs, and the data can be obtained from the cache. If a cache miss occurs, the data must be obtained from the slower main memory. The cache designer must determine the values of a number of parameters, including the mapping of main memory addresses to cache addresses, the selection of the line of the cache to be replaced when a new line is added, the size of the cache, the size of the cache line, and the method for performing memory writes. There may be more than one cache in a memory hierarchy, and instructions and data may have separate caches.

Virtual memory is used to give the appearance of a large memory—much larger than the main memory—at a speed that is, on average, close to that of the main memory. Most of the virtual address space is actually on the hard drive. To facilitate the movement of information between the memory and the hard drive, both are divided up in fixed-size address blocks called page frames and pages, respectively. When a page is placed in main memory, its virtual address must be translated to a physical address. The translation is done using one or more page tables. In order to perform the translation on each memory access without a severe performance penalty, special hardware is employed. This hardware, called a translation lookaside buffer (TLB), is a special cache that is a part of the memory management unit (MMU) of the computer.

Together with main memory, the cache and the TLB give the illusion of a large, fast memory that is, in fact, a hierarchy of memories of different capacities, speeds, and technologies, with hardware and software performing automatic transfers between levels.

REFERENCES

1. BARON, R. J. AND L. HIGBIE. *Computer Architecture*. Reading, MA: Addison-Wesley, 1992.

2. HANDY, J. *Cache Memory Book*. San Diego: Academic Press, 1993.

3. HENNESSY, J. L. AND D. A. PATTERSON. *Computer Architecture: A Quantitative Approach*, 5th ed. Amsterdam: Elsevier, 2011.

4. MANO, M. M. *Computer Engineering: Hardware Design*. Englewood Cliffs, NJ: Prentice Hall, 1988.

5. MANO, M. M. *Computer System Architecture*, 3rd ed. Englewood Cliffs, NJ: Prentice Hall, 1993.

6. MESSMER, H. P. *The Indispensable PC Hardware Book*, 2nd ed. Wokingham, U.K.: Addison-Wesley, 1995.

7. PATTERSON, D. A. AND J. L. HENNESSY. *Computer Organization and Design: The Hardware/Software Interface*, 5th ed. Amsterdam: Elsevier, 2013.

8. WYANT, G. AND T. HAMMERSTROM. *How Microprocessors Work*. Emeryville, CA: Ziff-Davis Press, 1994.

PROBLEMS

The plus (+) indicates a more advanced problem and the asterisk (*) indicates that a solution is available on the Companion Website for the text.

12-1. A CPU produces the following sequence of read addresses in hexadecimal: 54, 58, 104, 5C, 108, 60, F0, 64, 54, 58, 10C, 5C, 110, 60, F0, 64.

Supposing that the cache is empty to begin with, and assuming an LRU replacement, determine whether each address produces a hit or a miss for each of the following caches: **(a)** direct mapped in Figure 12-3, **(b)** fully associative in Figure 12-4, and **(c)** two-way set associative in Figure 12-6.

12-2. Repeat Problem 12-1 for the following sequence of read addresses: 0, 4, 12, 8, 14, 1C, 1A, 28, 26, 2E, 36, 30, 3E 38, 46, 40, 4E, 48, 56, 50, 5E, 58.

12-3. *A computer has a 32-bit address and a direct-mapped cache. Addressing is to the byte level. The cache has a capacity of 1 KB and uses lines that are 32 bytes. It uses write-through and so does not require a dirty bit.

(a) How many bits are in the index for the cache?

(b) How many bits are in the tag for the cache?

(c) What is the total number of bits of storage in the cache, including the valid bits, the tags, and the cache lines?

12-4. A cache memory system, which contains 32-bit data, uses direct mapping and has the following specifications:

There are 512 words (32 bits) in main memory, which are to be mapped to any of the 64-word locations in a cache. This assumes that a cache block, i.e., cache line has 4 bytes (words) only.

(a) In which location will the 0th word in main memory be mapped to?

(b) Which other words from main memory will be mapped to the same cache location?

(c) Explain the meaning of the following statement: "At any time, the cache contains only a copy of a portion of the main memory."

12-5. *Discuss the advantages and disadvantages of:

(a) instruction and data caches versus a unified cache for both.

(b) write-back cache versus a write-through cache.

12-6. Give an example of a sequence of program and data memory read addresses that will have a high hit rate for separate instruction and data caches and a low hit rate for a unified cache. Assume direct-mapped caches with the parameters in Figure 12-3. Both the instructions and data are 32-bit words, and the address resolution is to bytes.

12-7. *Give an example of a sequence of program and data memory read addresses that will have a high hit rate for a unified cache and a low hit rate for separate instruction and data caches. Assume that each of the instruction and data caches is two-way set associative with parameters as in Figure 12-6. Assume that the unified cache is four-way set associative with parameters as in Figure 12-6. Both the instructions and the data are 32-bit words, and the address resolution is to bytes.

12-8. Differentiate between "write back" and "write through", which are the write policies used in cache systems.

12-9. Consider the following case of a system with 2048 cache lines and 8192 main memory blocks. Find where in the cache will the main memory blocks MMB-19 and MMB-5031 be placed for the mapping policies of:

(a) direct mapping,

(b) fully associative mapping,

(c) 4-way set associative.

12-10. (a) Find the size of the tag, index, and offset for the two types of caches specified below.

(1) 16KB of data in a direct-mapped cache with 4-word blocks

(2) 16KB of data in a 2-way set associative cache with 4-word blocks.

(b) Why is fully associative mapping" never used?

(c) Draw diagrams to compare one-way associativity, 2-way associativity, and 4-way associativity.

12-11. *A cache memory has an access time from the CPU of 4 ns, and the main memory has an access time from the CPU of 40 ns. What is the effective access time for the cache–main memory hierarchy if the hit ratio is: **(a)** 0.91, **(b)** 0.82, and **(c)** 0.96?

12-12. Repeat Problem 12-11 if the cache access time from the CPU is 1 ns and the main memory has an access time from the CPU of 20 ns.

12-13. Redesign the cache in Figure 12-7 so that it is the same size, but is four-way set associative rather than two-way set associative.

12-14. +The cache in Figure 12-9 is to be redesigned to use write-back with write-allocate rather than write-through. Respond to the following requests, making sure to deal with all of the address and data issues involved in the write-back operation.

(a) Draw the new block diagram.

(b) Explain the sequence of actions you propose for a write miss and for a read miss.

12-15. *A virtual memory system uses 4 KB pages, 64-bit words, and a 48-bit virtual address. A particular program and its data require 4263 pages.

(a) What is the minimum number of page tables required?

(b) What is the minimum number of entries required in the directory page?

(c) Based on your answers to (a) and (b), how many entries are there in the last page table?

12-16. The figure below shows the format of a 32-bit address of a paged memory system.

31	22	21		12	11		0
DIR		Page			Offset		

Calculate the amount of physical memory addressable with this paging system.

12-17. The figure below gives a conceptual view of the TLB. Answer the below questions regarding the necessity and functioning of TLBs.

Linear address (X)	Physical address (Y)
X1	Y1
X2	Y2
X3	Y3
.....	.....
.....	.....

(a) Explain how this conceptual description matches an actual TLB description.

(b) Why is a TLB necessary in a paged memory system?

(c) What is meant by a TLB miss?

(d) For a generic computer, is the TLB realized in hardware or software?

12-18. (a) A TLB has a hit rate of 95 percent, and the TLB miss penalty $T_{MISS} = 150$ cycles. On a TLB hit, the time for address translation is $T_{HIT} = 0$. What is the average time for address translation?

(b) What do the bits Dirty and Used indicate?

(c) Page tables are stored in main memory and occupy space. How much is the size of the page table of a 32-bit computer with 4K page size?

12-19. Consider a system with 85 percent hit ratio, 60 ns to search in TLB, and 800 ns to access main memory. Find the time to access a page and read a desired word from the page for the following situations:

(a) When the page is found in the TLB.

(b) When there is a TLB miss.

(c) The average memory access time.

12-20. *In caches, we use both write-through and write-back as potential writing approaches. But for virtual memory, only an approach that resembles write-back is used. Give a sound explanation of why this is so.

12-21. In modern processors, there are many levels of caches. Make a study of cache structures and describe the multi-level cache structure in a typical processor used in desktop/laptop computers.

INDEX

664 ☐